THE OVARY

Volume I

THE OVARY

Edited by

SIR SOLLY ZUCKERMAN

Sands Cox Professor of Anatomy
in the University of Birmingham

Assisted by

ANITA M. MANDL and PETER ECKSTEIN

Department of Anatomy,
University of Birmingham

Volume I

1962

ACADEMIC PRESS · NEW YORK AND LONDON

ACADEMIC PRESS INC.
111 FIFTH AVENUE
NEW YORK 3, NEW YORK

U.K. Edition published by
ACADEMIC PRESS INC. (LONDON) LTD.
BERKELEY SQUARE HOUSE, BERKELEY SQUARE,
LONDON, W.1

Library of Congress Catalog Card Number 60-14868

Printed in Great Britain at
J. W. Arrowsmith Ltd., Bristol, England

176549

CONTRIBUTORS TO VOLUME I

E. C. AMOROSO, *Department of Physiology, Royal Veterinary College, London, England.*

S. A. ASDELL, *Department of Animal Physiology, Cornell University, New York, U.S.A.*

J. N. BALL, *Department of Zoology, University of Liverpool, England.*

P. M. F. BISHOP, *Guy's Hospital, London, England.*

I. CHESTER JONES, *Department of Zoology, University of Sheffield, England.*

P. ECKSTEIN, *Department of Anatomy, University of Birmingham, England.*

C. A. FINN, *Department of Physiology, Royal Veterinary College, London, England.*

L. L. FRANCHI, *Department of Anatomy, University of Birmingham, England.*

R. J. HARRISON, *Department of Anatomy, London Hospital Medical College, London, England.*

D. L. INGRAM, *Agricultural Research Council, Institute of Animal Physiology, Babraham, Cambridge, England.*

F. JACOBY, *Department of Anatomy, University of Wales, Cardiff.*

ANITA M. MANDL, *Department of Anatomy, University of Birmingham, England.*

L. HARRISON MATTHEWS, *Zoological Society of London, London, England.*

J. S. PERRY, *Agricultural Research Council, Institute of Animal Physiology, Babraham, Cambridge, England.*

I. W. ROWLANDS, *Agricultural Research Council, Institute of Animal Physiology, Babraham, Cambridge, England.**

A. SHARMAN, *Royal Samaritan Hospital for Women, Glasgow, and University of Glasgow, Scotland.*

SIR SOLLY ZUCKERMAN, *Department of Anatomy, University of Birmingham, England.*

* Present address: *Zoological Society of London, London, England.*

PREFACE

To the best of my knowledge no book on the normal ovary has appeared in English since the publication, in 1929, of Professor A. S. Parkes' monograph entitled "The Internal Secretions of the Ovary". The greater length of the present work, the object of which is to provide a detailed account of the principal aspects of ovarian development, structure and function as understood today, reflects the vigour with which researches on these subjects have been pursued over the past thirty years.

An almost unlimited number of topics could have been regarded as falling within the scope of the review. Since there was a necessary limit to size, the two volumes it constitutes cannot, accordingly, be claimed to exhaust the subject they were designed to cover. To whatever extent arbitrariness marks the fields dealt with, the treatise also partakes of a characteristic common to all scientific reviews, and one which reflects the fact that the content, pattern and emphasis of different fields of knowledge are always in a state of change.

The original intention was to publish the work in a single volume. When it became necessary to allocate the material to two, some rearrangement of chapters was called for, and the original sequence of topics which had been planned was changed. In the main, those chapters which relate to what might be called the natural history of the ovary are now included in Volume I, while information derived from more experimental and chemical studies is assembled in Volume II. The two volumes overlap to some extent, as do certain topics, but so far as possible this has been dealt with by means of cross-references.

I am deeply grateful to the many contributors for their generous assent to my invitation to participate in what has proved a lengthier and more arduous task than I, and perhaps they, anticipated at the outset. The authors of the various chapters are of course individually responsible for the content and bibliographic references as well as the style and accuracy of their contributions.

When manuscripts started to arrive, I had to turn to two of my colleagues, Dr. Anita Mandl and Dr. Peter Eckstein, for assistance in the work of editing, and of arranging for the translations of those chapters which were submitted in French. I am deeply grateful for their help, as I am also to the Academic Press for its tolerance during the long period in which this review has been in train. My thanks are also due to Miss Heather Paterson for her able help in preparing manuscripts and checking proofs, to Mr. L. T. Morton for compiling the Subject Index, and to the Academic Press for constructing the Author Index.

The delays which are inevitably associated with the production of a lengthy treatise have meant that a number of contributions appear less up-to-date in print than they did in typescript. Even though references to papers published in last year's scientific journals may be lacking, I nonetheless believe that at the moment the two volumes provide a more comprehensive picture of the whole subject than can be found in any other single work.

AUGUST, 1961   S. ZUCKERMAN

CONTENTS

CONTENTS OF VOLUME II

CHAPTER 1

THE DEVELOPMENT OF THE OVARY AND THE PROCESS OF OOGENESIS

L. L. FRANCHI, ANITA M. MANDL AND SIR SOLLY ZUCKERMAN

I. Development of the ovary

A. Introduction

The origin of the cellular components of the ovary has been the subject of unceasing debate for over 50 years, with the interest of the discussion focusing on the source of the primordial germ cells (see e.g. Waldeyer, 1870, 1906; Maréchal, 1907; Heys, 1931; Bounoure, 1939; Brambell, 1956). About this there are two main views. The first is Waldeyer's (1870) thesis that germ cells arise during embryonic development through the proliferation of the so-called germinal epithelium which covers the presumptive gonad. The contrary view,

2   L. L. FRANCHI, A. M. MANDL AND S. ZUCKERMAN

which gained considerable support from Weismann's (1885) theory of
the continuity of germ-plasm, is that the germ cells become segregated
before the formation of the organ systems of the embryo (e.g. Goette,
1875; Balfour, 1878; Nussbaum, 1880).

According to the view most widely accepted today, the development
of the ovary of vertebrates may be divided into four major phases.
During the first, *primordial germ cells* (i.e. undifferentiated germ cells
or 'Urkeimzellen'), which become segregated very early in development, migrate from their sites of origin and finally settle in bilateral
thickenings of the coelomic epithelium ventral to the developing
mesonephroi. This thickened epithelium is known as the *genital
ridge*.* Although adult females of some species have only one ovary
(e.g. cyclostomes), the genital ridges always appear bilaterally during
early development.

The second phase, which occurs after the arrival of the primordial
germ cells at the genital ridges, consists in the proliferation of both
non-germinal and germinal cells. This leads to the formation of distinct
gonadal primordia which are identical in both sexes (*the indifferent
gonad stage*).

During the third phase, the gonads become divided into a peripheral
cortex and a central *medulla*, separated by a primary *tunica albuginea*
(the medulla is absent in some lower vertebrates; see pp. 12 to 16).
The germ cells are at first mainly peripheral in position.

The fourth and final phase, characteristic of *sex differentiation*,
consists in the development of the cortex and involution of the medulla
in the female, and proliferation of the medulla and involution of the
cortex in the male. While the germ cells in the male are drawn into the
medulla, those in the female remain in the cortex, and in higher vertebrates become organized into cords (so-called Pflüger's cords). At
this stage, the germ cells in female embryos of some species may
enter *meiotic prophase* (see pp. 33 to 34) and therefore become morphologically distinguishable from corresponding cells in the male. (The
term *germ cell* is non-specific and is applicable equally to oogonia,
oocytes and ova, and to spermatogonia, spermatocytes, spermatids
and spermatozoa; see p. 69). Cells derived from the surface of the
gonad invest the female germ cells with a follicular envelope corresponding to the *granulosa cells* of the adult. The germ cells of the male
become associated with corresponding cells of epithelial origin ('supporting' cells or future *Sertoli cells*) and become arranged in *spermatic*

* Whether the genital ridges, when they first appear, also contain mesenchyme
cells is uncertain. As the development in most species studied (e.g. rodents) proceeds
very rapidly, it is unwise to consider that the gonads pass through a distinct 'genital
ridge stage'.

cords or *cysts* (future seminiferous tubules). The adjective 'germinal' has been in common use for many decades and is retained in the present discussion, even though the evidence is plain that the germinal epithelium lacks any ability to give rise to germ cells either during development or after birth (see pp. 57 to 58).

The first part of this chapter deals with the origin, development and differentiation of the individual constituents of the ovary in different vertebrate classes. Sex differentiation, except in its broadest outline, is beyond the scope of the discussion, since it includes such topics as the factors which underlie sex reversal and hermaphroditism, and the influence of alterations in chromosomal constitution. For detailed reviews of these matters, the reader is referred to Brambell (1930, 1956), Willier *et al.* (1955) and Dodd (1960).

B. Primordial germ cells

1. *Origin*

Numerous histological studies of invertebrates and vertebrates have indicated that certain specialized cytoplasmic components (see Hegner, 1914; Bounoure, 1939), called Keimbahn-determinants, can be traced from the unsegmented egg through successive developmental stages into the gonads of the sexually mature animal (for reviews, see also Hegner, 1914; Bounoure, 1939; Nieuwkoop, 1949). Experimental investigations have fully confirmed these histological inferences, and have established beyond doubt that Keimbahn-determinants are present in the vegetative pole of the amphibian egg shortly after fertilization and before the first cleavage (Bounoure, 1931a, b, 1935a, b, 1939; Bounoure *et al.*, 1954).

In all vertebrates that have been investigated (e.g. see Table I), the primordial germ cells originate extra-gonadally and migrate to the genital ridges. In most vertebrates, the cells appear in the endoderm or mesendoderm, though in urodele amphibians at least, they seem to originate in the mesoderm (Humphrey, 1925; Nieuwkoop, 1947). Both in mammals and in non-mammalian species which have telolecithal eggs and in which meroblastic cleavage* leads to the formation of a blastodermal disc, primordial germ cells may arise in the extra-embryonic area. In anuran amphibians, where holoblastic cleavage (cleavage of the entire zygote) occurs, the primordial germ cells first appear in relation to the floor of the archenteron. In urodele amphibians, they appear in the vicinity of the lateral or ventro-lateral lips of the blastopore (i.e. embryonic portion of the germ ring).

---

* Cleavage of part of the zygote only, while the yolk-laden part remains undivided.

TABLE I
Studies of the origin of germ cells in vertebrates*

Cyclostomes
Petromyzon   Butcher (1929)
Entosphenus   Wheeler (1899)
               Okkelberg (1921)

Fishes:
Elasmobranchs
Raja   Beard (1900)
Acanthias   Woods (1902)

Teleosts
Micrometrus   Eigenmann (1891)
Cymatogaster   Eigenmann (1897)
Salmo   Fedorow (1907)
Lophius   Dodds (1910)
Fundulus   Richards and Thompson
               (1921)
Xiphophorus   Essenberg (1923)
Cottus   Hann (1927)
Carassius   Stromsten (1929)
Platypoecilus Wolf (1931)
Lebistes   Dildine (1933)
               Goodrich et al. (1934)
Micropterus   Johnston (1951)

Other Fishes
Amia   Allen (1911)
Lepidosteus   Allen (1911)
Acipenser   Maschkowzeff (1934)

Amphibians: Anurans
Rana   Allen (1907)
               Dustin (1907)
               Kuschakewitsch (1910)
               Witschi (1914, 1929a)
               Bounoure (1924a, 1931a)
               Swingle (1926)
               Cheng (1932)
               Blackler (1958)
Bufo   Dustin (1907)
               King (1908)
               Bounoure (1924a)
               Perle (1927)
               Blackler (1958)
Xenopus   Blackler (1958, 1960)

Amphibians: Urodeles
Triton   Abramowicz (1913)
               Bounoure (1924b)
               Nieuwkoop (1947, 1951)
Amblystoma   Burns (1928)
               Humphrey (1929)
               McCosh (1930)
Hemidactylium Humphrey (1925)

Reptiles: Chelonians
Chrysemys   Allen (1906, 1907, 1911)
               Dustin (1910)
Caretta   Jordan (1917)
Sternotherus   Risley (1933a)

Reptiles: Lacertilians
Phrynosoma   Jarvis (1908)
Mabuia   Pasteels (1953)
Chamaeleo   Pasteels (1953)
Sphenodon   Tribe and Brambell,
               (1932)

Birds
Passer   Blocker (1933)
               Witschi (1935)
Circus   Stanley and Witschi
               (1940)
Gallus   Nussbaum (1901)
               D'Hollander (1904)
               Firket (1913)
               Swift (1914)
               Reagan (1916)
               Defretin (1924)
               Goldsmith (1928, 1935)
               Benoit (1930)
               Dantschakoff (1931b)

Mammals
Cavia   Celestino da Costa
               (1932)
Tatusia   Vanneman (1917)
Peromyscus   Everett (1943)
Mus   Everett (1943)
               Chiquoine (1954)
               Mintz (1957, 1959a, b)
               Mintz and Russell (1957)
Homo   Felix (1912)
               Fuss (1912)
               Politzer (1933)
               Debeyre (1933)
               Witschi (1948)
               McKay et al. (1953)

*For further references, see reviews by Hegner (1914), Heys (1931), Nieuwkoop 1949,) Zuckerman (1951, 1956, 1960), Brambell (1956) and Mintz (1959b).

Humphrey (1925) concludes that regardless of the germ layer in which the primordial germ cells eventually appear, "they may be said to be derived from the germ ring, or in meroblastic eggs, the equivalent blastodermic margin."

The paths by which the primordial germ cells migrate from their sites of origin to their final position in the genital ridges have been studied by standard histological as well as by histochemical methods, and by a variety of experimental techniques. The primordial germ cells are recognized histologically not only by their large size and by the presence of Keimbahn-determinants, but also in non-mammalian vertebrates by their high yolk content. The latter criterion is not a specific one at early stages of development, since most embryonic cells, particularly those of the presumptive endoderm, are also packed with yolk. At later stages of development, however, non-germinal cells lose their yolk before they divide and differentiate, whereas the primordial germ cells retain their primitive features for a longer period. Recent attempts to identify mammalian primordial germ cells by the histochemical reaction for alkaline phosphatase (e.g. Chiquoine, 1954; Mintz, 1957, 1959a, b) may be open to criticism, since this criterion may not be entirely specific. On the other hand, some circumstantial evidence is available to indicate that cells rich in alkaline phosphatase do, in fact, represent primordial germ cells. Mintz (1957, 1959b) and Mintz and Russell (1957) observed that mutant mice, characterized by female sterility, possessed a reduced number of primordial germ cells as early as the 10th day of embryonic life, due specifically to the lack of mitotic divisions and retarded migration of these cells. Mintz also observed that these cells originate extra-gonadally, and that their content of alkaline phosphatase decreases shortly after they arrive at the genital ridges, when some have already entered the prophase of meiosis and are thus identifiable as oocytes (see p. 32 and p. 88).

In all vertebrates (excluding amphibians and birds; see below) in which the zygote undergoes meroblastic cleavage, the primordial germ cells, originally segregated in the primitive extra-embryonic endoderm or mesendoderm, become incorporated into the embryo and are seen either in the endoderm, the mesoderm, or between these two layers. The formation of the coelom causes the primordial germ cells to become concentrated mainly in the lateral splanchnopleure, and subsequently in the region of either the caudal end of the developing gut or the stalk of the yolk sac. At later stages of development, the primordial germ cells are seen in the region of the developing dorsal mesentery, and later still, in the mesenchyme underlying the coelomic epithelium at the root of the mesentery. A concentration of primordial germ cells is thus formed ventral to the aorta, extending caudally from about the cranial* limits of the developing mesonephroi. From this position, the primordial germ cells migrate laterally to the genital ridges.

In anuran amphibians, the primordial germ cells, which arise in relation to the endoderm, form a median ridge along the roof of the archenteron, and through the apposition of the lateral mesodermal plates, become squeezed into the mesenchyme of the dorsal mesentery while the latter is being formed. In the urodeles, groups of germ cells arising in relation to the lateral plate mesoderm of the two sides are said to be carried towards the midline by the formation of the dorsal mesentery. Thus, whereas an undifferentiated median ridge is formed in anurans (Allen, 1907; Burns, 1925; Perle, 1927; Cheng, 1932; Jurand, 1957), the primordial germ cells in urodeles form a median collection or aggregation of cells which consists of two closely apposed but distinct halves. Grafting experiments on *Amblystoma* have shown that the primordial germ cells always migrate to their nearest genital ridge, i.e. they do not migrate from the right half of the median aggregate to the left genital ridge or *vice versa* (Humphrey, 1929a). The manner in which the median aggregation of primordial germ cells in amphibians splits to form lateral genital ridges is uncertain. Humphrey (1925) and Blackler (1958) consider that the separation is due to differential growth of tissues, whereas others (e.g. Allen, 1907; King, 1908; Nieuwkoop, 1947) believe that active migration is involved (see below).

In some reptiles and birds, the primordial germ cells that first become segregated in the area pellucida migrate into the developing mesodermal blood islands of the area vasculosa, and enter the peripheral circulation which then carries them to the genital ridge area (Swift, 1915; Goldsmith, 1928; Benoit, 1930; Dantschakoff, 1931a; Tribe and Brambell, 1932; Blocker, 1933; Pasteels, 1953).

2. *Modes of migration*

Four modes of migration of primordial germ cells have been postulated: (i) active, by amoeboid movements of the primordial germ cells themselves; (ii) passive, by differential growth of surrounding tissues; (iii) passive, by transport *via* the blood stream, and (iv) chemotactic, under the influence of some local inductors diffusing from the presumptive gonadal area.

---

* Topographical terms, such as upper, lower, anterior and posterior, are frequently ambiguous. The terms used in the present chapter are: cranial, caudal, ventral, dorsal, medial, median and lateral.

(i) *Active movements*. The view that the primordial germ cells migrate actively by an amoeboid form of movement is usually associated with the observation that they possess blunt pseudopodia-like processes. There is, however, no evidence that the pseudopodia are constantly present, regardless of the method of fixation, though Muratori (1937) claims to have observed them in the living germ cells of the chick cultured *in vitro*. A combination of active and passive (see below) migration is claimed to occur in a number of animals, including cyclostomes, fishes and some reptiles (Dodds, 1910; Okkelberg, 1921), but no experimental proof is provided.

Mammalian primordial germ cells are also claimed by some authors to migrate largely by their own active amoeboid movement (see e.g. Everett, 1943; Chiquoine, 1954), possibly aided by histiolytic action (Witschi, 1948). The only experimental evidence supporting this view derives from Mintz's (1959b) study (*op. cit.*) in which primordial germ cells were held up in their movement towards the genital ridges even though organogenesis appeared to be proceeding normally.

(ii) *Passive movements by differential growth of tissues*. Since differential growth of the germ layers occurs consistently in all vertebrates during organogenesis, it is clear that the primordial germ cells could be drawn passively from an extra- to an intra-embryonic position. Most of the evidence for amphibians indicates that germ cells reach the genital ridges solely by this means (e.g. Humphrey, 1925; Blackler, 1958).

(iii) *Passive movements by vascular transport*. Stanley and Witschi (1940) consider that the presence of germ cells in the blood stream in birds is accidental, and that any such cells are destined to degenerate. Other workers (e.g. Firket, 1913; Matsumoto, 1932; Witschi, 1935) believe that the avian germ cells migrate actively, and Berenberg-Gossler (1913) suggests that they migrate by differential tissue growth. Recent experimental work on the chick embryo (Simon, 1957; see also Willier, 1937) largely disposes of these earlier claims, in that it clearly demonstrates that in birds at least, the vascular path is responsible for the transport of the primordial germ cells.* Simon (1957) bisected the chick embryo at the level of the twentieth presumptive somite and found that the primordial germ cells situated in the germinal crescent reached the severed caudal region of the embryo, given that the vascular path remained intact. In a second experiment, he grafted the caudal half of another embryo on to the blastoderm, and found that, given that the graft became vascularized,

---

* The primordial germ cells also migrate *via* the blood stream in *Sphenodon*, a primitive diapsid reptile (Tribe and Brambell, 1932).

primordial germ cells originating from the cranial region of the host embryo were also able to reach the graft. In his final experiment, Simon united a chick embryo, whose germinal crescent had been removed, in parabiosis with a normal chick embryo. If a circulation became established between the two parabionts, the sterilized embryo's genital ridges became populated by some primordial germ cells. The implication of this experiment is that the cells were transported there *via* the blood stream from the non-sterilized partner. The view that the primordial germ cells in birds are carried to their definitive site of development by means of the blood stream is also supported by the repeated finding that the primordial germ cells are initially widely scattered in the embryo, particularly in the head (e.g. Swift, 1914), and that relatively large numbers become trapped in ectopic positions within fine capillaries. Such primordial germ cells as fail to reach the genital ridges degenerate.

The hypothesis that in certain teleosts the primordial germ cells also migrate *via* the blood stream (Stolk, 1958) requires substantiation.

(iv) *Chemotaxis*. The suggestion that the migration of the primordial germ cells to the presumptive gonads is aided by the emission of chemotactic or inductor substances from the gonad-forming areas has been put forward for fishes (Woods, 1902), birds (Firket, 1913, 1920; Willier, 1939) and mammals (Witschi, 1948, 1951a). It would appear probable, however, that although such specific influences might be responsible for directing the primordial germ cells at *later* stages of migration, when they are already in the vicinity of the future gonads, their initial movements are probably due to the differential growth of the germ layers in which the cells reside. The latter possibility is supported by the observation that anomalies arising in the course of grafting experiments, such as the formation of sterile gonads from grafts either containing or lacking the germinal crescent, are due, in birds at least, to the absence of a suitable transporting mechanism (in this instance, the blood stream: Willier, 1937; Simon, 1957). On the other hand, the final distribution of the primordial germ cells in the right and left presumptive ovaries in birds may well be mediated by chemotactic substances. An alternative explanation for the uneven distribution of primordial germ cells between the two avian ovaries is that the right ovary, which is destined to be non-functional (see below), and which receives fewer primordial germ cells than does the left, is poorly vascularized at very early stages of development (Dantschakoff, 1931a).

Experimental evidence supporting the view that inductor substances are responsible for the movement of mammalian primordial germ cells is lacking.

3. *Mitotic divisions during migration*

Although the numbers of primordial germ cells increase during the early stages of embryonic differentiation (Vanneman, 1917; Blackler, 1958), it is generally believed that no further multiplication occurs during the actual migration of the cells (fishes: Dodds, 1910; Johnston, 1951; amphibians: Swingle, 1926; McCosh, 1930; Cheng, 1932; Jurand, 1957; reptiles: Allen, 1906, 1907; Jordan, 1917; birds: Firket, 1913; Swift, 1915; Goldsmith, 1928; mammals: Celestino da Costa, 1932). The opposite view, that the cells divide during migration, is held by Blackler (1958), Matsumoto (1932) and Witschi (1948) and Chiquoine (1954) for anurans, birds and mammals, respectively. Experimental evidence supporting the latter view for mammals derives from Mintz's (1959b) observation that on the 8th day of gestation, mouse embryos contain about 100 primordial germ cells (identified by their high content of alkaline phosphatase; see p. 5), whereas 4 days later, the numbers are about 5,000. Mintz also makes the interesting suggestion that ovarian regeneration in mammals, which occasionally occurs after bilateral ovariectomy (see e.g. Parkes *et al.*, 1927) is due to a stimulation of ectopic primordial germ cells persisting in accessory ovarian structures. The persistence of ectopic primordial germ cells has also been recorded in some adult teleosts (Stolk, 1958).

The consensus of opinion, however, is that primordial germ cells undergo a period of mitotic proliferation once they have reached the genital ridges, and that, in general, those cells that fail to reach their destination degenerate and disappear.

4. *Fate of primordial germ cells*

The views that have been expressed about both the origin and fate of the definitive gonocytes range from a denial of the germinal nature of the primordial cells (e.g. Berenberg-Gossler, 1913; Simkins, 1923, 1925, 1928; Hargitt, 1925) to the belief in a continuous germ line (Keimbahn) from the embryo to the adult (e.g. Beard, 1900; Okkelberg, 1921; Bounoure, 1939; Nieuwkoop, 1947, 1949; Mintz, 1959b; Zuckerman, 1960). The view that the primordial germ cells degenerate and are replaced by later proliferations from the germinal epithelium (e.g. Kingery, 1917) has attracted a large number of supporters (see Zuckerman, 1951).

Much of the controversy about the identity of primordial and definitive gonocytes arises from the fact that soon after their arrival at the genital ridges, the gonocytes lose many or all of their distinguishing cytological features (see Brambell, 1956). Such experimental results as are available, particularly those of Bounoure (1924–1951), Goldsmith (1935), Nieuwkoop (1947, 1949) and more recently of Mintz (1959b), support the view that primordial germ cells not only give rise to *all* definitive gonocytes in both sexes, but also play an important role in the organization of the gonads. For detailed reviews of this problem, the reader is referred to Firket (1920), Heys (1931), Bounoure (1939), Willier (1939), Everett (1945), Tyler (1955), Brambell (1956), Mintz (1959b) and Zuckerman (1960).

C. The formation of the genital ridges

The presumptive gonads first appear as bilateral thickenings of the coelomic epithelium which covers the ventro-lateral aspects of the developing mesonephroi between the root of the dorsal mesentery and the Wolffian ducts. The extent of the thickened areas varies in different vertebrates (see Willier, 1939), but in general they reach from approximately the cranial end of the mesonephros to beyond its caudal end. Only the middle portion of the thickening is destined to contribute to the actual gonad in mammals (see Brambell, 1956), the germ cells becoming largely, if not entirely, segregated into this portion during the later stages of their migration. In amphibians, the cranial portion of the presumptive gonad forms the fat body (though in *Amblystoma* the latter may be of more localized origin; Burns, 1925). In toads, the indifferent genital ridge may be divided into three segments. The cranial portion (progonad) gives rise to the larval Bidder's organ, which shortly degenerates. The intermediate portion (mesogonad) forms the definitive Bidder's organ* (which occurs consistently in male toads, but may also develop in the females of some species; see Brambell, 1930). The caudal portion (metagonad) gives rise to the gonads themselves (see Ponse, 1924). In the female mammal, the sterile cranial portion of the genital ridge forms the suspensory ligament, while the sterile caudal portion contributes to the formation of the utero-ovarian ligament.

During development, the central portion of the bilateral gonadal area begins to project ventrally into the coelom in the form of a ridge which eventually becomes cylindrical (see below). The connection of the genital ridge with the mesonephros persists in the female as a mesentery (mesovarium) for vessels and nerves. In both sexes, the development of the ridges proceeds in a cranial-caudal direction (Brambell, 1927; Simkins, 1928), this trend being particularly clear in

---

* Bidder's organ in the male represents a suppressed cortical or ovarian field, held in abeyance by the developing testis. The removal of the testes causes a reactivation of Bidder's organ and sex reversal follows (see p. 24).

some fishes and in amphibians, in which the initially dorsal median concentration of primordial germ cells splits to form bilateral aggregates of cells, the division of the median concentration occurring first at the cranial end and proceeding caudally.

The time of appearance of the genital ridges varies in different classes of vertebrates, but is closely related to the arrival, in these regions, of the migrating primordial germ cells from their median concentration at the root of the dorsal mesentery.*

Some observers hold that the hypertrophy of the coelomic epithelium in the area of the presumptive genital ridge occurs as a direct result of the entry of the primordial germ cells (Allen, 1911; Brambell, 1927; Tribe and Brambell, 1932). Others (e.g. Firket, 1913; Swift, 1914) record that the epithelium has already thickened by the time the germ cells enter. Experimental findings are not consistent on this point. Thus, while Dantschakoff (1932) has shown that in the absence of primordial germ cells the coelomic epithelium fails to thicken or undergo subsequent proliferation to form a gonad, a large number of other workers (e.g. Reagan, 1916; Humphrey, 1927, 1928a,b; Benoit, 1930; Bounoure, 1935b; Willier, 1937, 1939, 1951; see also Burns, 1955) firmly contend that the primordial germ cells are by no means essential for the initiation of gonadal development. Dantschakoff destroyed the area of the germinal crescent in the chick embryo by means of a fine incandescent platinum wire, and observed that the gonadal regions of the embryo thereafter lacked primordial germ cells and failed to differentiate. In a further experiment, she transplanted early genital ridges to the allantois of another chick embryo, before the arrival of the primordial germ cells, and observed that the grafts never became organized into gonads, forming at the most only strands of somatic tissue (see Dantschakoff, 1951). The partial destruction of the germinal crescent, associated with the survival of some primordial germ cells, was followed by the formation of gonadal primordia which contained gonocytes and which subsequently differentiated. Willier (1951) studied isolated pieces of the chick blastoderm at certain critical stages (e.g. while the primordial germ cells were still situated in the germinal crescent; and at a time when they were migrating or just about reaching the gonadal areas), and reported that the genital ridges are capable of differentiating in the absence of primordial germ cells,

---

* The term 'median ridge' which has been adopted by some workers to denote this preliminary stage is perhaps an unfortunate one, since it refers to a temporary concentration of primordial germ cells which is not accompanied by specialization of the tissues immediately surrounding it. No vertebrates have as yet been shown to possess a gonad which is truly median in origin. The asymmetry of gonads which is seen at later developmental stages in some vertebrates is secondary, and is discussed on p. 25.

but that the ovarian cortex never forms and the ridges consist of male-like sex cords only.

At the same time, it is worth noting that Goldsmith (1935) and Bounoure (1937b) observed a marked reduction in the size of the developing gonads if the primordial germ cells were experimentally prevented from reaching the genital ridges; and that primordial germ cells which, as a result of grafting, aggregate in ectopic positions, are capable of inducing local thickenings of the coelomic epithelium which do not, however, differentiate to form a typical gonad (Humphrey, 1928b; Willier, 1933; Witschi, 1934).

In reviewing the available evidence, Burns (1955) concludes that: "(1) the local appearance of a genital ridge is conditioned by regional influences; (2) primordial germ cells alone cannot induce a genital ridge and are not essential for its origin; and (3) the formation of the ridge is an activity of the structural elements." The reasons underlying the discrepancy between the results obtained by Dantschakoff on the one hand, and those reported by all other students concerned with the differentiation of the genital ridges on the other, remain unresolved (see Zuckerman, 1960).

D. The indifferent gonad and the formation of medullary cords

Differentiation of the somatic cells in the genital ridges may begin before all the primordial germ cells have completed their migration, and the arrival of the latter, which then proliferate by mitosis, is associated with the further development of the non-germinal cells. As a result, the presumptive cortical region* thickens, the pattern followed being similar in the two sexes. Thus, in both, the genital ridges acquire a central or medullary zone formed by cells from the underlying mesenchyme and from the mesonephric rudiment. These cells, which are considered by some authorities to be the basic source of the medulla of the gonad, are related embryologically to the interrenal or adreno-cortical rudiments in some elasmobranchs, in amphibians and in amniotes (see pp. 13 to 16). No distinct counterpart to the gonadal medulla appears to exist in cyclostomes, ganoids and teleosts (Chieffi, 1949; Witschi, 1951a; D'Ancona, 1956b; Segal, 1959).

At this stage of development, the gonad is 'indifferent' sexually, since the course it will take in its further differentiation cannot be diagnosed from any histological feature.

* It is generally held that unlike the early genital ridge, the cortical region will not develop in the absence of the germ cells. This may not apply to birds (e.g. Dulbecco, 1946; Salzgeber, 1950; Marin, 1959) in which the cortex does develop, even after the destruction of the primordial germ cells by irradiation. It may also be of interest to note that the explanted gonadal epithelium and germ cells contained in it are capable of proliferating in the absence of the medulla (duck embryo: Wolff and Haffen, 1959).

1. *The origin of the medulla*

It is widely taught that two proliferations of the surface epithelium of the indifferent gonad invade the underlying mesenchyme. If the genetic sex of the embryo is male, the initial proliferation of the germinal epithelium results in the production of sex cords, which then differentiate into the definitive seminiferous tubules. In the female, the cells of the first proliferation give rise to sex cords which appear identical with those of the male. These do not branch, but elongate, and become separated from the cortical region of the gonad by a transient connective tissue layer or primary tunica albuginea. As a result, the medulla of the ovary becomes organized into radially arranged cords which come into contact with the distal ends of cords of cells that arise from the mesonephric rudiment, and which are themselves the rudiments of the rete system* (or 'urinogenital connection'; see Brambell, 1956).

The development of the medulla which, like the early genital ridge but unlike the cortex is largely independent of the presence of germ cells, is thus at first the same in both sexes and constitutes the main feature of the indifferent stage of gonad development. It has been described for marsupials (Fraser, 1919; Nelsen and Swain, 1942) and for many eutherian mammals, including the rat (Torrey, 1945), mouse (Brambell, 1927; Everett, 1943), rabbit (Winiwarter, 1901; Allen, 1904), pig (Allen, 1904), cow (Bascom, 1923), mole (Godet, 1949) and man (Winiwarter, 1910; Felix, 1912; Simkins, 1925; Gruenwald, 1942; Gillman, 1948). No information appears to be available for monotremes.

The second proliferation of the surface epithelium is generally held to give rise to the ovarian cortex in amphibians and amniotes. In males, the second, cortical, proliferation is either transitory or absent.

This conventional picture of the course of gonadal development is, however, controverted by a number of observations which suggest that the medulla is formed, not from the first proliferation of the germinal epithelium, but from extra-gonadal undifferentiated cells related to the mesonephric rudiment (mesonephric 'blastema'; see Witschi, 1914, 1951a, 1956), and is separated from the germinal epithelium by a previously formed core of mesenchyme cells known as the primary gonad cavity or albuginea. The presumptive rete cords also arise from the undifferentiated mesonephric 'blastema', the connection between the medulla and the rete apparatus being present from the earliest stages of development.

The evidence available for non-mammalian vertebrates is briefly summarized in Tables II–IV. Whereas the majority of authors contend

---

* Future vasa efferentia of the male.

TABLE II

The indifferent gonad in cyclostomes and fishes

Cyclostomes	Okkelberg (1921)	Gonad is mainly composed of epithelial cells and germ cells, and a small mesenchymal contribution. The stroma is derived from the peritoneal epithelium.
	Witschi (1951a)	The medulla is absent. The cortex is of epithelial origin and there is a mesenchymatous albuginea.
Ganoids	D'Ancona (1951, 1955)	Germ cells are located in the lateral margin of the gonads. The medulla is absent.
Teleosts	D'Ancona (1951)	The medulla is absent. The gonad arises from a single cortical anlage.
	Eigenmann (1897) Essenberg (1923) Hann (1927) Ashby (1957)	The stroma of the indifferent gonad is derived from the peritoneal epithelium (cf. Wolf's (1931) observations on *Platypoecilus*).
	D'Ancona (1951)	All teleosts are initally bisexual; in some, male and female gonocytes are distinct and segregated into separate regions of the gonad. (Bisexuality persists to the adult stage in some species.)
Elasmobranchs	Chieffi (1949, 1952, 1955a, 1959)	The medulla is present, and is clearly differentiated from an outer cortical region, which contains the germ cells. The medulla is derived from an epithelial 'blastema' situated at the angle of the dorsal mesentery and the somatopleure; this 'blastema' also gives rise to the interrenal bodies. Stromal elements, derived from haemopoietic tissue in the mesonephros, infiltrate into the medulla during the formation of the indifferent gonad.

TABLE III

The indifferent gonad in amphibians and reptiles

Amphibians	Witschi (1914, 1929a) Christensen (1930) Cheng (1932)	The germ cells are arranged peripherally. The medulla is formed from the mesonephric 'blastema' by downgrowths and proliferation in the form of pseudosegmentally arranged cords. The cortex and the medulla are separated by mesenchyme cells (albuginea or primary gonad cavity) up to the time of sex differentiation.
	Chieffi (1955a)	The medulla arises from an undifferentiated epithelial 'blastema' at the base of the kidney and median to the genital ridges.
	Vannini and Sabbadin (1954)	The medulla arises from the interrenal 'blastema' (cf. Witschi's discussion in Vannini, 1951).
Reptiles	Allen (1905) Simkins and Asana (1930) Risley (1933b, 1934) Forbes (1940, 1956)	The germ cells are distributed between the cortex and the medulla. The latter is formed by proliferations of the germinal epithelium in the form of a 'blastema' which becomes organized into solid medullary cords. The cortex and the medulla are derived from the same primordial elements, and are thus entirely homologous.
	Simkins and Asana (1930) Risley (1933b) Forbes (1940, 1956)	The early expansion of a cortical region, which is incompletely separated from the medulla by a primitive tunica albuginea, is characteristic of reptiles, and indicates a bisexual phase which persists for variable periods.
	Witschi (1951a) Witschi *et al.* (1953)	The medulla in the reptiles, as in other tetrapods, is derived from an undifferentiated mesonephric 'blastema' distinct from the coelomic epithelium. The initial components of the cortex and medulla are thus not homologous.

TABLE IV

The indifferent gonad in birds

Hoffmann (1892) D'Hollander (1904) Firket (1914) Swift (1915, 1916) Benoit (1924, 1951) Goldsmith (1928) Brode (1928) Willier (1939) amongst others	The germ cells are distributed between the cortex and the medulla. The medulla is formed by ingrowths of cells from localized parts of the germinal epithelium ('first proliferation').
Stanley and Witschi (1940) Witschi (1951a)	The medulla is derived as pseudosegmentally arranged cord-like downgrowths from an un-differentiated mesonephric 'blastema' which is distinct from the coelomic epithelium (see also Tables II and III).
Witschi (1935)	The germinal epithelium does not usually thicken appreciably during the indifferent stage.

that the gonadal medulla (where present) is derived from the germinal epithelium, Witschi (1951a) maintains that throughout the vertebrates, including the mammals, the medulla arises from an extra-gonadal mesonephric 'blastema': "The misconception that the medulla might arise as a 'first proliferation' from the 'germinal epithelium' could only arise from a study of mammalian materials, where the gonad cavity is reduced to a very narrow space or albuginea." It is worth noting, however, that from an independent examination of Witschi's (1948) material, Gillman (1948) concluded that the medullary cords arise from the germinal epithelium. At the same time, Gillman noted that the structure was looser in the area "just below the epithelium" (i.e. the region designated by Witschi as the albuginea) than elsewhere. This difference in interpretation indicates the great difficulty in reaching final conclusions about detailed embryological processes from histological study alone.

2. *The start of sex differentiation*

Towards the end of the indifferent stage, the gonad still retains a relatively broad connection with the mesonephros. Expansion of the interior of the gonad, and involution of the mesonephric kidney, later cause the 'nipping off' of the ovary so that it becomes suspended at the future hilar region by a narrow peduncle. The end of the indifferent stage of gonad development is also marked in the male by the further expansion of connective tissue cells in a layer under the germinal epithelium which is destined to become the definitive fibrous tunica albuginea of the testis.

In the earlier part of the indifferent phase, some of the germ cells which are scattered in and under the germinal epithelium become incorporated into the medullary cords, and thus pass down into the substance of the gonad. This process differs quantitatively in the two sexes and heralds the onset of sexual differentiation.

E. Sex differentiation

Before sex differentiation begins, the indifferent gonad contains all the cell-types it needs to render it capable of developing into either a testis or an ovary. The direction of further development depends upon both the genetic sex of the individual (see e.g. Dodd, 1960; Beatty, 1960) and on internal and external environmental factors.

Experimental evidence indicating that the direction of development is largely pre-determined genetically derives from Humphrey's (1928a,b) observation that after transplantation, the gonad-forming area develops into a testis or an ovary according to the sex of the donor, and regardless of that of the host. This sex-specificity may be evident even before the genital ridges are distinguishable, but the frequency with which a gonad of specific sex is formed in such grafts increases the later the transplantations are performed during the stages of development represented by the genital ridge and the indifferent gonad (see also Willier, 1939; Burns, 1955).

The fact that environmental factors, particularly internal ones, also play an essential role in gonad development is demonstrated by the ease with which the normal pattern of development for either sex can be modified by hormonal or other physiological disturbances (see Chapter 13, and Witschi, 1939, 1951b; Burns, 1955; Dodd, 1960).

The process of sex differentiation consists essentially of the proliferation of the cortex and regression of the medulla in the female, and of the reverse process in the male. Since the medulla is absent in cyclostomes and bony fishes, the process of sex differentiation in these animals differs from that in other vertebrates (elasmobranchs, amphibians, reptiles, birds and mammals).

1. Cyclostomes, teleosts and ganoids

Larval specimens of the lamprey *Entosphenus* possess a mixed population of germ cells consisting of variable proportions of oocytes and spermatogonia (individual specimens may possess 0 to 100 per

c

cent oocytes and 100 to 0 per cent spermatogonia). The onset of sexual differentiation is marked by the regression of the less dominant (i.e. less numerous) sex cells, although a few may occasionally be found even in the adult. As a result, the lampreys are characterized by a relatively long period of 'juvenile hermaphroditism' (Okkelberg, 1921), which according to D'Ancona (1951) would be more appropriately called 'intersexuality'.*

While the germ cells in amniotes become differentially distributed during sex differentiation (the germ cells in the male being carried into the interior of the gonad with the medullary cords, while those in the female remain peripheral), the distribution of germ cells in lampreys remains unaltered during the course of the process. The mechanism underlying the regression of the less dominant sex cells in these animals is not fully understood, though an attempt has been made to explain it (Okkelberg, 1921) on the basis of a process of local enzymic action as described by Goldschmidt (1917).

The hagfishes *Myxine* and *Bdellostoma* also possess potential germ cells of both sexes, but unlike the lampreys, where the cells are scattered more or less evenly throughout the gonadal tissue, the potential oocytes are situated in the cranial, and the potential spermatogonia in the caudal regions of the gonads (Cunningham, 1886; Schreiner, 1904, 1955; Cole, 1905; Conel, 1917). The process of sex differentiation in these animals consists essentially of the regression of either the cranial part of the gonad (leading to development in the male direction), or the regression of the caudal part (leading to development in the female direction). In some animals, the caudal (male) region fails to regress completely, while the cranial (female) part becomes fully differentiated (Schreiner, 1955). Animals in which this occurs are females. Adult males also occasionally contain vestiges of typically ovarian tissue (Schreiner, 1955).

The primordial germ cells in the sturgeon *Acipenser* have been claimed to be divisible into two size-groups even during the course of their migration to the genital ridges (Maschkowzeff, 1934), the larger cells being said to be presumptive oogonia and the smaller ones presumptive spermatogonia. D'Ancona (1951) has emphasized, however, that this type of dimorphism at so early a stage is unknown in all other vertebrates, and that the observation therefore requires confirmation.

In teleosts sexual differentiation is said to be first marked by the appearance of oocytes which enter the prophase of meiosis (see p. 32)

---

* The rate at which sex differentiation takes place has been found to differ between parasitic and non-parasitic lampreys, *Petromyzon marinus* and *Lampetra planeri*, respectively (Hardisty, 1960).

and which subsequently enlarge. Germ cells with the distinct characteristics of spermatogonia appear at a later stage of development (Hann, 1927; Wolf, 1931; Dildine, 1933; Johnston, 1951; Ashby, 1957). These observations have led many authors to postulate that an ovarian phase exists in the development of teleostean gonads regardless of the genetic sex of the individual. D'Ancona (1951) believes that the early appearance of typical oocytes does not warrant the assumption that all the animals possessing them necessarily pass through a female phase, since undifferentiated germ cells are also present at the same time: "Il semble plus exact de considérer comme indifférenciée la gonade à ce stade, dans laquelle coexistent des éléments des deux sexes, dont ceux du sexe femelle ont déjà pris leur aspect spécifique, tandis que ceux du sexe mâle sont encore indifférenciés." D'Ancona points out that, as in the lamprey, in which presumptive male and female germ cells are not topographically separated (as they are in the hagfishes), the sex of the gonad of the eel is determined by the differential regression of germ cells of one or the other type. D'Ancona concludes that most teleostean gonads initially contain the potential germ cells for both sexes, differentiation of sex being initially governed by their numerical proportions. The eel he regards as representing a more primitive condition of extended intersexuality. D'Ancona (1951) moreover suggests that considerable variation exists between different teleosts in the nature of the bisexual phase which precedes sex differentiation. Thus, for example, he observed that in two teleost families, the Sparidae and the Serranidae, male and female 'territories' are established in the gonad early in development and co-exist in the adult, leading to a condition of functional hermaphroditism as distinct from an initial transitory bisexuality. The latter, however, appears to be typical of many other teleosts, and is followed by a definite orientation in a male or female direction which may become evident at early stages of development (e.g. *Cottus:* Hann, 1927; *Salmo:* Ashby, 1957).

Dildine (1936) has reported that in *Lebistes,* the gonads of all individuals at early stages of development contain typical oocytes, and thus appear to be female. In 50 per cent of specimens the oocytes regress at a later stage of development, and are replaced by the development of testicular structures from the hilar region of the gonad. The mechanism by which sex differentiation takes place in *Lebistes* is not clear, but Dildine suggests that it is somewhat similar to that which occurs in elasmobranchs and tetrapods in that it is mediated by the relatively greater proliferation of the cortical region in the female than in the male, and by a relatively greater development of the hilar (cf. medulla in amniotes) region in the male than in the female. It is worth noting, however, that the suggestion that the gonads of *Lebistes* contain a medulla means that this species presumably differs from all other teleosts.

In many teleosts, the changes in the structure of the gonad during sex differentiation include the formation of an ovarian cavity by the establishment of deep longitudinal grooves on the ventro-lateral aspect of the organ. The cavity thus formed is a portion of the coelom and is lined by the 'germinal' epithelium (see p. 3). Ovigerous lamellae develop as folds of the epithelium which project into the cavity. (The ovary of the ganoid *Amia* also contains lamellae, but the ovarian cavity is absent; D'Ancona, 1955.) Fusion of the paired rudiments to form a median ovary occurs frequently among different species of teleosts. The testes develop an internal duct and usually remain paired (Essenberg, 1923; Wolf, 1931; Goodrich *et al.*, 1934; Fraser and Renton, 1940).

2. *Elasmobranchs, amphibians, reptiles, birds and mammals*

The process of sex differentiation in these groups of vertebrates consists essentially of the proliferation of the cortex and regression of the medulla in the female, and of the opposite process in the male. The recessive component (cortex in the male; medulla in the female) rarely differentiates further than the indifferent or bisexual stage. The germ cells become preferentially associated with the dominant component, frequently before sex differentiation has progressed to any extent. The distinction between the indifferent gonad stage and the onset of sex differentiation is therefore not clear-cut (see e.g. Allen, 1906; Swift, 1915, 1916; Bascom, 1923; Brambell, 1927), except perhaps in elasmobranchs (Chieffi, 1949, 1959) and amphibians (Witschi, 1914, 1929a, 1956; Christensen, 1930; Jurand, 1957).

In genetic males in these groups of vertebrates, the indifferent gonad becomes a testis earlier than it becomes transformed into an ovary in the genetic female, one of the earliest signs of testis-formation being the incorporation of the majority of germ cells into the developing medullary cords.*

According to those authors who maintain that the medulla originates from the first proliferation of the germinal epithelium (see pp. 13, 16 and Tables II–IV), the shift of the germ cells in the male entails little more than their inclusion within the proliferation during its advance into the underlying mescenchyme. Those who hold the view that the medulla originates from an extra-gonadal mesonephric 'blastema' (see

---

* In some species, the ovary may be recognized at early stages of development, not by the topographical distribution of the germ cells, but by the fact that a proportion of the latter enter the prophase of meiosis (see p. 23).

pp. 13 to 16) believe that during differentiation of the testis, the germ cells migrate into the developing medulla across the pre-existing albuginea. The latter process is said to be easily observed in amphibians, in which the albuginea is prominent (Witschi, 1914), and testicular differentiation is claimed to proceed similarly in man (Witschi, 1951a, 1956).

Regardless of its derivation, the medulla in the male consistently proliferates in the course of sex differentiation by the mitotic division of the germ cells and epithelial cells by which it is penetrated. The solid cords which arise from the latter cells become canalized and form a series of seminiferous tubules lined by supporting (future Sertoli) cells and germ cells. Connective tissue elements of mesenchymal origin further infiltrate between the tubules and also form a fibrous tunica albuginea which separates the tubules from the overlying epithelium, blood vessels following in their wake. Groups of interstitial cells (see pp. 27 to 28) commonly occur in the intertubular spaces.

The degree to which the cortex develops in the male is variable. In the majority of species, it does not develop beyond the indifferent stage and undergoes regression as the medulla proliferates. In most reptiles, some birds and a few mammals (also *Amblystoma*; Humphrey, 1929b), the cortex may develop beyond the indifferent stage. This development is transitory, for sooner or later, regression of the cortical region of the testis sets in, and any germ cells retained in it degenerate. As the testis enlarges, the cortex becomes attenuated and re-acquires the appearance of a flat coelomic epithelium. The seminiferous tubules acquire open connections with the tubules of the urinogenital complex (see p. 29) and thus with the Wolffian duct. These processes lead to the establishment of the full complement of structures characteristic of the immature testis.

(a) *The ovarian medulla*

Since the indifferent gonad stage is the same in both sexes, the ovarian medulla, at the onset of sex differentiation, is still voluminous and forms the bulk of the substance of the developing gonad. At this point of development, the ovarian medulla, which in some species (see Brambell, 1956) is separated from the cortex by a fine tunica albuginea, consists of germ cells and their associated epithelial cells, which form solid cords separated from each other by strands of connective tissue and blood vessels. Associated with the medulla are the rudiments of the rete ovarii system (see p. 29). The germ cells included in the medullary region eventually degenerate, but may persist for a considerable time (e.g. reptiles: Forbes, 1940; birds: Brode, 1928) and in mammals they may even enter the prophase of meiosis (Allen, 1904; Kingsbury, 1913; Brambell, 1956).

The medullary zone in female amniotes loses its individuality by the encroachment of cortical tissue from the surface of the ovary, and by the infiltration of vessels, nerves and connective tissue cells from the hilus. In elasmobranchs, the original medullary tissue in both sexes is displaced by the ingrowth of blood-forming elements from the haemopoietic tissue of the kidney. These elements persist only in the ovary (Chieffi, 1949, 1959). In the amphibian ovary, the weakly developed medullary cords, which are directly continuous with the rete cords, become hollow at their distal extremities and the cavities formed expand to obliterate the primary gonadal cavity. Since the cords were initially formed in relation to the somites ('pseudosegmental development'; see King, 1908; Witschi, 1914), a series of six or seven ovarial sacs are formed, giving the ovary a lobed appearance. The medulla in the amphibian ovary is generally represented by the walls of the sacs, which in the young frog fuse to form a secondary gonad cavity. Homologous cavitation occurs in reptiles (Forbes, 1940), birds (Brode, 1928; Witschi, 1956) and monotromes (Garde, 1930), resulting in a network of lacunae.

(b) *The ovarian cortex*

It is unanimously recognized that the ovarian cortex is derived from a proliferation of the germinal epithelium (the 'second proliferation'* described by many authors), that the majority of germ cells remain situated in the peripheral region of the gonad, i.e. in the cortex, and that they do not migrate into the medullary region as in the male. The early phases of sex differentiation in the female are therefore essentially an extension of the indifferent gonad stage, and typical ovarian features (e.g. marked proliferation of the cortex, appearance of nests of oocytes, and formation of the definitive tunica albuginea) do not become fully apparent until somewhat later (except in urodeles; see Burns, 1925, 1928; Humphrey, 1929b).

The rapid increase, through mitotic division, in the number of germ cells at early stages of ovarian differentiation has been recorded for elasmobranchs (Chieffi, 1959), amphibians (Witschi, 1914; Burns, 1925; Christensen, 1930; McCurdy, 1931), reptiles (Allen, 1906; Risley, 1933b), birds (Swift, 1915; Brode, 1928; Goldsmith, 1928; Willier, 1939) and mammals (Brambell, 1927; Mintz, 1959b; Beaumont, 1960b). Mitoses also occur in the epithelial cells and follicle cells (see pp. 26 to 27). These divisions result in an increase in the thickness

* Felix (1912) and Simkins (1928) do not believe that a second proliferation occurs in the human female. Brambell (1927), amongst others, considers that in some mammals, the first and second proliferations are continuous with one another.

of the cortex, and in amniotes, localized areas of proliferation may give rise to cord-like ingrowths towards the medulla which are known as Pflüger's tubules (dog: Jonckheere, 1930; cat: Winiwarter and Sainmont, 1909; rabbit: Winiwarter, 1901; Allen, 1904; man: Winiwarter, 1910).* In other species, a solid epithelial 'nucleus' later becomes split up into cords by the infiltration of connective tissue (Brambell, 1927; Hargitt, 1930). The cortical cords may be continuous with those of the medullary proliferation (see e.g. Torrey, 1945), and while they retain their connection with the outer epithelial layers for a considerable time, even after their ingrowth has ceased, they eventually become separated from the surface by a tunica albuginea which, in amphibians, arises from the mesenchyme of the primary gonad cavity (Brambell, 1930, 1956; Willier, 1939; Witschi, 1951a). Whether or not the cortex is arranged in cord-like structures primarily, or secondarily by the ingrowth of mesenchyme and connective tissue, the final result is the isolation of small nests of germ cells surrounded by follicular envelopes.†

After their initial phase of mitotic proliferation, the cortical germ cells (oogonia) enter meiotic prophase and become, by definition, oocytes (see pp. 32 to 33). (Corresponding stages in the male generally do not appear until after birth.) Not all oogonia enter meiotic prophase at the same time. Those situated relatively deeply develop earlier, so that in amphibians and birds, for example, oocytes in the more central areas of the ovary co-exist with oogonia at the periphery which are still undergoing mitotic proliferation (D'Hollander, 1904; Witschi, 1914; Burns, 1925; amongst others). Oogonial divisions eventually cease, either permanently (as in birds and mammals) or temporarily (as in amphibians and most reptiles). The persistence of oogonia after birth, and their capacity to divide mitotically (i.e. the process of oogenesis) is discussed in sect. II of this chapter.

(c) *Equipotentiality of germ cells*

The fact that in several vertebrates the embryo passes through a bisexual phase is shown by (i) the transitory development of features of the opposite sex (as in some elasmobranchs, urodeles, reptiles and mammals); (ii) the persistence of features characteristic of the opposite

---

* Ingrowths of cortical cords from the epithelium are said to continue for a considerable time (until birth or even to maturity) in some mammals, and some authors have reported the formation of a third proliferation. Such cords have also been described in the mouse after X-ray sterilization (Brambell et al., 1927a, b). For a detailed discussion, see Brambell (1956).

† In mammals, further ingrowth of fibrous tissue from the hilar region of the gonad (septa ovarii) radiates out towards the periphery of the ovary and incompletely divides the cortex into compartments.

sex (as in some amphibians and reptiles); or (iii) the failure of one gonad to acquire the full complement of female characteristics (as in birds).

Examples of the first form of bisexuality include the migration, in the female undergoing sexual differentiation, of germ cells into the medullary region (e.g. elasmobranchs: Chieffi, 1949, 1959). A similar phenomenon is seen during the indifferent gonad stage in a number of amniotes (see pp. 17, 21). The reverse situation is seen in male reptiles, the gonads of which develop a thick but transitory cortex.

The second form of bisexuality is illustrated by the formation of Bidder's organ (see p. 10) which differentiates from the intermediate portion of the genital ridge and which co-exists with the testes in the male toad (e.g. Ponse, 1924), and by the 'medullary rests' of the female alligator (Forbes, 1940).

The third form is represented by most birds, in which the right ovary contains only a small number of germ cells, mainly situated in the medullary region, which are capable, under certain conditions (e.g. after sinistral ovariectomy) of becoming transformed into typical spermatogonia (capable of division to complete the seminiferous series resulting in spermatozoa; Fell, 1923; Benoit, 1924; Brode, 1928; Brambell and Marrian, 1929; Gray, 1930; amongst others).

The examples of sex reversal in birds, in which an ovary showing clear signs of oogenesis may, under certain conditions, be partly or completely transformed into a testis in which functional sperm are produced, demonstrate that the sex chromosomes carried by the germ cells are not primarily responsible for the direction of differentiation into the gametes of the two sexes (sperm or ova). What these observations on sex reversal do demonstrate is that the direction of differentiation is determined by the region of the gonad in which the germ cells reside, and that the latter are initially bipotential. The latter conclusion also emerges from studies of natural and experimental sex reversal (see Chapter 13) in teleosts (D'Ancona, 1956a), elasmobranchs (Chieffi, 1959), amphibians (e.g. Witschi, 1914–1929b; Humphrey, 1929b; Burns, 1931; Foote and Witschi, 1939), reptiles (Risley, 1930) and mammals (see Burns, 1955).

The nature of the mechanism underlying sex differentiation is still not fully understood. The indifference or bisexuality of gonads at early stages of development, and the bipotential nature of the germ cells, show clearly that the differentiation of a testis or ovary depends on a complex sex-determining mechanism whose influence becomes manifest only gradually as development advances. Witschi's (1931) theory that differentiation is mediated by specific inductor substances, medullarin and cortexin, has received wide support (see also Witschi, 1914, 1929b, 1936), which largely derives from experimental investigations which are beyond the scope of this chapter. This subject was discussed in detail at the "Colloque sur la Différenciation Sexuelle chez les Vertébrés" held in Paris in 1950, to the Proceedings of which the reader is referred (as also to Witschi, 1951a; Burns, 1955).

F. Origin of ovarian asymmetry

Although the ovaries originate as bilateral primordia in all vertebrates, only a single ovary is present in the adults of certain groups, either due to the fusion of the two primordia, or to a failure of one gonad to complete its development. The fusion of the bilateral primordia to form a single median ovary may be complete (as in lampreys; Okkelberg, 1921), almost complete (as in some viviparous teleosts in which only some internal structures persisting after birth betray a bilateral origin; Goodrich et al., 1934; Turner, 1938a; Mendoza, 1940; Fraser and Renton, 1940) or partial (as in some teleosts where only the 'oviducts' fuse, e.g. *Phoxinus*; Bullough, 1939).

The failure of one ovary to develop fully, which is typical of some reptiles and most birds (e.g. Witschi, 1935; Stanley and Witschi, 1940; Pasteels, 1953) also occurs in Myxinoids (where the left gonad rudiment atrophies early in development; Felix and Bühler, 1906; Okkelberg, 1921), in some elasmobranchs (where the left rudiment disappears soon after birth; Matthews, 1950; Chieffi, 1955b, 1959), and for example, in the teleost *Micropterus* (where a smaller left ovary partially fuses on to the functional right ovary; Johnston, 1951).

The failure of one ovary to develop fully in birds (Firket, 1913, 1914; Swift, 1915; Defretin, 1924; Goldsmith, 1928; Brode, 1928; Dantschakoff, 1931a; Witschi, 1935, 1956) and probably in other groups also (elasmobranchs: Chieffi, 1955b, 1959; some reptiles: Stanley and Witschi, 1940) is due to the fact that at an early stage of migration, the majority of primordial germ cells migrate to the cortex of the opposite side, the number persisting in the cortical region of the nonfunctional ovary being very small (see p. 8).

The mechanism underlying ovarian asymmetry in monotremes (Garde, 1930) and certain bats (Matthews, 1937) is uncertain. It is possible that in these animals, as well as in the Myxinoids, there is an early differential distribution of the germ cells between the two sides.

G. Other cellular components of the ovary

Apart from the germ cells and the germinal epithelium, the following cells and structures are readily recognized in the ovaries of adult mammals: granulosa cells, theca interna and externa, corpora lutea, strands of connective tissue and, finally, clumps of variably shaped cells which fill the spaces between follicles and corpora lutea. Among these apparently non-specialized cells, which are usually referred to as the ovarian 'stroma', are single cells or nests of large cells which give positive histochemical reactions for lipids (see Chapter 3, sect. II, B) and which are often referred to as interstitial cells (see below). In some species, interstitial cells form separate glandular masses called 'interstitial glands' (e.g. rabbit, mole), but in the majority of mammals, they are scattered and not readily differentiated from neighbouring cells of the stroma.

The cellular components of the ovary, apart from the germ cells themselves, appear to be capable of undergoing considerable modification. Not only do the granulosa and theca cells become 'luteinized' under the influence of hypophysial hormones, but a variety of other cellular transformations appear to take place both spontaneously (e.g. in old age) and under various experimental conditions. From the information available, it is impossible to say which particular cells included under the non-specific term of 'stromal' cells can become transformed under what particular stimuli. All that can be said is that when observed at any given moment, the form of the ovary (and its cells) seems to all intents and purposes fixed, and that the processes of differentiation, regeneration and transformation which it may undergo cannot be accurately predicted from histological studies.

In view of the apparent pluripotentiality of 'stromal' cells and of the constant change in the pattern of their form and distribution; and because of the difficulty of recognizing interstitial cells in the majority of species, views about the embryological origin of these ovarian cells must be treated with reserve.

1. Follicle cells

In all vertebrates the oocyte becomes enveloped in an ovarian follicle during its growth and maturation (see Chapters 2B, sect. III, A and 2C, sect. III, A; see also Brambell, 1956).

Soon after they arrive in the genital ridges, the primordial germ cells acquire a covering of cells which flatten. It is generally believed that these cells are derived from the surface epithelium of the genital ridge, though in Amblystoma they are said to be mesenchymal in origin (Burns, 1925) and in Rana to be derived from the same epithelial 'blastema' which produces the medulla and the interrenal bodies (Vannini and Sabbadin, 1954). Since the germ cells are intimately connected at the earliest stages of development with both the surface epithelium and with subepithelial mesenchyme, it is possible that the follicle cells may arise from either tissue (Witschi, 1951a).

The close association between the germ cells and the somatic (granulosa) cells by which they are surrounded suggests that the former may exert some inductive influence upon the latter (see e.g. Brachet, 1950). This view is supported by the fact that the granulosa cells degenerate when oocytes become atretic or are damaged by ionizing radiations (see Chapters 4 and 22, respectively), and that typical follicles do not develop in ovaries which lack oocytes. While the early stages in follicular development are 'autonomous', the further growth of the follicle is dependent upon gonadotrophic stimulation (see Chapters 6, sect. I, B and 7, sect. III, A).

The follicle cells in the female are claimed to be homologous with the Sertoli cells in the male (see Witschi, 1951a).

2. *Secretory cells*

The theca interna cells, which surround the growing and mature follicle, the interstitial cells, and, at least in mammals, the cells of the corpus luteum (see Chapter 3, sect. II, B) are all regarded as probable sources of ovarian hormone whose output is directly dependent upon hypophysial stimulation (see Chapter 7, sect. III, A). The secretory capacity of the theca interna increases as the follicle which it surrounds approaches maturation, while the corpus luteum secretes hormones only during a variable and limited period.

The secretory cells of the ovaries of lower vertebrates have not been properly identified (see Chapters 5–7 and 17; also *Mem. Soc. Endocrin.* No. 4, 1955; and Gorbman, 1959). In cyclostomes, teleosts and elasmobranchs, they are said to be modified follicle cells which appear as components of pre- and post-ovulatory 'corpora lutea'. Amphibians and reptiles also develop corpora lutea which are derived, at least in part, from the theca layer which surrounds the follicle.

The formation and function of the theca interna and the corpus luteum are dealt with elsewhere in this book (Chapters 5 and 6).

The identity of interstitial cells, particularly in mammals, has been the subject of considerable discussion (see Chapter 2C, sect. IV; also Brambell, 1956). In birds and mammals, they are said to be large polyhedral cells with a clearly defined cell membrane, abundant cytoplasm and distinct rounded or ovoid nuclei and frequently contain fat globules (see Chapter 3). In birds, the cells are scattered singly or in small islets in the thecal walls of ovarian follicles and in the stroma. In mammals, the distribution of interstitial cells* is very variable (see Chapter 2C, sect. IV and V).

* For an account of the so-called 'sympathicotrophic cells' and 'Berger cells', the reader is referred to Sternberg (1949) and Brambell (1956).

Some authors support the view that the interstitial cells are formed *after* birth from the theca interna of atretic follicles by reference to certain structural and histochemical changes associated with the process of atresia (e.g. Dawson and McCabe, 1951; Rennels, 1951). There are, however, examples among birds (see e.g. Benoit, 1926) and mammals (e.g. Winiwarter, 1910; Kingsbury, 1914; O'Donoghue, 1916; Cole *et al.*, 1933; Davies *et al.*, 1957) where interstitial cells are claimed to be present in foetal or neonatal animals before the follicles have acquired distinct thecae, and thus before corpora lutea could have involuted and previously enlarged follicles become atretic. In these instances, it appears that the precursor interstitial cells are formed in the region which, in most vertebrate classes, constitutes the ovarian medulla during the late indifferent gonad stage (see Brambell, 1956; also Table III, p. 15).

The precursor interstitial cells have been claimed, mainly on the basis of arbitrary histological interpretation, to originate either from medullary cords derived from ingrowths of the surface epithelium of the genital ridges, or from the so-called 'true' medullary cells (see Witschi, 1951a) derived from the mesonephric 'blastema'. The claim that the functional similarity of gonadal interstitial cells and adrenocortical cells (see Chapter 16, sect. I; and Segal, 1959) demonstrates a common embryological origin is based on, at the most, no more than highly circumstantial evidence. It is also clear that little progress will be made towards the establishment of the origin of interstitial cells until such time as histochemical methods are devised whereby these cells become consistently and unequivocally identifiable in both foetal and adult material.

3. *Ovarian stroma*

The origin of the ovarian stroma, which is more prominent in amniotes than in lower vertebrates, is no more clearly understood than that of the interstitial cells. It is probable that it is derived, like the interstitial cells, from the elements of the regressing ovarian medulla. It is also possible that further ingrowths from the ovarian hilar region, and perhaps to a lesser extent from germinal epithelial cells, contribute to its formation. The derivation of the cells which later become transformed into connective tissue cells, fibroblasts, smooth muscle cells, capillaries, and other derivatives of the primary mesenchyme, is not established (see p. 26). It has been suggested that in cyclostomes and teleosts (see Table II), the stroma largely consials of epithelial cells (in addition to the vascular and mesenchymst elements).

H. Associated ovarian structures

1. *Rete ovarii*

A connection between the mesonephros and the gonads, which is related to the gonadal medulla,* is formed in both sexes during the indifferent period of gonad development. The connection remains rudimentary in the female, and does not participate in the adult in the transport of gametes, which are discharged directly into the coelom. In the males of elasmobranchs, amphibians and amniotes, spermatozoa are transferred from the testis to the exterior through a complex system of ducts, the most distal parts of which represent the embryological mesonephric connection.

Before sex differentiation sets in, solid cellular cords called rete cords connect the medulla with the more cranially situated tubules of the mesonephros. The precise region from which these cords originate (gonadal medulla, portions of the glomerular apparatus of the kidney, or a relatively undifferentiated region intermediate in position), appears to vary considerably in different classes of vertebrates. There is also some diversity of opinion regarding the origin of the cords in individual species (see Brambell, 1956).

In the female, the rete cords do not develop after the onset of sexual differentiation. In mammals, they persist at the base or hilus of the gonad in the form of a small mass of blind tubules or solid cords. In amphibians, the rete ovarii is continuous with the inflated sac-like medullary cords and forms part of the epithelial lining of the ovarial sac (see p. 22). In reptiles (Forbes, 1940) and birds (Witschi, 1956), the cavities of the medullary cords are homologous with those in amphibians and with the rete tubules of the testis. The rete ovarii remains capable of becoming functional for a certain time during ovarian differentiation, and may form a functional urinogenital connection if sex reversal occurs (Witschi, 1931; Foote and Witschi, 1939).

2. *Ovarian bursa*

The ovaries of certain mammals are surrounded by a peritoneal capsule or ovarian bursa which varies considerably between species in the extent to which it communicates with the coelomic cavity (see Eckstein and Zuckerman, 1956; also Chapter 2C, sect. I). The ovarian bursa is absent in man; forms a wide open cup in the cat, hyena, guinea pig, mole and pig; and wholly encapsulates the ovary in the rat and the mouse.

* According to Witschi (1951a), no urinogenital connections are formed during development in cyclostomes and teleosts, in which the medullary component of the gonad is also absent.

The development of the ovarian bursa has been described for the rat and the mouse by Kellogg (1941) and Agduhr (1927) respectively. In the rat, the bursa arises mainly from the mesosalpinx, with contributions from the mesovarium and the ligamentum ovarii proprium, and from a ligament which is loosely attached to the dorsal body wall and leads cranially as far as the diaphragm. The earliest stage of development at which the bursa becomes apparent is the 16th day of intra-uterine life (i.e. shortly after the onset of sexual differentiation). The ovary is attached to the mesosalpinx (which is derived partly from the peritoneum of the degenerating mesonephros, and partly from the tubal ridge) by a short mesentery or mesovarium. Between the 16th day of gestation and the time of birth, the oviduct, together with its elongating mesosalpinx, moves across the surface of the ovary, and by the 19th day, the rat ovary is already seen to lie in a shallow cup formed by the mesosalpinx and bounded laterally by the oviduct. The cranial part of the oviduct is then pulled over the caudal surface of the ovary, and, at term, a closed bursa is fully established except for a very small ventro-caudal opening. According to Kellogg, the latter finally closes on about the 7th day after birth. In the mouse, the opening appears to close at an earlier stage of development (Agduhr, 1927). There is some evidence, however, that a small opening remains patent throughout life in both rats and mice (Alden, 1942; Wimsatt and Waldo, 1945; see also Kingery, 1917) and that it closes periodically in phase with the oestrous cycle.

Embryological studies in other mammalian species are reviewed by Kellogg (1941) who concluded that, in general, "the peritoneal sac arises in some way from the mesentery of the oviduct or uterus and that its formation is accompanied by the elongation of the oviduct. The exact manner of its development has not been made very clear."

3. Vestiges of mesonephros

In amniote embryos, the entire mesonephros involutes in both sexes after the formation of the metanephros. Vestiges do, however, persist and can be recognized after birth. The cranial portion of the mesonephros, which contributed to the urinogenital connection, is retained in the female as the epoöphoron, a small mass of tissue in the mesovarium similar in character to the rete ovarii. In the male, the cranial portion of the mesonephros is functional and forms the epididymis. The caudal portion of the mesonephros is also retained in a rudimentary non-functional form as the paroöphoron and para-didymis respectively.

I. Conclusion

In seeking to understand why opinion is so uncertain on a variety of aspects of ovarian development, in particular about the origin of the primordial germ cells, it is useful to remember that the embryologist has essentially only three techniques at his disposal, of which two are inevitably subjective in their application. The method nearest to hand is the histological description of a series of presumed successive developmental stages, the object being to recognize and trace individual cellular elements. Because of the complex morphogenetic movements which occur during ontogeny, this approach is necessarily arbitrary unless the cells that are being traced possess some characteristic feature or 'marker' which is revealed by conventional histological techniques, and which distinguishes them from other cellular elements in the embryo. For example, it must be certain that characteristic features like 'pseudopodia' occasionally claimed to be visible in primordial germ cells (see p. 7) are not the result of crenation of the cell membrane induced by inadequate fixation.

This kind of histological approach was the earliest to be used in the study of the origin of germ cells, and since the microscopic and chemical procedures required for its application had reached a high standard nearly a century ago, the earliest reports based on this method are in no way inferior to those published more recently. Indeed, the main elements in the story of oogenesis were firmly established by the time Winiwarter and Sainmont (1909) published their classic observations on oogenesis in the cat.

The second line of approach open to the embryologist concerned with the origin of germ cells is to use histochemical reagents which specifically mark some particular structural, chemical or enzymic component of a lineage of cells which would not normally become distinguishable by standard staining methods. This method is of value only if the histochemical reaction is positive for one type of cell, and is therefore also somewhat arbitrary in its application.

The third method is the experimental modification of the normal pattern of development by such procedures as extirpation, transplantation or irradiation of tissues, parabiosis, and administration of chemical substances (e.g. hormones). The techniques of extirpation and transplantation of gonadal primordia, which have been very successfully used in amphibian larvae and avian embryos, are hardly applicable to early embryos of placental animals.

In assessing such information as has been published, it is therefore necessary to differentiate between conclusions that are based on possibly arbitrary interpretations of simple histological observations, and those founded on solid experimental proof. The brief survey given in this chapter suggests that there is substantial support for the view that throughout the vertebrates, the primordial germ cells become segregated, and are distinct from other embryonic cells, at very early stages of development, and that frequently they arise in sites which are quite unrelated to those of the presumptive gonadal regions. There is also experimental evidence to indicate that the primordial germ cells migrate from their extra-gonadal sites of origin to the genital ridges, and that after multiplying, they differentiate at varying times during the life-cycle of the individual into spermatogonia or oogonia. The method by which the germ cells migrate has not been fully established for the majority of vertebrates. Apart from a few decisive experiments such as those of Willier (1937), Simon (1957) and Mintz (1959b), much of the available evidence for a particular mode of migration has been inferred from studies of histological material alone, and is therefore open, as indicated above, to arbitrary interpretation.

A critical survey of the published reports on the embryological origin of non-germinal ovarian cells reveals an urgent need for experimental studies. It is plain that the many conflicting statements on this subject which appear in the literature are unlikely to be resolved until the results of properly controlled experiments become available.

II. Oogenesis

A. Introduction

The term oogenesis is used to denote the transformation of oogonia, which themselves multiply in the ovary by the process of mitotic divisions, into oocytes. The primary oocytes so formed must of necessity undergo reduction division (meiosis) to yield, first, a secondary (haploid) oocyte and a first polar body, and subsequently, by mitotic division of the secondary oocyte, the definitive gamete (the haploid ovum, or ovum for short) and a second polar body. This pattern occurs uniformly throughout the vertebrates. Oogenesis as such is therefore dependent in the first place upon the mitotic division of primordial germ cells and oogonia. The chromosomal changes characteristic of meiosis occur only in primary oocytes that have been formed from oogonia.

It should be noted that the term oogenesis has frequently been used incorrectly in the past, and occasionally still is, to apply to the growth of the oocyte and its follicular envelope, associated in some species with vitellogenesis—processes which are known to occur after part of the meiotic prophase has already taken place.* For this reason, the following cytological terms are described below in the sense they are used in the ensuing discussion.

B. Terminology

Essentially the process of meiosis consists of two nuclear divisions, of which the first involves the halving of the number of chromosomes. The second division (of cells which are already haploid) is mitotic in character, and results in the production of two haploid daughter cells.

The first division is subdivided into four main phases: prophase, metaphase, telophase and anaphase, of which all but the first, though differing in detail, are essentially similar to the corresponding phases of mitosis. The prophase of meiosis is further divided into four major stages:

Leptotene: the nucleus contains individual single chromosomes, usually with clearly marked chromomeres. The chromosomes are frequently polarized, that is to say, they are not distributed randomly, but lie clumped to one side with a clear space at the opposite pole of the nucleus. This arrangement, which occurs commonly in vertebrate oocytes, is also called *synizesis*.

Zygotene: homologous pairs of chromosomes come to lie parallel to each other. The pairing process, also called *synapsis*, may begin at any of several places along the length of the chromosomes (e.g. terminal or intermediate).

Pachytene: the paired chromosomes or bivalents become thicker, and in some species appear to be coiled around each other. The number of visible threads becomes halved, but cross-sections of individual threads show that each consists of two separate components. The chromosomes are frequently polarized, and their arrangement, appearing to originate from one pole of the nucleus, resembles that of a bunch of flowers ('bouquet').† Pachytene is a relatively stable phase and, with the exception of diplotene in animals bearing yolky eggs (see below), is the longest individual phase of meiotic prophase.

Diplotene: the paired chromosomes begin to split longitudinally, and each of the two individual chromosomes splits further into two threads; cross-sections will therefore show tetrads (four threads).

* The process of vitellogenesis is outside the scope of this chapter, and the reader is referred to Loyez (1906), Sonnenbrodt (1908), Van Durme (1914), Brambell (1925), Marza and Marza (1936), Flynn and Hill (1939), Boyd (1941), Olsen (1942) and Olsen and Fraps (1944) amongst others.

† The 'bouquet' configuration may occur at zygotene also.

D

The homologous chromosomes begin to separate from each other, but are held together at one or more points along their length (chiasmata). The final separation involves the phenomenon of 'crossing over', whereby variable portions of chromatids are exchanged. The chromosomes become shorter and their coiled structure becomes more apparent. In those species that have yolky eggs, the diplotene phase is prolonged and is characterized by the appearance of very long chromosomes with radiating hairs or side-loops which appear to originate from the chromomeres. The structural and functional significance of these giant 'hairy' chromosomes, called *lampbrush chromosomes*, has been studied in detail, particularly in Amphibia (see p. 44). During their formation, the lampbrush chromosomes become looser in structure and lose their affinity for nuclear stains.

The prophase of meiosis occurs at variable times during the life-span of different vertebrates. The duration of the individual phases has been estimated for some laboratory rodents (see p. 69), in which they are limited to the period immediately preceding and following birth.

The typical diplotene phase of meiosis is followed, in mammals, by a resting phase of variable length, usually referred to as the *dictyate* stage.* In practically all mature mammals (see pp. 54 to 57), the chromosomal configuration of all oocytes seen in the ovary (other than those undergoing maturation division; see below) is characteristic of the dictyate phase. This phase may be absent in vertebrates bearing yolky eggs, being replaced by an excessively prolonged diplotene phase (see above) during which the chromosomes, as in the mammalian dictyate phase, lose some of their staining properties.

Meiotic metaphase, telophase and anaphase, yielding two haploid daughter cells, do not appear to occur during the embryonic development of any vertebrate, being limited to the sexually mature female and characteristically occurring shortly before ovulation or the liberation of the mature ovum (see Chapters 5, 6 and 8). (Cells undergoing degeneration may show pseudo-maturation spindles and precocious expulsion of the first polar body. This problem, with respect to mammals, is considered in Chapter 4.)

The discussion in this section will be focused on evidence relating to the process of oogenesis, as defined above, during the life-cycle of different classes of vertebrates.

C. Cyclostomes

The oogonia are derived exclusively from primordial germ cells of extra-gonadal origin which had previously migrated to the genital

---

* This is distinct from *interphase*, which usually denotes the resting period between two mitotic divisions.

ridges (Okkelberg, 1921). These germ cells divide mitotically a number of times, yielding daughter cells which, before reaching the stage of cell-growth, undergo a series of changes characteristic of meiotic pro-phase (leptotene, synapsis, pachytene, diplotene; Okkelberg, 1921). Oocytes remain in a stage which Okkelberg called 'diakinese' (charac-terized by the presence of discrete paired chromosomes, some in contact with the nuclear envelope in the form of tetrads) during the growth period, and probably up to the time of sexual maturity. Boyd (1941) considers that Okkelberg's 'diakinese' stage probably represents diplotene, since his description suggests that later in development the chromosomes assume a typical lampbrush configuration.

After arrival at the genital ridges, the primordial gonocytes of the lamprey *Entosphenus* remain quiescent for a short period and then undergo division to form either isolated cells or nests of cells. The larvae remain sexually indifferent until they are 35 mm long, clear-cut bisexual elements persisting (Okkelberg, 1921). There is some evidence to suggest that the isolated cells represent presumptive oogonia, whereas those arranged in nests will later participate in the formation of spermatic cysts. The presumptive oogonia are scattered amongst the male germ cell cysts in the lampreys, but are topographically separated in both larval and adult myxinoids into a male caudal and a female cranial portion (Schreiner, 1904, 1955; Cole, 1905; Conel, 1917). (The gonadal medulla is absent in cyclostomes, but early differentiation depends not only on the germ cells but also on the ingrowths of epithelial cells forming either granulosa cell coverings for the oogonia, or investing layers for the cysts of the male gonocytes; see pp. 14 and 18).

The composition of the gonads of larval lampreys varies consider-ably between individual specimens. Some contain a high proportion of actively dividing germ cells (presumptive male), while others consist mainly of enlarged cells which divide more rarely (presumptive female). The same is also true of adult myxinoids, in which the less dominant portion of the gonad later becomes vestigial.

It may thus be concluded that in the lamprey, no oogonia capable of mitotic proliferation persist up to the time of sexual maturity, oogenesis, as defined above, being restricted to very early stages of development. It is also clear that pachytene is followed by a prolonged phase of diplotene (characteristic of most vertebrates bearing yolky eggs; see p. 34) before the maturation division followed by ovulation takes place. Lampreys discharge eggs only once during their life-time and die shortly after reaching sexual maturity.

Information for adult myxinoids which experience more than one reproductive cycle does not appear to be available.

D. Fishes

The conclusion that primordial germ cells are derived from extra-gonadal cells and later give rise to oogonia appears to have been first reached by Balfour (1878) from his studies of selachian embryos. His view was supported, amongst others, by Eigenmann (1891, 1897) and Beard (1900, 1902), and vigorously opposed by a number of authors including Waldeyer (1870, 1906) who, following Pflüger's classical studies of mammalian material, believed that during embryonic development definitive oocytes are derived from the germinal epithelium. For a detailed discussion of the pioneer studies which led to much controversy as long as 50 years ago, the reader is referred to Maréchal (1907).

Rückert (1892) established the occurrence of giant lampbrush chromosomes in *Pristiurus*, and described a sequence of nuclear changes which is clearly meiotic in character. Examining sexually immature fish, he observed that mitotic divisions are very rare even in the smallest of all the germ cells present (22 μ in diameter) to which he refers as 'Ureier' or primordial germ cells. Oocytes measuring 28 μ in diameter contain fine faintly staining chromatin threads arranged in a loose knot filling the entire intranuclear space (leptotene). Rückert noted that as the germ cells increased in size, the chromosomes enlarged greatly but later shrank to less than a thousandth of their previous size. He concluded that the longitudinal splitting of the chromosomes (i.e. diplotene) occurs long (months or even years) before the germ cell is fully grown. Since his material was limited to sexually immature specimens, Rückert provides no information about the occurrence of mitotic and meiotic phenomena after the onset of maturity.

A further and very detailed study of oogenesis in the elasmobranch was undertaken by Maréchal (1904, 1907) who, unlike Rückert, was able to use Winiwarter's (1901) classic description of nuclear changes associated with meiotic prophase as a guide. He studied young and adult *Pristiurus* and *Scyllium*, and concluded that the smallest germ cells, which are no longer capable of dividing mitotically, represent oocytes in a resting phase that precedes meiotic prophase: "nous n'oserions affirmer que nous ayons recontré une seule division oogoniale bien authentique." The rarity or absence of mitotic divisions observed by both Maréchal and Rückert indicates that neoformation of oocytes, as defined above, probably does not occur in either adolescent or sexually mature elasmobranchs of the two species studied.

Maréchal's description of meiotic phenomena in elasmobranchs suggests that the pattern is identical with that found in higher vertebrates, including mammals, though it differs from the latter by the presence of lampbrush chromosomes. It also establishes clearly what Rückert had been unable to demonstrate, namely that a clear-cut resting phase exists between the last oogonial mitotic telophase and the onset of meiotic prophase, and that the chromosomes, though losing some of their affinity for stain during part of diplotene, retain their identity and structure and later enlarge to assume the lampbrush configuration.

A more recent study of the sexually mature basking shark (Matthews, 1950) indicates that at any given time, the number of germ cells containing some yolk and measuring more than 0·5 mm in diameter may be as high as 6×10^6. The smallest follicles are about 80 μ in diameter and are composed of cells within which the germ cell cannot be distinguished histologically. "In the next recognizable stage, one of the cells has become considerably larger than the others, measuring up to 70 μ in diameter; it has taken up a more or less central position in the follicle, now 150–200 μ in diameter, and is definitely recognizable as the oocyte." Mitotic and meiotic changes are not reported, and it is difficult to discover from Matthews' description whether oogenesis occurs in the adult female of this species. It is possible that by the time the female becomes sexually mature, all oogonial mitoses have ceased and the small cells situated in the centre of the primary follicles have already passed through the earliest stages of meiotic prophase. In view of the growth of the oocyte during late diplotene described for *Scyllium* and *Pristiurus*, however, it would be expected that even the smallest oocytes in the basking shark would be histologically identifiable. On the other hand, this creature is viviparous, and appears to differ from the other two species by the absence of lampbrush chromosomes. Moreover, Matthews was only able to capture specimens at restricted seasons of the year, and the possibility exists that oogenesis occurs at times when the sharks migrate off-shore.

The scanty evidence that is available would thus appear to indicate that oogenesis, as defined above, does not occur in elasmobranchs after the onset of sexual maturity.

The only other non-teleostean species investigated is the sturgeon. Moltchanova (1941) and Loukine (1941a, b) noted that after sexual maturity, when the fish are 6–7 years old, the ovaries undergo a succession of changes in phase with the spawning season. Cells described as oogonia and small oocytes occur, in the early part of the annual cycle, in scattered nests mingled with connective tissue cells. These small germ cells remain in the peripheral area of the gonad, while those at the centre enlarge and acquire yolk. The ovary does not return to its original state following the first spawning season. In addition to the small 'oocytes and oogonia', some growing oocytes and remains of old follicles persist. Moltchanova could not distinguish chromosomes in these germ cells, nor did she describe the occurrence of mitotic divisions. Hence the cells she described as oogonia may have been oocytes which had undergone early meiotic prophase before the onset of sexual maturity. From the evidence presented, it is impossible to say how the 'new' batches of oocytes following spawning arise.

A wide variety of teleosts has been studied, and the observations reported are both variable and controversial. The conclusions reached by the investigators fall into four main categories: (a) oocytes are derived from proliferations of the germinal epithelium; (b) they are derived from mitotic divisions of the follicular cells; (c) some oocytes are formed from pre-existing oogonia, while others are formed from epithelial cells; and (d) all definitive germ cells arise from pre-existing oogonia which have remained in the ovary from the time of their arrival (as primordial germ cells undergoing division) in the genital ridges during embryonic development. In addition, a number of reports on seasonal changes in the ovaries of teleosts have appeared, the authors not expressing any definite views as to the origin of 'new' germ cells which may make their appearance after sexual maturity (Fraser and Renton, 1940; Merriman and Schedl, 1941; James, 1946; Rosenthal, 1952; Yamamoto, 1956a, b).*

(a) *Oocytes are derived from proliferations of the germinal epithelium*

None of the authors who has supported this hypothesis provides an unequivocal demonstration of intermediate stages between epithelial cells and oocytes (e.g. Stuhlmann, 1887; Cunningham, 1898; Wallace, 1904; Franz, 1909; Philippi, 1909; Essenberg, 1923; Bailey, 1933; for a full discussion, see Eggert, 1931). In most cases, the author bases his conclusion on the simultaneous occurrence of large numbers of mitoses in epithelial cells on the one hand, and the appearance of young germ cells on the other. Moreover, none of the reports specifies early meiotic changes in the cells which are derived from the germinal epithelium. Since the latter may well show a seasonal peak in mitotic activity, the daughter cells resulting from such divisions being no more than vegetative cells, little reliance can be placed upon the conclusions of these reports in so far as oogenesis is concerned. On the other hand, Bullough (1939) states that in the minnow, *Phoxinus laevis*, oogonia 'appear' in the germinal epithelium, which in this species covers only part of the ovarian surface, and that the oogonia

---

* For a review of the seasonal changes in the reproductive organs of fishes, the reader is referred to Matthews and Marshall (1956). It must be emphasized, however, that the term oogenesis in their account does not necessarily signify the formation of new germ cells, but occasionally denotes the growth of pre-existing oocytes.

become directly 'transformed' into oocytes following a short period of rest. The oocytes are then said to enter prophase which is followed by a period of cell growth. (Bullough also suggests that shortly after spawning, new oogonia are formed from the cells of discharged follicles in which mitotic divisions are common.) In a later study, Bullough (1942a) proposed that oogonia, having arisen by the mitotic division of the germinal epithelium, pass through the tunica, remaining attached to it on the inner surface. He further suggests that when dividing, the epithelial cells might also give rise to new associated vegetative cells which form investing layers around the oogonia. Bullough estimates that five to six oogonia arise at the same time from each patch of the germinal epithelium, though the subsequent nuclear changes are not necessarily synchronized in each nest. Mitotic divisions in the germinal epithelium decrease in frequency and are absent in the winter, while increased environmental temperature is said to be associated with an increase in the number of oocytes.

Although Bullough was able to demonstrate the presence of meiotic prophase in oocytes of the minnow, his conclusion that the definitive germ cells are derived from epithelial cells is open to the same type of criticism as those he reached from his studies of the mouse (see p. 70; also Zuckerman, 1951).

(b) *Oocytes are derived from follicular cells*

Evidence supporting this view is equally speculative and unsatisfactory. Andreu *et al.* (1957), in their investigations on the pilchard *Sardinia pilchardus* (a species which is able to spawn many times during a single season), observed a large number of mitoses in the follicular tissue and the appearance of 'transitional stages' between follicular and germ cells. It may well be that in this species, oogonia lack any morphological features by which they could be histologically differentiated from follicular cells which, in the course of differentiation, may vary in size.

(c) *Oocytes are derived from both pre-existing oogonia and from epithelial cells*

Wheeler (1924) reported that in the dab, *Pleuronectes*, the number of eggs visible in the ovary does not seem to have diminished after each yearly spawning of large crops of ova. Oocytes pass through their whole cycle in one season preceding spawning, but no germinal nests which might produce later generations could be detected. After spawning, the ovary quickly 'fills' with small oocytes, but Wheeler was unable to find any signs of oogonial stages, nor could he demonstrate any transformation of somatic cells into oocytes. The small oocytes present after spawning showed synapsis, contraction, pachytene, diplotene and dictyate stages. Since he could not define intermediate stages between vegetative and germ cells, Wheeler concluded that some new oocytes arise from follicle cells belonging to the recently ovulated eggs.

Wolf (1929, 1931), working on immature female *Platypoecilus*, suggests that some transformations of epithelial cells into gametes can be seen. At the same time he considered many definitive germ cells to be derived from primordial germ cells. Transition stages between epithelial and germ cells were said to occur in the female only, Wolf being of the opinion that in the male all definitive germ cells are derived from primordial gonocytes.

According to Mendoza (1941), who studied the viviparous teleost *Neotoca bilineata*, production of oocytes does not cease entirely during gestation. Nests of small oocytes are always present, but only in small numbers until the end of gestation. A sharp rise in the number of oocytes was claimed to occur at this period, associated with atresia which, however, was believed not to vary considerably in phase with the reproductive cycle. The oocytes were seen to lie in the walls of ovigerous folds (see p. 20), the smallest (7 μ in diameter) undergoing meiotic prophase, having originated, according to Mendoza, from the epithelial invaginations of the folds. Germ cells were also often seen in the surface epithelium of the folds, a finding which led Mendoza (1943) to conclude that oocytes may differentiate *before* the epithelium has invaginated, and that only a proportion of definitive germ cells arise from the epithelial cells.

Ashby's (1957) observations on the brown trout show that the gonadal folds of the ovary of 5½-months-old fish contain 'protogonia' of which some are in the leptotene stage of meiosis. Large nests of these 'protogonia' are said to occur in the cranial part of the gonad, scattered individually between other ovarian elements. These cells are said to degenerate subsequently. At the age of 192–206 days, several oocytes were in the diplotene stage of meiosis, entering a period of cell-growth by 232 days. At 300 days, oocytes "seen earlier" (but clearly not identifiable as being the same cells as those seen in younger specimens) had enlarged, and an increase was said to occur in the number of small oocytes, associated with a hypertrophy of the epithelium lining the ovigerous folds. Ashby concluded that this epithelium was responsible for the production not only of follicular and stroma cells, but of oogonia also. Ashby's interpretation of his observations is thus reminiscent of that of some workers (e.g. Kingery, 1917) who have studied oogenesis in mammals (see p. 55). Whilst the presence of germ cells in early meiotic prophase is recognized, these workers assume, without evidence, that such degeneration as may be occurring in *some* cells is in effect responsible for the destruction of *all* pre-existing germ cells, viable oocytes then arising from vegetative cells. This conclusion can have little substance in the absence of quantitative studies.

As none of the authors describes mitotic divisions of oogonia, the possibility exists that the youngest germ cells, whose small size may make them difficult to identify, represent pre-meiotic oocytes which subsequently, and in phase with the reproductive cycle, enter the leptotene stage of meiosis and enlarge. It is equally probable, however, as Eggert (1931) points out, that the observers in question missed the restricted period of the year during which oogonial divisions occur, or else mistook epithelial cell divisions for oogonial divisions.

(d) *Oocytes are derived exclusively from pre-existing oogonia*

In his study of *Cottus bairdii*, Hann (1927) observed that oogonia are present throughout the year. Oogonial divisions occur in young fish (7 weeks old), and are followed by early maturation phases in June and October. Small oocytes which start to grow in the first year mature in 2-year old fish, and subsequent oogonial divisions commence in May of each year, spawning having taken place in April. Oocytes clearly showing synizesis are formed only from oogonial divisions, and none is formed from somatic cells. Hann concluded as follows: "Thus each year after the first, a portion of the oogonia changes to oocytes and increases the reserve supply, and at the same time a portion of the reserve supply enters the secondary growth phase and develops during the year into mature ova."

A similar conclusion was reached by Craig-Bennett (1930) who observed many oogonial divisions in the stickleback shortly after spawning, though a small number could be detected at other times of the year also. The oogonia grow into primary oocytes from July to September, and secondary yolk formation takes place between September and May. Maturation division and discharge of ripe ova occurs in May. Unlike Hann, however, Craig-Bennett did not describe chromosomal changes corresponding to the prophase of meiosis.

In an exhaustive study of a number of species belonging to the Gobiiformes and Blenniiformes, Eggert (1931) observed that oogonia are present at all times of the year, and that they divide mitotically to give rise to oocytes shortly after spawning. The newly formed cells undergo the prophase of meiosis, and Eggert believes that the pre-meiotic resting phase, as claimed by Maréchal (1904, 1907) for elasmobranchs and by Franz (1909) for teleosts, is unlikely to occur. On the contrary, he believes that the time interval between the last division of oogonia and the onset of the prophase of meiosis is brief. Like Hibbard and Parat (1927) and Narain (1930), he was able to detect cytological features which characterize the germ cells, and concluded that (i) there is no evidence that oocytes are derived from the germinal epithelium and (ii) in all teleosts, oocytes proliferate through the multiplication of oogonia. In his view earlier authors did not detect the divisions of oogonia because oogonia are small and not readily differentiated from large cells situated in the germinal epithelium (though some differences are detectable), and because the divisions of oogonia occur only during one relatively short season of the year. The division of oogonia is synchronized within the nests of cells which are relatively small, the maximum number of divisions visible in any one aggregate of germ cells being eight to twelve. Eggert also gives a detailed description of the nuclear changes taking place in the course of the growth of the oocytes, and remarks that *Periophthalmus chrysospilos* and *P. vulgaris*, species which do not experience restricted breeding cycles, are the only teleosts which he has examined in which cyclical oogenesis fails to occur. Spawning in these species occurs sporadically throughout the year, and is associated with divisions of oogonia and growth of oocytes independently of seasonal changes.

The evidence provided by Matthews' (1938) study of the killifish *Fundulus* is less satisfactory in so far as he did not trace the origin or recognize the nature of the large numbers of small cells which he observed immediately under the epithelium of the ovigerous folds in the ovary. He noted that the cells persist throughout the year, that they divide actively in a cyclical manner, and that they are characterized by relatively large nuclei and scanty cytoplasm. The description he provides suggests that these cells may be oogonia. Matthews does not suggest that the new oocytes formed seasonally are derived from the germinal epithelium.

Turner (1938a) investigated the origin of germ cells in a viviparous teleost, *Cymatogaster*, and observed that the ovary is histologically immature at birth and that it is characterized by rudiments of ovigerous folds containing single germ cells or nests of germ cells, together with developing oocytes. Mitoses are frequent in some cells and synizesis was observed 6 weeks *post partum*. The dorsal parts of the ovigerous folds contain cavities, while the ventral parts are solid and contain nests of germ cells in the leptotene stage of meiosis, and in mitosis. The growth of the oocytes takes place in the dorsal portions. The female is inseminated at the age of 5 months *post partum*. The ovigerous folds undergo extensive growth, while the nests of germ cells remain quiescent. The parental ovary involutes after parturition but then enlarges, while mitoses occur in the nests of germ cells, those oocytes that had not previously matured also enlarging at the same time.

A second example of a topographical segregation of immature germ cells is provided by Suzuki's (1939) report on a local Japanese race of *Plecoglossus altivelis* (Salmonidae). Eggs are matured in the right ovary and the caudal part of the left, but the cranial part of the left ovary contains a stock of oogonia and oocytes which occur in nests and provide the material for a second spawn. (In other regions of Japan, animals of this species spawn once and then die.) The illustration provided shows no indication of the prophase of meiosis in the reserve stock of germ cells.

Turner's (1938b) second study is less convincing than his first in that waves of oogonial divisions are not reported. He noted, however, that in the ovoviviparous teleost *Brachyraphis*, oocytes retained in the ovary of the gravid female remain small until the brood is hatched. This species, like other Poeciliidae, undergoes short reproductive cycles, a proportion of specimens recovered at any time of the year being pregnant.

The possibility that divisions of oogonia cease early in the life-history of some teleosts is supported by a number of observations, particularly those of Dildine (1933, 1936) and Goodrich et al. (1934) on the guppy *Lebistes*. The embryonic gonads of this species are hermaphrodite, and changes in the female germ cells typical of meiotic prophase are said to occur as early as 10–15 days before birth. All specimens at the initial stages of differentiation contain germ cells in the zygotene phase of meiosis. Approximately 50 per cent of the animals retain their female characteristics, and the germ cells in synapsis continue to enlarge and form the definitive oocytes (the other 50 per cent differentiate in the male direction; Dildine, 1933, 1936). Goodrich et al. (1934) noted that widespread degeneration of primordial germ cells occurs in the gonads, but that nevertheless a sufficient number survive to give rise to the future gametes. These authors considered that no conclusive evidence was available that the definitive germ cells arise from proliferations of vegetative cells.

Maréchal (1907) examined the ovaries of *Trigla hirundo* and *Gasterosteus aculeatus* and concluded that the smallest germ cells present do not divide mitotically but, as in elasmobranchs, directly enter the prophase of meiosis. Hickling (1936), in a careful study of the hake, *Merlucius merluccius*, similarly observed that oogonia dividing by mitosis are no longer seen in fish aged 3 to 4 years, some 6 years before the first spawning. The ovary contains nests of germ cells immediately under the surface of the ovigerous lamellae. Some nuclei are in inter-phase (i.e. Maréchal's pre-meiotic resting phase), some show synaptic changes and others are described as 'post-synaptic'. According to Hickling, the numbers of 'pre-synaptic', 'synaptic'' and 'post-synaptic' germ cells vary in phase with the season of the year even before sexual maturity is reached. The seasonal variation is more pronounced in adult animals, a large number of oocytes undergoing synapsis during the winter months, followed by an enlargement and maturation during the early summer. In an earlier study, Hickling (1930) searched in the adult hake for mitoses in the smallest germ cells, but failed to find any. He suggested that "the sudden re-appearance of young oocytes in the spent ovary, after their apparent scarcity in the ripe ovary, is an illusion, consequent upon the collapse of the ovigerous lamellae after the ripe eggs have been spawned or reabsorbed." In discussing Wheeler's (1924) suggestion that a 'reserve fund' of eggs is regenerated from follicular cells, Hickling comments: "The numbers of new eggs added to the reserve fund are very easily covered by the reserve of undeveloped oocytes and oogonia* which are always to be seen, even in very old fish, lying beneath the ovigerous lamellae, in the spent ovary." Hickling's studies are of particular interest since (i) he examined a large number of specimens recovered at different times of the year; and (ii) he specifically looked for divisions of oogonia.

It may thus be concluded that all definitive germ cells of fish are consistently derived from primordial oocytes, and that oogenesis continues during adult life in some species but not in others. Such evidence as is available suggests that dividing oogonia occur rarely, if at all, in some elasmobranchs and that in at least three of the teleostean species investigated, they are absent after sexual maturity. In most other teleosts, however, oogenesis proper appears to occur cyclically with a peak shortly after spawning.

E. Amphibians

The majority of authors who have studied oogenesis in this class of vertebrates agree that definitive oocytes are formed from pre-existing oogonia which undergo mitotic division, the daughter cells at a later period showing the changes characteristic of meiotic prophase that mark the female germ cell. The latter are particularly easy to identify by the presence of large lampbrush chromosomes in the diplotene phase of meiosis (see e.g. Koltzoff, 1938; Dodson, 1948; Duryee, 1950; Gall, 1952, 1954; Alfert, 1954). It is nevertheless difficult to obtain a precise estimate of the duration of the individual phases of the prophase of meiosis. It appears that the oocyte grows considerably during

---

* By oogonia, Hickling presumably means germ cells which have ceased to divide mitotically and which have not as yet entered meiotic prophase.

pachytene and diplotene—phases during which the mammalian oocyte remains almost constant in size. In particular, diplotene appears to last for a considerable period if one can judge by the increase in the size of the oocyte. After the initial longitudinal splitting of the chromosomes characteristic of diplotene, the threads lose some of their affinity for basic stains, the chromosomes acquire a typical lampbrush configuration, and the oocytes continue to enlarge. Although the period during which the chromosomes lose their affinity for stain is reminiscent of the dictyate phase in mammals, it may not be strictly homologous since it appears to occur during, rather than after, diplotene.

Among the minority of reports claiming that cells of the germinal epithelium divide to form oocytes are those of Dustin (1907), Gatenby (1916) and McCosh (1930). These reports are open to the same criticism as corresponding reports on fish. The fact that the ovary at any one time contains fewer oocytes than the very large number of eggs which are shed during the entire life-span of the animal (Gatenby, 1916) does not necessarily imply that the rapidly dividing germinal epithelium is the source of new oocytes. Nor does Gatenby's other observation, that in the early spring extensive invaginations of the germinal epithelium surround 'pockets' of germ cells at various stages of development and differentiation, indicate anything other than that the rate of division of the germinal epithelium varies seasonally. Gatenby himself commented on the fact that oocytes which he believed to be derived from the germinal epithelium did not undergo heterotypic prophase, the only nuclear change being loss in stainability.

Observations of this type are difficult to reconcile with the many clear-cut accounts of meiotic changes in the germ cells of amphibians, and with the conclusive experimental evidence provided, for example, by Bounoure (1937b) and Foote and Witschi (1939). Bounoure irradiated the vegetative pole of the fertilized egg with ultra-violet rays and observed that the population of germ cells in the young frog after metamorphosis (formed from the irradiated egg) decreases rapidly and is not re-stocked by the mitotic proliferation of other cell-types in the ovary. Foote and Witschi demonstrated that during sex reversal, oocytes disappear due to the migration of oogonia into the medulla of the gonad and their subsequent transformation into spermatogonia. A similar conclusion emerges from Nieuwkoop's (1951) and Blackler's (1960) transplantation studies. Nieuwkoop exchanged the extra-gonadal presumptive germ cell material of two species of *Triton* which are readily differentiated from each other by their pigmentation. The ovaries of the host subsequently contains only germ cells whose pigmentation is characteristic of the donor species, an unexpected result if vegetative cells of the genital ridge give rise secondarily to 'new' oogonia. Blackler removed the site of the germ cells in *Xenopus laevis*, and replaced it by an identical site derived from a donor mutant embryo (carrying the so-called 'Oxford nuclear marker'). Blackler succeeded in rearing the host *Xenopus* beyond the stage of metamorphosis, when follicular growth and differentiation was observed to have set in.

Experimental evidence that oogonia persist in the adult and give rise to oocytes derives from Humphrey's (1931) observation on sex reversal in *Amblystoma*. The transplantation of a testis into a female larva causes a reduction in the number of cortical germ cells in the host. No regeneration of germ cells occurs after the grafted testis is removed. This result indicates a loss of oogonia and a lack of transformation of somatic into germ cells.

Careful embryological and histological studies fully confirm the experimental evidence. King's (1908) early study of sexual differentiation in *Bufo* indicated that the primordial female germ cells (all of which she believed had arisen by mitotic division of gonocytes which existed before the onset of sexual differentiation) become distributed peripherally, while the presumptive male germ cells are situated in the medullary region. The peripheral primary oogonia divide mitotically and give rise to nests of secondary oogonia. Further divisions, which King estimated to represent four or five generations, then occur within the nests, though not necessarily involving all the cells at any one time. The final division gives rise to resting oogonia which are tightly packed within the nests, and are characterized by large polygonal nuclei. The oogonia become transformed into oocytes, some of which grow and undergo meiotic changes at varying times. Four weeks after metamorphosis, all the nuclei contain either an excentric concentration of chromatin or a mass of threads. The chromosomes become evenly distributed throughout the nucleus, and each thread then becomes thinner before splitting longitudinally, each half lying parallel to its other half. These changes first occur in nests of oocytes nearest to the ovarian cavity, while more distally situated nests remain quiescent. King was also able to identify lampbrush chromosomes in oocytes throughout their growth period. Although she did not study the ovaries of sexually mature toads, her findings imply that a reserve of potential oogonia situated distally from the ovarian cavity persists for some time after metamorphosis.

These observations on *Bufo* were later confirmed by Swingle's (1926) report on *R. catesbeiana*, according to which oogonia persist peripherally and give rise to later generations of oocytes. Undifferentiated oocytes, i.e. oogonia, were also observed in larvae and immature adults by Jurand (1957), and in adult anurans, in which they divide seasonally to give rise to oocytes (Witschi, 1929a; Christensen, 1930; Cheng, 1932).

Essentially similar observations have been made on urodeles. A differential distribution of oogonia and oocytes in the adult has been reported for *Triturus torosus* (in which the oogonia occur more frequently in the hilar region; McCurdy, 1931) and for *Amblystoma punctatum* and *Plethodon cinereus* (in which the oogonia are peripheral; Burns, 1925 and Burger, 1937, respectively). Miller and Robbins (1954) state that in *Triturus torosus* ovulation occurs in January–February, and a resumption of ovarian activity is seen between April and July, associated with a peak of mitoses in the oogonia and growth of the smallest oocytes. Other reports on seasonal changes in urodeles which, however, provide no specific information about oogonial divisions include those of Hilsman (1934) and Adams (1940).

It may be concluded, therefore, that the evidence indicates that (i) all definitive oocytes in amphibians are derived from primordial gonocytes which initially originate in extra-gonadal parts of the embryo (see also pp. 3 to 6), and (ii) that cyclical neoformation of oocytes by the mitotic division of pre-existing oogonia, i.e. true oogenesis, occurs consistently after the onset of sexual maturity in all species.

F. Reptiles

Almost all observations reported hitherto indicate that primordial germ cells are responsible for the production of all oogonia which, in turn, proliferate to give rise to all the oocytes that are ever formed. An exception is Simkins' (1925) belief that, because he found it inconceivable that a 300-year old turtle should still possess the germ cells with which it was furnished during embryonic life, such germ cells as are present must be derived from continuous proliferations of either the germinal epithelium or the stroma. This claim is pure speculation and is not substantiated by any cytological evidence. However inconceivable the idea, there are many, in the field of biological phenomena, which are even more so, but which are nonetheless true—for example the fact that the various contributors to this book were once single cells.

A careful embryological study by Tribe and Brambell (1932) showed that during early development in *Sphenodon*, primordial germ cells of extra-gonadal origin lose their yolk granules when they settle in the genital ridges, and shortly thereafter enter the prophase of meiosis. It is difficult to say from the available evidence whether all the oogonia become transformed into oocytes and enter the leptotene phase of meiosis before hatching, or whether some oogonia persist and divide later. The possibility exists that *Sphenodon* hatches with a finite stock of oocytes, as do the birds (see below).

Similar observations have been reported for the musk turtle (*Sternotherus*) by Risley (1930, 1933b). Many nuclei in meiotic prophase were seen in the gonadal cortex of embryos immediately after the germ cells had ceased multiplying. Sex differentiation still proceeds at this time; regression of germ cells occurs in the medullary cords, but some of these persist also, and as a result the gonad assumes a bisexual appearance. Risley observed that many germ cells in meiotic prophase persisted in the ovaries until the end of embryonic life, but shortly before hatching entered a period of cell-growth. Although Risley's observations do not prove that neoformation of oocytes ceases at the time of hatching, they show that changes characteristic of meiotic prophase occur in at least some of the germ cells very early in the life-history of the animal.

Loyez (1906) examined the ovaries of a number of adult reptiles (five species of *Lacerta*; *Anguis fragilis*, L.; *Tropidonotus natrix*, Gesn.; *T. viviperinus*, Schl.; *Vipera aspis*, Merr.; *Testudo graeca*, L.; *T. radiata*; *Cistudo europaea*, Schneid.; and *Crocodilus niloticus*) and concluded that oogonia divide mitotically to give rise to cells which undergo a series of changes typical of meiotic prophase. In some species the oogonia are arranged in nests, while in others they are scattered singly. The oocytes enlarge relatively little during leptotene, pachytene and the early stages of diplotene. The latter phase is extremely long, and is interrupted by a phase which is similar to, but not identical with, the dictyate resting phase in mammals. The chromosomes remain in diplotene while the oocytes increase in size, and in all species examined except the Ophidia, acquire a lampbrush configuration. The relationship between chromosomal changes and the growth of the oocyte is therefore somewhat similar to that in amphibians (and birds, see below). The appearance of the lampbrush chromosomes, and the long duration of the diplotene phase, may well be associated with vitellogenesis since it appears to occur typically in animals bearing telolecithal eggs.

The classical observations of Loyez have been confirmed more recently by Boyd (1941) who studied the gecko *Hoplodactylus maculatus*. This worker was also able to trace the division of oogonia, situated in 'oogonial beds' (restricted to a small part of the ovarian surface in this species), and the formation of oocytes which enter leptotene, zygotene, pachytene and a very prolonged phase of diplotene. Boyd specifies that the lampbrush chromosomes in reptiles remain compact, and do not spread out evenly throughout the enlarging nucleus, a feature which she considers to be peculiar to this class.

Other reports on oogenesis in reptiles are less detailed (e.g. Cieslak, 1945, on *Thamnophis*). It is worth noting, however, that Munson (1904) claims to have observed mitotic divisions of oogonia in the adult turtle *Clemmys*, and that Allen (1906) observed synaptic oocytes shortly after hatching in *Chrysemys*. The ovary of the sexually immature terrapin (*Malachlemmys centrata*) contains oogonia and small oocytes in synapsis, associated with growing oocytes (Risley, 1941). The numbers of mitotic divisions in oogonia and the numbers of oocytes in synapsis are claimed to increase following the injection of gonadotrophic hormones. Injections of testosterone and oestradiol dipropionate cause atresia of oocytes, but some oogonia were said to survive and continue to divide. Risley does not specify whether dividing oogonia are seen in the adult terrapin.

Oogonia are reported to occur for at least 18 months after hatching in the alligator, a species which becomes sexually mature at the age of 5–6 years (Forbes, 1940). Vitellogenesis, a process which occurs after the early stages of meiotic prophase, begins in some oocytes as early as 6 months after hatching. This observation indicates that at least some oocytes are likely to have passed through meiotic prophase some 5 years before sexual maturity. Whether these oocytes survive to ovulate, or whether they degenerate and are replaced by more recently matured oocytes, is not specified. It is of interest to note that degeneration of small oocytes as well as atresia of follicles are known to occur in reptiles (see Loyez, 1906; Boyd, 1941).

It would thus appear that in most reptiles, oogonia may persist until after sexual maturity, and that they give rise to oocytes by mitotic divisions. The only possible exceptions are *Sphenodon* and *Sternotherus*, in which changes typical of meiotic prophase occur during embryonic life. The latter observations, as already mentioned, do not preclude the possibility that some oogonia persist in these two forms until after hatching and that they divide to form oocytes.

G. Birds

It is generally held that all definitive oocytes in birds are derived from oogonia of extra-gonadal origin, and that none arises during embryonic development from proliferations of the germinal epithelium (Swift, 1914, 1915). The few who have postulated a contrary view are D'Hollander (1904), who believed that during the early stages of incubation, some of the follicular cells derived from the germinal epithelium may become transformed into germ cells, and Firket (1913, 1920) who claimed, again on the basis of histological evidence alone, that from the 15th day of incubation onwards, most of the primordial gonocytes in the gonad of the chick undergo degeneration, to be

E

replaced by new cells derived from the germinal epithelium. Firket also observed that most primordial germ cells which had failed to reach the genital ridges and had been 'trapped' in the mesentery and the rete regions degenerate at the time of hatching. The few surviving 'stragglers' undergo the prophase of meiosis and enlarge, but then degenerate. Firket was also able to detect changes typical of meiotic prophase in the germ cells situated in the ovary itself, but assumed that they had been formed by proliferations of the germinal epithelium and represented secondary, rather than primary, germ cells.

Gatenby's (1924) statement that germ cells arise from the germinal epithelium was based on his observations of transformations of epithelial cells during sex reversal. He recorded a series of changes in the affinity for cytoplasmic dyes in a number of peritoneal epithelial cells, and took these to imply that a direct transformation of somatic into germinal elements was necessarily taking place. The fact that oogonia frequently persist in the right ovary of the bird has been well established. As long as the active left ovary is in situ, the right ovary remains rudimentary. After the removal of the functional ovary, the germ cells in the right ovary undergo nuclear changes characteristic of spermatogenesis, and sex reversal follows (Fell, 1923; Benoit, 1923, 1924, 1951; Brode, 1928; Brambell and Marrian, 1929; Crewe, 1933; amongst others). Brode's (1928) observations clearly indicate, however, that proliferations of the germinal epithelium contribute nothing to the formation of the germ cells. If gonocytes are congenitally absent from the right ovary, as they occasionally are, then sinistral ovariectomy is not followed by a transformation of the right gonad into a fully functional testis. In other words, the formation of male germ cells depends on pre-existing gonocytes and is independent of such mitotic activity and/or cell changes in the germinal epithelium as may occur.

The belief that the germinal epithelium gives rise to oocytes in the functional ovary of the adult bird appears to be held solely by Bullough and Gibbs (1941), who linked the peaks of mitotic proliferation of the germinal epithelium in the starling with cyclical neoformation of oocytes. The fact that the germinal epithelium of the adult bird divides actively after ovulation does not, of course, imply that oogenesis is taking place. It may well be correlated with repair of the surface epithelium which is damaged during the expulsion of the very large mature eggs (see p. 58).

Waldeyer (1870) appears to have been one of the first to suggest that at the time of hatching, the ovary of the bird contains a finite stock of germ cells which becomes exhausted as the animal ages, and also that the number of germ cells does not increase after birth. He based this view on his own observations of adult avian ovaries, in which he could find neither mitotic divisions of germ cells nor the changes characteristic of early meiosis. His conclusion received considerable support from the detailed study of germ cells of the chick during the late incubation period carried out by D'Hollander (1904) and from exhaustive studies of the nuclear changes associated with post-natal growth of oocytes in a wide variety of species (Loyez, 1906; Sonnenbrodt, 1908; Van Durme, 1914). The absence of mitotic divisions of germ cells in adult birds has been confirmed by several more recent workers (e.g. Brambell, 1925; Fauré-Fremiet and Kaufman, 1928; Marza and Marza, 1936).

In his classical descriptions of germ cells during embryonic development, D'Hollander (1904) noted that cords of primary gonocytes are clearly seen on the 10th day of incubation of the chick. Mitotic divisions occur frequently up to the 15th day in the central part of the ovary, and up to the time of hatching in the peripheral regions. Many germ cells with interphase nuclei are present between the 10th and the 15th days. Changes characteristic of leptotene and zygotene occur between the 16th and 20th days. Thickening of the chromosome threads, i.e. pachytene, occur in many cells between the 19th day and hatching. At the time of hatching, and for several days thereafter, many oocytes display longitudinal splitting of the chromosomes characteristic of diplotene. D'Hollander divided the latter phase into four stages, of which the first two last up to the 6th day and the second two up to the 20th day after hatching. The growth of the oocyte before it becomes invested with a layer of granulosa cells is referred to as 'extra-follicular growth'. The subsequent and more extensive enlargement of the oocyte is called by D'Hollander 'intra-follicular growth'.

The sequence of later changes was described meticulously by a number of D'Hollander's contemporaries, including Loyez (1906), Sonnenbrodt (1908) and Van Durme (1914). These authors described a complete series characteristic of meiotic prophase at the time of hatching and during the first few days following it. The sequence of changes is essentially the same as that described for mammals by Winiwarter (1901), but differs from what Goldsmith (1928) claims to occur. According to the latter worker, synizesis in birds occurs before leptotene (at about the 20th day of incubation), followed by a long resting phase up to 65-69 days after hatching, when pachytene sets in. A further resting period is then said to occur, without diplotene intervening. It would appear probable that the stage described by Goldsmith as pachytene represents changes associated with the end of diplotene and the appearance of lampbrush chromosomes (for a description of the latter, see Koltzoff, 1938). Loyez, Sonnenbrodt and Van Durme all failed to establish the

E*

occurrence of pachytene as late as 9–10 weeks after hatching. On the contrary, their descriptions indicate that diplotene lasts for a considerable period, during which the oocyte enlarges, as in amphibians and some reptiles. Lampbrush chromosomes, which identify the stage of meiosis as diplotene, are present in oocytes towards the end of the 'extra-follicular phase' of growth defined by D'Hollander (1904). It is of interest to note that the many species of birds examined by Loyez (1906) were remarkably uniform in the nuclear changes associated with the growth of the oocyte.*

Fauré-Fremiet and Kaufman's (1928) quantitative study of the number of oocytes in the fowl is of particular interest, in that it clearly demonstrates that the population of germ cells decreases with age. These authors estimated that 2 days after birth, the ovary of the White Leghorn chick contains some $3 \cdot 6 \times 10^6$ oocytes, and that of the Rhode Island Red chick approximately $12 \cdot 5 \times 10^6$. By the time the birds are 15 days old, the numbers of oocytes have fallen to approximately 5,300 and 5,800 respectively. This rapid depletion (however approximate the estimates may be) is reminiscent of what occurs during the first few days after birth in mammals (see p. 57), but the speed with which the oocytes 'disappear' is even more dramatic. Unfortunately, no information is available about the histological changes associated with the early wave of post-natal atresia in birds which affects the small oocytes. Both Fauré-Fremiet and Kaufman (1928) and Brambell (1925) provide ample evidence of atresia affecting large oocytes. Measurements of oocytes (Brambell, 1925) indicate that all the oocytes present enlarge between the 4th and 21st day after hatching (corresponding to D'Hollander's 'intra-follicular growth phase' during late diplotene). Thereafter, only some continue to grow, while others remain essentially constant in size for considerable periods, even until after the onset of sexual maturity. Brambell observed that oocytes exceeding 75μ at 6 weeks, and those exceeding 100μ at 11 weeks, undergo atresia, the latter showing more advanced stages of degeneration. These observations led him to conclude that all the oocytes which enter upon a period of rapid growth between the 3rd and 6th weeks after birth are fated to become atretic without ever reaching maturity. A description of atresia in oocytes of many other avian species, provided by Loyez (1906), indicates that the process occurs uniformly throughout the carinate birds.

Further evidence, though of a less direct nature, that the stock of oocytes decreases with age derives from the repeated observations that the number of eggs laid by hens declines progressively (Brody et al.,

* For a detailed description of the maturation and fertilization of avian eggs, the reader is referred to Olsen (1942) and Olsen and Fraps (1944).

1923; Fauré-Fremiet and Kaufman, 1928; Greenwood, 1937; Clark, 1940; Insko *et al.*, 1947), and that hens which have been partially ovariectomized lay fewer eggs than their controls (Hutt and Grussendorf, 1933). Fauré-Fremiet and Kaufman (1928) established that the reduction in egg-laying with age is exponential, and that the rate of decrease differs between two varieties of fowl (White Leghorn and Rhode Island Red). The latter observation is of particular interest in view of the recent demonstration of the differential rate of decrease in the number of oocytes in two strains of mice (p. 59).

Pearl and Schoppe's (1921) claim that the number of oocytes increases with age appears to be, at first sight, contradictory to all other reports. These authors, however, counted only those oocytes that were visible under a dissecting microscope, and clearly omitted from their counts all the many primordial oocytes which had not passed beyond the end of their early 'extra-follicular growth phase'.

It may thus be concluded that in contrast to the majority of fishes and reptiles, and all amphibians, oogenesis, as defined in the Introduction, does not occur in carinate birds after birth. Information about rattite birds is lacking.

H. Monotremes and marsupials

The ovaries of adult and adolescent *Ornithorhynchus* and *Echidna* contain neither oogonia nor oocytes in early meiotic prophase (see Gatenby, 1922; Flynn and Hill, 1939). Follicular atresia (see Garde, 1930) is observed frequently (Flynn and Hill, 1939) in oocytes at all stages of development. These authors concluded that all the oocytes visible after birth have undergone meiotic prophase long before the animal is fully grown, and that no neoformation of oocytes occurs. Germ cells in embryonic and early post-natal monotremes have not so far been studied.

Very little is known about oogenesis in marsupials, and no studies appear to have been published on the germ cells in embryonic and pouch-young specimens. Hartman (1923) claimed that neoformation of oocytes occurs in the adult opossum "in a circumscribed nest of embryonic epithelium from which ova are periodically fed into the ovary". The area in which oogenesis is said to occur is near the ovarian hilus, the germinal epithelium in other parts of the ovary being inactive. Hartman, however, provides no cytological evidence that the cells formed in the hilar region are in fact oocytes. Changes characteristic of meiotic prophase were not seen, but he comments that polynuclear oocytes and other aberrant structures tend to be hilar in position. The incidence of polynuclear oocytes is also said to be higher in the opossum than in a number of eutherian mammals studied (Hartman, 1926), and is related to the age of the animal, the younger the opossum the greater the number of polynuclear oocytes. It is worth noting, however, that Hartman also observed these aberrant structures in the ovary of a dog—a species in which the number of oocytes is known to decrease with age (see p. 57), and in which neoformation of oocytes does not occur.

Everett (1942) also claimed that divisions of the germinal epithelium cells are correlated with neoformation of oocytes throughout the reproductive life of the opossum. But he, too, failed to provide any evidence that the newly formed cells undergo changes typical of meiotic prophase.

The absence of oogonia and oocytes in early meiotic prophase in adult marsupials suggests that oogenesis does not persist, but a full investigation of the gonads of embryos and pouch-young is clearly necessary to establish this conclusion.

I. Eutherian mammals

Until recently, there were as many students who contended that oogenesis continues uninterruptedly throughout the reproductive life of a mammal as claimed that the female begins her period of reproduction furnished with a finite stock of oocytes which gradually becomes exhausted. The latter view is associated with the name of Waldeyer by whom it was proposed in 1870 in his monograph "Eierstock und Ei". Waldeyer believed that neoformation of oocytes in the adult mammal, as in the bird, would have to be associated with mitotic divisions of persisting oogonia, and since he could find no such divisions in either avian or mammalian adult ovaries, he concluded that oogonial divisions must cease very early in the life-history of these animals. His hypothesis was later given precision by the careful cytological work of Winiwarter (1901, 1910, 1920a, b) and Winiwarter and Sainmont (1908, 1909), and this in turn stimulated further studies not only on mammals, but also on lower vertebrates. Thus in the first decade following Winiwarter's (1901) now classic paper, a number of painstaking studies on lower vertebrates and birds (e.g. D'Hollander, 1904; Maréchal, 1904, 1907; Loyez, 1906; Sonnenbrodt, 1908; King, 1908) were undertaken, and in every instance the same sequence of meiotic phenomena described for mammals was found to occur, with only slight modifications associated with vitellogenesis and the duration of the diplotene stage. In view of the overwhelming evidence that the process of oogenesis follows the same steps in most vertebrates, it is surprising that subsequently a view gained currency that mammalian oocytes arise from the germinal epithelium without undergoing meiotic prophase, and even more so that it was ever seriously entertained in view of the speculative nature of the evidence on which it was based. This contrary belief begins with Kingery's (1917) remarkable suggestion that the primitive germ cells, which are known to undergo synizesis, are fated to degenerate and that "synizesis may represent a stage in degeneration, wherein the normal relations of nucleus and cytoplasm, and the forces governing them are disturbed". These views were taken a step further by Allen (1923) and Evans and Swezy (1931) who suggested that new oocytes are formed throughout life, and in phase with the reproductive cycle, from the germinal epithelium of the adult mammal, at the same time as vast numbers of already-formed oocytes become eliminated through atresia (see Chapter 4). This thesis, in spite of further advances in the understanding of chromosomal behaviour during gametogenesis, prevailed until some 10 years ago (see Pincus, 1936). Since then it has been shown to be totally inconsistent with the results of a series of experimental and quantitative studies specially designed to test its validity (see Zuckerman, 1951, 1956).

It should be noted, however, that dividing cells which have been diagnosed as oogonia and/or cells which show chromatin configurations characteristic of meiotic prophase have been reported to occur in a few specimens of a small number of mammalian species. Thus cells corresponding in all cytological respects with oogonia and synaptic oocytes have been observed in *Galago senegalensis moholi*, *G. crassicaudatus*, *G. demidoffi* and *Periodicticus potto* (Gérard, 1919/1920, 1932; Gérard and Herlant, 1953). Gérard and Herlant themselves point out that "la persistence de poussées pflügeriennes constitue indubitablement un phénomène exceptionnel chez les Mammifères adultes", and conclude "il nous est impossible à l'heure actuelle de comprendre la raison pour laquelle l'épithelium ovarien des Lémuriens conserve son activité oogénétique chez l'adulte." Hamlett (1935a) described cells in early meiotic prophase in one single pregnant armadillo; but on examining the ovaries of a larger series of twenty-one armadillos (of which two were pregnant), which had been injected with gonadotrophic preparations, he was unable to find any more examples of post-pubertal oogenesis (Hamlett, 1935b). It is unlikely that the treatment would have inhibited oogenesis if, in fact, it was occurring previously. Hamlett's claims have recently been re-examined by Enders (1960) who studied over 300 ovaries derived from foetal, neonatal and adult armadillos. Enders concludes that although meiotic figures persist in 'intersex cords' (which resemble seminiferous tubules more than they do Pflüger's cords), neoformation of oocytes does not occur in the adult armadillo. Such meiotic figures as occur are usually associated with karyolysis and other degenerative processes. The last exceptional species is the loris (Rao, 1927; Brambell, 1930). Here, Brambell's comment

is that "there can be no doubt that these oocytes are actually undergoing the prophase changes in the adult ovaries, but further research
is necessary to determine whether they originate by the transformation of epithelial cells or from oogonia, which may have arisen from
primordial germ-cells and have persisted in the ovaries without
entering on the prophase changes of the meiotic division until adult
life." He adds that "the latter supposition is rendered more probable
by the observation of de Winiwarter (1920) that the formation of
oocytes in the immediate vicinity of the hilum is delayed and may
still be in progress after it has ceased elsewhere." Winiwarter has
observed such oocytes, still exhibiting meiotic prophase stages, in the
ovaries of young cats shortly after puberty. Similar observations have
been made more recently by Aron et al. (1952, 1954a,b) on the guinea
pig, though the interpretation of their findings differs from Winiwarter's
and is discussed below.

The confusion which led to the temporary abandonment of Waldeyer's hypothesis derives primarily from three sources. First, from the
fact that the epithelium which covers the mature ovary has always
been called the germinal epithelium (though Beard, 1900, pointed out
60 years ago that this was a misnomer), and from the fact that the cells
of this epithelium can frequently be seen to be undergoing mitotic multiplication. Second, from the fact that at any given moment a very high
proportion of the oocytes present in an ovary appears to be undergoing
degeneration. And third, from the fact that larger-sized follicles clearly
fluctuate in number according to the phases of the reproductive cycle
(e.g. Myers et al., 1936; Boling et al., 1941; Mandl and Zuckerman,
1952).

No single writer, however, who has claimed that the total number of
oocytes and follicles present in the ovary, or the number which undergoes atresia, fluctuate in accordance with the phases of the oestrous
cycle (see Pincus, 1936), has based his view on anything but purely
subjective impressions or at best on incomplete, and sometimes very
incomplete, counts of the oocytes and follicles in the ovary. Those who
were led to reject Waldeyer's thesis because of these two claims gave no
weight to the fact that plainly recognizable primordial oocytes, i.e. all
those that lack an epithelial cover or are covered by a single layer of
granulosa cells, make up 90 per cent or more of the germ cell population
of the ovary (see Green et al., 1951). When these are taken into account,
analysis both in the rat (Mandl and Zuckerman, 1950) and monkey
(Green and Zuckerman, 1951, 1954) shows that there are no variations
in the total number of oocytes in phase with the reproductive cycle,
in spite of the very conspicuous variations which occur in the numbers
of larger follicles.

Carefully controlled observations have also shown that the total number of oocytes in an animal declines with age (rat: Arai, 1920a; Slater and Dornfeld, 1945; Mandl and Zuckerman, 1951a; Mandl and Shelton, 1959; mouse: Jones, 1957; Krohn, 1959; Jones and Krohn, 1959, 1961; monkey: Green and Zuckerman, 1951, 1954; dog: Schotterer, 1928; human: Block, 1951, 1952, 1953). The rate of decline can be readily expressed in terms of simple regression coefficients (rat: Mandl and Zuckerman, 1951a; mouse: Jones and Krohn, 1959, 1961; monkey: Green and Zuckerman, 1951, 1954). There is also a considerable variation in the total number of oocytes found in animals of the same age belonging to the same species, but this variation is significantly greater between unrelated rats of the same age than between litter-mates (Mandl and Zuckerman, 1950), and between mice belonging to different inbred strains (see p. 59; also Jones, 1957; Jones and Krohn, 1959, 1961). Whenever careful attempts have been made to control the criteria whereby an oocyte is diagnosed as atretic (see Chapter 4, sect. II, B), it has also been found that no variation occurs in the total number of degenerating oocytes in phase with the oestrous cycle (Mandl and Zuckerman, 1950).

1. *Experimental investigations*

These numerical considerations alone cast ample doubt on the presumed evidence underlying the view that oogenesis continues uninterruptedly during the reproductive life of the mammal. The definitive experimental evidence which necessitates the rejection of this view derives from a large series of observations which are summarized under the following three sub-headings.

(a) *The germinal epithelium*

It has been established that the germinal epithelium persists unchanged in the X-irradiated ovary, in spite of the total and permanent loss of oocytes (see p. 60 and Chapter 22, sect. II, B). It follows either that the germinal epithelium is not the source of oocytes in the mature animal, or that irradiation, without affecting the physical appearance, suppresses a capacity it has to produce oocytes (Everett, 1943).

The argument against the latter view is that the destruction of the germinal epithelium of an ovary of the rat by means of corrosive substances is not associated with any changes in the size of the oocyte population. In these experiments comparisons were made with the untreated ovary of the same animal, or with the two ovaries of a control litter-mate, and observations were extended over a period of nearly $1\frac{1}{2}$ years (i.e. 50% or more of the reproductive life of the animal; Mandl and Zuckerman, 1951b). The results of this experiment amplify a corresponding study made on numerous species by Moore and Wang (1947). The conclusion to which both sets of studies point is that mitotic divisions in the germinal epithelium bear no necessary relation to the process of oogenesis.

(b) *The numbers of oocytes in ovarian grafts*

Oocytes have been reported to persist in ovarian auto- and homografts for considerable periods in spite of the disappearance from such grafts of any trace of the germinal epithelium (e.g. Herlitzka, 1900; Marshall and Jolly, 1907, 1908; Pettinari, 1928; Mandl and Zuckerman, 1949). The grafting procedure is followed by a rapid and considerable decrease in the population of oocytes. The latter does not increase in successful autografts of ovarian tissue re-implanted after freezing at very low temperatures ($-190°C$) or after having been kept at normal room temperature (Green *et al.*, 1956). Further information about the effect of grafting on the survival of oocytes is given in Chapter 4, sect. III, H and in Chapter 21, sect. IV.

(c) *Experimental variations in the decline of the oocyte population*

(i) *Partial ovariectomy.* Compensatory hypertrophy of an ovary is not associated with an increase in the total number of oocytes, but the single hypertrophied ovary contains as many follicles with antra as do the two ovaries of a normal animal (Mandl and Zuckerman, 1951c). These findings confirm Arai's (1920b) earlier study of compensatory hypertrophy in the rat. They also accord with Lipschütz's observations (1925, 1928; see also Lipschütz and Voss, 1925) on the cat and the rabbit, and Jones and Krohn's (1960) later studies on the mouse. The results of all these experiments indicate that no new oocytes are formed when an ovary or fragment of an ovary undergoes compensatory hypertrophy, and that the number of oocytes present in a small piece of ovarian tissue left in the body is gradually exhausted by recurrent phases of follicular maturation. The latter conclusion has also been confirmed in a more extensive series of experiments (Mandl *et al.*, 1952) in which litter-mate rats were subtotally ovariectomized, and the remaining fragment of ovarian tissue in some animals painted with tannic acid in order to destroy the germinal epithelium. Compensatory hypertrophy occurred in the ovarian fragment left in the body whether or not the germinal epithelium persisted. The rate of loss of the oocytes was substantially greater than would be expected to occur in a single ovary of a normal animal, and increased inversely with the amount of ovarian tissue left in the body. The latter findings, together with Jones's (1957) corresponding observations on the mouse, thus indicate that the smaller an ovarian fragment, the more quickly will it become depleted of its oocytes.

(ii) *Hypophysectomy.* Certain early findings of Swezy (1933) which she interpreted as indicating that the number of oocytes rises after hypophysectomy are open to a contrary conclusion (Zuckerman, 1951) and have failed to be supported by properly controlled experiments (Ingram, 1953), which clearly demonstrated that only the rate of decline in oocyte numbers with age is retarded by the operation. The possibility has also been suggested that the rate of atresia diminishes following hypophysectomy (see Chapter 4, sect. III, D).

Corresponding results have recently been obtained in the mouse. Hypophysectomy was found to retard the rate of loss of oocytes significantly, so that the ovaries of an hypophysectomized mouse of the CBA strain would still be found to contain oocytes at an age (about 450 days) when a normal unoperated control animal's ovaries would be devoid of germ cells (Jones and Krohn, 1959). If the ovaries of such an hypophysectomized animal are orthotopically transplanted into a young ovariectomized female of the same strain, ovulation and breeding will be resumed. Transplantation into an old host of the same strain is followed by growth of small follicles to Graafian size (Jones and Krohn, 1959).

(iii) *Inter-strain differences in oocyte numbers.* The size of the oocyte population was found to decline at significantly different rates in two inbred strains of mice (CBA and RIII). In the former, the number of oocytes drops to zero when the animals reach the age of about 450 days (*op. cit.*), while mice of either RIII or the Strong A strains retain as many as 300 to 1,000 oocytes at that age, apparently never becoming devoid of oocytes within their entire life-span. Calculations of the rate of loss of oocytes show that 25 per cent of existing oocytes are lost every 20 days in the CBA strain, and only 10 per cent in the Strong A strain. Hybrid animals of the F_1 generation of CBA × Strong A possess a higher number of oocytes in middle- and old age than do either of the parent strains (Jones and Krohn, 1961).

For a discussion of the reduction in fertility associated with ageing, and hence with the reduction in the population of oocytes, the reader is referred to Ingram et al. (1958) and Krohn (1959).

(iv) *Parity in relation to oocyte numbers.* The rate of loss of oocytes was found to be about the same in breeding as in virgin rats (Shelton, 1959) and mice (Jones, 1957; Jones and Krohn, 1961). There is a slight tendency for animals subjected to forced-breeding to have a higher number of oocytes (Jones, 1957).

(v) *The effect of X-irradiation on oocyte numbers.* The effect of X-irradiation on the numbers of oocytes is dealt with in a later chapter

(Chapter 22, sect. II, B). It is of interest to note here, however, that the number of oocytes which survives exposure to ionizing radiations is directly related to (i) the dose of rays in roentgen units and (ii) the time after exposure when the count is made (Mandl, 1959). The number of oocytes declines even after exposure to very low doses which have a negligible effect on the non-germinal elements of the ovary. It has also been shown that following sub-sterilization doses, those oocytes which survive are functionally normal in so far as breeding continues. The number of litters, and the litter-size, are also related to the dose of X-rays to which the animals were exposed, and to the time after exposure (Ingram, 1958).

A further point worth mentioning is that the irradiation of foetuses with heavy doses is followed by life-long sterility (Raynaud and Frilley, 1946, 1947), and that the peak of ovarian radiosensitivity occurs at 15 days after conception in the foetal rat, at a time when mitotic divisions of the oogonia are most frequently seen (Beaumont, 1961; see also Part I and the following section of this chapter).

2. *The life-history of the oocyte in the mouse and the rat*

The primordial gonocytes of the mouse divide mitotically in the course of their migration to the genital ridges (Mintz, 1959b). Mitotic divisions continue to occur after the arrival of the germ cells at the genital ridges (about the 12th day after conception; Mintz, 1959a, b; Beaumont, 1960, 1961). In the female, the germ cells probably enter the leptotene stage of meiosis shortly after cessation of mitotic divisions, many cells at this stage being visible on about the 16th day of gestation Brambell, 1927; Mintz, 1959a; our own observations; see also Cowperthwaite, 1925). In other strains of mice, however, leptotene changes are said to occur about 12 hours after birth (Slizynski, 1958). Following a short period of zygotene (Fig. 1), the germ cells enter pachytene, a phase which is longer than any of the other pre-dictyate phases. Diplotene is characterized by the appearance of nucleolar-like chromatin granules (Fig. 2), and the threads begin to lose their definition shortly before entering the dictyate or resting condition. It should be pointed out, however, that the recognition of different stages of the prophase of meiosis in fixed tissue sections is difficult, and that not all of the above observations have been confirmed by studies of squash preparations. Within 3–4 days of birth, the oocytes of mice and rats have entered the resting phase (Fig. 3), which continues throughout pre-pubertal and adult life until pre-ovulation maturation (or pseudo-maturation associated with atresia; see Chapter 4, sect. II, A) takes place. The resting phase may thus last for a period ranging from a few weeks in

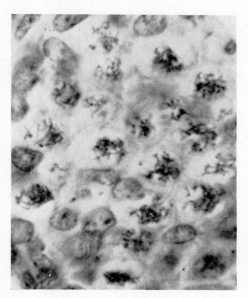

Fig. 1.   Oocytes in the zygotene stage of meiosis (rat embryo
on the 18th day of intra-uterine life).   (×900).

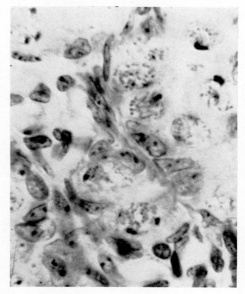

Fig. 2.   Oocytes in the diplotene phase of meiosis (rat embryo
on the 22nd day of intra-uterine life, i.e. full term).   (×900).

F

small rodents to several decades in primates (see preceding section of this chapter, p. 34; also Brambell, 1956). The resting phase of mammalian oocytes possibly differs from that in many lower vertebrates in that it appears to follow diplotene and may not constitute a phase of diplotene itself during which the chromosomes become diffuse and lose their affinity for nuclear stains. The possibility that the resting phase in mammals is, in effect, a continuation of the diplotene phase of meiosis cannot, in the light of present knowledge, be dismissed.

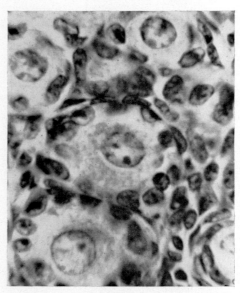

FIG. 3.   Oocytes in the dictyate or resting phase (rat 4 days after birth). (×900).

The histological appearance of the nucleus of the oocyte changes very little while the follicular cells multiply and the Graafian follicle (differentiation of theca, formation of antrum, etc.; see Brambell, 1928, 1956) becomes organized. The possibility, however, that changes occur which are not detectable by standard histological techniques is indicated by the observation that the radiosensitivity of the primordial oocyte is considerably greater than that of medium-sized follicles (Mandl, 1959).

While the majority of oocytes undergo atresia at varying times in the course of their development (see Chapter 4), those destined to survive undergo a series of changes immediately before ovulation. The sequence of changes leading to the maturation division which precedes ovulation (for details of follicular changes, see Brambell, 1956) has recently been investigated in considerable detail by Odor (1955), Edwards and Gates (1959) and Mandl (unpublished data). The timing of the changes was followed by Odor (1955) by the onset of heat, as judged by lordosis; and by the period following the administration of gonadotrophin by Edwards and Gates (1959). Mandl's animals were killed at different times during the afternoon and evening of the day when the vaginal smear was typically pro-oestrous.

A few hours before ovulation, the nucleolus of the oocyte becomes less chromophilic, and the vacuole within it becomes clearly marked. The chromatin material outside the nucleolus becomes less abundant, and the nucleus appears as an empty vesicular structure ('germinal vesicle') within which floats the large nucleolus. The nucleolus later shrinks in size to form a densely staining 'chromatin mass' of about 3μ in diameter. The shrinkage appears to take place very rapidly, inter- mediate stages between the lightly staining nucleolus and the 'chromatin mass' being extremely difficult to find. The 'chromatin mass' enlarges by opening out, with the resulting appearance of a cluster of oval chromatin bodies (Fig. 4). The nuclear membrane disappears at about this stage, which is followed by pre-spindle formation. The chromo- somes then become organized on a metaphase spindle (Fig. 4). Odor (1955) estimates that the process from chromatin condensation to the formation of the metaphase spindle takes some 2–3 hours. Metaphase is followed by anaphase and telophase and the extrusion of the first polar body (Figs. 5 and 6).* The formation of the first polar body appears to take place before ovulation in all mammalian species examined, including the primates (Hartman and Corner, 1941; see also Odor, 1955). The chromatin of the oocyte undergoes rapid condensation immedi- ately before undergoing the second metaphase. This stage is usually not completed until after fertilization. Odor (1955) estimates that ovulation occurs in the rat some 7–8 hours after chromatin condensa- tion, and 9–10 hours after the onset of heat, as judged by lordosis. Similar findings were reported for the mouse following injection of gonadotrophins (Edwards and Gates, 1959). The oocytes were in dictyate phase until 2 hours after the injection. They then completed the prophase of the first maturation division, and the first metaphase plates were found 30 min. later. From about 4–8 hours all oocytes were in metaphase. Edwards and Gates estimate that metaphase lasts $6 \cdot 00 \pm 0 \cdot 30$ hours, anaphase $1 \cdot 22 \pm 0 \cdot 26$ hours and telophase $0 \cdot 28 \pm 0 \cdot 20$ hours. Ovulation began just under 12 hours after the injection of chorionic gonadotrophin, and was virtually complete by 14 hours. For general

* For an account of these changes as seen under the electron microscope, see Odor and Renninger (1960).

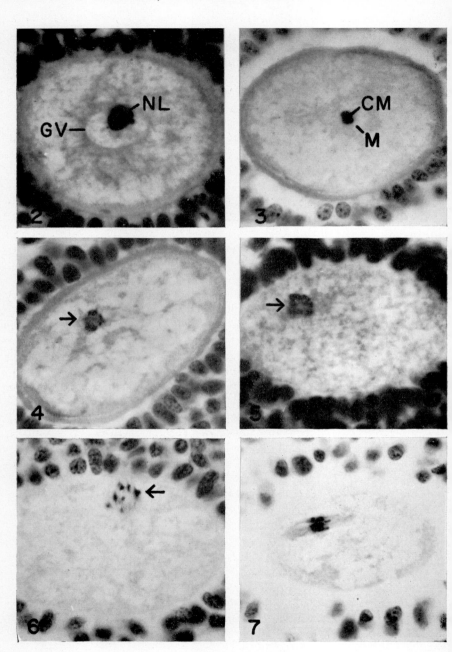

Fig. 4.

information about the maturation division in other species, the reader is referred to Brambell (1956).

The actual process of ovulation has been studied in the living rat by Blandau (1955), who estimates that it lasts between 5 and 760 seconds, depending largely on the position of the cumulus oöphorus in relation to the stigma (see also Chapter 8, sect. I, E).

Austin and Braden (1954) report that in the rat and rabbit, penetration of eggs occurs some $2\frac{1}{2}$–4 hours after ovulation, and that a change, possibly a final stage of maturation, must take place in the egg membranes of the rat before sperm can enter. Penetration of all eggs in any one Fallopian tube takes about 2 hours, the sperm spending an average of $\frac{1}{2}$ hour in the perivitelline space. The telophase of the second maturation division in the rat is near completion about 2 hours after the entry of the spermatozoon into the vitellus (Austin, 1951). Pronuclei were observed in the mouse about 4 hours, and the first cleavage division about 25 hours, after sperm penetration had taken place (Edwards and Gates, 1959).

3. Comparison between male and female gametogenesis in laboratory rodents

The male primordial germ cells arrive at the gonadal ridges at about the same time as do the female (mouse: 12 days after conception; Mintz, 1959a, b), and undergo a series of mitotic divisions up to about the 16th day of gestation (see e.g. Hargitt, 1926; Beaumont, 1960). In the strain of mice studied by Mintz, the earliest differences between the male and female germ cells may be seen at about the 15th–16th day, when the female germ cells enter the first stage of the heterotypic prophase. The male germ cells rarely divide after the 17th day of gestation, and degenerative processes appear in an increasing proportion of them (Beaumont, 1960). The surviving cells grow in size and

---

FIG. 4. *2* Resting stage of ovum. GV=germinal vesicle; NL=one large nucleolus. ($\times$810). *3* Stage of chromatin mass. CM=chromatin mass, surrounded by a somewhat indefinite membrane (M). ($\times$790). *4* Transitional phase. The chromatin mass is seemingly replaced by a structure (see arrow) consisting of a number of chromatin particles. No spindle fibres are visible. ($\times$790). *5* Transitional phase (continued). The chromatin masses are considerably larger than those in *4*. ($\times$810). *6* The forming stage of the first metaphase spindle. Many chromosomes (see arrow) are arranged irregularly along the spindle fibres. ($\times$790). *7* Definitive first metaphase spindle. This spindle is broader than the second metaphase spindle (see *17* in Fig. 6); it possesses finer spindle fibres and its chromosomes are less densely concentrated at the equator. ($\times$790). (Reproduced by permission from Odor, 1955.)

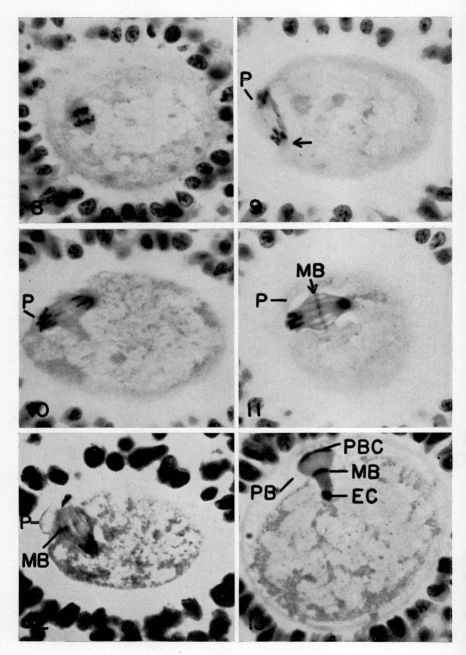

FIG. 5.

on the 4th day *post partum*, mitotic divisions appear, giving rise to the first generation of spermatogonia type-A (Clermont and Perey, 1957). Six days after birth, the type-A cells proliferate and give rise to new type-A cells (stem cells which later provide for the formation of new generations of spermatogonia) and to intermediate and type-B spermatogonia, the latter in turn producing primary spermatocytes. From the 15th day *post partum* onwards, it becomes evident that cyclical changes of the seminiferous epithelium similar to those observed in the adult are already established (Clermont and Perey, 1957). All the divisions up to and including the formation of primary spermatocytes are mitotic. Primary spermatocytes undergo heterotypic division by entering leptotene shortly after being formed. The leptotene phase is followed by zygotene and pachytene, the latter phase being the longest of the heterotypic prophase, as in the female. Diakinesis follows a short phase of diplotene. The second division ensues very rapidly, with the result that secondary spermatocytes are rarely seen in sections of the adult testis. The divisions of secondary spermatocytes give rise to spermatids which then undergo a sequence of transformations (spermiogenesis) to form fully differentiated spermatozoa. Cyclical changes occurring in the seminiferous tubules of adult rodents have been studied by Leblond and Clermont (1952), Clermont and Leblond (1953) and Oakberg (1957). More recently, a similar study of the testis of the monkey has been published (Clermont and Leblond, 1959). The total duration of the cycle in the rat is 12 days, and four cycles are necessary for the complete process from spermatogonia type-A to spermatozoa (Clermont *et al.*, 1959). The corresponding time for the mouse is a little shorter (Oakberg, 1957). It is clear that the major difference between the two sexes lies in the fact that continuous proliferation of germ cells occurs in the male,* whereas

* Even so, it has been established that some reduction in the capacity to produce spermatozoa occurs in the ageing human testis (Segal and Nelson, 1959). The secretory capacity of the gland, in contrast, is maintained in a relatively high proportion of cases, the rise in gonadotrophins, characteristic of menopausal women (see for instance, Loraine, 1958; and Chapters 7 and 10) occurring only rarely.

FIG. 5. *8* Early anaphase of first maturation. (× 790). *9* Late anaphase. *P* = protrusion on the surface of the egg, the forerunner of the first polar body. (× 790). *10* Late anaphase (continued). (× 790). *11* Early telophase. *MB* = mid-body. (× 790). *12* Early telophase (continued). The mid-body (*MB*) is now located on a line which is continuous with the indentation marking the beginning of constriction of the non-granular protrusion (*P*) which will become the polar body. (× 810). *13* Late telophase. *PBC* = chromatin of polar body; *EC* = chromatin of secondary oocyte; *MB* = mid-body. (× 790). (Reproduced by permission from Odor, 1955).

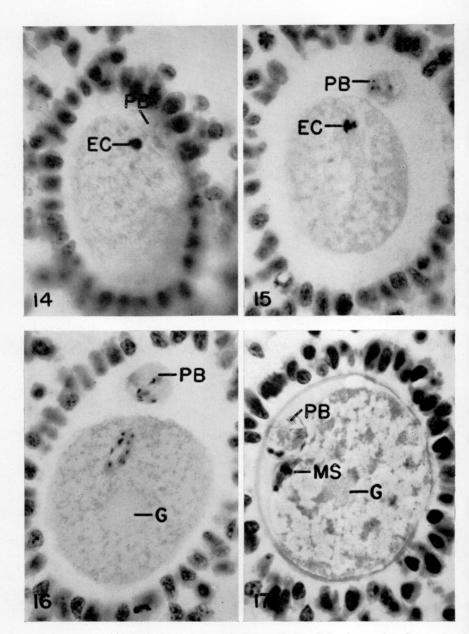

FIG. 6. *14* Dissolution of the telophase spindle. *EC*=chromatin of secondary oocyte; *PB*=polar body. (×790). *15* Same stage (continued). (×790). *16* The forming second metaphase spindle. (×790). *17* The definitive second metaphase spindle; *G*=area of unknown significance containing a relatively large amount of granular material. (×790). (Reproduced by permission from Odor, 1955.)

the female is born with a finite stock. Secondly, the mieotic process in the male is relatively rapid, whereas in the female it is interrupted by a long resting phase between the first few days after birth and ovulation at any time after puberty.

The analogous stages of gametogenesis (in the mouse) are summarized in Table V.

TABLE V.

Analogous stages in gametogenesis in male and female mice

MALE	FEMALE
Divisions of primordial germ cells between the 12th and 16th days of foetal life. Similar in both sexes.	
Birth	
Divisions of primordial germ cells to form spermatogonia	—
Divisions of spermatogonia type-A to form intermediate spermatogonia	—
Divisions of intermediate spermatogonia to form spermatogonia type-B	—
Divisions of spermatogonia type-B to form primary spermatocytes	—
Heterotypic division of spermatocytes: Leptotene 31.2 hr. Zygotene 37.5 hr. Pachytene 175.3 hr. Diplotene 21.4 hr. (Oakberg, 1957)	Leptotene ⎫ Zygotene ⎬ 16th day of foetal life to 1–2 days *post partum**. Pachytene ⎭ Diplotene Total duration 200–250 hr. (Brambell, 1927). (12 hr. to 72 hr. after birth; duration *ca.* 50 hr. according to Slizynski, 1958).
	BIRTH
Diakinesis ⎫ Metaphase ⎬ 10.4 hr. (Oakberg, 1957)	Metaphase 6.0 hr. Anaphase 1.2 hr. Telophase 0.3 hr. (Edwards and Gates, 1959).
Formation of secondary spermatocytes	Expulsion of first polar body.
Division of secondary spermatocytes to form spermatids.	Formation of second polar body, usually completed after fertilization.
Transformation of spermatids into differentiated spermatozoa	—

J. Conclusion

Although available information is anything but exhaustive, such observations as have been made on vertebrates and many invertebrates suggest that the process of oogenesis follows a uniform pattern, of which there are two main variants. In the one oogenesis appears to continue either uninterruptedly or cyclically throughout reproductive life (e.g. most teleosts, all amphibians, most reptiles and conceivably a few mammals). In the other, meiotic prophase occurs very early in life, oogonia neither persisting nor dividing mitotically after the onset of sexual maturity (e.g. cyclostomes, elasmobranchs, a few teleosts, perhaps some reptiles, all birds, monotremes, and with a few possible exceptions, all eutherian mammals).

It would be surprising indeed if the eutherian mammals and the marsupials, on the study of which much of the controversy about oogenesis has focused, were to deviate from such a uniform pattern. The observations listed in this chapter are illustrative of many others (see Zuckerman, 1951, 1956, 1960) which lead unequivocally to the conclusion that the female mammal begins its reproductive life furnished with a finite stock of oocytes. Conversely, the available facts are inconsistent with the alternative hypothesis that oogenesis in mammals* continues uninterruptedly throughout reproductive life. It cannot be too strongly emphasized that (i) there is no possible way of ever proving the latter hypothesis experimentally, whereas it has been disproved, as already indicated, by a variety of experimental tests, and (ii) that views about oogenesis based purely on histological evidence are necessarily arbitrary. Thus, to take one example, the claim that either one or another constituent cell of the ovary can become directly transformed into an oocyte in effect completely dismisses the problem of how and when oogenesis occurs. A belief of this kind would demand attention only if it were supported by an unequivocal demonstration of a consecutive series of intermediate cellular stages. But no such demonstration has ever been offered. It is equally unscientific to base hypotheses about the formation of germ cells only on the histological observation of mitoses in the germinal epithelium and the topographical relationship between epithelial cells and oocytes in the dictyate phase (e.g. Allen, 1923; Bullough, 1942b; Aron et al., 1952, 1954a, b). In the last resort, the only acceptable histological evidence of neoformation of germ cells in the adult mammalian ovary would be the observation of mitotic divisions in oogonia; and in the absence of such evidence

* A list of the few mammalian species which may be exceptional in this respect is given on p. 55.

for the overwhelming majority of eutherian mammals, the view that oogenesis persists after the onset of sexual maturity is clearly untenable.

REFERENCES

Abramowicz, H. (1913). Die Entwicklung der Gonadenanlage und Entstehung der Gonocyten bei *Triton taeniatus* (Schneid.). *Morph. Jb.* **47**, 593–644.
Adams, A. E. (1940). Sexual conditions in *Triturus viridescens*. III. The reproductive cycle of the adult aquatic form of both sexes. *Amer. J. Anat.* **66**, 235–275.
Agduhr, E. (1927). Studies on the structure and development of the bursa ovarica and the tuba uterina in the mouse. *Acta zool., Stockh.* **8**, 1–133.
Alden, R. H. (1942). The periovarial sac in the albino rat. *Anat. Rec.* **83**, 421–433.
Alfert, M. (1954). Composition and structure of giant chromosomes. *Int. Rev. Cytol.* **3**, 131–175.
Allen, B. M. (1904). The embryonic development of the ovary and testis of the mammals. *Amer. J. Anat.* **3**, 89–146.
Allen, B. M. (1905). The embryonic development of the rete-cords and sex-cords of *Chrysemys*. *Amer. J. Anat.* **5**, 79–94.
Allen, B. M. (1906). The origin of the sex-cells in *Chrysemys*. *Anat. Anz.* **29**, 217–236.
Allen, B. M. (1907). An important period in the life history of the sex-cells of *Rana pipiens*. *Anat. Anz.* **31**, 339–347.
Allen, B. M. (1911). The origin of the sex-cells of *Amia* and *Lepidosteus*. *J. Morph.* **22**, 1–36.
Allen, E. (1923). Ovogenesis during sexual maturity. *Amer. J. Anat.* **31**, 439–481.
Andreu, B. and Dos Santos Pinto, J. (1957). Histology and biometrical features of the ovary of the pilchard in ripening, spawning and recovering. The origin of ovocytes. *Invest. Pesq.* **6**, 3–38 (from *Biol. Abstr.*).
Arai, H. (1920a). On the postnatal development of the ovary (albino rat) with especial reference to the number of ova. *Amer. J. Anat.* **27**, 405–462.
Arai, H. (1920b). On the cause of the hypertrophy of the surviving ovary after semispaying (albino rat) and the number of ova in it. *Amer. J. Anat.* **28**, 59–79.
Aron, C., Marescaux, J. and Petrovic, A. (1952). Formation d'ovogonies aux dépens de l'épithelium superficiel de l'ovaire chez le cobaye prémature ou mûr. *C.R. Ass. Anat.* **39**, 421–423.
Aron, C., Marescaux, J. and Petrovic, A. (1954a). Ovogenèse postnatale chez le cobaye prémature ou mûr. *C.R. Soc. Biol., Paris*, **148**, 388–390.
Aron, C., Marescaux, J. and Petrovic, A. (1954b). Etat actuel du problème de l'ovogenèse postnatale chez les mammifères. *Arch. Anat., Strasbourg*, **37**, 1–46.
Ashby, K. R. (1957). The effect of steroid hormones on the brown trout (*Salmo trutta*, L.) during the period of gonadal differentiation. *J. Embryol. exp. Morph.* **5**, 225–249.
Austin, C. R. (1951). The formation, growth and conjugation of the pronuclei in the rat egg. *J. R. micr. Soc.* **71**, 295–306.

Austin, C. R. and Braden, A. W. H. (1954). Time relations and their significance in the ovulation and penetration of eggs in rats and rabbits. *Austr. J. biol. Sci.* **7**, 179–194.

Bailey, R. J. (1933). The ovarian cycle in the viviparous teleost *Xiphophorus hellerii*. *Biol. Bull., Wood's Hole*, **64**, 206–225.

Balfour, F. M. (1878). On the structure and development of the vertebrate ovary. *Quart. J. micr. Sci.* **18**, 383–438.

Bascom, K. F. (1923). The interstitial cells of the gonads of cattle with especial reference to their embryonic development and significance. *Amer. J. Anat.* **31**, 223–259.

Beard, J. (1900). The morphological continuity of the germ cells in *Raja batis*. *Anat. Anz.* **18**, 465–485.

Beard, J. (1902). The germ cells. Part I. *Raja batis*. *Zool. Jb.* **16**, 615–702.

Beatty, R. A. (1960). Chromosomal determination of sex in mammals. *In* "Sex Differentiation and Development" (C. R. Austin, ed.). *Mem. Soc. Endocrin.* No. 7, 45–48.

Beaumont, H. M. (1960). Changes in the radiosensitivity of the testis during foetal development. *Int. J. Radiation Biol.*, **2**, 247–256.

Beaumont, H. M. (1961). The radiosensitivity of oogonia and oocytes in the foetal rat. *Int. J. Radiation Biol.* **3**, 59–72.

Benoit, J. (1923). A propos du changement expérimental de sexe par ovariotomie chez la poule. (Présentation d'animaux et de préparations microscopiques). *C.R. Soc. Biol., Paris*, **89**, 1326–1328.

Benoit, J. (1924). Sur la signification de la glande génitale rudimentaire droite chez la poule. *C.R. Acad. Sci., Paris*, **178**, 341–344.

Benoit, J. (1926). Sur l'origine des cellules interstitielles de l'ovaire de la poule. *C.R. Soc. Biol., Paris*, **94**, 873–875.

Benoit, J. (1930). Contribution à l'étude de la lignée germinale chez le poulet. Déstruction précoce des gonocytes primaires par les rayons ultra-violets. *C.R. Soc. Biol., Paris*, **104**, 1329–1331.

Benoit, J. (1951). Différenciation sexuelle chez les oiseaux au cours du développement normal et de l'intersexualité expérimentale par ovariectomie. *In* "Colloque sur la Différenciation Sexuelle chez les Vertébrés", pp. 213–232. Centre national de la recherche scientifique, Paris.

Berenberg-Gossler, H. von (1913). Die Urgeschlechtszellen des Hühnerembryos am 3. und 4. Bebrütungstage, mit besonderer Berücksichtigung der Kern- und Plasmastrukturen. *Arch. mikr. Anat.* **81**, Abt. II, 24–72.

Blackler, A. W. (1958). Contributions to the study of germ cells in the Anura. *J. Embryol. exp. Morph.* **6**, 491–503.

Blackler, A. W. (1960). Transfer of germ-cells in *Xenopus laevis*. *Nature, Lond.* **185**, 859–860.

Blandau, R. J. (1955). Ovulation in the living albino rat. *Fertil. and Steril.* **6**, 391–404.

Block, E. (1951). Quantitative morphological investigations of the follicular system in women. Methods of quantitative determinations. *Acta anat.* **12**, 267–285.

Block, E. (1952). Quantitative morphological investigations of the follicular system in women. Variations at different ages. *Acta anat.* **14**, 108–123.

Block, E. (1953). A quantitative morphological investigation of the follicular system in newborn female infants. *Acta anat.* **17**, 201–206.

Blocker, H. W. (1953). Embryonic history of the germ-cells in *Passer domesticus*, (L.). *Acta zool., Stockh.* **14**, 111–152.

Boling, J. L., Blandau, R. J., Soderwall, A. L. and Young, W. C. (1941). Growth of the Graafian follicle and the time of ovulation in the albino rat. *Anat. Rec.* **79**, 313–331.

Bounoure, L. (1924a). Dérivés endodermiques dorsaux et première ébauche génitale chez les batraciens anoures. *C.R. Acad. Sci., Paris*, **178**, 339–341.

Bounoure, L. (1924b). Origine des gonocytes primaires chez les urodèles et signification de ces éléments chez les amphibiens en général. *C.R. Acad. Sci., Paris*, **179**, 1082–1084.

Bounoure, L. (1931a). Sur la nature golgienne d'un élément cytoplasmique caractéristique du germen dans les premiers stades du développement de la grenouille. *C.R. Acad. Sci., Paris*, **193**, 297–300.

Bounoure, L. (1931b). Sur l'existence d'un déterminant germinal dans l'oeuf indivis de la grenouille rousse. *C.R. Acad. Sci., Paris*, **193**, 402–404.

Bounoure, L. (1935a). Sur la possibilité de réaliser une castration dans l'oeuf de la grenouille rousse; résultats anatomiques (avec projections). *C.R. Soc. Biol., Paris*, **120**, 1316–1319.

Bounoure, L. (1935b). Une preuve expérimentale du rôle du déterminant germinal chez la grenouille rousse. *C.R. Acad. Sci., Paris*, **201**, 1223–1225.

Bounoure, L. (1937a). Le déterminant germinal est-il bien en cause dans l'atrophie des gonades consécutive à l'action des rayons ultra-violets sur le pôle inférieur de l'oeuf de grenouille? *C.R. Soc. Biol., Paris*, **125**, 895–897.

Bounoure, L. (1937b). Les suites de l'irradiation du déterminant germinal, chez la grenouille rousse, par les rayons ultra-violets: résultats histologiques. *C.R. Soc. Biol., Paris*, **125**, 898–900.

Bounoure, L. (1939). "L'Origine des Cellules Reproductrices et le Problèm de la Lignée Germinale." Gauthiers-Villars, Paris.

Bounoure, L. (1951). Sur le développement sexuel des glandes génitales de la grenouille en l'absence de gonocytes. *In* "Colloque sur la Différenciation Sexuelle chez les Vertébrés", pp. 65–74. Centre national de la recherche scientifique, Paris.

Bounoure, L., Aubry, R. and Huck, M.-L. (1954). Nouvelles recherches expérimentales sur les origines de la lignée reproductrice chez la grenouille rousse. *J. Embryol. exp. Morph.* **2**, 245–263.

Boyd, M. M. M. (1941). The structure of the ovary and the formation of the corpus luteum in *Hoplodactylus maculatus*, Gray. *Quart. J. micr. Sci.* **82**, 337–376.

Brachet, J. (1950). "Chemical Embryology." Interscience Publishers, Inc., New York.

Brambell, F. W. R. (1925). The oogenesis of the fowl (*Gallus bankiva*). *Phil. Trans. B.* **214**, 113–151.

Brambell, F. W. R. (1927). The development and morphology of the gonads of the mouse. Part I. The morphogenesis of the indifferent gonad and of the ovary. *Proc. roy. Soc. B.* **101**, 391–409.

Brambell, F. W. R. (1928). The development and morphology of the gonads of the mouse. Part III. The growth of the follicles. *Proc. roy. Soc. B.* **103**, 258–272.

Brambell, F. W. R. (1930). "The Development of Sex in Vertebrates." Sidgwick and Jackson, Ltd., London.

Brambell, F. W. R. (1956). Ovarian changes. In "Marshall's Physiology of Reproduction" (A. S. Parkes, ed.) Vol. I, Part I, pp. 397–542. Longmans, Green and Co., London.

Brambell, F. W. R. and Marrian, G. F. (1929). Sex reversal in a pigeon (Columbia livia). Proc. roy. Soc. B. 104, 459–470.

Brambell, F. W. R., Parkes, A. S. and Fielding, U. (1927a). Changes in the ovary of the mouse following exposure to X-rays. Part I. Irradiation at three weeks old. Proc. roy. Soc. B. 101, 29–56.

Brambell, F. W. R., Parkes, A. S. and Fielding, U. (1927b). Changes in the ovary of the mouse following exposure to X-rays. Part II. Irradiation at or before birth. Proc. roy. Soc. B. 101, 95–114.

Brode, M. D. (1928). The significance of the asymmetry of the ovaries of the fowl. J. Morph. 46, 1–57.

Brody, S., Henderson, E. W. and Kempster, H. L. (1923). The rate of senescence of the domestic fowl as measured by the decline in egg production with age. J. gen. Physiol. 6, 41–45.

Bullough, W. S. (1939). A study of the reproductive cycle of the minnow in relation to the environment. Proc. zool. Soc. Lond. A. 109, 79–102.

Bullough, W. S. (1942a). Gametogenesis and some endocrine factors affecting it in the adult minnow (Phoxinus laevis, L.). J. Endocrin. 3, 211–219.

Bullough, W. S. (1942b). Oogenesis and its relation to the oestrous cycle in the adult mouse. J. Endocrin. 3, 141–149.

Bullough, W. S. and Gibbs, H. F. (1941). Oogenesis in adult mice and starlings. Nature, Lond. 148, 439–440.

Burger, J. W. (1937). The continuity of the germ cells in the urodele Plethodon cinereus (Green). J. Morph. 60, 489–519.

Burns, R. K. (1925). The sex of parabiotic twins in Amphibia. J. exp. Zool. 42, 31–89.

Burns, R. K. (1928). The transplantation of larval gonads in urodele amphibians. Anat. Rec. 39, 177–191.

Burns, R. K. (1931). The process of sex transformation in parabiotic Amblystoma. II. Transformation from male to female. J. exp. Zool. 60, 339–387.

Burns, R. K. (1955). Urinogenital system. In "Analysis of Development" (B. H. Willier, P. A. Weiss and V. Hamburger, eds.) pp. 462–491. W. B. Saunders Co., Philadelphia and London.

Butcher, E. O. (1929). The origin of the germ cells in the lake lamprey (Petromyzon marinus unicolor). Biol. Bull., Wood's Hole, 56, 87–99.

Celestino da Costa, A. (1932). Les gonocytes primaires chez les mammifères. C.R. Ass. Anat. 27, 198–212.

Cheng, T. H. (1932). The germ cell history of Rana cantabrigensis Baird. I. Germ cell origin and gonad formation. II. Sex differentiation and development. Z. Zellforsch. 16, 497–541 and 542–596.

Chieffi, G. (1949). Ricerche sul differenziamento dei sessi negli embrioni di Torpedo ocellata. Pubbl. Staz. zool., Napoli, 22, 57–78.

Chieffi, G. (1952). Sull' organogenesi dell' interrenale e della medulla della gonade in Torpedo ocellata e in Scylliorhinus canicula. Pubbl. Staz. zool., Napoli, 23, 186–200.

Chieffi, G. (1955a). Nuove osservazioni sull' organogenesi della medulla della gonade nei vertebrati: Ricerche istochimiche in Rana esculenta, Bufo viridis e Scylliorhinus canicula. Pubbl. Staz. zool., Napoli, 27, 62–72.

Chieffi, G. (1955b). Sull' origine dell' asimmetria dell' ovario negli embrioni di *Scylliorhinus canicula*. *Monit. zool. ital.* **63**, 31–41 (from Chieffi, 1959).

Chieffi, G. (1959). Sex differentiation and experimental sex reversal in elasmobranchs. *Arch. Anat. micr. Morph. exp.* **48**, 21–36.

Chiquoine, A. D. (1954). The identification, origin and migration of the primordial germ cells in the mouse embryo. *Anat. Rec.* **118**, 135–146.

Christensen, K. (1930). Sex differentiation and development of oviducts in *Rana pipiens*. *Amer. J. Anat.* **45**, 159–187.

Cieslak, E. S. (1945). Relations between the reproductive cycle and the pituitary gland in the snake *Thamnophis radix*. *Physiol. Zoöl.* **18**, 299–329.

Clark, T. B. (1940). The relation of production and egg weight to age in White Leghorn fowls. *Poult. Sci.* **19**, 61–66 (from *Biol. Abstr.*).

Clermont, Y. and Leblond, C. P. (1953). Renewal of spermatogonia in the rat. *Amer. J. Anat.* **93**, 475–501.

Clermont, Y. and Leblond, C. P. (1959). Differentiation and renewal of spermatogonia in the monkey, *Macacus rhesus*. *Amer. J. Anat.* **104**, 237–273.

Clermont, Y. and Perey, B. (1957). Quantitative study of the cell population of the seminiferous tubules in immature rats. *Amer. J. Anat.* **100**, 241–267.

Clermont, Y., Leblond, C. P. and Messier, B. (1959). Durée du cycle de l'épithelium séminal du rat. *Arch. Anat. micr. Morph. exp.* **48**, 37–55.

Cole, F. J. (1905). Notes on Myxine. I. *Anat. Anz.* **27**, 323–326.

Cole, H. H., Hart, G. H., Lyons, W. R. and Catchpole, H. R. (1933). The development and hormonal content of fetal horse gonads. *Anat. Rec.* **56**, 275–293.

Conel, J. le Roy (1917). The urogenital system of Myxinoids. *J. Morph.* **29**, 75–163.

Cowperthwaite, M. H. (1925). Observations on pre- and postpubertal oogenesis in the white rat, *Mus norvegicus albinus*. *Amer. J. Anat.* **36**, 69–89.

Craig-Bennett, A. (1930). The reproductive cycle of the three-spined stickleback, *Gasterosteus aculeatus*, Linn. *Phil. Trans.* B. **219**, 197–281.

Crew, F. A. E. (1933). A case of non-disjunction in the fowl. *Proc. roy. Soc. Edinb.* **53**, 89–100.

Cunningham, J. T. (1886). On the structure and development of the reproductive elements in *Myxine glutinosa*, L. *Quart. J. micr. Sci.* **27**, 49–76.

Cunningham, J. T. (1898). On the histology of the ovary and of the ovarian ova in certain marine fishes. *Quart. J. micr. Sci.* **40**, 101–163.

D'Ancona, U. (1951). Détermination et différenciation du sexe chez les poissons. *In* "Colloque sur la Différenciation Sexuelle chez les Vertébrés", pp. 92–112. Centre national de la recherche scientifique, Paris.

D'Ancona, U. (1955). Osservazioni sulle gonadi giovanili di *Amia calva*. *Arch. ital. Anat. Embriol.* **60**, 184–200.

D'Ancona, U. (1956a). Inversions spontanées et expérimentales dans les gonades des téléostéens. *Année Biol.* **52**, 89–99 (from *Biol. Abstr.*).

D'Ancona, U. (1956b) Morphogenèse et différenciation sexuelle chez les poissons téléostéens. *Bull. Soc. zool. Fr.* **81**, 219–229.

Dantschakoff, V. (1931a). Keimzelle und Gonade. I. A. Von der entodermalen Wanderzelle bis zur Urkeimzelle in der Gonade. *Z. Zellforsch.* **13**, 448–510.

Dantschakoff, V. (1931b). Keimzelle und Gonade. Die entodermale Wanderzelle als Stamzelle in der Keimbahn. Experimentelle Beweise. *Z. Zellforsch.* **14**, 376–384.

Dantschakoff, V. (1932). Keimzelle und Gonade. IIb. Ganzheit des Gewebekomplexes als Faktor in der Entwicklung der Gonade. *Z. Zellforsch.* **15**, 581–644.

76   L. L. FRANCHI, A. M. MANDL AND S. ZUCKERMAN

Dantschakoff, V. (1951). La différenciation du sexe chez les vertébrés. In "Colloque sur la Différenciation Sexuelle chez les Vertébrés", pp. 185–212. Centre national de la recherche scientifique, Paris.

Davies, J., Dempsey, E. W. and Wislocki, G. B. (1957). Histochemical observations on the fetal ovary and testis of the horse. J. Histochem. Cytochem. 5, 584–590.

Dawson, A. B. and McCabe, M. (1951). The interstitial tissue of the ovary in infantile and juvenile rats. J. Morph. 88, 543–572.

Debeyre, A. (1933). Sur la présence de gonocytes chez un embryon humain au stade de la ligne primitive. C.R. Ass. Anat. 28, 240–250.

Defretin, M. (1924). Origine et migration des gonocytes chez le poulet. C.R. Soc. Biol., Paris, 91, 1082–1084.

D'Hollander, F. (1904). Recherches sur l'oogénèse et sur la structure et la signification du noyau vitellin de Balbiani chez les oiseaux. Arch. Anat. micr. 7, 117–180.

Dildine, G. C. (1933). Germ cell origin and gonad differentiation in the viviparous top minnow, Lebistes reticulatus. Anat. Rec. 57, Suppl., 88.

Dildine, G. C. (1936). Studies in teleostean reproduction. I. Embryonic hermaphroditism in Lebistes reticulatus. J. Morph. 60, 261–277.

Dodd, J. M. (1960). Genetic and environmental aspects of sex determination in cold-blooded vertebrates. In "Sex Differentiation and Development" (C. R. Austin, ed.). Mem. Soc. Endocrin. No. 7, 17–44.

Dodds, G. S. (1910). Segregation of the germ-cells of the teleost, Lophius. J. Morph. 21, 563–610.

Dodson, E. O. (1948). A morphological and biochemical study of lampbrush chromosomes of vertebrates. Univ. Calif. Publ. Zool. 53, 281–314.

Dulbecco, R. (1946). Sviluppo di gonadi in assenza di cellule sessuali nell' embrioni di pollo. Sterilizazione completa mediante esposizione a raggi γ allo stadio di linea primitiva. Rend. Acc. Naz. Lincei, Ser. VIII. 1, 1211–1213 (from Burns, 1955).

Duryee, W. R. (1950). Chromosomal physiology in relation to nuclear structure. Ann. N.Y. Acad. Sci. 50, 920–952.

Dustin, A. P. (1907). Recherches sur l'origine des gonocytes chez les amphibiens. Arch. Biol., Paris, 23, 411–522.

Dustin, A. P. (1910). L'origine et l'évolution des gonocytes chez les reptiles (Chrysemys marginata). Arch. Biol., Paris, 25, 495–534.

Eckstein, P. and Zuckerman, S. (1956). Morphology of the reproductive tract. In "Marshall's Physiology of Reproduction" (A. S. Parkes, ed.) Vol. I. Part I, pp. 43–155. Longmans, Green and Co., London.

Edwards, R. G. and Gates, A. H. (1959). Timing of the stages of the maturation divisions, ovulation, fertilization and the first cleavage of eggs of adult mice treated with gonadotrophins. J. Endocrin. 18, 292–304.

Eggert, B. (1931). Die Geschlechtsorgane der Gobiiformes und Blenniformes. Z. wiss. Zool. 139, 249–558.

Eigenmann, C. H. (1891). On the precocious segregation of the sex-cells of Micrometrus aggregatus, Gibbons. J. Morph. 5, 481–492.

Eigenmann, C. H. (1897). Sex differentiation in the viviparous teleost Cymatogaster. Arch. EntwMech. 4, 125–179.

Enders, A. C. (1960). A histological study of the cortex of the ovary of the adult armadillo, with special reference to the question of neoformation of oocyces. Anat. Rec. 136, 491-499.

Essenberg, J. M. (1923). Sex differentiation in the viviparous teleost *Xiphophorus hellerii* Heckel. *Biol. Bull.*, *Wood's Hole*, **45**, 46–96.

Evans, H. M. and Swezy, O. (1931). Ovogenesis and the normal follicular cycle in adult mammalia. *Mem. Univ. Calif.* **9**, 119–224.

Everett, N. B. (1942). The origin of ova in the adult opossum. *Anat. Rec.* **82**, 77–91.

Everett, N. B. (1943). Observational and experimental evidences relating to the origin and differentiation of the definitive germ cells in mice. *J. exp. Zool.* **92**, 49–91.

Everett, N. B. (1945). The present status of the germ-cell problem in vertebrates. *Biol. Rev.* **20**, 45–55.

Fauré-Fremiet, E. and Kaufman, L. (1928). La loi de décroissance progressive du taux de la ponte chez la poule. *Ann. Physiol. Physicochim. biol.* **4**, 64–122.

Fedorow, V. (1907). Ueber die Wanderung der Genitalzellen bei *Salmo fario*. *Anat. Anz.* **31**, 219–223.

Felix, W. (1912). The development of the urinogenital organs. *In* "Manual of Human Embryology" (F. Keibel and F. P. Mall, eds.). Vol. 2, pp. 752–979. J. B. Lippincott Co., Philadelphia and London.

Felix, W. and Bühler, A. (1906). Die Entwickelung der Keimdrüsen und ihrer Ausführungsgänge. *In* "Handbuch der vergleichenden und experimentellen Entwickelungslehre der Wirbeltiere" (O. Hertwig, ed.). Vol. III, Part I. pp. 619–896. Gustav Fischer, Jena.

Fell, H. B. (1923). Histological studies on the gonads of the fowl. I. The histological basis of sex reversal. *J. exp. Biol.* **1**, 97–130.

Firket, J. (1913). Recherches sur les gonocytes primaires (Urgeschlechtszellen) pendant la période d'indifférence sexuelle et le développement de l'ovaire chez le poulet. *Anat. Anz.* **44**, 166–175.

Firket, J. (1914). Recherches sur l'organogenèse des glandes sexuelles chez les oiseaux. *Arch. Biol.*, *Paris*, **29**, 201–351.

Firket, J. (1920). Recherches sur l'organogenèse des glandes sexuelles chez les oiseaux. *Arch. Biol.*, *Paris*, **30**, 393–516.

Flynn, T. T. and Hill, J. P. (1939). The development of the Monotremata. Part IV. Growth of the ovarian ovum, maturation, fertilisation and early cleavage. *Trans. zool. Soc. Lond.* **24**, 445–622.

Foote, C. L. and Witschi, E. (1939). Effect of sex hormones on the gonads of frog larvae (*Rana clamitans*): Sex inversion in females; stability in males. *Anat. Rec.* **75**, 75–83.

Forbes, T. R. (1940). Studies on the reproductive system of the alligator. IV. Observations on the development of the gonad, the adrenal cortex and the Müllerian duct. *Contr. Embryol. Carneg. Instn.* **28**, 129–156.

Forbes, T. R. (1956). The development of the reproductive system of a lizard, *Anolis carolinensis. Amer. J. Anat.* **98**, 139–157.

Franz, V. ((1909). Die Eiproduktion der Scholle (*Pleuronectes platessa*, L.). *Wiss. Meersuntersuch.* (*Abtl. Helgoland*), **9**, 59–141.

Fraser, E. A. (1919). The development of the urogenital system in the Marsupialia, with special reference to *Trichosurus vulpecula*. Part II. *J. Anat.*, *Lond.* **53**, 97–129.

Fraser, E. A. and Renton, R. M. (1940). Observations on the breeding and development of the viviqarous fish, *Heterandria formosa. Quart. J. micr. Sci.* **81**, 479–520.

Fuss, A. (1912). Ueber die Geschlechtszellen des Menschen und der Säugetiere. *Arch. mikr. Anat.* **81**, Abt. II, 1–23.

Gall, J. G. (1952). The lampbrush chromosomes of *Triturus viridescens*. *Exptl. Cell Res. Suppl.* **2**, 95–102.

Gall, J. G. (1954). Lampbrush chromosomes from oocyte nuclei of the newt. *J. Morph.* **94**, 283–351.

Garde, M. L. (1930). The ovary of *Ornithorhynchus*, with special reference to follicular atresia. *J. Anat., Lond.* **64**, 422–453.

Gatenby, J. W. B. (1916). The transition of peritoneal epithelial cells into germ cells in some amphibian Anura, especially in *Rana temporaria*. *Quart. J. micr. Sci.* **61**, 275–300.

Gatenby, J. W. B. (1922). Some notes on the gametogenesis of *Ornithorhynchus paradoxus*. *Quart J. micr. Sci.* **66**, 475–496.

Gatenby, J. W. B. (1924). The transition of peritoneal epithelial cells into germ cells in *Gallus bankiva*. *Quart. J. micr. Sci.* **68**, 1–16.

Gérard, P. (1919/1920). Contribution à l'étude de l'ovaire des mammifères. L'ovaire de *Galago mossambicus* (Young). *Arch. Biol., Paris*, **30**, 357–391.

Gérard, P. (1932). Etudes sur l'ovogenèse et l'ontogenèse chez les lémuriens du genre *Galago. Arch. Biol., Paris*, **43**, 93–151.

Gérard, P. and Herlant, M. (1953). Sur la persistence de phénomènes d'oogenèse chez les lémuriens adultes. *Arch. Biol., Paris*, **64**, 97–111.

Gillman, J. (1948). The development of the gonads in man, with a consideration of the role of fetal endocrines and the histogenesis of ovarian tumors. *Contr. Embryol. Carneg. Instn.* **32**, 81–131.

Godet, R. (1949). Recherches d'anatomie, d'embryologie normale et expérimentale sur l'appareil génital de la taupe (*Talpa europœa*, L.). *Bull. biol.* **83**, 25–111.

Goette, A. (1875). "Die Entwickelungsgeschichte der Unke (*Bombinator igneus*) als Grundlage einer vergleichenden Morphologie der Wirbelthiere." Leopold Voss, Leipzig.

Goldschmidt, R. (1917). A further contribution to the theory of sex. *J. exp. Zool.* **22**, 593–617.

Goldsmith, J. B. (1928). The history of the germ cells in the domestic fowl. *J. Morph.* **46**, 275–315.

Goldsmith, J. B. (1935). The primordial germ-cells of the chick. I. The effect on the gonad of complete and partial removal of the 'germinal crescent' and of removal of other parts of the blastodisc. *J. Morph.* **58**, 537–553.

Goodrich, H. B., Dee, J. E., Flynn, C. M. and Mercer, R. M. (1934). Germ cells and sex differentiation in *Lebistes reticulatus. Biol. Bull., Wood's Hole*, **67**, 83–96.

Gorbman, A. (1959). "Comparative Endocrinology." John Wiley & Sons, Inc., New York.

Gray, J. C. (1930). The development, histology and endocrine functions of the compensatory right gonad of the hen. *Amer. J. Anat.* **46**, 217–259.

Green, S. H. and Zuckerman, S. (1951). The number of oocytes in the mature rhesus monkey (*Macaca mulatta*). *J. Endocrin.* **7**, 194–202.

Green, S. H. and Zuckerman, S. (1954). Further observations on oocyte numbers in mature rhesus monkeys (*Macaca mulatta*). *J. Endocrin.* **10**, 284–290.

Green, S. H., Mandl, A. M. and Zuckerman, S. (1951). The proportion of ovarian follicles in different stages of development in rats and monkeys. *J. Anat., Lond.* **85**, 325–329.

Green, S. H., Smith, A. U. and Zuckerman, S. (1956). The numbers of oocytes in ovarian autografts after freezing and thawing. *J. Endocrin.* **13**, 330–334.

Greenwood, A. W. (1937). Constitutional vigor in poultry. *Emp. J. exp. Agric.* **5**, 32–37 (from *Biol. Abstr.*).

Gruenwald, P. (1942). The development of the sex cords in the gonads of man and mammals. *Amer. J. Anat.* **70**, 359–397.

Hamlett, G. W. D. (1935a). Extra-ovarial sex cords on an armadillo ovary. *Anat. Rec.* **62**, 195–199.

Hamlett, G. W. D. (1935b). The effects of Antuitrin S and pituitary extract upon the armadillo ovary. *Anat. Rec.* **62**, 201–207.

Hann, H. W. (1927). The history of the germ cells of *Cottus bairdii* Girard. *J. Morph.* **43**, 427–497.

Hardisty, M. W. (1960). Development of the gonads in parasitic and non-parasitic lampreys. *Nature, Lond.* **187**, 341-342.

Hargitt, G. T. (1925). The formation of the sex glands and germ cells of mammals. I. The origin of the germ cells in the albino rat. *J. Morph.* **40**, 517–557.

Hargitt, G. T. (1926). The formation of the sex glands and germ cells of mammals. II. The history of the male germ cells in the albino rat. *J. Morph.* **42**, 253–305.

Hargitt, G. T. (1930). The formation of the sex glands and germ cells of mammals. III. The history of the female germ cells in the albino rat to the time of sexual maturity. IV. Continuous origin and degeneration of germ cells in the female albino rat. *J. Morph.* **49**, 277–331 and 333–353.

Hartman, C. G. (1923). Postpubertal oogenesis in the opossum. *Anat. Rec.* **32**, 209.

Hartman, C. G. (1926). Polynuclear ova and polyovular follicles in the opossum and other mammals, with special reference to the problem of fecundity. *Amer. J. Anat.* **37**, 1–51.

Hartman, C. G. and Corner, G. W. (1941). The first maturation division of the macaque ovum. *Contr. Embryol. Carneg. Instn.* **29**, 1–6.

Hegner, R. W. (1914). "The Germ Cell Cycle in Animals." Macmillan Co., New York.

Herlitzka, A. (1900). Recherches sur la transplantation. La transplantation des ovaires. *Arch. ital. Biol.* **34**, 89–106.

Heys, F. (1931). The problem of the origin of germ cells. *Quart. Rev. Biol.* **6**, 1–45.

Hibbard, H. and Parat, M. (1927). Oogenesis in certain teleosts with special reference to the chondriome, vacuome and yolk formation. *J. Anat., Lond.* **61**, 494–497.

Hickling, C. F. (1930). The natural history of the hake. Part III. Seasonal changes in the condition of the hake. *Fish. Invest.* Series II, **12**, 1–78.

Hickling, C. F. (1936). Seasonal changes in the ovary of the immature hake, *Merluccius merluccius* L. *J. Mar. Biol. Assn. U.K.* **20**, 443–461.

Hilsman, H. M. (1934). The ovarian cycle in *Triturus viridescens. Anat. Rec.* **57**, Suppl., 82.

Hoffmann, C. K. (1892). Etude sur le développement de l'appareil urogénital des oiseaux. *Verh. Koningl. Akad. Wetensch.*, Amsterdam (from Maréchal, 1907).

Humphrey, R. R. (1925). The primordial germ cells of *Hemidactylium* and other Amphibia. *J. Morph.* **41**, 1–43.

Humphrey, R. R. (1927). Modification or suppression of the so-called migration of primordial germ cells in anuran embryos. *Anat. Rec.* 35, 41.

Humphrey, R. R. (1928a). Sexual differentiation in gonads developed from transplants of the intermediate mesoderm of *Amblystoma*. *Biol. Bull., Wood's Hole*, 55, 317–338.

Humphrey, R. R. (1928b). The developmental potencies of the intermediate mesoderm of *Amblystoma* when transplanted into ventrolateral sites in other embryos: the primordial germ cells of such grafts and their rôle in the development of a gonad. *Anat. Rec.* 40, 67–101.

Humphrey, R. R. (1929a). The early position of the primordial germ cells in urodeles: evidence from experimental studies. *Anat. Rec.* 42, 301–314.

Humphrey, R. R. (1929b). Studies on sex reversal in *Amblystoma*. I. Bisexuality and sex reversal in larval males uninfluenced by ovarian hormones. *Anat. Rec.* 42, 119–155.

Humphrey, R. R. (1931). Studies on sex reversal in *Amblystoma*. V. The structure of ovaries of *A. tigrinum* subjected for long periods to the influence of a testis resident in the same animal. *Anat. Rec.* 51, 135–153.

Hutt, F. B. and Grussendorf, D. T. (1933). On the fecundity of partially ovariotomized fowls. *J. exp. Zool.* 65, 199–214.

Ingram, D. L. (1953). The effect of hypophysectomy on the number of oocytes in the adult albino rat. *J. Endocrin.* 9, 307–311.

Ingram, D. L. (1958). Fertility and oocyte numbers after X-irradiation of the ovary. *J. Endocrin.* 17, 81–90.

Ingram, D. L., Mandl, A. M. and Zuckerman, S. (1958). The influence of age on litter-size. *J. Endocrin.* 17, 280–285.

Insko, W. M., Steele, D. G. and Wightman, E. T. (1947). Reproductive phenomena in ageing hens. *Bull. Ky. agric. Exp. Sta.* No. 498, 1–23 (from *Biol. Abstr.*).

James, M. F. (1946). Histology of gonadal changes in the bluegill, *Lepomis macrochirus* Rafinesque, and the largemouth bass, *Huro salmoides* (Lacépède). *J. Morph.* 79, 63–91.

Jarvis, M. M. (1908). The segregation of the germ-cells of *Phrynosoma cornutum*: preliminary note. *Biol. Bull., Wood's Hole*, 15, 119–126.

Johnston, P. M. (1951). The embryonic history of the germ-cells of the large-mouth black bass, *Micropterus salmoides salmoides* (Lacépède). *J. Morph.* 88, 471–542.

Jonckheere, F. (1930). Contribution à l'histogénèse de l'ovaire des mammifères. L'ovaire de *Canis familiaris*. *Arch. Biol., Paris*, 40, 357–436.

Jones, E. C. (1957). "The ageing ovary." Thesis, University of Birmingham.

Jones, E. C. and Krohn, P. L. (1959). Influence of the anterior pituitary on the ageing process in the ovary. *Nature, Lond.* 183, 1155–1158.

Jones, E. C. and Krohn, P. L. (1960). The effect of unilateral ovariectomy on the reproductive life-span of mice. *J. Endocrin.* 20, 129–134.

Jones, E. C. and Krohn, P. L. (1961). The relationship between age, numbers of oocytes and fertility in virgin and multiparous mice. *J. Endocrin.* 21, 469–495.

Jordan, H. E. (1917). Embryonic history of the germ-cells of the loggerhead turtle (*Caretta caretta*). *Publ. Carneg. Instn.* 11, 313–344.

Jurand, A. (1957). Rozwój i róznicowanie gonad u "*Xenopus laevis*" Daud. *Folia Biol.* 5, 123–149 (from *Biol. Abstr.*).

Kellogg, M. P. (1941). The development of the periovarial sac in the white rat. *Anat. Rec.* 79, 465–477.

King, H. D. (1908). The oogenesis of *Bufo lentiginosus*. *J. Morph.* **19**, 369–438.

Kingery, H. M. (1917). Oogenesis in the white mouse. *J. Morph.* **30**, 261–315.

Kingsbury, B. F. (1913). The morphogenesis of the mammalian ovary: *Felis domestica*. *Amer. J. Anat.* **15**, 345–387.

Kingsbury, B. F. (1914). The interstitial cells of the mammalian ovary: *Felis domestica*. *Amer. J. Anat.* **16**, 59–95.

Koltzoff, N. K. (1938). The structure of the chromosomes, and their participation in cell metabolism. *Biolghicheskii Zh., Mosk.* **7**, 3–46.

Krohn, P. L. (1959). Ageing processes in the female reproductive tract. *In* "Lectures on the Scientific Basis of Medicine", Vol. VII, pp. 285–313. The Athlone Press, London.

Kuschakewitsch, S. (1910). Die Entwicklungsgeschichte der Keimdrüsen von *Rana esculenta*. Ein Beitrag zum Sexualitätsproblem. *Festschr. R. Hertwig, Jena*, **2**, 61–224 (from Simkins, 1923).

Leblond, C. P. and Clermont, Y. (1952). Definition of the stages of the cycle of the seminiferous epithelium in the rat. *Ann. N.Y. Acad. Sci.* **55**, 548–573.

Lipschütz, A. (1925). Dynamics of ovarian hypertrophy under experimental conditions. *Brit. J. exp. Biol.* **2**, 331–346.

Lipschütz, A. (1925). New developments in ovarian dynamics and the law of follicular constancy. *Brit. J. exp. Biol.* **5**, 283–291.

Lipschütz, A. and Voss, H. E. V. (1925). Further developments on the dynamics of ovarian hypertrophy. *Brit. J. exp. Biol.* **3**, 35–41.

Loraine, J. A. (1958). "Clinical Applications of Hormone Assay." E. & S. Livingstone, Edinburgh and London.

Loukine, A. V. (1941a). La fréquence du frai chez le sterlet. *C.R. Acad. Sci., U.R.S.S.* **32**, 166–168.

Loukine, A. V. (1941b). Les stades de maturité sexuelle du sterlet. *C.R. Acad. Sci., U.R.S.S.* **32**, 374–376.

Loyez, M. (1906). Recherches sur le développement ovarien des oeufs méroblastiques à vitellus nutritif abondant. *Arch. Anat. micr.* **8**, 69–397.

Mandl, A. M. (1959). A quantitative study of the sensitivity of oocytes to X-irradiation. *Proc. roy. Soc. B.* **150**, 53–71.

Mandl, A. M. and Shelton, M. (1959). A quantitative study of oocytes in young and old nulliparous laboratory rats. *J. Endocrin.* **18**, 444–450.

Mandl, A. M. and Zuckerman, S. (1949). Ovarian autografts in monkeys. *J. Anat., Lond.* **83**, 315–324.

Mandl, A. M. and Zuckerman, S. (1950). The numbers of normal and atretic ova in the mature rat. *J. Endocrin.* **6**, 426–435.

Mandl, A. M. and Zuckerman, S. (1951a). The relation of age to numbers of oocytes. *J. Endocrin.* **7**, 190–193.

Mandl, A. M. and Zuckerman, S. (1951b). The effect of destruction of the germinal epithelium on the numbers of oocytes. *J. Endocrin.* **7**, 103–111.

Mandl, A. M. and Zuckerman, S. (1951c). Numbers of normal and atretic oocytes in unilaterally spayed rats. *J. Endocrin.* **7**, 112–119.

Mandl, A. M. and Zuckerman, S. (1952). Cyclical changes in the number of medium and large follicles in the adult rat ovary. *J. Endocrin.* **8**, 341–346.

Mandl, A. M., Zuckerman, S. and Patterson, H. D. (1952). The number of oocytes in ovarian fragments after compensatory hypertrophy. *J. Endocrin.* **8**, 347–356.

Maréchal, J. (1904). Ueber die morphologische Entwickelung der Chromosomen im Keimbläschen des Selachiereies. *Anat. Anz.* **25**, 383–398.

Maréchal, J. (1907). Sur l'ovogénèse des sélaciens et de quelques autres chordates. *Cellule*, **24**, 7–239.

Marin, G. (1959). Gonadogenesi in assenza di gonociti e azione radiazioni ionizzanti sul differenziamento sessuale dell' embrione di pollo. *Arch. ital. Anat. Embriol.* **64**, 211–235.

Marshall, F. H. A. and Jolly, W. A. (1907). Results of removal and transplantation of ovaries. *Trans. roy. Soc. Edinb.* **45**, 589–599.

Marshall, F. H. A. and Jolly, W. A. (1908). On the results of heteroplastic ovarian transplantation as compared with those produced by transplantation in the same animal. *Quart. J. exp. Physiol.* **1**, 115–120.

Marza, V. D. and Marza, E. V. (1936). The formation of the hen's egg. Parts I–IV. *Quart. J. micr. Sci.* **78**, 133–189.

Maschkowzeff, A. (1934). Zur Phylogenie der Geschlechtsdrüsen und der Geschlechtsausführgänge bei den Vertebrata. *Zool. Jb.* **59**, 1–68.

Matsumoto, T. (1932). On the early localization and history of the so-called primordial germ-cells in the chick embryo. (Preliminary report). *Sci. Rep. Tohoku Imp. Univ., Biol.* **7**, 89–127.

Matthews, L. H. (1937). The female sexual cycle in the British horseshoe bats, *Rhinolophus ferrum-equinum insulanus* Barrett-Hamilton and *R. hipposideros minutus* Montagu. *Trans. zool. Soc. Lond.* **23**, 224–255.

Matthews, L. H. (1950). Reproduction in the basking shark, *Cetorhinus maximus* (Gunner). *Phil. Trans. B.* **234**, 247–316.

Matthews, L. H. and Marshall, F. H. A. (1956). Cyclical changes in the reproductive organs of the lower vertebrates. In "Marshall's Physiology of Reproduction" (A. S. Parkes, ed.). Vol. I, Part I, pp. 156–225. Longmans, Green and Co., London.

Matthews, S. A. (1938). The seasonal cycle in the gonads of *Fundulus. Biol. Bull., Wood's Hole*, **75**, 66–74.

McCosh, G. K. (1930). The origin of the germ cells in *Amblystoma maculatum. J. Morph.* **50**, 569–611.

McCurdy, H. M. (1931). Development of the sex organs in *Triturus torosus. Amer. J. Anat.* **47**, 367–403.

McKay, D. G., Hertig, A. T., Adams, E. C. and Danziger, S. (1953). Histochemical observations on the germ cells of human embryos. *Anat. Rec.* **117**, 201–219.

Mendoza, G. (1940). The reproductive cycle of the viviparous teleost, *Neotoca bilineata*, a member of the family Goodeidae. II. The cyclic changes in the ovarian soma during gestation. *Biol. Bull., Wood's Hole*, **78**, 349–365.

Mendoza, G. (1941). The reproductive cycle of the viviparous teleost, *Neotoca bilineata*, a member of the family Goodeidae. III. The germ cell cycle. *Biol. Bull., Wood's Hole*, **81**, 70–79.

Mendoza, G. (1943). The reproductive cycle of the viviparous teleost, *Neotoca bilineata*, a member of the family Goodeidae. IV. The germinal tissue. *Biol. Bull., Wood's Hole*, **84**, 87–97.

Merriman, D. and Schedl, H. P. (1941). The effects of light and temperature on gametogenesis in the four-spined stickleback, *Apeltes quadracus* (Mitchill). *J. exp. Zool.* **88**, 413–449.

Miller, M. R. and Robbins, M. E. (1954). The reproductive cycle in *Taricha torosa* (*Triturus torosus*). *J. exp. Zool.* **125**, 415–445.

Mintz, B. (1957). Embryological development of primordial germ-cells in the mouse: Influence of a new mutation W^j. *J. Embryol. exp. Morph.* **5**, 396–403.

1. OVARIAN DEVELOPMENT AND OOGENESIS 83

Mintz, B. (1959a). Nuclear differentiation in early gonia of the mouse embryo. *Anat. Rec.* **134**, 608.

Mintz, B. (1959b). Continuity of the female germ cell line from embryo to adult. *Arch. Anat. micr. Morph. exp.* **48**, 155–172.

Mintz, B. and Russell, E. S. (1957). Gene-induced embryological modifications of primordial germ cells in the mouse. *J. exp. Zool.* **134**, 207–237.

Moltchanova, I. (1941). La structure histologique des oeufs des sterlets aux stades différents de maturité sexuelle. *C.R. Acad. Sci., U.R.S.S.* **32**, 163–165.

Moore, C. R. and Wang, H. (1947). Ovarian activity in mammals subsequent to chemical injury of cortex. *Physiol. Zoöl.* **20**, 300–321.

Munson, J. P. (1904). Researches on the oogenesis of the tortoise, *Clemmys marmorata. Amer. J. Anat.* **3**, 311–347.

Muratori, G. (1937). Embryonal germ-cells of the chick in hanging-drop cultures. *Contr. Embryol. Carneg. Instn.* **26**, 59–69.

Myers, H. I., Young, W. C. and Dempsey, E. W. (1936). Graafian follicle development throughout the reproductive cycle in the guinea pig, with especial reference to changes during oestrus (sexual receptivity). *Anat. Rec.* **65**, 381–401.

Narain, D. (1930). Cytoplasmic inclusions in the oogenesis of *Ophiocephalus punctatus. Z. Zellforsch.* **11**, 237–243.

Nelsen, O. E. and Swain, E. (1942). The prepubertal origin of germ-cells in the ovary of the opossum (*Didelphys virginiana*). *J. Morph.* **71**, 335–355.

Nieuwkoop, P. D. (1947). Experimental investigations on the origin and determination of the germ cells, and on the development of the lateral plates and germ ridges in urodeles. *Arch. néerl. Zool.* **8**, 1–205.

Nieuwkoop, P. D. (1949). The present state of the problem of the "Keimbahn" in the vertebrates. *Experientia,* **5**, 308–312.

Nieuwkoop, P. D. (1951). Causal analysis of the early development of the primordial germ cells and the germ ridges in urodeles. *In* "Colloque sur la Différenciation Sexuelle chez les Vertébrés" pp. 75–86. Centre national de la recherche scientifique, Paris.

Nussbaum, M. (1880). Zur Differenzierung des Geschlechts im Thierreich. *Arch. mikr. Anat.* **18**, 1–120.

Nussbaum, M. (1901). Zur Entwickelung des Geschlechts beim Huhn. *Verh. Anat. Ges., Jena,* (from Hegner, 1914).

Oakberg, E. F. (1957). Duration of spermatogenesis in the mouse and timing of stages of the cycle of the seminiferous epithelium. *Amer. J. Anat.* **99**, 507–516.

O'Donoghue, C. H. (1916). On the corpora lutea and interstitial tissue of the ovary in the Marsupialia. *Quart. J. micr. Sci.* **61**, 433–473.

Odor, D. L. (1955). The temporal relationship of the first maturation division of rat ova to the onset of heat. *Amer. J. Anat.* **97**, 461–491.

Odor, D. L. and Renninger, D. F. (1960). Polar body formation in the rat oocyte as observed with the electron microscope. *Anat. Rec.* **137**, 13–23.

Okkelberg, P. (1921). The early history of the germ cells in the brook lamprey *Entosphenus wilderi* (Gage), up to and including the period of sexual differentiation. *J. Morph.* **35**, 1–151.

Olsen, M. W. (1942). Maturation, fertilization and early cleavage in the hen's egg. *J. Morph.* **70**, 513–533.

Olsen, M. W. and Fraps, R. M. (1944). Maturation, fertilization and early cleavage of the egg of the domestic turkey. *J. Morph.* **74**, 297–309.

Parkes, A. S., Fielding, U. and Brambell, F. W. R. (1927). Ovarian regeneration in the mouse after complete double ovariotomy. *Proc. roy. Soc.* B. **101**, 328–354.

Pasteels, J. (1953). Contribution à l'étude du développement des reptiles. I. Origine et migration des gonocytes chez deux Lacertiliens (*Mabuia megalura* et *Chamaeleo bitaeniatus*). *Arch. Biol., Paris,* **64**, 227–245.

Pearl, R. and Schoppe, W. F. (1921). Studies on the physiology of reproduction in the domestic fowl. XVIII. Further observations on the anatomical basis of fecundity. *J. exp. Zool.* **34**, 101–118.

Perle, G. (1927). Origine de la première ébauche génitale chez *Bufo vulgaris*. *C.R. Acad. Sci., Paris,* **184**, 303–304.

Pettinari, V. (1928). "Greffe Ovarienne et Action Endocrine de L'Ovaire." Gaston Doin, Paris.

Philippi, E. (1909). Fortpflanzungsgeschichte der viviparen Teleosteer *Glaridichthys januarius* und *G. decem-maculatus* in ihrem Einfluss auf Lebensweise, makroskopische und mikroskopische Anatomie. *Zool. Jb. (Abt. Anat.)* **27**, 1–94.

Pincus, G. (1936). "The Eggs of Mammals." Macmillan Co., New York.

Politzer, G. (1933). Die Keimbahn des Menschen. *Z. Anat. EntwGesch.* **100**, 331–361.

Ponse, K. (1924). L'organe de Bidder et le déterminisme des caractères sexuels sécondaires du crapaud (*Bufo vulgaris* L.). *Rev. suisse Zool.* **31**, 177–336.

Rao, C. R. N. (1927). On the structure of the ovary and the ovarian ovum of *Loris lydekkerianus* Cabr. *Quart. J. micr. Sci.* **71**, 57–74.

Raynaud, A. and Frilley, M. (1946). Irradiation, au moyen des rayons X, des ébauches génitales de l'embryon de souris, au quinzième jour de la vie intra-utérine. *C.R. Acad. Sci., Paris,* **233**, 1187–1189.

Raynaud, A. and Frilley, M. (1947). Déstruction des glandes génitales de l'embryon de souris par une irradiation au moyen des rayons X, à l'âge de treize jours. *Ann. Endocrin., Paris,* **8**, 400–419.

Reagan, F. P. (1916). Some results and possibilities of early embryonic castration. *Anat. Rec.* **11**, 251–267.

Rennels, E. G. (1951). Influence of hormones on the histochemistry of ovarian interstitial tissue in the immature rat. *Amer. J. Anat.* **88**, 63–107.

Richards, A. and Thompson, J. T. (1921). The migration of the primary sex-cells of *Fundulus heteroclitus*. *Biol. Bull., Wood's Hole,* **40**, 325–348.

Risley, P. L. (1930). Bisexuality and sex differentiation in embryos of the musk turtle, *Sternotherus odoratus* (Latreille). *Anat. Rec.* **47**, 323.

Risley, P. L. (1933a). Contributions on the development of the reproductive system in *Sternotherus odoratus* (Latreille). I. The embryonic origin and migration of the primordial germ cells. *Z. Zellforsch.* **18**, 459–492.

Risley, P. L. (1933b). Contributions on the development of the reproductive system in *Sternotherus odoratus* (Latreille). II. Gonadogenesis and sex differentiation. *Z. Zellforsch.* **18**, 493–543.

Risley, P. L. (1941). A comparison of effects of gonadotropic and sex hormones on the urogenital systems of juvenile terrapins. *J. exp. Zool.* **87**, 477–515.

Rosenthal, H. L. (1952). Observations on reproduction of the Poeeiliid *Lebistes reticulatus* (Peters). *Biol. Bull., Wood's Hole,* **102**, 30–38.

Rückert, J. (1892). Zur Entwickelungsgeschichte des Ovarialeies bei Selachiern. *Anat. Anz.* **7**, 107–158.

Salzgeber, B. (1950). Stérilisation et intersexualité obtenues chez l'embryon de poulet par irradiation aux rayons X. *Bull. biol.* **84**, 225–233.

1. OVARIAN DEVELOPMENT AND OOGENESIS 85

Schotterer, A. (1928). Beitrag zur Feststellung der Eianzahl in verschiedenen Altersperioden bei der Hündin. *Anat. Anz.* **65**, 177–192.

Schreiner, K. E. (1904). Über das Generationsorgan von *Myxine glutinosa* (L.). *Biol. Zbl.* **24**, 91–104, 121–129 and 162–173.

Schreiner, K. E. (1955). Studies on the gonad of *Myxine glutinosa* L. *Univ. Bergen Arb. naturv. R.* **8**, 1–36.

Segal, S. J. (1959). Comparative aspects of gonadal morphology, physiology and antigenicity. In "Comparative Endocrinology" (A. Gorbman, ed.) pp. 553–567. John Wiley & Sons, Inc., New York.

Segal, S. J. and Nelson, W. O. (1959). Initiation and maintenance of testicular function. In "Recent Progress in the Endocrinology of Reproduction" (C. W. Lloyd, ed.) pp. 107–129. Academic Press, Inc., New York and London.

Shelton, M. (1959). A comparison of the population of oocytes in nulliparous and multiparous senile laboratory rats. *J. Endocrin.* **18**, 451–455.

Simkins, C. S. (1923). On the origin and migration of the so-called primordial germ cells in the mouse and the rat. *Acta. zool., Stockh.* **4**, 241–278.

Simkins, C. S. (1925). Origin of the germ cells in *Trionyx*. *Amer. J. Anat.* **36**, 185–213.

Simkins, C. S. (1928). Origin of the sex cells in man. *Amer. J. Anat.* **41**, 249–293.

Simkins, C. S. and Asana, J. J. (1930). Development of the sex glands in *Calotes*. I. Cytology and growth of the gonads prior to hatching. *Quart. J. micr. Sci.* **74**, 133–149.

Simon, D. (1957). La migration des cellules germinales de l'embryon de poulet vers les ébauches gonadiques; preuves expérimentales. *C.R. Soc. Biol., Paris*, **151**, 1576–1580.

Slater, D. W. and Dornfeld, E. J. (1945). Quantitative aspects of growth and oocyte production in the early prepubertal rat ovary. *Amer. J. Anat.* **76**, 253–275.

Slizynski, B. M. (1958). Meiotic prophase in female mice. *Nature, Lond.* **179**, 638.

Sonnenbrodt (1908). Die Wachstumsperiode der Oocyte des Huhnes. *Arch. mikr. Anat.* **72**, 415–480.

Stanley, A. J. and Witschi, E. (1940). Germ cell migration in relation to asymmetry in the sex glands of hawks. *Anat. Rec.* **76**, 329–342.

Sternberg, W. H. (1949). The morphology, androgenic function, hyperplasia and tumors of the human ovarian hilus cells. *Amer. J. Path.* **25**, 493–521.

Stolk, A. (1958). Extra-regional oocytes in teleosts. *Nature, Lond.* **182**, 1241.

Stromsten, F. A. (1929). History of the germ cells in the goldfish. *Anat. Rec.* **44**, 254.

Stuhlmann, F. (1887). Zur Kenntnis des Ovariums der Aalmutter (*Zoarces viviparus* Cuv.). *Abh. Naturw., Hamburg*, **10** (from Eggert, 1931).

Suzuki, K. (1939). Regeneration of gonads in *Plecoglossus altivelis* after spawning season. *Cytologia*, **10**, 113–126.

Swezy, O. (1933). "Ovogenesis and its Relation to the Hypophysis." Science Press, Lancaster, Pennsylvania.

Swift, C. H. (1914). Origin and early history of the primordial germ-cells in the chick. *Amer. J. Anat.* **15**, 483–516.

Swift, C. H. (1915). Origin of the definitive sex-cells in the female chick and their relation to the primordial germ-cells. *Amer. J. Anat.* **18**, 441–470.

H

Swift, C. H. (1916). Origin of the sex-cords and definitive spermatogonia in the male chick. *Amer. J. Anat.* **20**, 375–410.

Swingle, W. W. (1926). The germ cells of anurans. 2. An embryological study of sex differentiation in *Rana catesbeiana*. *J. Morph.* **41**, 441–546.

Torrey, T. W. (1945). The development of the urinogenital system of the albino rat. II: the gonads. *Amer. J. Anat.* **76**, 375–397.

Tribe, M. and Brambell, F. W. R. (1932). The origin and migration of the primordial germ cells of *Sphenodon punctatus*. *Quart. J. micr. Sci.* **75**, 251–282.

Turner, C. L. (1938a). Histological and cytological changes in the ovary of *Cymatogaster aggregatus* during gestation. *J. Morph.* **62**, 351–373.

Turner, C. L. (1938b). The reproductive cycle of *Brachyraphis episcopi*, an ovoviviparous poeciliid fish, in the natural tropical habitat. *Biol. Bull., Wood's Hole*, **75**, 56–65.

Tyler, A. (1955). Ontogeny of immunological properties. *In* "Analysis of Development" (B. H. Willier, P. A. Weiss and V. Hamburger, eds.) pp. 556–573. W. B. Saunders Company, Philadelphia and London.

Van Durme, M. (1914). Nouvelles recherches sur la vitellogenèse des oeufs d'oiseaux aux stades d'accroissement, de maturation, de fécondation et du début de la segmentation. *Arch. Biol., Paris*, **29**, 71–200.

Vanneman, A. S. (1917). The early history of the germ cells in the armadillo, *Tatusia novemcincta*. *Amer. J. Anat.* **22**, 341–363.

Vannini, E. (1951). Organogenèse des gonades et déterminisme du sexe chez les amphibiens et les amniotes. *In* "Colloque sur la Différenciation Sexuelle chez les Vertébrés", pp. 113–131. Centre national de la recherche scientifique, Paris.

Vannini, E. and Sabbadin, A. (1954). The relation of the interrenal blastema to the origin of the somatic tissues of the gonad in frog tadpoles. *J. Embryol. exp. Morph.* **2**, 275–289.

Waldeyer, W. (1870). "Eierstock und Ei." Engelmann, Leipzig.

Waldeyer, W. (1906). Die Geschlechtszellen. *In* "Handbuch der vergleichenden und experimentellen Entwicklungslehre der Wirbeltiere" (O. Hertwig, ed.) pp. 86–476. Gustav Fischer, Jena.

Wallace, W. (1904). Observations on ovarian ova and follicles in teleostean and elasmobranch fishes. *Quart. J. micr. Sci.* **47**, 161–213.

Weismann, A. (1885). "Die Continuität des Keimplasmas als Grundlage einer Theorie der Vererbung." Jena (from Hegner, 1914).

Wheeler, J. F. G. (1924). Growth of the egg in the dab (*Pleuronectes limanda*). *Quart. J. micr. Sci.* **68**, 641–660.

Wheeler, W. M. (1899). The development of the urinogenital organs of the lamprey. *Zool. Jb.* **13**, 1–88.

Willier, B. H. (1933). Potencies of the gonad-forming area in the chick as tested by chorio-allantoic grafts. *Arch. mikr. Anat.* **130**, 616–648.

Willier, B. H. (1937). Experimentally produced sterile gonads and the problem of the origin of germ cells in the chick embryo. *Anat. Rec.* **70**, 89–112.

Willier, B. H. (1939). The embryonic development of sex. *In* "Sex and Internal Secretions" (E. Allen, ed.) pp. 64–144. Baillière, Tindall and Cox, London.

Willier, B. H. (1951). Sterile gonads and the problem of the origin of germ cells in the chick embryo. *In* "Colloque sur la Différenciation Sexuelle chez les Vertébrés", pp. 87–91. Centre national de la recherche scientifique, Paris.

Willier, B. H., Weiss, P. A. and Hamburger, V. (1955). "Analysis of Development." W. B. Saunders Co., Philadelphia and London.

Wimsatt, W. A. and Waldo, C. M. (1945). The normal occurrence of a peritoneal opening in the bursa ovarii of the mouse. *Anat. Rec.* **93**, 47–57.

Winiwarter, H. de (1901). Recherches sur l'ovogenèse et l'organogenèse ed l'ovaire des mammifères (lapin et homme). *Arch. Biol., Paris,* **17**, 33–199.

Winiwarter, H. de (1910). Contribution à l'étude de l'ovaire humain. I. Appareil nerveux et phéochrome. II. Tissu musculaire. III. Cordons médullaires et corticaux. *Arch. Biol., Paris,* **25**, 683–756.

Winiwarter, H. de (1920a). Couche corticale définitive au hile de l'ovaire et pseudoformation ovulaire. *C.R. Soc. Biol., Paris,* **83**, 1406–1408.

Winiwarter, H. de (1920b). Formation de la couche corticale définitive et origine des oeufs définitifs dans l'ovaire de chatte. *C.R. Soc. Biol., Paris,* **83**, 1403–1405.

Winiwarter, H. de and Sainmont, G. (1908). Über die ausschliesslich postfötale Bildung der definitiven Eier bei der Katze. *Anat. Anz.* **32**, 613–616.

Winiwarter, H. de and Sainmont, G. (1909). Nouvelles recherches sur l'ovogenèse et organogenèse de l'ovaire des mammifères (chat). *Arch. Biol., Paris,* **24**, 1–142 and 165–276.

Witschi, E. (1914). Experimentelle Untersuchung über die Entwicklungsgeschichte der Keimdrüsen von *Rana temporaria. Arch. mikr. Anat.* **85**, 9–113.

Witschi, E. (1929a). Studies on sex differentiation and sex determination in amphibians. I. Development and sexual differentiation of the gonads of *Rana sylvatica. J. exp. Zool.* **52**, 235–265.

Witschi, E. (1929b). Studies on sex differentiation and sex determination in amphibians. II. Sex reversal in female tadpoles of *Rana sylvatica* following the application of high temperature. *J. exp. Zool.* **52**, 267–291.

Witschi, E. (1931). Studies on sex differentiation and sex determination in amphibians. V. Range of the cortex-medulla antagonism in parabiotic twins of Ranidae and Hylidae. *J. exp. Zool.* **58**, 113–145.

Witschi, E. (1934). Genes and inductors of sex differentiation in amphibians. *Biol. Rev.* **9**, 460–488.

Witschi, E. (1935). Origin of asymmetry in the reproductive system of birds. *Amer. J. Anat.* **56**, 119–141.

Witschi, E. (1936). Studies on sex differentiation and sex determination in amphibians. VIII. Experiments on inductive inhibition of sex differentiation in parabiotic twins of salamanders. *Anat. Rec.* **66**, 483–503.

Witschi, E. (1939). Modification of the development of sex in lower vertebrates and mammals. *In* "Sex and Internal Secretions" (E. Allen, ed.) pp. 145–226. Baillière, Tindall and Cox, London.

Witschi, E. (1948). Migration of the germ cells of human embryos from the yolk sac to the primitive gonadal folds. *Contr. Embryol. Carneg. Instn.* **32**, 67–80.

Witschi, E. (1951a). Embryogenesis of the adrenal and the reproductive glands. *Rec. Progr. Hormone Res.* **6**, 1–27.

Witschi, E. (1951b). Génétique et physiologie de la différenciation du sexe. *In* "Colloque sur la Différenciation Sexuelle chez les Vertébrés" pp. 33–64. Centre national de la recherche scientifique, Paris.

Witschi, E. (1956). "Development of Vertebrates." W. B. Saunders Co., Philadelphia.

Witschi, E., Bruner, J. A. and Segal, S. J. (1953). The pluripotentiality of the mesonephric blastema. *Anat. Rec.* **115**, 381.

Wolf, L. E. (1929). Transformation of epithelial cells into germ cells in *Platypoecilus maculatus*. *Anat. Rec.* **44**, 261.

Wolf, L. E. (1931). The history of germ cells in the viviparous teleost *Platypoecilus maculatus*. *J. Morph.* **52**, 115–153.

Wolff, E. and Haffen, K. (1959). La culture *in vitro* de l'épithélium germinatif isolé des gonades mâles et femelles de l'embryon de canard. *Arch. Anat. micr. Morph. exp.* **48**, 331–345.

Woods, F. A. (1902). Origin and migration of the germ-cells in *Acanthias*. *Amer. J. Anat.* **1**, 307–320.

Yamamoto, K. (1956a). Studies on the formation of fish eggs. I. Annual cycle in the development of ovarian eggs in the flounder *Liopsetta obscura*. *J. Fac. Sci. Hokkaido Univ. Zool.* **12**, 362–373.

Yamamoto, K. (1956b). Studies on the formation of fish eggs. II. Changes in the nucleus of the oocyte of *Liopsetta obscura*, with special reference to the activity of the nucleolus. *J. Fac. Sci. Hokkaido Univ. Zool.* **12**, 375–390.

Zuckerman, S. (1951). The number of oocytes in the mature ovary. *Rec. Progr. Hormone Res.* **6**, 63–109.

Zuckerman, S. (1956). The regenerative capacity of ovarian tissue. *Ciba Foundation Coll. Ageing*, **2**, 31–54.

Zuckerman, S. (1960). Origin and development of oocytes in foetal and mature mammals. *In* "Sex Differentiation and Development" (C. R. Austin, ed.). *Mem. Soc. Endocrin.* No. 7, 63–70.

ADDENDUM

The developmental history of germ cells in the human ovary during foetal life (and early childhood) has recently been re-investigated by histochemical methods. Mitotic activity of germ cells was found to be maximal from the 8th (17 mm) to the 20th (160 mm) week, after which it gradually diminishes and ceases about the time of birth.

Pinkerton, J. H. M., McKay, D. G., Adams, C. E. and Hertig, A. T., 1961, *Obstet. & Gynec.* **18**, 152–181.

THE STRUCTURE OF THE OVARY
A. Invertebrates

L. HARRISON MATTHEWS

I. General

Sexual reproduction, with the production of ova and spermatozoa, is found in the simplest invertebrates. In many Protozoa, such as the Sporozoa, mega- and micro-gametes are formed directly from the merozoite stage. In the Parazoa, the ova of Porifera are derived from wandering amoebocytes which increase in size and undergo a reduction division; they are found in all stages in the dermal jelly and are fertilized in the inhalant canals whither they migrate by amoeboid movement. Although these animals produce eggs, they have no specialized ovary for their formation and nourishment.

In the Metazoa, however, the gonads are universally recognizable as discrete structures, and their rudiments are often evident at very early stages of embryological development. The ovary has been the subject of close study in some species of mammals, but much less work has been done on the organ in other groups, especially in many of the invertebrates. The mammals are only one of five classes in the subphylum Vertebrata of the phylum Chordata, and the Chordata themselves are only one of some twenty phyla of Metazoa which include all the vertebrate and invertebrate animals. It is not possible in this chapter to give more than a brief survey of the structure and histology of the ovary, as far as it is known, in some of the more important invertebrate phyla.

II. The ovary in the different phyla of invertebrates

A. Coelenterata

1. *Cnidaria*

In the Coelenterata, usually regarded as the most primitive of the acoelomate Metazoa, the gonads are distinct, although in the Hydrozoa they are often no more than aggregations of sex cells at definite sites. In Hydrozoa the sex cells generally originate from interstitial cells of the epidermis or gastrodermis, from which they migrate to the gonads where they complete their development. Most of the young oocytes in the ovary serve as nourishment for the minority, sometimes no more than one, that mature. In the Scyphozoa, which are nearly all dioecious, the sex cells are found at the base of the gastrodermis, which forms an epithelium covering the gonad. The ovaries are four or eight in number and generally project into the sides or floor of the gastric pockets. The ova are generally discharged through the mouth by rupture of the ovarian wall into the gastro-vascular cavity. In the Anthozoa, which may be dioecious or hermaphrodite, the sex cells are derived from the gastrodermis and migrate into the mesogloea. The gonads of both sexes are situated on some or all of the septa of the gastro-vascular cavity (Hyman, 1940).

2. *Ctenophora*

The ctenophores are hermaphrodite and the gonads lie on the wall of the eighth meridional canal, the ovaries and testes on opposite sides. The germ cells are derived from the endoderm, and the ovary is arranged as a single or discontinuous strip on the wall of its meridional canal. Many ctenophores show dissogeny, in which sexual maturity is reached in the larva after which the gonads degenerate but return to maturity in the adult. The eggs are discharged through the mouth (Hyman, 1940).

B. Platyhelminthes

Most of the platyhelminths are hermaphrodite. Each animal generally contains complete and separate male and female reproductive systems, but a few are dioecious. As there is no coelom, the gonads are embedded in the mesenchyme, from certain cells of which the sex cells are derived (Hyman, 1951a).

1. *Turbellaria*

In the primitive forms, the oogonia are not concentrated into ovaries, but in the higher forms, where the ovaries are separate from the mesenchyme, they may be of diverse shapes, and single, paired or multiple. In a few forms, some of the oocytes take on nutritive functions and form a follicle surrounding the oocytes that become eggs. In others, the ovary, there termed germovitellarium, is divided into egg- and yolk-producing parts. In most Turbellaria the female gonads are thus differentiated into separate ovaries and yolk glands which discharge into a common duct.

2. *Trematoda*

The ovary is generally single and may be rounded, branched, coiled or lobed. The organ is lined by a layer of spherical resting oogonia with large nuclei and little cytoplasm. The oogonia divide to give rise to oocytes which move to the centre of the ovary during their rapid growth. They are so closely packed that they appear polyhedral, but become spherical or ovoid on release from the ovary. The yolk glands, which appear to be more concerned with shell secretion than with yolk production, are nearly always separate and of a complex shape (Dawes, 1946).

3. *Cestoda*

There is usually a single ovary in each, generally hermaphrodite, proglottis, but sometimes there is a pair. The ovary is often more or less lobulated and sometimes of a complex shape. Yolk glands are not always present. Where they occur they are distinct from the ovary and discharge into its duct; they may be multiple or single.

C. Nemertea

Most species of nemertines are dioecious. The ovaries are derived from small masses of mesenchyme cells generally arranged in a row along both sides of the gut and between its pouches; at sexual maturity, a short duct opening on to the body surface arises for the discharge of the ova. The ovaries, which develop into a series of thin walled sacs embedded in the mesenchyme, are filled with cells, some of which become yolk cells that are absorbed by the others, the ripening oocytes.

Numerous eggs are generally produced simultaneously by each ovary, but in some species each ovary produces a single large egg at intervals (Hyman, 1951a). Fertilization may be internal or external and the eggs are usually laid in batches, though in a few viviparous genera development takes place within the ovaries.

D. Nematoda

Nematodes are usually dioecious, although the males of many species are rare and parthenogenesis occurs in some. Terrestrial species are frequently protandrous hermaphrodites. The sperm produced in the

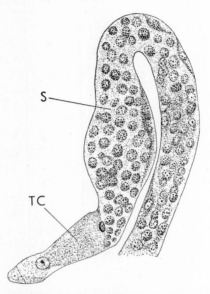

FIG. 1. NEMATODA: The blind proximal end of the ovary of *Ascaris lumbricoides*, showing the terminal cell, *TC*, and syncytium, *S*. (Redrawn by permission from Musso, 1930.)

male stage is stored and used to fertilize the eggs produced by the same gonad in its subsequent female stage. In the female of dioecious species, there are generally two tubular ovaries which range in form from short and straight to complexly coiled; they are continuous with the oviduct. The germinal zone may be confined to the closed proximal end of the organ, or spread throughout its length. The oogonia are attached to a central rachis during their enlargement and differentiation, but the oocytes become detached before their final maturation. In *Ascaris* and other genera, the ova arise from a polynucleated syncytium near the proximal end of the ovary (Fig. 1). Musso (1930), who gives an extensive bibliography of the sexual apparatus of Nematoda, describes the process of division by which the nuclei of the syncytium are derived from a large terminal or primordial germ cell lying at the blind end of the ovary. The epithelium of the ovarian wall arises from sterile germ cells which originate in the same way as the sex cells.

E. Nematomorpha

In the gordiids, or hair-worms, the egg sacs arise as longitudinal splits in the mesenchyme which fills the body with a solid mass of cells in the young stage. The ovaries are formed from mesenchyme cells lateral to the splits which form the egg sacs or egg tubes (Vejdovsky, 1886). The numerous lateral diverticula have been described, probably erroneously, as segmentally arranged. As the eggs enter the egg sacs and pass caudally down the oviducts, the partly emptied ovary becomes a hollow organ.

F. Acanthocephala

The Acanthocephala are dioecious, and in the female the ovary is single or double. The ovary divides into separate pieces called ovarian balls which float unattached in the dorsal ligament sac, or the single sac when that alone is present (Hyman, 1951b). The central part of the ovarian ball is a syncytium which gives rise to the oogonia. The latter move to the outer part of the ball where they produce the oocytes. When ripe, the oocytes are released from the ovarian balls and are fertilized and undergo development in the pseudocoel or ligament sac. A shell is formed when the larvae are provided with rostellum and hooks, and they are then discharged to the exterior.

G. Rotifera

The ovary is generally single and consists of a syncytium lying between the gut and the syncytial vitellarium or yolk-gland which covers it (Hartog, 1910). A single membrane envelops both, and forms a tubular oviduct leading to the cloaca. The membrane constricts each maturing egg from the syncytium and ruptures to allow yolk material to reach it from the vitellarium. The number of eggs produced is small, seldom more than fifty and often much less, and is determined by the number of nuclei in the syncytium at birth (Hyman, 1951b). Although some species are either habitually or occasionally parthenogenetic, insemination is generally hypodermic, the sperm being injected into the pseudocoel through the penis of the male which is used to bore through the integument of the female.

H. Gastrotricha, Kinorhyncha, Priapulida

In the Gastrotricha the ovaries appear to be somewhat similar to those in the Rotifera; in the Kinorhyncha they resemble those of the nematodes, and in Priapulida there is a pair of urogenital organs which consist of gonadal tubules on one side and masses of solenocytes on the other, all opening into a cavity continuous with the urogenital duct.

J. Entoprocta

Some species are dioecious, others hermaphrodite, and yet others sometimes one or the other. The pair of ovaries are small sacs lying ventral to the stomach; their short ducts unite to form a median common oviduct which opens at the genital pore near a depression on the calyx which forms a brood chamber protected by the tentacles. In hermaphrodite forms the pair of testes lies posterior to the ovaries and their ducts unite with those of the ovaries. In *Loxosoma tethyae* the ovary consists of a small number of cells only one of which becomes mature at a time. This cell grows by fusing with neighbouring cells, and obtains its yolk by ingesting so-called gland cells produced near the edge of the calyx (Harmer, 1885).

K. Annelida

1. *Polychaeta*

Nearly all polychaete worms are dioecious, the germ cells of both sexes being derived from cells of the coelomic epithelium. The ovaries thus formed are generally very numerous as they occur in each of many segments of the body. The site of the areas of proliferation of coelomic epithelium varies greatly, but it is frequently the wall of a septum or the sheaths of the blood vessels. The cells which become oocytes are invested by a layer of smaller ones which form a follicle, the ovisac, and act as nurse cells. When ripe and yolk-laden, the oocytes are liberated, either free or still enclosed in the ovisac, into the coelom, which may become almost entirely filled with them. In some species the eggs are liberated into the sea water by rupture of the body wall, but generally they are discharged through the nephridia (nephromixia) or the coelomoducts. In some forms such as the Arenicolidae, the proliferating areas are formed into definite ovaries which are comparatively few and correspond in number with that of the nephridia, the extreme being reached in one genus which has only a single pair. Even those forms with relatively few ovaries produce large numbers of eggs which distend most of the body cavity. In the few hermaphrodite forms, the eggs and sperm are usually produced by the segments of different parts of the body. In some species the gonads are confined to the hinder part of the body in which the parapodia are modified to form appendages for swimming as opposed to crawling, and the eggs are liberated when the worms swim to the surface layers of the sea. In others the modified sexual hind part of the body is budded off and develops a head so that the sexual individual parts from the asexual one. A further elaboration of the process leads to the development of the sexual individual's head before detachment, and the budding of a chain of similar sexual individuals which are successively liberated. In these forms the phenomenon of swarming is common, vast numbers of ripe individuals congregating at the surface of the sea to spawn simultaneously.

2. Oligochaeta

All the oligochaetes are hermaphrodite, and have a sexual apparatus much more complex than that of the polychaetes, especially in its male components. Almost universally there is a single pair of ovaries constantly located in a definite segment; in a few exceptional species there are two pairs of ovaries. The ovaries are attached to the posterior surface of the anterior septum of the ovarian segment, and hang freely in the coelom. They are comparatively small organs and the free end from which the oocytes are shed may be single or multiple, producing a compact pear-shaped, or branched fan-shaped, organ. The ovary is derived from cells of the coelomic epithelium; it often consists of a basal zone, sometimes syncytial, at the attachment to the septum, an intermediate zone of proliferation, and a distal zone filled with growing oocytes enclosed by a layer of flattened cells. The ripe oocytes are detached from the apex, or the ends of the distal processes, of the ovary and pass to the exterior through short ducts with ciliated funnels opening into the coelom. In some species the unripe oocytes, invested by a membrane of very thin cells derived from what appear to be potential oocytes, are liberated from the ovary and stored in sacs, produced by a backward evagination of the posterior septum of the ovarian segment, where they undergo growth with the accumulation of yolk material. Although oligochaetes are hermaphrodite, most species appear to be functionally protandric so that self-fertilization does not occur; the sperm received from a partner are stored in spermathecae and fertilize the oocytes when they are laid in a cocoon produced during the female functional phase. In some species insemination is hypodermic, since the sperm make their way through the body wall from spermatophores deposited on its surface. In species which produce large eggs they appear to be liberated by rupture of the body wall (Stephenson, 1930).

3. *Hirudinea*

The leeches, like the oligochaetes, are hermaphrodite. There is a single pair of ovaries derived from coelomic epithelium; each is surrounded by a capsule of similar origin which fuses with the oviduct. The ovary thus becomes a hollow organ filled with ovarian tissue and continuous with its duct. The male part of the reproductive apparatus is much more complex than that of the female (Beddard, 1910).

4. *Sipunculida*

Sipunculids are normally dioecious, although hermaphrodite specimens have been reported; female individuals greatly outnumber males. The ovaries (and testes) are aggregations of cells derived from the coelomic epithelium, and arranged as small ridges lying on the wall of the coelom at the origins of one or more of the retractor muscles of the introvert. The oocytes are shed into the coelom at an early stage and undergo growth and maturation for many months while floating in the coelomic fluid. When liberated from the ovary they are invested in a tenuous layer of flattened cells which is lost in later stages of growth. The oocyte is then heavily laden with yolk supplied from the coelomic fluid, and becomes surrounded by a thick non-cellular surrounding membrane (Paul, 1910).

5. *Echiuroidea*

The ovary consists of a mass of cells derived from the coelomic epithelium aggregated along the wall of the ventral blood vessel. The cells break off and undergo growth and maturation, floating freely in the body cavity. In some species the cells break away in masses, one of which enlarges to become the ovum and is nourished by the others. The ripe ova are discharged through the nephridia (Shipley, 1910).

L. Arthropoda

Owing to the reduction of the coelom, the gonads are always directly continuous with their ducts, which are probably coelomoducts.

1. *Onychophora*

The sexes are separate and each has a single pair of gonads. The ovaries are tubular and lie in the posterior part of the body attached to the pericardial septum by a ligament. In viviparous forms the eggs are small, but in oviparous ones they are large and rich in yolk. In the former all the oocytes are produced during embryonic life, and the ovary in the adult is filled with growing oocytes enclosed in cellular follicles. In the latter the eggs bulge from the surface of the ovary as they accumulate yolk material. The germinal tissue forms part of the wall of the ovary and bulges internally towards the sterile wall so that the lumen is more or less occluded. The nuclei of the younger oocytes are scattered in a syncytium from which they derive their cytoplasm and, in later stages, a thin follicular wall. In

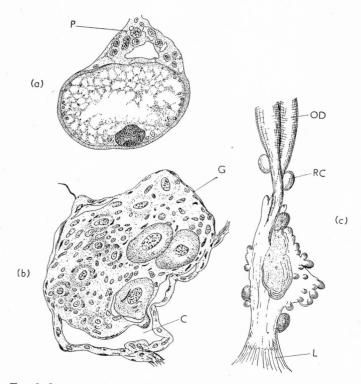

FIG. 2. ONYCHOPHORA: (a) Section of a mature oocyte of *Peripatopsis capensis* within its pedunculated follicle. *P*, peduncle. (b) Transverse section of the ovary of *Opistopatus blainvillei* with oocytes in various stages of development. *C*, cavity of the ovary bounded below by sterile epithelium; *G*, germinal epithelium. (c) Ovaries of *Eoperipatus weldoni* with pedunculated follicles. *L*, ligament of attachment; *OD*, oviduct; *RC*, receptaculum seminis. (Redrawn by permission from Bouvier, 1905.)

oviparous forms with large eggs the follicles become pedunculated. On dehiscence the oocytes leave the follicles and pass through the cavity of the ovary on their way to the oviduct. Fertilization is hypodermic in some species, the spermatophores being deposited on the surface of the body of the female; in others there is a receptaculum seminis into which the sperm is believed to be introduced by the male (Bouvier, 1905) (see Fig. 2).

2. Crustacea

The sexes are generally separate in the Crustacea, and hermaphroditism is uncommon except in some sedentary or parasitic forms such as the cirripedes and parasitic isopods. Parthenogenesis occurs in some branchiopods, ostracods, and isopods. The ovaries are hollow organs, generally paired, connected directly to the oviducts which lead to the exterior.

(a) Among the Branchiopoda the ovaries of the Anostraca are simple tubes, but in the Notostraca they are large and complexly branched. Here the surface is arranged as rounded follicles each containing four epithelial cells of which the outermost becomes an oocyte, growing at the expense of the other three nurse cells. In some Cladocera the ovaries are fused to form a single organ. The germinal area (germarium) consists of a syncytium at one end of the ovary from which masses of cytoplasm containing four nuclei are detached into the ovarian cavity where they become separate cells arranged in line one after the other. The third cell of each group of four develops into an oocyte at the expense of the others, which provide it with nourishment and yolk materials. The eggs thus formed are 'summer' eggs and develop parthenogenetically in the brood pouch of the parent's carapace. At certain times 'winter' eggs are formed: the ovarian epithelium becomes swollen and absorbs several, sometimes many, sets of four cells derived from the germarium, and provides nourishment for the third cell of another set of four which receives nourishment also from its own three sister cells. 'Winter' eggs are generally produced only one at a time and are fertilized before development starts (Wagler, 1927).

(b) Ostracoda. The ovaries are paired and lie on each side of the gut in the hinder part of the body. Many species are parthenogenetic, and their males have never been discovered.

(c) In free living Copepoda such as *Calanus* the single median ovary lies dorsal to the gut, filling about two-thirds of the thorax and tapering to a blunt point posteriorly. Paired oviducts arise from its anterior end and run at first forwards and then backwards to open together on the first abdominal segment. The posterior end of the ovary is filled with actively dividing oogonia which produce the oocytes filling the rest of the ovary, in progressively advanced stages of growth as they approach the oviducts. Yolk formation begins in half-grown oocytes, the yolk droplets appearing first at the periphery of the cell. Fertilization takes place as the eggs pass the openings of the spermathecae when they are laid (Hilton, 1931). In the more specialized parasitic forms such as *Lernea* the ovaries move from the cephalothorax to the genital segment during metamorphosis. Although they fuse together two oviducts lead to the external openings, and two ovisacs are produced. In the cyclops stage the ovaries consist of a mass of minute cells; in the adult there are no tubules and all the oocytes lie in close contact. Spermatophores are received in the cyclops stage when the animal is attached to its first host, and are retained during metamorphosis to fertilize the oocytes matured in the adult while attached to the second host (Scott, 1901).

(*d*) Cirripedia. Among the Cirripedia the Thoracica are generally hermaphrodite, and the ovary lies in the peduncle or the basal part of the mantle, from which it may extend into the parietal part. The ovary is follicular, and ducts of the follicles join to form an oviduct on each side. According to Darwin (1851) the follicles are formed by a bulging out of the ovarian tube to form a sac containing three to five oocytes, and the ovarian tube itself forms an inextricable ramifying mass of branching tubes lined by the germinal epithelium which produces the oocytes where it is evaginated to form the follicles. In the Rhizocephala,which are generally parasitic on decapod Crustacea, most of the organs are lost in the adult female and the animal consists of little more than a bag of eggs.

(*e*) Among the Malacostraca the ovaries in the Leptostraca and Syncarida are simple paired tubes lying in the abdomen, and sometimes extending as far as the head, lined with epithelial cells and containing the oocytes arranged in a row.

In the Hoplocarida (Stomatopoda) the ovaries are joined posteriorly and lie closely applied to each other along the rest of their length so that they appear superficially to be a single organ; they are arranged as lateral lobes in each segment. The germinal epithelium lies on the inner side of the ovary, and the cells of the rest of the ovarian epithelium appear to provide nourishment and yolk material to the growing oocytes (Grobben, 1876).

Among the Peracardia similar paired, tubular ovaries are connected by a median part containing the germinal epithelium in the Mysidacea; in the Cumacea the arrangement is the same in some species, but in others and in the Tanaidacea the median part is lacking and the germinal epithelium lines the lateral walls of the ovarian tubes (Zimmer, 1927). In the Isopoda the paired ovaries are generally separate, but are fused together anteriorly in a few species. They lie at each side of and beneath the heart and when ripe they fill a large part of the dorsal segment of the body cavity; the oviducts leave their lateral borders a little posterior to their centres (Hewitt, 1907). The germinal epithelium lines the lateral side of the ovary and developing oocytes fill its central

cavity. Many species possess rudimentary testes attached to the
anterior end of the lateral side of the ovary, and in males rudimentary
ovaries are attached to the vesiculae seminales. Some of the parasitic
isopods are protandric hermaphrodites. Fertilization is internal and
the eggs are usually carried in a brood pouch on the underside of the
female's body. In the Amphiphoda the ovaries in *Gammarus* are paired,
straight cylindrical tubes lying between the heart and gut and extending through most of the thorax and into the abdomen; they open
through short oviducts towards their posterior ends. The ovarian wall
is lined internally by cylindrical epithelium and is covered externally
by a thin tunica propria. The oocytes are produced from the epithelial
cells, which enlarge and accumulate a thick layer of granular yolk so
that the single row of eggs gives the ovarian tube a slightly lobulated
appearance. The eggs when laid are carried in a brood pouch on the
underside of the female (Cussans, 1904).

In the Eucarida the ovaries of Euphausiacea are two elongated tubular
masses fused anteriorly; the oviducts arise from a lobe on each side
in the posterior half. The germinal epithelium lies on the ventral
side.

In the Decapoda the ovary consists basically of two sacs lying above
the gut and under the heart, but there is much variation in shape,
position, and degree of intercommunication between them among the
widely differing forms of the sub-order. The germinal epithelium forms
a band along the inner side of the ovary extending along most of its
length. The oocytes become enclosed in follicles formed from cells
indistinguishable from those which become oocytes, and are heavily
yolked when ripe. The growth of the epithelial cells gives rise to lobules
which project into the lumen of the ovary and are attached to the wall
by short stalks. One cell of the mass increases in size to become the
oocyte and the others form a layer of cells lining the follicle inside a
thin tunica. As the oocyte grows a vitelline membrane is formed
between it and the epithelial cells, and when the egg is ripe and full
of yolk, the follicle bursts and releases the egg into the lumen of the
ovary whence it finds its way to the oviduct (Huxley, 1880).

3. *Myriapoda*

The sexes are separate, and the ovary is a long unpaired tube opening
through two oviducts near the base of the second legs in millipedes,
and by a single duct at the posterior end of the body in centipedes.
The fundamentally paired nature of the ovary is shown in some Diplo-
poda by the arrangement of the germinal epithelium in two bands
on the floor of the ovarian sac.

4. *Insecta*

The ovary in insects is essentially a tubular structure made up of a number of individual ovarioles which open into the oviduct. The ovarioles are usually multiple, but the number varies from one ovariole in each ovary to an extreme of over 2,400 in some white ants (Imms, 1957). In a few forms only one ovary with a single ovariole is developed on one side of the body, that of the other side being suppressed. In the Collembola the ovaries are sac-like and are not divided into ovarioles.

The ovarioles end proximally in a terminal filament which is a continuation of the investing peritoneal membrane and generally forms a ligament anchoring the ovary in the body cavity. The ligament produced by the fusion of the terminal filaments takes various forms but is sometimes absent.

Proximally each ovariole is a solid mass of cells, the germarium, from which both primordial germ cells, and nurse cells when present, are derived; the main part of the ovariole, however, is tubular. The ovarioles were classified into two types by Brandt (1874): panoistic, in which nurse cells are absent, and meroistic, in which they are present. Gross (1903) divided the latter type into two sub-divisions: polytrophic, with numerous follicles of nurse cells; and telotrophic (or acrotrophic), with a single follicle of nurse cells at the proximal end (Fig. 3).

In all three types, the larger part of the ovariole, the vitellarium, is tubular and contains the developing oocytes, each enclosed in a follicle produced by an ingrowth of the epithelium of the vitellarium. The epithelial cells of the ovarian follicles secrete the shell or 'chorion' and in addition, particularly in the panoistic type, they nourish the oocyte.

In meroistic types of ovariole, nurse cells are present in addition to oocytes; their function is to secrete yolk granules which are incorporated in the oocyte (Palm, 1948). In polytrophic ovarioles the nurse cells are gathered into follicles invested with an epithelium derived from that lining the ovariole; they alternate with the oocytes along the length of the ovariole. In some Hymenoptera, at least, the nurse cells become incorporated in the oocyte. Peacock and Gresson (1928) find that in the Tenthredinidae, as in the honeybee, the cell boundaries in the nurse follicles break down and their cytoplasm and nuclei flow into the oocyte in the next proximal follicle and become absorbed in the ooplasm. In some species material also passes from the follicle cells surrounding the larger oocytes and becomes indistinguishable from accessory nuclei. Ahrens (1935), working on termites, showed that the yellow pigment found in the 'corpus luteum' of insects that appears in the degenerating remains of the follicle is not the same as the luteal

I

pigments found in the corpus luteum of higher vertebrates. In acro-trophic ovarioles the nurse cells are concentrated towards the apex and are sometimes connected with the more proximal oocytes by protoplasmic strands. Palm (1948) finds that in *Bombus* the nurse cells degenerate when they have finished secreting and that the 'corpus luteum' is normally formed only from the nurse follicular epithelium

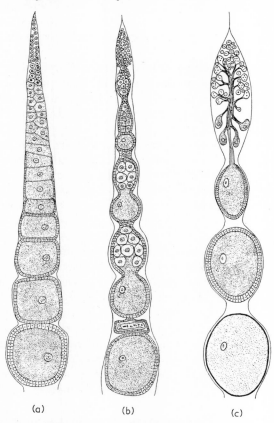

(a)   (b)   (c)

FIG. 3. INSECTA: Schematic figures of the three types of ovarioles: (a) panoistic; (b) polytrophic; (c) acrotrophic. (Redrawn by permission from Imms, 1957).

which grows after secretion has ended, and removes the remains of the degenerate nurse cells. When oocytes are resorbed in pathological conditions 'corpora lutea' may be formed by the epithelium of the egg follicle as well.

Many insects are viviparous, the embryos usually being lodged in the oviducts during development, though in some Dermaptera they are retained in the ovarioles. A few viviparous forms have no oviducts, and a breakdown of the ovaries disperses the eggs into the haemocoel where they develop. This phenomenon is associated with partheno-genetic paedogenesis in some cecidomyid Diptera. In many social insects, and especially among the Isoptera, the ovary of the inseminated female undergoes great post-metamorphic hypertrophy.

5. *Arachnida*

(*a*) Xyphosura. The sexes are separate, and the ovary is a system of ramified and anastomosing tubes in the dorsal part of the body, spreading forward from the opisthosoma to extend laterally in the prosoma (Owen, 1873). The oocytes lie in the ovarian epithelium of the ovary and not in its lumen. Fertilization is external (Fage, 1949).

(*b*) Scorpionidea. Each ovary consists of a pair of longitudinal tubes connected by transverse branches; the medial longitudinal tubes of each side may be partly or completely fused (Fig. 4). Primordial germ cells, oogonia, and small oocytes lie among the epithelial cells of the tubes. As the oocytes grow they push the walls of the tube before them so that they come to lie in follicles projecting from the walls, and in the final stages the follicles become pedunculated. The fertilized eggs develop in the follicles, and as growth proceeds the embryos distend the follicles and the ovarian tubes into which they project. In species with little or no yolk a pseudoplacenta is formed (Wahab, 1945). In pairing, the spermatophores are transferred to the female after a preliminary dance of the sexes. In the Scorpionidea, as also in the Solifuga and Phalangida, the genital cells are differentiated at a very early stage and are recognizable already in the blastoderm of the gastrula.

(*c*) Pseudoscorpionidea. The ovaries are fused into a single median tube but the oviducts are paired. The oocytes lie in pedunculated follicles which bulge through the outer surface of the ovary and are lined with flattened cells. The space between the oocytes is filled with secretory cells which produce the nourishment for the embryos or larvae, but not apparently the yolk material. A ritual behaviour at pairing results in the formation and deposition of a spermatophore by the male and the removal of the sperm from it into the spermatheca of the female. The oocytes are shed into the ovarian cavity where they are fertilized, and the secretory cells then become active. The female constructs a nest, and the eggs are laid into an incubation chamber formed under, and attached to, the ventral surface of the female by special glands. The secretory cells of the ovary continue to provide nourishment for the embryos because the chamber is in uninterrupted contact with the ovary, and in one species at least, the nourishment is

I*

suddenly injected into the gut of the larvae by the mother. As a result of this manoeuvre, the larvae immediately triple their volume, while the body of the mother is almost completely emptied (Vachon, 1938).

(d) Solifuga. The ovaries extend from the ninth to the fifth segment of the opisthosoma and bear numerous bunches of follicles on their outer sides, the remainder of the ovarian wall being apparently sterile. Anteriorly, the ovaries join the dilated oviducts, which have thick

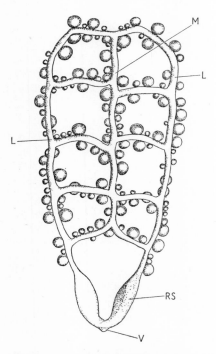

Fig. 4. Scorpionidea: The female genital system of *Buthus quin-questriatus* with lateral ovarian tubes (L) and fused median ovarian tubes (M) connected by transverse branches. The walls of the tubes are covered with projecting follicles. *RS*, receptaculum seminis; *V*, vagina. (Redrawn by permission from Wahab, 1945.)

glandular and muscular walls, and unite to form the genital chamber into which the male inserts with his chelicerae a mass of spermatophores which he has deposited on the ground (Vachon, 1945).

(e) Palpigrada and Uropyga. The ovaries lie in the opisthosoma, and in some species of the latter, are fused into a single mass. In the Amblipyga the eggs are carried in a pouch derived from a secretion of the genital ducts and applied to the ventral side of the opisthosoma.

The eggs are few, large and yolky and are not, as in the pseudoscorpions, supplied with nourishment from a secretion of the ovary (Millot, 1939).

(*f*) Areneida. The ovaries are paired elongated sacs lying on each side of the mid-line of the ventral part of the opisthosoma. In some species they are partly fused together. When ripe they frequently almost completely fill the opisthosoma, surrounding and compressing the other organs. Externally a thin muscular coat lies inside the peritoneal covering, and internally they are lined by a single layer of epithelial cells, which are generally cubical, but may become flattened or columnar according to their state of activity; all can become oogonia, follicle or secretory cells. The derived oocytes are nourished by the epithelial cells, and pass to the outer surface of the ovary where they push the peritoneum outwards to form the follicular membrane; the bulging follicle is connected to the ovary by a peduncle of epithelial cells. During the growth of the oocyte, the cytoplasm becomes filled with yolk granules elaborated in connection with a 'yolk nucleus' formed of concentric laminations of lipo-protein together with enlarged mitochondria. When the ripe oocyte is discharged from the follicle, the epithelial cells of the peduncle become filled with lipid droplets so that a body analogous to the corpus luteum of vertebrates is formed. Such bodies are also formed after the degeneration of an oocyte within a follicle. When the eggs are ready for deposition the epithelial cells of the ovary become greatly enlarged and intensely active, and pour secretion into the lumen of the ovary where it forms the cement that coats the eggs and binds them together in a mass in the cocoon. When the eggs are laid they are fertilized by sperm released from the spermathecae into which they have been introduced by the pedipalps of the male after a frequently very complicated procedure of ritual behaviour (Millot, 1949).

(*g*) In the Phalangida, or harvest-men, the ovaries are fused posteriorly to form a horseshoe-shaped organ connected with the oviducts by the anteriorly extended arms. The sperm are transferred to the uterus by direct copulation, and the eggs are laid through an extrusible ovipositor which is often comparatively long (Berland, 1949).

(*h*) Acarina. The ovaries are frequently fused to form a single structure which varies greatly in size and shape between different species, and even in the same individual according to its state of activity. It is a median sac-like organ connected with two oviducts and the receptaculum seminis. Some species produce only a few large eggs, but in many the ripe ovary fills the body and nearly obliterates the other organs. A few species are ovoviviparous. In some mites there is a central syncytial mass containing nuclei which give rise to oocytes and become surrounded by cytoplasm in which yolk granules are developed. Sperm stored in the receptaculum seminis, where it has been deposited directly or, in some species, within spermatophores conveyed by the chelicerae of the male, fertilize the eggs as they pass from the ovary to the oviduct. The ovary appears to contain its full complement of oocytes at an early stage of development when the animal emerges from the nymphal skin (Michael, 1884, 1901).

(*j*) In the Pycnogonida, in which the body is extremely reduced and the limbs are very long, lateral expansions of the paired ovaries extend into the eight legs and in some species reach to the sixth segment of them. In the legs the oocytes increase in size while lodged in follicles containing a liquid which apparently produces nourishment for them. When ripe they pass inwards towards the body again to be released from the female ovipores at the bases of the second coxae. Fertilization is external (Loman, 1917).

(*k*) In the Tardigrada (water bears) the single gonad is a sac lying above the gut and suspended anteriorly from the dermal body wall. There is a single asymmetrical oviduct. In some species there is a small receptaculum seminis lying beside the oviduct opening with it into the terminal portion of the intestine. The oocytes that mature appear to develop at the expense of others which are used by them for nourishment. The eggs are fertilized in the ovary, where they also acquire their shells.

(*l*) Pentastomida. The ovary is a single tube, blind posteriorly and dorsal in position, supported by a median mesentery. It communicates with a pair of oviducts. The developing oocytes bulge from the surface of the ovary and then re-enter its cavity for final maturation before entering the oviduct where they are fertilized (Cuénot, 1949).

M. Mollusca

1. *Amphineura*

Among the Amphineura the Polyplacophora, which are dioecious, have ovaries that are with few exceptions unpaired and median, but in mature individuals may be displaced by other organs and appear asymmetrical. The ovary is a hollow organ, and the oocytes are derived from the epithelium which is folded as projecting processes into the lumen. They are contained in follicles, the cells of which become highly flattened as the oocytes increase in size (Plate, 1901).

2. *Gastropoda*

In the Gastropoda the Prosobranchiata are generally dioecious, and the oviduct discharges through the right kidney in the Diotocardia (e.g. *Patella*), but through separate ducts in the mantle cavity in the Monotocardia (e.g. *Buccinum*). In *Patella* the single ovary occupies the ventral face of the left side of the visceral mass. The ovary is formed from a single cavity lined by germinal epithelium which, with its underlying connective tissue, grows inwards as folds that unite into trabeculae, and convert the ovary into a mass of tubules containing the oocytes surrounded by epithelium. The ripe oocytes are expelled by rupture of the ovary into the cavity of the right kidney (Davis and Fleure, 1903). In *Buccinum* the unpaired ovary lies upon the digestive gland, and in close contact with it; it extends along the right side of it to the tip of the spire. It consists of numerous acini arranged botryoidally and set at right angles to its surface; it penetrates into the substance

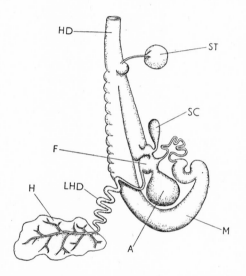

FIG. 5. GASTROPODA: Reproductive system of *Aplysia punctata* from the ventral side. *A*, albumen gland; *F*, fertilization chamber; *H*, hermaphrodite gland; *HD*, large hermaphrodite duct; *LHD*, little hermaphrodite duct; *M*, mucus gland; *SC*, spermatocyst; *ST*, spermatotheca. (Redrawn by permission from Eales, 1921.)

of the hepatopancreas. The acini are lined with a thin layer of flattened germinal epithelium which here and there gives rise to the oocytes, which project into the lumen of the tubules. They are attached to the wall of the tubules and covered by a thin layer of flattened follicle cells. The first part of the oviduct is a narrow tube with delicate walls which runs from the tip of the ovary along the right side of the digestive gland to join the distal glandular part which opens into the mantle cavity (Dakin, 1912). Kostitzine (1949) finds that degeneration of oocytes within the acini is frequent.

The Opisthobranchiata are hermaphrodite. In *Aplysia* the gonad is an unpaired ovotestis with a common genital duct, to which a complicated system of accessory glands and ducts is connected (Fig. 5). The ovotestis is a compact gland of irregular shape embedded in the visceral mass on its right posterior border. It is a racemose gland consisting of innumerable acini, each of which produces oocytes and sperm which are discharged into the cavity of the acinus. The acini are connected with the hermaphrodite duct. Young individuals are protandrous, but in older ones both oocytes and sperm are found in the same acinus. The oocytes are unripe when discharged so that self-fertilization cannot occur at this stage (Eales, 1921).

The Pulmonata, too, are hermaphrodite. In *Helix* the ovotestis occupies the apex of the spire, and oocytes and sperm are produced in the same follicles. Both leave the gland by a common duct which, however, separates into male and female ducts in the lower part of its course. There is great complication of accessory glands and ducts. The foreign sperm are received in spermatophores and pass to a spermatotheca where they are released; immediately before ovulation the native sperm degenerate within the hermaphrodite duct so that cross-fertilization is ensured.

3. *Lamellibranchiata*

In the Lamellibranchiata the sexes are generally separate, though some species are always, and others occasionally, hermaphrodite. In some the gonad discharges into the kidney, but in most there is a separate gonoduct. In those species of *Pecten* (Filibranchiata) which are hermaphrodite the paired gonads lie posterior and ventral to the rudimentary foot, forming a tongue-like mass attached to the adductor muscle and traversed in part by the alimentary canal. The male part occupies the dorsal and anterior part of the gland, the female part the hinder end, and small islets of tissue from each part may be found in the other as there is no regular boundary; the spermary is cream in colour, the ovary vermilion pink. The oocytes and sperm appear to ripen at different times, separated, however, by only a short interval so that the animal is functionally protandrous. The gonads open into the kidney through which their products are discharged into the sea water for external fertilization. The gonad consists of many branched tubules bearing numerous sac-like alveoli lined by germinal epithelium. The tubules are lined with tall ciliated epithelium which is continuous with the flattened germinal epithelium of the alveoli. The young oocytes are attached to the wall of the alveolus but gradually project more and more until they are liberated into the lumen (Dakin, 1909; Coe, 1945).

In the species of *Cardium* (Eulamellibranchiata) in which the sexes are separate there is little difference between the gonads of the two sexes except in their contents. The gonads are paired and consist of a branching, tubular gland opening on the lateral and posterior body wall near the posterior retractor muscle of the foot. Three main ducts, dorsal, ventral and intermediate, join the short terminal duct of each side. Smaller branches join the main ducts and ramify among the muscles and viscera. They bear botryoidal clusters of alveoli in which the oocytes are produced. The ducts are lined with ciliated epithelium, but in the alveoli the germinal epithelium consists of small cells. Many of these enlarge and project into the lumen, the largest ones being attached to the wall by a short stalk. On release they lie freely in the cavity and frequently adhere to each other by the thick vitelline membrane which is secreted, apparently from their surface, in their later stages. Fertilization is external (Johnstone, 1899).

4. Cephalopoda

In the Cephalopoda the sexes are separate, and the single ovary occupies the posterior end of the visceral mass. It is a large hollow organ, the cavity being part of the coelom, with the germinal epithelium confined to the ventral region, and the oviducts leaving its anterior part. The wall of the ovary bearing the germinal epithelium projects inwards as folds so that the oocytes are carried on numerous racemes. The oocytes are derived from cells of the germinal epithelium which sink below the epithelial surface and then protrude into the ovary, pushing the wall before them until they are completely surrounded by an epithelial layer several cells thick forming an investing follicle. As the oocyte grows the follicular layer becomes folded and the folds project into the substance of the oocyte so that the surface of contact is greatly increased. Further protrusion and folding of the ovarian wall gives rise to the characteristic racemes. The follicle when ripe secretes the 'chorion' round the mature oocyte, which is liberated by rupture of the follicle and passes out of the ovarian cavity by the oviduct (Isgrove, 1909).

N. Ectoprocta (Bryozoa)

Most gymnolaemate ectoprocts are hermaphrodite, many of them protandrous or protogynous. Each zooid generally contains one ovary, sometimes two, as well as one or more testes. The ovary may be attached to the body wall, intestine, or funiculus, and consists of a bunch of developing oocytes covered with a thin layer of peritoneum. The germ cells are derived from peritoneal cells during early development, and when ripe the oocytes are shed into the coelom, and in some species pass out into the sea water through the intertentacular organ. In most forms, however, very few ripe eggs are produced and arrangements of various complexities exist for brooding them (Hyman, 1959). The phylactolaemate ectoprocts are hermaphrodite and viviparous. In *Cristatella* the ovaries lie on the inner side of the common wall of the colony attached to, and covered by, the peritoneum from cells of which the germ cells are derived. Only one egg matures in each ovary; it is brooded in an embryo sac attached to the inside of the wall of the colony until the ciliated larva is ready to escape by passing through the orifice produced by the degeneration of the maternal polypide (Harmer, 1910).

O. Brachiopoda

With the exception of one genus all the brachiopods are dioecious, the gonads being derived from mesodermal cells of the coelomic epithelium concentrated in four places to produce four gonads, two on each side of the body, generally a pair in each mantle lobe. A nutrient blood vessel runs along the axis of the gonad, and the perivisceral fluid bathes its free surface. The ripe oocytes are discharged into the body cavity, and find their way to the exterior through the duct of the segmental organs. In some species the fertilized egg develops in a brood pouch generally formed by an invagination of the body wall (Shipley, 1895). In *Lingula* the developing oocytes lie amongst numerous yolk cells, and are surrounded by tenuous follicle cells in some stages of development (Schaeffer, 1926).

P. Chaetognatha

The arrow-worms are hermaphrodite, and possess one pair of ovaries and one pair of testes lying in the coelom, the former anterior, the latter posterior, to the tail septum. The ovaries are elongated solid organs lying on each side of the intestine, separated from each other by the intestine and its mesenteries. They are invested by peritoneum and suspended from the lateral body wall by a short mesovarium. The oviduct, which encloses the sperm reservoir, runs along the lateral side of the ovary. The germinal epithelium lies adjacent to the oviduct, the oogonia and oocytes more medially, the latter progressively laden with yolk granules. The maturing oocyte comes into contact with two enlarged accessory cells of the epithelium of the oviduct which penetrate the vitelline membrane, and between which sperm enters from the sperm duct. The polar bodies are formed in succession, and fertilization takes place, whereupon the egg passes between the oviducal cells, which show some signs of degenerating in the neighbourhood of the rupture, and passes into the lumen of the duct (Burfield, 1927).

Q. Phoronida

Most phoronids are hermaphrodite, but in some the sexes are separate. In *Phoronis australis* the testes and ovaries lie on the left side of the stomach separated by the efferent blood vessel. The diverticula or coeca of the vessel penetrate the gonads in all directions and the sex cells are produced from peritoneal cells covering the blind coeca. The coelomic epithelial cells covering a vascular coecum enlarge at different rates so that the larger ones become invested in a follicle formed by the smaller flattened ones. When the oocyte is ripe it escapes from the follicle into the coelom and is discharged to the exterior through the nephridia (Benham, 1890). After spawning, the flat peritoneal cells of the diverticula enlarge to regenerate the gonad. In some species fertilization occurs in the coelom.

R. Echinodermata

The reproductive system is primitively a single gonad opening by a pore in the interradius that accommodates the hydropore and the anus. This arrangement persists in Holothuroidea but is modified in most echinoderms to produce radially symmetrical gonads, corresponding to the body symmetry, by the growth of the gonad round the under-surface of the aboral pole as a genital stolon that gives off gonadal primordia pentamerously. Hyman (1955) also states that the primordial germ cells arise from the wall of one of the coelomic compartments, usually the left somatocoel close to the axial complex, but that the gonad definitely does not arise from the axial gland.

1. *Crinoidea*

In *Antedon* the sexes are separate and the gonads are situated in the pinnules. As there may be fifty or more pinnules fringing each of the five pairs of arms, a ripe female may posses over 500 ovaries. The ovaries are oval cavities lined with germinal epithelium; some of its cells enlarge and become oocytes but others remain small and form follicles surrounding the oocytes. The ovaries in the proximal pinnules are the first to ripen and, according to Chadwick (1907), the eggs probably escape by rupture of the ovarian walls at one or more points of least resistance; fertilization takes place in the water. All the numerous ovaries are connected to each other by the genital rachis, which lies in the genital sinus in the wall dividing the coeliac from the subtentacular canals. The rachis extends along the whole length of each arm giving branches to each pinnule, and proximally the rachids extend into the disc, where they are believed to arise from the axial complex in the larva. The rachids are at first solid strands but later

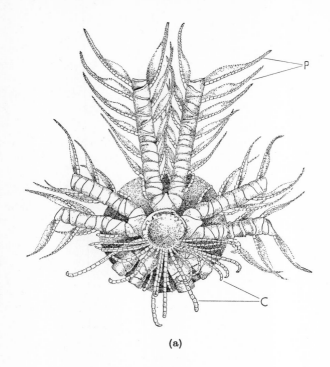

(a)

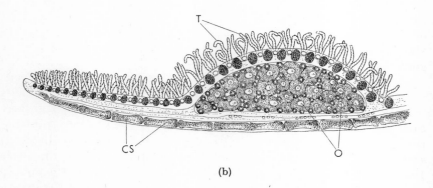

(b)

FIG. 6. ECHINODERMATA: *Crinoidea:* (a) Aboral surface of the disc and bases of the arms of *Antedon bifida.* The cirra (*C*) have been removed from the upper part to show the bases of the arms. *P*, pinnules with ovaries. (b) Section through a pinnule with its ovary. *CS*, jointed calcareous skeleton of the pinnule; *O*, oocytes; *T*, tentacles. (Redrawn by permission from Chadwick, 1907.)

become tubes, lined with germinal epithelium, which form the gonads in the pinnule (see Fig. 6).

2. *Holothuroidea*

The single gonad represents a primitive condition which is known in other echinoderms only in certain extinct groups. The ovary lies in the anterior part of the coelom in the mid-dorsal interradius; it is made up of numerous tubules which join at their bases to form the one or two ovarian tufts attached to one or both sides of the dorsal mesentery. The tubules are generally, but not always, numerous and elongated and may be variously branched. When ripe the ovary is very large and occupies many times the volume that it filled when unripe. The ovarian tubules join at the attachment of the ovary to the mesentery to form a common duct that opens on the surface of the mid-dorsal interradius. The walls of the tubules consist of muscular and connective tissue layers clothed externally by coelomic epithelium and internally by germinal epithelium which invests the oocytes with a thin follicular wall (Hamann, 1883). Clark (1907) reported that in some hermaphrodite forms each tubule produces sperm and eggs at the same time, but that other hermaphrodite species are probably protandrous. In *Cucumaria laevigata* Ackerman (1902) showed that the tubules of the gonad are at first indifferent but as they grow they form and release eggs. With further elongation the oocytes are destroyed by coelomocytes, and the tubules then produce sperm. The tuft of the gonad is then made up of small indifferent tubules, together with larger female, and very long male ones. The spent tubules are destroyed by coelomocytes and new ones develop from the indifferent tubules of the base. Hyman (1955) points out that the process of destruction and formation of new tubules from a growing zone at the base of the gonad is probably general in holothurians.

3. *Asteroidea*

In the common starfish *Asterias rubens* there are ten ovaries, two in each ray. They are branched and much lobulated sacs lying free in the perivisceral cavity except at their single point of attachment to the aboral body wall, close to the proximal ends of the rays (Chadwick, 1923). The ripe ova are discharged through a single duct from each gonad which opens by a pore on the latero-aboral surface close to the interradial line. At the breeding season the ovaries are much enlarged and fill each ray, extending from near the ends almost into the body cavity of the disc. The germinal epithelium lining the gonads consists of cubical or polygonal cells which give rise to the oocytes and also form follicles enclosing them. Yolk granules, presumably derived from the follicle cells, are deposited in the cytoplasm of the ova, and the egg membrane becomes thickened in the later stages of growth. The sexes are separate, and fertilization of the several million eggs extruded by each female occurs in the water at the time of spawning. In some asteroids (Luidiidae, some Astropectenidae and others) the gonads are serial and lie in a row at the side of each arm; they may open by individual ducts and pores, or by a common duct with a pore in the usual position (Hyman, 1955). A few forms are normally hermaphrodite.

4. *Echinoidea*

In sea-urchins the ovaries are five arborescent glands suspended by mesenteric folds from the inner wall of the apical half of the test (Chadwick, 1900). They are interradial and open to the exterior through the pores of the basal plates of the apical system. The walls of the ovaries are extremely sacculated and form numerous follicles within which the oocytes are formed and nourished. When ripe the ovaries fill most of the body cavity of the test and in some parts of the world are used as food—one of our common species is *Echinus esculentus*.

5. *Ophiuroidea*

In the brittle-stars the body wall is invaginated at the bases of the arms to form usually ten, but sometimes more or fewer, bursae through which a respiratory current of water is maintained. The gonads are stated to discharge their products into the bursae, which also serve as protective chambers in those species that brood their young. The work of Smith (1940), however, showing that there are permanent gonoducts in the mature *Ophiothrix fragilis*, throws some doubt on this statement which requires further investigation. In this species the genital products are discharged through gonoducts and after fertilization, development of the egg and metamorphosis, young individuals creep into the bursae of adults. The ovaries are small sacs attached to the internal wall of the bursae, which is lined by coelomic epithelium. They arise from the genital rachis which contains the primordial germ cells, and sends branches into the coelomic sacs budded from the genital sinus where it makes contact with the coelomic surface of the bursae. Hyman (1955) points out that there may be one, two, or larger numbers of ovaries attached to each bursa, and quotes the discovery of Mortensen (1923) that in *Gorgonocephalus* there may be several thousand. In some species that lack bursae the eggs are said to be discharged directly through the body wall. Some species are hermaphrodite with distinct ovaries and testes simultaneously functional, others are protandric, and some apparently experience several successive changes of sex; in others the large females carry epizoic dwarf males. Smith (1940) describes the ovary of *Ophiothrix fragilis* as a sac invested with a connective tissue sheath covered externally by a thin layer of epithelium. The central lumen is filled by germ cells, and in the mature gonad septa develop which partition the organ into numerous compartments, and contain muscle fibres as does the cortical layer. The oocytes lie in follicles amongst the mass of primary germ cells and mature in batches; they are discharged when ripe into the lumina of the ovaries and pass to the exterior through the gonoducts. Pigment occurs in some quantity in the interstitial tissue.

S. Chordata

1. *Hemichorda*

In the Hemichorda the sexes are generally separate. The ovaries of the Enteropneusta lie on each side of the gut in the anterior part of the trunk as a series of sacs which may be simple, as in *Saccoglossus horsti* (Brambell and Goodhart, 1944), or lobulated, as in *Ptychodera bahamensis*. In addition to the primitive germ cells, oogonia, and oocytes, the ovary is lined with a thin epithelium that appears in some cases to invest the oocytes. It also contains yolk cells whose contents, in some stages of development at least, are not only transferred to the oocytes but are released into the ovarian lumen (Van der Horst, 1939). Each ovary opens externally by a pore either directly or through a short duct; in many species the ovaries fill longitudinal lateral extensions of the body, the genital wings. The ovaries are hollow organs, though the lumen becomes filled by the developing oocytes, and in *Protoglossus koehleri* Burdon-Jones (1956) found that each ovary contained several oocytes of varying ages. The most mature of these were large and had a clearly defined germinal vesicle visible through the walls of the ovisacs and the overlying epidermis. The cytoplasm of the large oocytes that measured a little less than half a millimetre in diameter was granular and heavily yolked.

Among the Pterobranchia the ovaries of the Cephalodiscida are a pair of sacs projecting into the trunk coelom on each side of the median dorsal trunk mesentery at the anterior end of the stomach, between the pharynx and the terminal part of the intestine, and connected with the gonopore by a short duct. Hermaphrodites with one male and one female gonad have been recorded (Hyman, 1959). The ovary in the Rhabdoplurida is single and rounded, and lies in the right metacoel; it is hollow and is connected to the gonopore by a short duct. The germinal region lies near the oviduct and the developing oocytes, enveloped with epithelium, move towards the hind end of the ovary; when ripe they lie in the hind end (Schepotieff, 1907). In some species the oocytes lie between the peritoneum and the inner epithelium of the ovary, the latter forming a follicular epithelium. The fore part of the ovary contains young oocytes in varying stages of growth, but the hinder part contains only a single, very large yolky egg at any one time. The yolk material is apparently not derived from special yolk cells.

2. Urochorda

Most of the Urochorda are hermaphrodite. Among the solitary Ascidiacea the gonads of *Ascidia* lie close together on the left side of the body between the stomach and intestine, and have a separate duct opening into the atrium. In some other ascidians gonads are present on both sides of the body, and in others there are many complete sets of both male and female systems on the inner surface of the body wall on both sides projecting into the peribranchial cavity. The ovary is a slightly ramified gland occupying most of the intestinal loop. It is hollow, and the ripe oocytes are released into its cavity. Most of the germinal cells form follicles around the future oocyte; some of these form a layer in contact with the oocyte and produce a thin gelatinous coating over it inside the follicle. The other follicle cells produce two layers, the outer of which remains in the ovary when the oocyte is discharged; the cells of the inner layer become large and vacuolated, and some of them form papillae which are believed to help the egg to float in the sea water. These cells may then proliferate to form up to seven cell layers investing the oocyte (Herdman, 1899). In the compound Ascidiacea such as *Botryllus* the gonads are in general similar, but the formation of oocytes is complicated by the colonial organization. In the oozooid the paired gonads appear as undifferentiated cells a few of which are recognizable as young oocytes. These migrate in the common blood stream to the first blastozooids where they form lateral gonads. They continue to develop and migrate similarly into the next generation of blastozooids and so on until the seventh or eighth generation, when they are fertilized. Only one or two oocytes reach maturity in the sexually mature blastozooid, and they escape by rupture of the epithelium lining the peribranchial cavity. Thereafter the male part of the gonad ripens and produces sperm (Herdman, 1924). Nearly all the Larvacea are hermaphrodite, and the large gonads lie at the posterior end of the body; there is no oviduct and the ova break through the body wall at one point. The oocytes are surrounded by follicle cells, and in some species of *Oikopleura* they lie in a mass of amoeboid parenchyma cells (Lohman, 1933). Among the Thaliacea the organization of the gonads is complicated by the colonial structure in compound

forms, and in others by the alternation of asexual with sexual generations. In *Pyrosoma* the gonads are derived from a cord of germinal
tissue which forms a part of every budding stolon; on the ventral
edge of the body a portion of the germinal tissue gives rise to a lobed
testis, and to a single oocyte surrounded by follicle cells. In *Salpa*
the hermaphrodite gonads are protogynous and the ovary generally
contains a single oocyte, seldom more. It is formed from germinal
tissue derived from the stolon-bearing generation. This generation
has been interpreted as a female producing a series of males by asexual
gemmation, and depositing in each of these an ovum which will develop
after fertilization in the body of the male into a solitary or female
individual. This view, however, is not universally adopted (Harmer,
1904).

3. *Cephalochorda*

The sexes are separate, and the gonads are generally but not always
paired. There may be two dozen or more pairs of ovaries projecting
into the atrial cavity at the sides of the pharynx and intestine. Each
is primarily surrounded by a layer of coelomic epithelium which becomes
folded inwards to form a cavity within the genital chamber which itself
is covered by the atrial epithelium. The ovary is attached by a hilus
carrying the blood vessels supplying a system of lacunae. The germinal
epithelium is confined to one side of the ovary, and the growing oocytes
are contained in individual follicles covered with epithelium and protruding into its cavity. When the oocytes are ripe they burst into the
atrium and the eggs, which are fertilized in the sea water, escape by
the atriopore or more rarely by the mouth (Pietschmann, 1929).

REFERENCES

Ackerman, A. (1902). Über die Anatomie und Zwittrigkeit der *Cucumaria
laevigata*. Z. wiss. Zool. **72**, 721–749.
Ahrens, W. (1935). Die Entwicklung des "Corpus luteum" bei den Insekten.
Z. mikr-anat. Forsch. **37**, 467–500.
Beddard, F. E. (1910). Earthworms and leeches. *In* "Cambridge Natural
History", vol. II, London.
Benham, W. B. (1890). The anatomy of *Phoronis australis*. Quart. J. micr. Sci.
30, 125–158.
Berland, L. (1949). Ordre des Opilions. *In* "Traité de Zoologie" (P.-P. Grassé,
ed.), vol. VI, p. 761–793. Paris, Masson.
Bouvier, E. L. (1905). Monographie des Onychophores. Ann. Sci. nat. Zool.
Ser. 9, 2, 1–384.
Brambell, F. W. R. and Goodhart, C. B. (1944). *Saccoglossus horsti* sp.n.,
an Enteropneust occurring in the Solent. J. Mar. biol. Ass. U.K. **25**, 283–301.
Brandt, A. (1874). Ueber die Eiröhren der *Blatta* (*Periplaneta*) *orientalis*.
Mem. Acad. Sci. St. Petersb. Ser. 7, **21**, No. 12.

Burdon-Jones, C. (1956). Observations on the enteropneust *Protoglossus koehleri* (Caullery & Mesnil). *Proc. zool. Soc. Lond.* 127, 35–58.

Burfield, S. T. (1927). Sagitta. *L.M.B.C. Mem.* 28.

Chadwick, H. C. (1900). Echinus. *L.M.B.C. Mem.* 3.

Chadwick, H. C. (1907). Antedon. *L.M.B.C. Mem.* 15.

Chadwick, H. C. (1923). Asterias. *L.M.B.C. Mem.* 25.

Clark, H. L. (1907). The apodous holothurians. *Smithson. Contr. Knowl.* 35, (1916). No. 1723.

Coe, W. R. (1945). Development of the reproductive system and variations in sexuality in *Pecten* and other pelecypod mollusks. *Trans. Conn. Acad. Arts Sci.* 36, 673–700.

Cuénot, L. (1949). Les Tardigrades. Les Pentastomides. *In* "Traité de Zoologie" (P.-P. Grassé, ed.), vol. VI, p. 39–59; 61–75. Paris, Masson.

Cussans, M. (1904). Gammarus. *L.M.B.C. Mem.* 12.

Dakin, W. J. (1909). Pecten. *L.M.B.C. Mem.* 17.

Dakin, W. J. (1912). Buccinum. *L.M.B.C. Mem.* 20.

Darwin, C. (1851). A monograph of the Cirripedia. The Lepadidae. *Ray Soc. Publ.*

Davis, J. R. A. and Fleure, H. J. (1903). Patella. *L.M.B.C. Mem.* 10.

Dawes, B. (1946). "The Trematoda." Cambridge University Press.

Eales, N. B. (1921). Aplysia. *L.M.B.C. Mem.* 24.

Fage, L. (1949). Mérostomacés. *In* "Traité de Zoologie" (P.-P. Grassé, ed.), p. 219–262. Paris, Masson.

Grobben, C. (1876). Die Geschlechtsorgane von *Squilla mantis*, Rodn. *S.B. Akad. Wiss. Wien*, 74, Abt. 1, 389–406.

Gross, J. (1903). Untersuchungen über die Histologie des Insektenovariums. *Zool. Jb.* (Anat.), 18, 72–186.

Hamann, O. (1883). Beiträge zur Histologie der Echinodermen. *Z. wiss. Zool.* 39, 145–190.

Harmer, S. F. (1885). On the structure and development of *Loxosoma*. *Quart. J. micr. Sci.* 25, 261–337.

Harmer, S. F. (1904). Hemichordata. *In* "Cambridge Natural History", vol. VII, London.

Harmer, S. F. (1910). Polyzoa. *In* "Cambridge Natural History", vol. II, London.

Hartog, M. (1910). Rotifers. *In* "Cambridge Natural History", vol. II, London.

Herdman, E. C. (1924). Botryllus. *L.M.B.C. Mem.* 26.

Herdman, W. A. (1899). Ascidia. *L.M.B.C. Mem.* 1.

Hewitt, C. G. (1907). Ligia. *L.M.B.C. Mem.* 14.

Hilton, I. F. (1931). The oogenesis of *Calanus finmarchicus*. *Quart. J. micr. Sci.* 74, 193–222.

Horst, C. J. van der. (1939). Hemichordata. *In* Bronn "Die Klassen und Ordnungen des Thierreiches", 4, Abt. 4, Buch 2, Tl. 2.

Huxley, T. H. (1880). "The Crayfish." London, Kegan Paul and Co.

Hyman, L. H. (1940). "The Invertebrates", vol. I, New York, McGraw-Hill.

Hyman, L. H. (1951a). "The Invertebrates", vol. II, New York, McGraw-Hill.

Hyman, L. H. (1951b). "The Invertebrates", vol. III, New York, McGraw-Hill.

Hyman, L. H. (1955). "The Invertebrates", vol. IV, New York, McGraw-Hill.

Hyman, L. H. (1959). "The Invertebrates", vol. V, New York, McGraw-Hill.

Imms, A. D. (1957). "A General Textbook of Entomology." 9th ed. London.

Isgrove, A. (1909). Eledone. *L.M.B.C. Mem.* **18**.

Johnstone, J. (1899). Cardium. *L.M.B.C. Mem.* **2**.

Kostitzine, J. (1949). L'appareil réproducteur femelle de quelques mollusques prosobranches marins. *Arch. Zool. exp. gén.* **86**, 145–167.

Lohman, H. (1933). Appendiculariae. *In* Kükenthal "Handbuch der Zoologie", Bd. V, Tl. 2. Tunicata, pp. 15–202.

Loman, J. C. C. (1917). Beiträge zur Anatomie und Biologie der Pantopoden. *Tijdschr. ned. dierk. Verh.*, Sér. 2, **16**, 53–102.

Michael, A. D. (1884). British Oribatidae. *Ray Soc. Publ.*

Michael, A. D. (1901). British Tyroglyphidae. *Ray Soc. Publ.*

Millot, J. (1939). L'appareil génital des Pédipalpes. *Int. Congr. Ent.* **7**, **2**, 846–865.

Millot, J. (1949). Ordre des Aranéides. *In* "Traité de Zoologie" (P.-P. Grassé, ed.), vol. VI, p. 589–743. Paris, Masson.

Mortensen, T. (1932). Biological observations on ophiurids. *Vidensk. Medd. naturh. Foren. Kbh.* **93**, 171–194.

Musso, R. (1930). Die Genitalröhren von *Ascaris lumbricoides* und *megalocephala*. *Z. wiss. Zool.* **137**, 274–363.

Owen, R. (1873). On the anatomy of the American king-crab (*Limulus polyphemus*, Latr.). *Trans. Linn. Soc. Lond.* **28**, 459–506.

Palm, N.-B. (1948). Normal and pathological histology of the ovaries in *Bombus* Latr. (Hymenoptera). *Opusc. ent.* Suppl. **7**.

Paul, G. (1910). Über *Petalostoma minutum* Keferstin und verwandte Arten nebst einigen Bemerkungen zur Anatomie von *Onchnesoma steenstrupii*. *Zool. Jb.* (Anat.) **29**, 1–50.

Peacock, A. D. and Gresson, R. A. R. (1928). The roles of the nurse-cells, oocytes and follicle-cells in tenthredinid oogenesis. *Quart. J. micr. Sci.* **71**, 541–561.

Pietschmann, V. (1929). Acrania. *In* Kükenthal "Handbuch der Zoologie", Bd. VI, Tl. 1, pp. 3–124.

Plate, L. H. (1901). Die Anatomie und Phylogenie der Chitonen. *Zool. Jb.* Suppl. **5**, 281–592.

Schaeffer, C. (1926). Untersuchungen zur vergleichenden Anatomie und Histologie der Brachiopodengattung Lingula. *Acta zool. Stockh.* **7**, 329–402.

Schepotieff, A. (1907). Die Pterobranchien.—Die Anatomie von *Rhabdopleura*. *Zool. Jb.* (Anat.) **23**, 463–534.

Scott, A. (1901). Lepeophtheirus and Lernaea. *L.M.B.C. Mem.* **6**.

Shipley, A. E. (1895). Brachiopods (Recent). *In* "Cambridge Natural History", vol. III, London.

Shipley, A. E. (1910). Gephyrea and Phoronis. *In* "Cambridge Natural History", vol. II, London.

Smith, J. E. (1940). The reproductive system and associated organs of the brittle-star *Ophiothrix fragilis*. *Quart. J. micr. Sci.*, **82**, 267–309.

Stephenson, J. (1930). "The Oligochaeta." Oxford University Press.

Vachon, M. (1938). Recherches anatomiques et biologiques sur la réproduction et développement des pseudoscorpions. *Ann. Sci. nat. Zool.* Ser. 11. **1**, 1–207.

Vachon, M. (1945). Remarques sur les organes genitaux de quelques solifuges (Arachnides). *Bull. Mus. Hist. nat., Paris*, **17**, 476–482.

Vejdovsky, F. (1886). Zur Morphologie der Gordiiden. *Z. wiss. Zool.* **43**, 369–433.

Wagler, E. (1927). Branchiopoda, Phyllopoda = Kiemfüsser. *In* Kükenthal "Handbuch der Zoologie", Bd. III, Tl. 1, pp. 305–398.

Wahab, A., Abd-El-. (1945). The female genital system of the scorpion *Buthus quinquestriatus* (H.E.). *Bull. zool. Soc. Egypt*, **11**, 1–11.

Zimmer, C. (1927). Mysidacea, Cumacea, Tanaidacea. *In* Kükenthal "Handbuch der Zoologie", Bd. III, Tl. 1, pp. 606–696.

CHAPTER 2

THE STRUCTURE OF THE OVARY
B. Vertebrates

L. L. FRANCHI

I. Introduction

The purpose of this section is to provide a short comparative account
of the general structure shown by the ovary in different classes of
vertebrates. It is, as a rule, restricted to the condition in non-
mammalian vertebrates, but occasionally refers to mammals where it
seems pertinent to do so. A detailed description of the structure of
the mammalian ovary is given in part C of this chapter.

II. Comparative morphology of the vertebrate ovary

There is considerable variation in the structure of the ovary between
the different classes and orders, and, to a more limited extent, genera
in the vertebrate sub-phylum. In spite of this ultimate diversity, the
initial development of the ovary is essentially similar in all vertebrates
(see Chapter 1). Like the testes in the male, the ovaries differentiate
from bilaterally symmetrical, indifferent gonadal rudiments in the
young embryo. Modifications of the general pattern of development
may occur subsequently and are most frequently found amongst
species which produce large ova (see below).

K

Throughout the vertebrates the ovaries, unlike the testes of many mammals, lie within the peritoneal cavity. The primitive position—close to the dorsal body wall, extending caudally from the cranial extremity of the kidneys—is retained in all vertebrates including birds. In mammals, the ovaries may undergo a moderate degree of descent in a ventro-caudal direction so that, according to the species, the organs are found anywhere between the caudal poles of the kidneys and the pelvis. The ostia of the oviducts are normally closely related in position.

With the exception of *Ornithorhynchus* among the monotremes (Flynn and Hill, 1939) and certain bats (Matthews, 1937), the ovaries of mammals are bilateral organs of equal size and function (see Chapter 2C). By contrast, the development of the right ovary is suppressed in the majority of birds. Certain of the birds of prey, however, possess both ovaries in a functional condition, although the right oviduct may be vestigial (Stanley and Witschi, 1940; see below, p. 132).

Reptiles, amphibians and many fishes have paired ovaries. Only that on the right side, however, develops in the basking shark *Cetorhinus maximus* (Matthews, 1950), the dogfish *Scylliorhinus canicula* (Chieffi, 1955, 1959) and in certain other elasmobranchs. Among the teleosts several species, of which *Heterandria formosa* (Fraser and Renton, 1940), *Oryzias latipes* (Robinson and Rugh, 1943) and *Lebistes reticulatus* (Goodrich *et al.*, 1934) are typical examples, possess a single ovary. In the majority of teleosts the ovaries are paired and fusion is only evident in the oviducts at their junction with the ovaries (e.g. *Phoxinus laevis*; Bullough, 1939). In the lampreys the ovary is a median un-paired organ, and only that of the right side develops in hagfishes (Conel, 1917; Okkelberg, 1921). The origin of asymmetry in the ovaries of lower vertebrates is discussed in Chapter 1.

Ambisexuality of the gonads is not uncommon among fishes and amphibians, and individuals may change their functional sex in a seasonal manner. Among teleosts, members of the families Sparidae and Serranidae possess hermaphroditic gonads, male and female gametes being produced in distinct regions of the same organ. Nor-mally these fishes exhibit the functional characteristics of one sex during one season and those of the other in the following season (Fig. 1). Some species, however, are capable of self-fertilization (van Oordt, 1933; D'Ancona, 1949, 1951). Both natural and experimental sex reversal have been described for amphibians. The functional ovary may become atrophic and eventually be replaced by testicular tissue (e.g. Humphrey, 1929; Foote and Witschi, 1939; Witschi, 1939; Gallien, 1955; see also Chapter 13). Bidder's organ, a structure associ-ated with the urogenital complex in male toads, is histologically similar to an immature ovary, and may become a functional ovary following

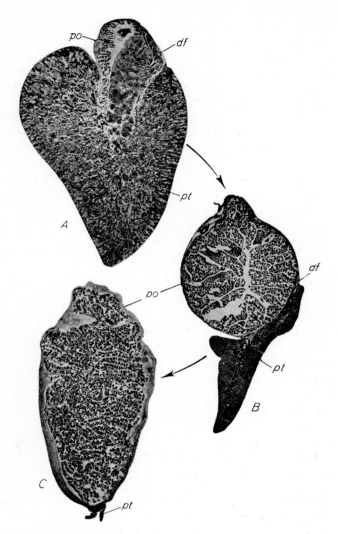

FIG. 1. Transverse sections of the gonad of the teleost *Sparus auratus*, showing successive stages in its transformation from a functional testis to a functional ovary. *A:* male phase; *B:* during inversion; *C:* female phase, in which the testis is reduced to a small vestige and the ovary develops a highly complex system of ovigerous lamellae. *pt*, testicular portion; *po*, ovarian portion; *df*, d. deferens. (Reproduced from D'Ancona (1951), by permission of Centre National de la Recherche Scientifique.)

removal of the testes (see Witschi, 1939). Okkelberg (1921) has described a type of hermaphroditism in the lamprey *Entosphenus wilderi*, in the gonad of which male and female sexual elements occur side by side. This condition, however, does not normally persist in the mature adult. In the gonad of the hagfishes *Myxine* and *Bdellostoma*, there are clearly demarcated cranial female and caudal male portions (Cunningham, 1886; Cole, 1905; Conel, 1917; Schreiner, 1904, 1955), although only one portion attains sexual maturity in the adult in both sexes. The other portion (cranial in the male, caudal in the female) either remains in an immature condition or becomes rudimentary. The rule among cyclostomes, therefore, as in many fishes with initially bisexual gonads, is to become functionally unisexual according to the predominance of male or female germ cells. The less dominant elements become atrophic at the onset of sexual maturity and eventually disappear. The factors underlying ambisexual tendencies in lower vertebrates are discussed by Brambell (1930), D'Ancona (1951) and in outline in Chapters 1 and 13.

III. Patterns of ovarian structure

The ovaries of both non-mammalian and mammalian vertebrates show several important differences, and may be broadly classified according to the presence or absence of certain structural components (see p. 125). Alternatively, they may be divided into *compact* and *saccular* types. In the latter the organ is hollow; this condition is encountered in more than one vertebrate class, but according to Nelsen (1953) only the amphibians can be said to possess true saccular ovaries. Compact ovaries occur in reptiles, birds and, typically, mammals.

A. General morphology and histology

In all vertebrates the ovary is covered by a germinal epithelium which is continuous with the peritoneal epithelium lining the body cavity. The cells are frequently cuboidal and are capable of rapid mitotic proliferation to accommodate the extensive changes in size and shape of the ovary which occur during breeding cycles. Like the peritoneal cells, they are phagocytically active (Latta and Pederson, 1944). The term 'germinal' is still used in reference to the ovarian epithelium, since it was formerly considered to be the source of germ cells in the embryo and of additional oocytes in the adult (see Chapter 1). The only possible relevance that this term may be said to retain at present is that the epithelium consists of non-germinal (somatic) cells amongst which germ cells occasionally reside. The extent of such germinal portions is restricted in a few species, such as the minnow

(Bullough, 1939), geckos (Boyd, 1941) and the mare (Hammond and Wodzicki, 1941).

Immediately under the germinal epithelium lies a thin layer of mesenchymal connective tissue which is known as the tunica albuginea. Although characteristic, this layer is generally poorly developed in the ovary compared with the testis, where it forms a thick fibrous tunica.

The bulk of the ovary in most vertebrates is made up of the cortex, surrounding a central core or medulla. The relative proportions of these two regions vary widely between different classes, and it is claimed that a true medullary region is lacking, from the earliest developmental stages of the gonad, in cyclostomes, teleosts and ganoids (see Chapter 1). Accordingly, a urogenital connection is absent in these groups. The embryonic ovarian medulla of other vertebrates undergoes regressive changes, although it persists in a variety of structural forms (see below). In mammals, much of the original medullary tissue may be displaced by a 'secondary medulla' consisting of connective tissue and vascular and nervous elements. In general, the medulla of adult vertebrates, with the exception of the above three groups, is a loose spongy and highly vascular tissue. The blood vessels, nerves and lymphatics which supply the ovary pass into the medulla along its region of attachment to the body wall. The latter is extensive in lower vertebrates, in which the ovary itself is frequently elongated and suspended by a long mesovarium. In mammals the ovary is small and compact and the region of attachment is represented by a short, thick hilus.

The comparatively dense cortex is composed of a stroma of connective tissue fibres, fibroblasts, cells of epithelial origin, and spindle-shaped cells among which numbers of oocytes are distributed. The latter are enclosed within a follicular epithelium, the extent and complexity of which vary both according to the species and the reproductive state of the individual. In all vertebrates the primordial oocyte acquires a follicular epithelium early on in the life of the animal. At first the follicle consists of only a few flattened cells which closely surround the oocytes. When a proportion of the latter have entered upon their characteristic growth phase the follicle (granulosa) cells divide mitotically and may become cuboidal or columnar. The epithelium remains as a single layer of cells in cyclostomes, teleosts and amphibians, but may become several layers thick in elasmobranchs, reptiles and birds. In mammals, the multilayered condition is characteristic, and the Graafian follicle, unlike the corresponding structure in non-mammals, contains a fluid-filled cavity or antrum (see Chapter 2C). In many vertebrates, too, the ovarian follicle, after reaching a certain size, develops an outer covering, or theca, which may differentiate into a highly vascularized inner zone of glandular cells and an outer fibrous zone. For details of follicular structure in different vertebrates see Chapters 2C and 5; also Hoar (1955) and Brambell (1956).

Although the mammalian ovary may contain follicles representative of all stages of growth, the organ in lower vertebrates may contain only certain stages, depending upon the particular phase of the breeding cycle (see Chapter 5; and Matthews and Marshall, 1956).

In addition to large numbers of follicles the ovaries of most vertebrates contain other structures which are derived from growing and mature follicles. These are atretic follicles (corpora atretica) and corpora lutea. The extent to which they form prominent features of the ovary depends, mainly, upon breeding habits of the species concerned. Large numbers of follicles undergo atretic degeneration during the life of the animal and may persist for a time as dense fibrous or glandular structures. They are normally of no functional significance, but their nature in some lower vertebrates has led to them being termed 'pre-ovulatory corpora lutea' (Miller, 1955). Post-ovulatory corpora lutea occur in representatives of most vertebrate classes and are formed from remnants of the follicle after ovulation (i.e. liberation of the ripe ovum). In most non-mammals these bodies are transitory and of doubtful functional significance. On the other hand, true corpora lutea are of universal occurrence among mammals,* and their endocrine function is of great significance both in the control of the reproductive cycle and the maintenance of gestation. The formation and histology of these structures in non-mammals is discussed on p. 137†.

The relative degree of development of the cortex and medulla may be regarded as one of the main sources of structural variation in the ovaries among different vertebrates. On the other hand, whereas in the ovary of the sexually mature adult the medulla remains structurally and functionally constant, the size, shape and composition of the cortex is considerably influenced by the breeding habits of the species. Comparatively small changes take place in animals which breed continuously; in those with a well-defined sexual season there are marked fluctuations in cortical development. This becomes especially evident in species in which multiple ovulation is the rule and in those that produce large, telolecithal eggs. Therefore in fishes, amphibians, reptiles, birds and, to a smaller extent in monotremes, the ovary/body weight ratio can at times be very high. Much of the increase in size

* A corpus luteum occurs in monotremes, but whether it has the same significance as in higher mammals remains doubtful (see Brambell, 1956; Hisaw, 1959).

† Additional information about cyclical ovarian changes in different vertebrates, and the formation of corpora lutea, may be found in *Comparative Physiology of Reproduction* (1955) and in *Comparative Endocrinology* (1959).

and weight of the ovary is due to the development of oocytes and not to the growth of accessory follicular structures. In marsupial and placental mammals, which have microlecithal eggs, the ratio is low. Changes in the size, shape and weight of the ovary are due primarily to the formation of Graafian follicles and corpora lutea, and the growth of the oocyte does not materially affect the ovary/body weight ratio; this, in consequence, varies only within comparatively narrow limits.

B. Cyclostomes

The ovary is elongated, extending through the greater part of the body cavity, and is suspended along its entire length by a mesovarium through which vascular elements pass. The lamprey ovary is composed mainly of masses of small follicles and a rather sparse interfollicular stroma, which appears to be of epithelial origin (Okkelberg, 1921). The organ is surrounded by a thin envelope of germinal epithelium. The ovary of hagfishes consists of little more than a ventral continuation of the mesovarium and is very compressed from side to side. The smallest oocytes occur in groups in the ventral margin, between the folds of epithelium. As growth and vitellogenesis proceed the oocyte acquires a follicle, consisting of epithelial cells and connective tissue, and passes towards the proximal border of the mesovarium (Cunningham, 1886; Conel, 1917). The caudal portion of the mesovarium, which contains immature testicular tissue in the young animal, is normally sterile in the mature female, although nonfunctional testicular 'rests' may persist (Schreiner, 1955). During breeding, mature eggs are shed into the body cavity by rupture of the wall of the ovary. No ducts connect the ovary with the exterior in cyclostomes, although pores appear in the cloacal wall during sexual maturity.

C. Fishes

The ovary of most fishes resembles that of the lamprey, although variable degrees of elaboration in internal structure may occur, particularly among teleosts, which appear to be related to the breeding habits of the species. The ovary of elasmobranchs, however, like that of higher vertebrates, contains a distinct medullary region, the original cellular elements of which become replaced during development by haematopoietic cells derived from the kidney (Chieffi, 1949, 1959; see also Chapter 1). No medulla is present in ganoids or teleosts.

Typically, the ovary and mesovarium are elongated. Blood vessels enter the organ along the length of the mesovarium and ramify through the mediodorsal portion. Oocytes undergoing growth and maturation occur in the more ventral portion of the ovary and are ovulated from the ventro-lateral surface, sometimes into a special sinus, or 'ovarian cavity' (see below).

During the breeding season the surface of the ovary assumes a beaded appearance as it becomes distended with maturing oocytes. Frequently also, the organ undergoes striking colour changes owing to the deposition, first of yolk, and second of pigment within the enlarging oocytes. This is clearly seen in the sturgeon (Loukine, 1941; Moltchanova, 1941). In this animal, as in elasmobranchs and cyclostomes, mature eggs are released by rupture of the ovarian wall.

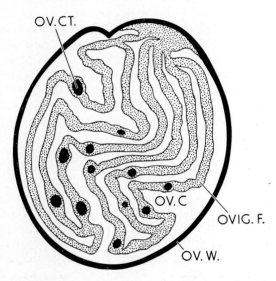

FIG. 2. Diagrammatic transverse section of ovary of a teleost fish (*Cymatogaster*), to show the system of ovigerous lamellae suspended in an ovarian cavity. *OV.CT.* developing oocyte; *OV.C.* ovarian cavity; *OVIG.F.* ovigerous fold; *OV.W.* ovarian wall. (Reproduced by permission from Turner, 1938.)

In many teleosts, eggs are ovulated into an ovarian cavity on the ventro-lateral wall of the ovary, and pass to the exterior through a duct which joins the caudal portion of the organ. The cavity may be formed in different ways: in some, particularly viviparous species, a portion of the coelom becomes enclosed by an infolding of the ovarian wall. The cavity is thus lined by germinal epithelium and a number of 'ovigerous folds' project into it from the walls (Figs. 1, 2; e.g. Craig-Bennett, 1930; Matthews, 1938; Turner, 1938; Mendoza, 1940). The folds consist of masses of follicles in varying stages of growth, lying in a loose connective tissue stroma. The youngest follicles are situated distally and the mature ones more proximally. The ovarian cavity is formed at or about the time of hatching in most of the species which have been studied. In some teleosts, however, it is formed only when the mature follicles rupture, by a hollowing-out of the internal tissues (e.g. *Tilapia*: Aronson and Holz-Tucker, 1949). The ovigerous folds in the ganoid *Amia calva* are not suspended in a separate ovarian cavity (D'Ancona, 1955).

Among species in which external fertilization occurs, many thousands of eggs may be spawned in one season. In viviparous and ovoviviparous species smaller numbers of oocytes become mature at any one time, and as a result the ovary often assumes the appearance of a bunch of grapes. This is typically seen in elasmobranchs, which produce heavily yolked eggs. The ovary and reproductive tract in these animals is adapted for the development of fertilized eggs *in situ*. Embryos develop within the ovarian cavity in several teleosts (for example, *Neotoca bilineata*: Mendoza, 1940), and the hollow ovary of *Heterandria formosa* becomes distended with several broods of young fish in varying stages of development (Fraser and Renton, 1940). Modifications in size and shape occur in the ovaries of other members of the families Poeciliidae and Anablepidae, in which both fertilization and embryonic development occur within modified ovarian follicles (see Hoar, 1955; Matthews, 1955; Matthews and Marshall, 1956).

The ovaries of many fishes, therefore, undergo marked fluctuations in form and composition. At the height of the breeding season they expand and may distend the body wall of the female. After spawning they rapidly shrink, and in species like the minnow are reduced to thin, thread-like organs consisting mainly of immature oocytes and a few stromal cells (Bullough, 1939).

D. Amphibians

The ovaries of adult amphibians are lobed structures composed mainly of cortex covered by germinal epithelium. A compact medullary region is present during early embryonic development but largely disappears subsequently. In its place large hollow sacs are formed in the centre of the organ by extensive modification of the medullary and rete cords (Chapter 1). The ovarian cavity is thus lined by cells which represent the remains of the medulla (Fig. 3).

Amphibian ovaries are also characterized by the persistence, during adult life, of groups of oogonia in the germinal epithelium. These give rise by division to successive generations of oocytes (see Chapter 1, sect. II, E).

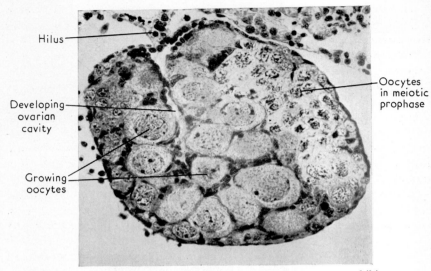

FIG. 3(a). Transverse section of the ovary of a young amphibian (*Rana temporaria*) during metamorphosis. (Reproduced by permission of Prof. L. Gallien.)

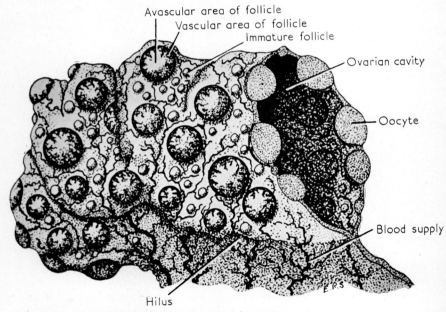

FIG. 3(b). Diagrammatic representation of part of the ovary of an adult amphibian (*Necturus maculosus*). (Reproduced by permission from *Comparative Embryology of the Vertebrates*, by O. E. Nelsen. Copyright, 1953. McGraw-Hill Book Company Inc.)

The folded cortical walls contain large numbers of oocytes which, in some species, may be divisible into a number of generations according to their stage of growth (De Allende, 1939; Smith, 1955). At the onset of the breeding season many small follicles begin to grow; the ovary therefore also enlarges and its surface assumes a mulberry-like appearance. At spawning time, mature eggs are ovulated directly into the body cavity. Prior to spawning the whole of the reproductive tract is enormously enlarged and, as in many fishes, may distend the abdomen of the female. At the end of the breeding season, however, the tract may undergo regression to juvenile proportions (Jordan, 1893; Alexander and Bellerby, 1938). March (1937) has estimated that in the frog at this time the ovaries are one-tenth of their pre-spawning weight.

After spawning, the ovaries contain the remains of discharged follicles, immature oocytes and corpora atretica (Smith, 1955). Post-ovulatory corpora lutea have been described in some species (p. 138).

E. Reptiles

The reptilian ovary is a somewhat irregular oval structure, the medulla of which contains a network of fluid-filled cavities, or lacunae (Fig. 4). These are derived from the medullary cords of the embryonic ovary and are therefore homologous with the ovarian sac of amphibians (see above). Under certain conditions these cavities may become distended (Forbes, 1940).

There is little stroma in the cortex, and the bulk of the ovary is composed of numerous follicles. At the onset of breeding the ovaries assume a grape-like appearance owing to the rapid increase in size of a relatively small number of oocytes, which accumulate abundant yolk. The follicle, compared with that in fishes and amphibians, is highly complex in composition, and as the oocyte matures the theca (see p. 126) differentiates into glandular and connective tissue layers (see Boyd, 1941; Brambell, 1956; Miller, 1959). Before ovulation occurs the mature follicles project from the surface of the ovary on short stalks. In some lizards very few eggs are shed in each season. Only one is ovulated from each ovary in the geckos (Boyd, 1941). The cellular elements of the discharged follicle persist for a variable time in most reptiles and form a corpus luteum (see p. 137).

F. Birds

The general features of ovarian structure and physiology in birds have been repeatedly reviewed, more recently by Benoit (1950), Sturkie (1954) and Breneman (1955). As mentioned above, only the left ovary normally reaches a fully functional state, the right one remaining in a rudimentary condition from an early stage in the embryo (Fig. 5). This, however, does not apply to all birds. According to the data collected by Romanoff and Romanoff (1949), a well-developed right ovary is present in over 50 per cent of mature hawks and in about 24 per cent of ring doves; it is also occasionally present in chicks and pigeons (see also Stanley and Witschi, 1940).

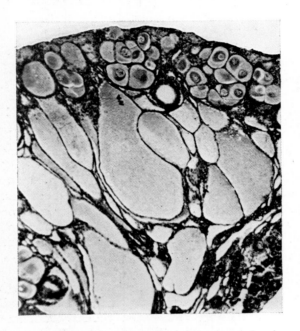

Fɪɢ. 4. Transverse section of a portion of the ovary of an immature alligator. A narrow cortical zone, containing numbers of small oocytes, is at the top of the figure, and the extensive medullary lacunae occupy the centre. (Reproduced by permission from Forbes, 1940.)

In the typical, asymmetrical condition the right ovary persists as a microscopic vestige in the adult, but it may become an active gonad if the left one is removed or functionally impaired.* The structure of this vestige in the domestic fowl was studied by Brode (1928). In

* Impairment can occur, for example, by tumorous growths (Crew, 1923; Brambell and Marrian, 1929) or by experimental sinistral ovariectomy (Benoit, 1923; Domm, 1924, 1939; Kornfeld, 1960). The right gonad then develops into a testis or an ovotestis. This organ is frequently hormonally active and may cause reversal of the secondary sexual characters. The occasional ability to produce sperm (Crew, 1923) depends upon the persistence of undifferentiated germ cells (Brode, 1928).

61 per cent of the specimens examined it consisted of medullary tissue only, while in the remaining 39 per cent a cortical rudiment was also present. The smaller proportion of primordial germ cells which migrate

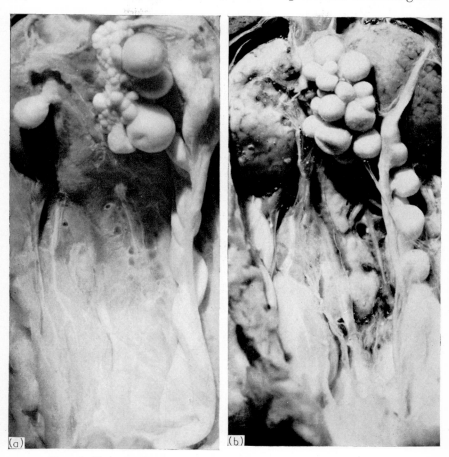

FIG. 5. Ventral dissections of the reproductive tract of the adult female broad-winged hawk (*Buteo*), to show the asymmetrical development of the ovaries. In (a) the right ovary is represented by a single enlarged follicle. In (b) the right ovary is absent. In both specimens the remainder of the reproductive tract of the right side is completely atrophied. (By courtesy of Prof. A. J. Stanley; Fig. 5b reproduced from *J. Morph.* (1937), **61**, 321).

into the right gonadal rudiment during embryonic development (cf. Chapter 1) persist for a period of up to 3 weeks after hatching, with occasional exceptions. This finding would explain the almost invariable sterility of the hypertrophied right gonad which follows removal of the left one in older birds (see footnote on p. 132).

As in reptiles, the ovarian medulla of birds contains an extensive network of lacunae. The cortex of the left ovary possesses little stromal tissue, but is subject to wide structural variation according to the reproductive state of the individual. The marked changes in size coloration and weight of the ovary are due largely to the rapid growth of oocytes during breeding cycles. In the starling, for example, the ovary may show an increase in weight from 8 mg in early winter to as much as 1400 mg immediately prior to ovulation in spring (Witschi, 1956).

The ovary of the newly hatched bird has an endowment of several million oocytes (see Chapter 1, sect. II, G), some of which enlarge slightly but remain relatively quiescent until sexual maturity is attained. By this time some of the oocytes have reached a diameter of 6 mm in the fowl. They then enter upon a phase of rapid growth, brought about mainly by the deposition of yolk, and increase in diameter at the rate of some 4 mm per day. Similarly, in the starling, the largest oocytes in the winter ovary are about 0·5 mm in diameter. As the breeding season approaches, a proportion of them enlarge to 4 mm. Only a few of these normally undergo further enlargement in the following days and are eventually ovulated.

The rapid and extensive increase in size of the oocytes causes the follicles to bulge conspicuously from the surface of the ovary (Fig. 6). Ultimately the mature follicle is suspended from the surface by a narrow pedicle on which, after ovulation, other oocytes mature and become pedunculated. Associated with the rapid growth of the oocyte a many-layered vascular theca, containing an elaborate venous supply, forms around the follicle (Nalbandov and James, 1949; Nelsen, 1953). The arterial supply, however, is poorly developed. Prior to release of the oocyte in the fowl an elongated, relatively avascular area, the stigma, appears on the outer aspect of the theca (Fig. 6, inset). Rupture of the follicular wall occurs in the centre of this area at the time of ovulation. Excessive loss of blood from the torn theca is prevented by the contraction of the blood-vessel walls. The additional coats of the egg, such as the albumen layer and shell, are laid down in specialized regions of the oviduct.

Atresia of oocytes is a prominent feature of the bird ovary, particularly in species which have a short breeding season. All oocytes that enter the growth phase are potential gametes, but only a small proportion are ovulated and the remainder become resorbed, either *in situ* or after the breakdown of the follicular wall (see Brambell, 1956).

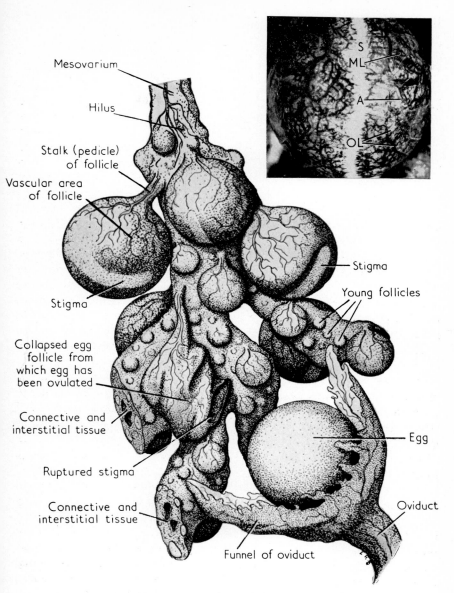

Mesovarium

Hilus

Stalk (pedicle) of follicle

Vascular area of follicle

Stigma

Collapsed egg follicle from which egg has been ovulated

Connective and interstitial tissue

Ruptured stigma

Connective and interstitial tissue

S

ML

A

OL

Stigma

Young follicles

Egg

Oviduct

Funnel of oviduct

FIG. 6. Diagram to show the external structure of the functional ovary of a bird during breeding. Follicles in various stages of growth are present. The stigma marks the position in which the follicle wall ruptures at the time of ovulation. (Reproduced by permission from *Comparative Embryology of the Vertebrates* by O. E. Nelsen. Copyright, 1953. McGraw-Hill Book Company Inc.)
Inset.—Surface view of a large follicle of the chicken ovary, injected to show the vascular system. The stigma (*S*) clearly marked by the absence of large blood vessels (*A; OL; ML*). (Reproduced by permission from Nalbandov and James, 1949.)

G. Mammals

The structure of the mammalian ovary is reviewed in detail in part C of this chapter, and only a few comparative aspects will be considered here.

1. *Monotremes*

The ovary resembles that in birds by the tendency for bilateral asymmetry and by the presence of characteristic vascular medullary lacunae. The structure of the follicle is also similar, except that the oocyte, in the mature follicle of the monotremes, is suspended in a fluid-filled cavity which is considered to be homologous with the antrum of the Graafian follicle of higher mammals (Flynn and Hill, 1939). The oocyte accumulates abundant yolk, and only one or two eggs are laid during each breeding cycle. For details concerning the corpus luteum, see Brambell (1956) and Chapter 2C.

2. *Marsupial and placental mammals*

The ovary is of the typically compact type. There are no extensive lacunae in the medulla as in other amniotes, and the only well-marked cavities are those present in the fully developed Graafian follicles in the cortex. The bulk of the ovary is therefore made up of an extensive cortex and a relatively small medulla. The cortex is rich in stromal elements, amongst which lie follicles in various stages of development, corpora lutea and groups of interstitial cells. The smallest follicles lie peripherally, whereas those in the early growth phase are placed more deeply. As the Graafian follicles reach maturity they (and the corpora lutea derived from them) tend to become superficial again. Nests of interstitial cells are usually found in the deeper zones of the cortex. Variations in the proportion and distribution of the ovarian components in different mammals are considered in Chapter 2C.

As mentioned earlier, the ratio of ovary weight to body weight is low in mammals, and does not fluctuate markedly according to breeding habits (see also Chapter 2C). The attachment of the organ to the body wall is relatively short and the ovary itself correspondingly smaller than in lower vertebrates. The total increase in size of the oocyte during the growth phase is very small compared with that in reptiles and birds, and the enlargement of the ovary which occurs during breeding cycles is almost entirely due to the development of Graafian follicles and corpora lutea.

Degenerative changes (atresia) are common in the ovarian follicles both of mammals and of lower vertebrates. These changes can take place in a number of ways and may occur at any stage in the cycle of

2B. OVARIAN STRUCTURE: LOWER VERTEBRATES 137

follicular development, but the process invariably leads to the cessation of growth and eventual resorption of the oocyte. In mammals a wave of atresia, starting from the time of birth, accounts for the greater part of the observed fall in oocyte numbers (see Chapter 1, sect. II, I). Even after the onset of sexual maturity, the loss in numbers from atresia exceeds that due to ovulation (Arai, 1920; Mandl and Zuckerman, 1950). The subject of atresia is fully considered in Chapter 4.

IV. The fate of the discharged follicle in non-mammalian vertebrates

The discharged follicles of elasmobranch fishes and of reptiles give rise to structures closely resembling mammalian corpora lutea. Similar structures develop in the follicles of other fishes, amphibians and birds but are not as prominent (Harrison, 1948; Hoar, 1955; Matthews, 1955; Brambell, 1956; Hisaw and Hisaw, 1959). There is, as yet, no clear evidence that these structures exhibit endocrine activity, although they may well do so in viviparous species.

Descriptions of luteal-like bodies developing in the post-ovulatory follicle of the fowl are given by Pearl and Boring (1918), Hett (1923), Yocom (1924) and Davis (1942). Pearl and Boring state that the 'corpus luteum' of the hen develops from the theca interna cells. Davis maintains that the post-ovulatory follicle in birds is not identical with the corpus luteum of mammals because there is no hypertrophy or proliferation of the granulosa cells (see Chapter 2 C). The post-ovulatory follicle quickly shrinks to half its original size and contains a mass of highly vacuolated granulosa cells and phagocytes. The thecal cells also become vacuolated and the thecal layer frequently contains hyalin.

Cunningham and Smart (1934) consider that the essential character of the corpus luteum in lower vertebrates is the persistence and hypertrophy of the ruptured follicle. In their opinion, the latter only occurs in viviparous species, whereas in oviparous ones the discharged follicle undergoes degeneration (see Weekes, 1934). In reptiles, however, the corpus luteum is formed irrespective of the presence or absence of a placenta. Since the corpora lutea are formed in oviparous reptiles they may have appeared before the evolution of the placenta, and later have acquired a function connected with placentation (Boyd, 1941). In reptiles, therefore, the development of a corpus luteum is not associated exclusively with viviparity, but also with the mere retention of eggs in the oviduct (Rahn, 1938; see also Miller, 1959). Bragdon (1946) considers that in the ovoviviparous snakes *Thamnophis* and *Natrix* the morphological appearance of the corpora lutea antedates their possible utilization as endocrine organs.

L

Luteal tissue in the ovaries of the snakes *Thamnophis* and *Potamophis* is apparently derived solely from the granulosa cells of the discharged follicle, the theca interna cells providing only the supporting tissue. Such luteal tissue has also been found in seven species of viviparous snakes, in the horned toad lizard and in the snapping turtle. The corpora lutea are well vascularized and are maintained throughout gestation, but they degenerate slowly after parturition.

The formation of the corpus luteum both in viviparous and ovoviviparous lizards has been described by a number of authors (Mingazzini, 1893; Lucien, 1903; Hett, 1924; Cunningham and Smart, 1934; Weekes, 1934). A review of the relevant literature is given by Boyd (1941), who made a detailed study of the corpus luteum in *Lacerta vivipara* and in the gecko *Hoplodactylus maculatus*. In these species the follicular epithelium persists after ovulation and forms the main cellular constituent of the corpus luteum. Fibroblasts from the theca interna penetrate between the individual luteal cells and also form septa. Boyd states that the few theca interna cells which are seen to penetrate with the fibroblasts are of little or no functional importance in the corpus luteum. Thecal cells are involved to a greater or lesser extent in other reptiles (see Weekes, 1934; Miller, 1959). In *Hoplodactylus* there is no overgrowth by thecal cells of the rupture point of the follicle such as occurs in most reptiles, and the corpus luteum, as in a number of other viviparous lizards (Weekes, 1934), remains avascular. Also in this species, the luteal cells develop lipid-filled vacuoles in the pregnant female and the vacuolation steadily increases in amount during gestation.

It has been claimed that true corpora lutea are developed in the ovaries of the viviparous toad, *Nectophrynoides occidentalis*, after the release of eggs into the oviducts. The structures are formed by the thickening of the thecal layer and the occlusion of the cavity by follicle cells (Lamotte and Rey, 1954). They are thought to be concerned in the maintenance of gestation (Gallien, 1959), but no experimental studies have been made to confirm this conclusion. The occurrence of short-lived corpora lutea has also been described in the newt, *Taricha torosa* (Miller, 1955; see also Gallien, 1959).

REFERENCES

Alexander, S. S. and Bellerby, C. W. (1938). Experimental studies on the sexual cycle of the South African clawed toad (*Xenopus laevis*). *J. exp. Biol.* **15**, 74–81.

Allende, I. C. L. de. (1939). Cycle sexuel du crapaud *Bufo arenarum* femelle. *C.R. Soc. Biol., Paris*, **130**, 676–679.

Arai, H. (1920). On the postnatal development of the ovary (albino rat), with especial reference to the number of ova. *Amer. J. Anat.* **27**, 405–462.

Aronson, L. R. and Holz-Tucker, A. M. (1949). Ovulation in the mouth-breeding cichlid fish, *Tilapia macrocephala* (Bleeker). *Anat. Rec.* **105**, 568–569.

Benoit, J. (1923). A propos du changement expérimental de sexe par ovariotomie, chez la poule. *C.R. Soc. Biol., Paris*, **89**, 1326–1328.

Benoit, J. (1950). Organes uro-génitaux. *In* "Traité de Zoologie" (P.-P. Grassé, ed.), Vol. XV, p. 341–377. Masson, Paris.

Boyd, M. M. M. (1941). The structure of the ovary and the formation of the corpus luteum in *Hoplodactylus maculatus* Gray. *Quart. J. micr. Sci.* **82**, 337–376.

Bragdon, D. E. (1946). Follicular atresia in ovoviviparous snakes. *Anat. Rec.* **96**, 542–543.

Brambell, F. W. R. (1930). "The Development of Sex in Vertebrates." Sidgwick and Jackson, London.

Brambell, F. W. R. (1956). Ovarian changes. *In* "Marshall's Physiology of Reproduction" (A. S. Parkes, ed.), 3rd ed. Vol. I, Pt. I, p. 397–542. Longmans, Green and Co., London.

Brambell, F. W. R. and Marrian, G. F. (1929). Sex reversal in a pigeon (*Columba livia*). *Proc. roy. Soc.* B. **104**, 459–470.

Breneman, W. R. (1955). Reproduction in birds: the female. *In* "Comparative Physiology of Reproduction" (I. Chester Jones and P. Eckstein, eds.). *Mem. Soc. Endocrin.* No. 4, 94–113.

Brode, M. D. (1928). The significance of the asymmetry of the ovaries of the fowl. *J. Morph.* **46**, 1–57.

Bullough, W. S. (1939). A study of the reproductive cycle of the minnow in relation to the environment. *Proc. zool. Soc. Lond.* A. **109**, 79–102.

Chieffi, G. (1949). Ricerche sul differenziamento dei sessi negli embrioni di *Torpedo ocellata*. *Pubbl. Staz. zool. Napoli*, **22**, 57–78.

Chieffi, G. (1955). Sull'origine dell'asimmetria dell'ovario negli embrioni di *Scylliorhinus canicula*. *Monit. zool. ital.* **63**, 31–41.

Chieffi, G. (1959). Sex differentiation and experimental sex reversal in elasmobranchs. *Arch. Anat. micr. Morph. exp.* **48**, 21–36.

Cole, F. J. (1905). Notes on Myxine. I. *Anat. Anz.* **27**, 323–326.

"Comparative Endocrinology" (1959). (A. Gorbman, ed.). John Wiley and Sons, Inc., New York.

"Comparative Physiology of Reproduction" (1955). (I. Chester Jones and P. Eckstein, eds.). *Mem. Soc. Endocrin.* No. 4, Cambridge University Press.

Conel, J. le Roy. (1917). The urogenital system of Myxinoids. *J. Morph.* **29**, 75–163.

Craig-Bennett, A. (1930). The reproductive cycle of the three-spined stickleback, *Gasterosteus aculeatus*, Linn. *Phil. Trans.* B. **219**, 197–281.

Crew, F. A. E. (1923). Studies in intersexuality. II. Sex-reversal in the fowl. *Proc. roy. Soc.* B. **95**, 256–278.

Cunningham, J. T. (1886). On the structure and development of the reproductive elements in *Myxine glutinosa*, L. *Quart. J. micr. Sci.* **27**, 49–76.

Cunningham, J. T. and Smart, W. A. M. (1934). The structure and origin of the corpora lutea in some of the lower vertebrata. *Proc. roy. Soc.* B. **116**, 258–281.

D'Ancona, U. (1949). Ermafroditismo e intersessualità nei Teleostei. *Experientia*, **5**, 381–389.

D'Ancona, U. (1951). Détermination et différenciation du sexe chez les poissons. *In* "Colloque sur la Différenciation Sexuelle chez les Vertébrés", p. 92–112. Centre national de la recherche scientifique, Paris.

D'Ancona, U. (1955). Osservazioni sulle gonadi giovanili di *Amia calva*. *Arch. ital. Anat. Embriol.* **60**, 184–200.

Davis, D. E. (1942). Regression of the avian post-ovulatory follicle. *Anat. Rec.* **82**, 297–307.

Domm, L. V. (1924). Sex-reversal following ovariotomy in the fowl. *Proc. soc. exp. Biol.*, *N.Y.* **22**, 28–28.

Domm, L. V. (1939). Modifications in sex and secondary sexual characters in birds. *In* "Sex and Internal Secretions" (E. Allen, ed.), p. 227–327. Baillière, Tindall and Cox, London.

Flynn, T. T. and Hill, J. P. (1939). The development of the Monotremata. IV: Growth of the ovarian ovum, maturation, fertilisation and early cleavage. *Trans. zool. Soc. Lond.* **24**, 445–622.

Foote, C. L. and Witschi, E. (1939). Effect of sex hormones on the gonads of frog larvae (*Rana clamitans*): Sex inversion in females; stability in males. *Anat. Rec.* **75**, 75–83.

Forbes, T. R. (1940). Studies on the reproductive system of the alligator. IV. Observations on the development of the gonad, the adrenal cortex and the Müllerian duct. *Contr. Embryol. Carneg. Instn.* **28**, 129–156.

Fraser, E. A. and Renton, R. M. (1940). Observations on the breeding and development of the viviparous fish, *Heterandria formosa*. *Quart. J. micr. Sci.* **81**, 479–520.

Gallien, L. (1955). The action of sex hormones on the development of sex in Amphibia. *In* "Comparative Physiology of Reproduction" (I. Chester Jones and P. Eckstein, eds.), *Mem. Soc. Endocrin.* No. 4, 188–204.

Gallien, L. (1959). Endocrine basis for reproductive adaptations in Amphibia. *In* "Comparative Endocrinology" (A. Gorbman, ed.), p. 479–487. John Wiley and Sons, Inc., New York.

Goodrich, H. B., Dee, J. E., Flynn, C. M. and Mercer, R. M. (1934). Germ cells and sex differentiation in *Lebistes reticulatus*. *Biol. Bull.*, *Wood's Hole*, **67**, 83–96.

Hammond, J. and Wodzicki, K. (1941). Anatomical and histological changes during the oestrous cycle in the mare. *Proc. roy. Soc. B.* **130**, 1–23.

Harrison, R. J. (1948). The development and fate of the corpus luteum in the vertebrate series. *Biol. Rev.* **23**, 296–331.

Hett, J. (1923). Das Corpus luteum der Dohle. *Arch. mikr. Anat.* **97**, 718–838.

Hett, J. (1924). Das Corpus luteum der Zauneidechse (*Lacerta agilis*). *Z. mikr.-anat. Forsch.* **1**, 41–48.

Hisaw, F. L. (1959). Endocrine adaptations of the mammalian estrous cycle and gestation. *In* "Comparative Endocrinology" (A. Gorbman, ed.), p. 533–552. John Wiley and Sons, Inc., New York.

Hisaw, F. L. Jr. and Hisaw, F. L. (1959). Corpora lutea of elasmobranch fishes. *Anat. Rec.* **135**, 269–277.

Hoar, W. S. (1955). Reproduction in teleost fish. *In* "Comparative Physiology of Reproduction" (I. Chester Jones and P. Eckstein, eds.). *Mem. Soc. Endocrin.* No. 4, 5–24.

Humphrey, R. R. (1929). Studies on sex reversal in *Amblystoma*. I. Bisexuality and sex reversal in larval males uninfluenced by ovarian hormones. *Anat. Rec.* **49**, 119–155.

Jordan, E. O. (1893). The habits and development of the newt (*Diemyctylus viridescens*). *J. Morph.* **8**, 269–366.

Kornfeld, W. (1960). Experimentally induced proliferation of the rudimentary gonad of an intact domestic fowl. *Nature, Lond.* **185**, 320.

Lamotte, M. and Rey, P. (1954). Existence de *corpora lutea* chez un Batracien anoure vivipare, *Nectophrynoides occidentalis* Angel; leur évolution morphologique. *C.R. Acad. Sci., Paris*, **238**, 393–395.

Latta, J. S. and Pederson, E. S. (1944). The origin of ova and follicle cells from the germinal epithelium of the ovary of the albino rat as demonstrated by selective intravital staining with India ink. *Anat. Rec.* **90**, 23–35.

Loukine, A. V. (1941). Les stades de maturité sexuelle du sterlet. *C.R. Acad. Sci., U.R.S.S.* **32**, 374–376.

Lucien, M. (1903). Note préliminaire sur les premières phases de la formation des corps jaunes chez certain reptiles. *C.R. Soc. Biol., Paris*, **55**, 1116–1117.

Mandl, A. M. and Zuckerman, S. (1950). The numbers of normal and atretic ova in the mature rat. *J. Endocrin.* **6**, 426–435.

March, F. (1937). Relative growth in Amphibia. *Proc. zool. Soc. Lond.* A. **107**, 415–469.

Matthews, L. H. (1937). The female sexual cycle in the British horseshoe bats, *Rhinolophus ferrum-equinum insulanus* Barrett-Hamilton and *R. hipposideros minutus* Montagu. *Trans. zool. Soc. Lond.* **23**, 224–255.

Matthews, L. H. (1950). Reproduction in the basking shark, *Cetorhinus maximus* (Gunner). *Phil. Trans.* B. **234**, 247–316.

Matthews, L. H. (1955). The evolution of viviparity in vertebrates. *In* "Comparative Physiology of Reproduction" (I. Chester Jones and P. Eckstein, eds.), *Mem. Soc. Endocrin.* No. 4, 129–148.

Matthews, L. H. and Marshall, F. H. A. (1956). Cyclical changes in the reproductive organs of the lower vertebrates. *In* "Marshall's Physiology of Reproduction" (A. S. Parkes, ed.), 3rd ed., Vol. I, Pt. I, p. 156–225. Longmans, Green and Co., London.

Matthews, S. A. (1938). The seasonal cycle in the gonads of *Fundulus*. *Biol. Bull., Wood's Hole*, **75**, 66–74.

Mendoza, G. (1940). The reproductive cycle of the viviparous teleost, *Neotoca bilineata*, a member of the family Goodeidae. II. The cyclical changes in the ovarian soma during gestation. *Biol. Bull., Wood's Hole*, **78**, 349–365.

Miller, M. R. (1955). In discussion to Hoar (1955), q.v.

Miller, M. R. (1959). The endocrine basis for reproductive adaptations in reptiles. *In* "Comparative Endocrinology" (A. Gorbman, ed.), p. 499–516. John Wiley and Sons, Inc., New York.

Mingazzini, P. (1893). Corpi lutei veri e falsi dei rettili. *Ric. Lab. Anat. norm. Univ. Roma*, **3**, 105–126.

Moltchanova, I. (1941). La structure histologique des oeufs des sterlets aux stades différents de maturité sexuelle. *C.R. Acad. Sci., U.R.S.S.* **32**, 163–165.

Nalbandov, A. V. and James, M. F. (1949). The blood-vascular system of the chicken ovary. *Amer. J. Anat.* **85**, 347–377.

Nelsen, O. E. (1953). "Comparative Embryology of the Vertebrates", chap. 2. The Blakiston Company Inc., New York.

Okkelberg, P. (1921). The early history of the germ cells in the brook lamprey *Entosphenus wilderi* (Gage), up to and including the period of sexual differentiation. *J. Morph.* **35**, 1–151.

Oordt, G. J. van (1933). Zur Sexualität der Gattung *Epinephelus* (Serranidae, Teleostei). *Z. mikr.-anat. Forsch.* **33**, 525–533.

Pearl, R. and Boring, A. M. (1918). Sex studies, X: The corpus luteum in the ovary of the domestic fowl. *Amer. J. Anat.* **23**, 1–35.

Rahn, H. (1938). The corpus luteum of reptiles. *Anat. Rec.* **72**, Suppl. p. 55.

Robinson, E. J. and Rugh, R. (1943). The reproductive processes of the fish *Oryzias latipes*. *Biol. Bull., Wood's Hole*, **84**, 115–125.

Romanoff, A. L. and Romanoff, A. J. (1949). "The Avian Egg." John Wiley and Sons, Inc., New York.

Schreiner, K. E. (1904). Über das Generationsorgan von *Myxine glutinosa* (L.). *Biol. Zbl.* **24**, 91–104; 121–129; 162–173. (Cited by Conel, 1917).

Schreiner, K. E. (1955). Studies on the gonad of *Myxine glutinosa* L. *Univ. Bergen Arb. Naturv. R.* **8**, 1–36.

Smith, C. L. (1955). Reproduction in female Amphibia. *In* "Comparative Physiology of Reproduction" (I. Chester Jones and P. Eckstein, eds.), *Mem. Soc. Endocrin.* No. 4, 39–56.

Stanley, A. J. and Witschi, E. (1940). Germ cell migration in relation to asymmetry in the sex glands of hawks. *Anat. Rec.* **76**, 329–342.

Sturkie, P. D. (1954). "Avian Physiology." Comstock Publishing Assoc., New York.

Turner, C. L. (1938). Histological and cytological changes in the ovary of *Cymatogaster aggregatus* during gestation. *J. Morph.* **62**, 351–373.

Weekes, H. C. (1934). The corpus luteum in certain oviparous and viviparous reptiles. *Proc. Linn. Soc., N.S.W.* **59**, 380–391.

Witschi, E. (1939). Modification of the development of sex in lower vertebrates and in mammals. *In* "Sex and Internal Secretions" (E. Allen, ed.), p. 145–226. Baillière, Tindall and Cox, London.

Witschi, E. (1956). "Development of Vertebrates." W. B. Saunders and Co., Philadelphia.

Yocom, H. B. (1924). Luteal cells in the gonad of the phalarope. *Biol. Bull., Wood's Hole*, **46**, 101–105.

CHAPTER 2

THE STRUCTURE OF THE OVARY
C. Mammals

R. J. HARRISON

I. General

The mammalian ovaries are paired organs, approximately equal in size (apart from functional changes), except in the duckbill (*Ornithorhynchus*) in which the right ovary is atrophied and in certain bats (e.g. Vespertilionidae) in which the left one shows atrophy. They are found within the abdominal or pelvic cavity as far cranial as the lower pole of the kidney (duckbill) and as caudal as the true pelvis (*Homo*); ectopic ovaries may be present in the inguinal canal. The organs are attached by a mesentery (mesovarium) to the dorsal aspect of the broad ligament, the medial and lateral edges of which may be condensed as suspensory or infundibulo-pelvic 'ligaments'. The ovarian vessels pass to the organ through the mesovarium, and anastomoses between them and uterine vessels may occur at its base; the ovarian arteries are spiral (Reynolds, 1950).

The ovaries may be enclosed in a peritoneal capsule or ovarian bursa which varies considerably in development and in the extent to which it communicates with the coelomic cavity (Insectivora, Chiroptera, Carnivora, Rodentia). There is a periovarian space between the ovary and the peritoneal lining of the bursa which may become distended with fluid of unknown origin (e.g. in carnivores). The periovarian space is closed in species like the weasel, otter and shrew, but communicates with the peritoneal cavity by a narrow passage, which allows interchange of fluid in the rat and mouse (Alden, 1942; Wimsatt and Waldo, 1945) as well as in dogs, bears and several other carnivores (cf. Kellogg, 1941). A wide capsule communicating freely with the abdominal cavity is present in the cat, hyaena, guinea pig, mole, pig, ewe and rabbit. In catarrhine and lower primates the bursa is of variable depth and wholly or partially encloses the ovary; in catarrhine monkeys it is generally represented by a 'peritoneal recess'. The bursa is very poorly developed in the mare and man, and is completely absent in whales (see Kellogg, 1941; Eckstein and Zuckerman, 1956). In the mare the bursa is a cleft-like structure which conceals the 'ovulation fossa' (see below); it is probably the result of a closer attachment of the fimbriated end of the uterine tube to ovarian tissue than occurs in other mammals. In the dugong (Sirenia) the ovaries are hidden in pouches in the dorsal abdominal wall (Hill, 1945).

In many mammals the quiescent ovary is a small flattened ovoid or spherical organ, compact in structure and with a relatively smooth surface. At the onset of the breeding season the organ begins to swell owing to the growth of follicles, and mound-like protrusions appear on its surface as the follicles mature. A grape-like appearance may be assumed by the ovary in animals in which multiple ovulation is the rule (e.g. the sow); in others, such as the horse, sheep, and primates, the regular outline of the organ is only locally disturbed (for instance, by a large corpus luteum or Graafian follicle).

The adult ovary is covered by a so-called 'germinal' epithelium beneath which lies a connective tissue tunica albuginea of varying thickness. It contains the follicular apparatus, stromal and connective tissue, interstitial tissue to a very varying degree, and vascular and lymphatic elements. The following pages briefly review the chief characteristics of these components of the ovary in mammals (see also Eckstein and Zuckerman, 1956; Brambell, 1956; Watzka, 1957). The subject of atresia is considered in Chapter 4.

II. The 'germinal' or covering epithelium

All mammalian ovaries are covered by a continuous sheet, usually single layered, of cuboidal or low columnar epithelium. This covering or *'germinal' epithelium* is supported on a distinct basement membrane and invests the contours of the ovary whether smooth or lobulated.

It is only disrupted when follicles rupture at ovulation; repair occurs over the stigmata within 2 to 4 days. Mitoses are alleged to be seen in the epithelial cells at oestrus. Bullough (1946) suggested that these are the result of oestrogenic stimulation, but Zuckerman (1951) believes they merely reflect a response to an increase in ovarian volume with follicular development. Stein and Allen (1942), however, injected oestrone into the periovarian space of normal young mice and hypophysectomized adults. They counted mitoses in the germinal epithelium, after colchicine treatment, and found more in treated than control animals. It could nevertheless still be argued that the oestrogen caused overall ovarian hypertrophy and that mitotic activity in the epithelium is still secondary to ovarian enlargement. The role of the germinal epithelium during development of the ovary is discussed in Chapter 1, sect. I.

The covering epithelium is often invaginated into the subjacent *tunica albuginea* to form small folds, pits or sub-surface crypts (Harrison and Matthews, 1951). These formations are particularly developed in Pinnipedia (Harrison *et al.*, 1952; Laws, 1956) and Proboscidea (Perry, 1953). These authors found a periodic increase in the number and extent of the surface crypts possibly associated with the oestrous cycle, although the nature of the relationship is obscure. In some carnivores the crypts lead to islands of granulosa-like cells, resembling anovular follicles, lying deep to the tunica albuginea. Neal and Harrison (1958) describe an extensive intra-ovarian system of tubules in the badger (*Meles*) that appears to be continuous with well-developed surface invaginations lined by covering epithelium. The significance of crypts and their connections with intra-ovarian tubules is difficult to assess. Mossman (1938) has pointed out that follicular epithelium is to be regarded as modified coelomic epithelium and follicular antra as isolated portions of peritoneal cavity filled with somewhat modified peritoneal fluid. The intra-ovarian crypts may represent a vestige of a primitive pattern of ovarian structure (Harrison and Matthews, 1951; see also Chapter 2B, above), or else their development may reflect a natural propensity of the covering epithelium to contribute epithelial elements to the cortical region that, in some forms, is continued into adult life.

In the horse the originally complete covering of germinal epithelium becomes modified soon after birth and in the mature mare is restricted to a narrow groove known as the *ovulation fossa*, the remainder of the surface being covered by serosa (Küpfer, 1928; Hammond and Wodzicki, 1941). The follicles are distributed throughout the substance of the bean-shaped ovary, but Graafian follicles rupture only into the ovulation fossa.

III. The characteristics of the ovarian follicle in mammals

Primordial follicles consist of a single layer of flattened epithelial cells surrounding each oocyte. They lack a connective tissue or thecal investment. They may be as small as $16 \cdot 5\mu$ in diameter in mice (Brambell, 1928) but are usually somewhat larger. They may form a pronounced peripheral zone throughout the cortex, as in the rabbit and cat, but can be more widely distributed, or even more numerous near the hilus of the ovary.

Rarely, a primordial follicle may contain more than one oocyte (see Hartman, 1926). Such polyovular follicles are more common in foetal or immature ovaries, but have been described in a wide variety of mammals, including man (see Brambell, 1956, for references). They are frequently found in the opossum, in which a record number of 100 oocytes was found in a single follicle by Hartman. It has been suggested that they result either from division of an original single oocyte or from coalescence of adjacent primordial follicles. More probably, however, they result from failure of groups of germ cells to become separated by intervention of epithelial and connective elements. There is so far only one record of polyovular follicles (except perhaps in marsupials) reaching maturity and rupturing (Allen *et al.*, 1947); the majority invariably undergo atresia or else all but one of the oocytes die. Kent (1959) was able to demonstrate a reduction in the incidence of polyovular follicles and polynuclear ova to 17—18 per cent of the control values after treatment of young female golden hamsters with oestradiol monobenzoate. He suggests that the results are due to alleviation of an oestrogen deficiency in the young animal.

The follicles sink gradually deeper into the cortex of the ovary as they increase in size. The single layer of flattened cells enveloping the oocyte increases in thickness and its cells become cuboidal or columnar to form a distinct *membrana granulosa*. The layer rapidly becomes several cells thick. Robinson (1918) thought that the young granulosa cells had indistinct plasma membranes and might form a syncytium, but this has not been confirmed. The enlargement of the granulosa layer is soon accompanied by the development of an outer encapsulating sheath derived from the stroma. This constitutes the theca, later to become divided into a glandular, well vascularized inner layer, the *theca interna*, and an outer one, or *theca externa*, composed of connective tissue. The latter may contain smooth muscle fibres, although Claesson (1947) found none in a number of mammalian types; it usually lacks elastic fibres (Corner, 1932). Numerous blood vessels and lymphatics penetrate the theca externa to communicate with a fine plexus of vessels in the theca interna. The granulosa layer is avascular until after ovulation. A thin membrana propria separates it from the theca interna. According to Solomons and Gatenby (1924) it is formed from the theca interna, but some regard it as two-layered, each component attached to, and perhaps formed by, the adjacent cellular layer (Robinson, 1918).

Mossman (1938) has discussed the homology of ovarian follicles with the coelom, and concluded that follicles are not direct outpouchings of the coelom but develop secondarily to meet specialized conditions associated with ovulation of very small ova.

The follicle enlarges as a result of proliferation of granulosa and thecal layers and, in the majority of mammals (except the Centetidae), one or more cavities soon form in the granulosa. The cavities enlarge, coalesce into an antrum and the fluid-filled follicle becomes surrounded by a remarkably uniform wall, except at the point of attachment of the oocyte. Here the oocyte is surrounded by an irregular cluster of granulosa cells destined to become the *corona radiata*, the whole conglomerate being attached to cells forming the discus proligerus or *cumulus oöphorus*. Each of these features will now be considered in some detail.

The germinal epithelium phagocytoses dye-stuff and India ink particles. Latta and Pederson (1944) tried to label the cells of the epithelium in this way and, following such treatment, observed ink particles in follicle cells and even in oocytes. Jones (1949) was unable, however, to find any particles in oocytes five or more cycles after the start of a similar experiment. Other investigations of the adult germinal epithelium in grafted ovarian tissue, after its destruction by salicylic acid and other corrosives, and after exposure to X-irradiation are reviewed in Chapters 1 and 22.

A. The membrana granulosa

The granulosa cells of multi-layered follicles are small, polygonal or cuboidal, with granular cytoplasm and densely stained nuclei. The antrum appears after the first phase of follicular growth (see p. 152) has ended; the follicle is then less than 400μ in large mammals and about 150μ to 200μ in small mammals (except in the Centetidae, see p. 148). The antrum is sometimes lined at its periphery by an internal limiting membrane that has been considered to have arisen either as a condensation of the antral, or follicular, fluid containing cellular debris (Robinson, 1918), or from the inner granulosa cells, or else from invading theca interna cells (Brambell, 1956).

Mitoses occur frequently in the granulosa cells during follicular growth (Robinson, 1918), particularly when the antrum develops (Bullough, 1942). Lane and Davis (1939) have measured the changes in volume of the granulosa and the number of mitoses therein during the oestrous cycle.

Caldwell (1887) was probably the first to observe that the follicles of monotremes contain a fluid (called pro-albumen by him) around the oocyte. The amount of fluid is small because the large oocyte of monotremes almost fills the follicle; in *Echidna* and *Ornithorhynchus* the fluid completely surrounds the oocyte (Flynn and Hill, 1939). Small follicles have an epithelium of a single layer of cubical cells; later it rapidly thickens (Hill and Gatenby, 1926; Garde, 1930). There follows a phase, when the oocyte increases from 1·0 to 2·0 mm in diameter, during which the follicular epithelium decreases in thickness. During the final phases of oocyte growth the follicular epithelium becomes further thickened (up to 30μ across) and is relatively thicker than in mature follicles of Sauropsida. Mature follicles measure about 4·75 mm in diameter and the wall consists of large polyhedral cells with oval nuclei. The theca interna differentiates, when the follicle is about 0·75 mm in diameter, from the stromal cells of the primitive theca. It consists of several layers of small cells with small oval nuclei and vacuolated cytoplasm.

Several authors have studied the growth changes in the follicles of bats (Guthrie and Jeffers, 1938a, b; Wimsatt, 1944; Guthrie *et al.*, 1951; Sluiter and Bels, 1951).

The formation of the antrum in *Myotis* is foreshadowed by accumulation of a watery secretion within and between granulosa cells. There is pronounced hypertrophy of the granulosa and a reduction in intrafollicular tension which results in disappearance of the antrum just before ovulation. A unique specialization has been described in the follicles of hibernating vespertilionid bats which may provide a source of energy to facilitate the long survival of the follicle during hibernation with reduced body metabolism (Wimsatt and Kallen, 1957). Marked hypertrophy and vesiculation is present in the granulosa cells of the discus proligerus, and enormous quantities of glycogen accumulate.

Ripe follicles of *Corynorhinus rafinesquei* differ from those of most other mammals in the relative smallness of the antrum and in enormous 'balls' of cumulus cells surrounding the ovum (Pearson *et al.*, 1952). The authors suggest that 'secretions' of the follicle cells are retained and not released into the antral fluid.

There is no true antrum in the follicles of certain insectivores such as *Hemicentetes* and *Ericulus* (Landau, 1938; Strauss, 1938a). The granulosa cells swell and prevent formation of an antrum; later they become loosened to form a sponge-like arrangement. The theca also shows some loosening towards maturity. Niklaus (1950) has described changes in the size of the nuclei of granulosa cells in *Ericulus*.

Marked folding occurs in the granulosa layer of the mature follicles of *Vulpes fulva* (Pearson and Enders, 1943) and in the bitch (Evans and Cole, 1931; Mulligan, 1942). Each complicated fold of mural granulosa projects into the antrum and contains delicate connective tissue and blood vessels from the thecal plexus. Accessory granulosa cells, have been described in the follicular wall in kittens (Wotton and Village, 1951). They have long processes that make contact with the zona pellucida and may provide nutriment to the oocyte.

Growth changes in the granulosa of rats have been described by Deane (1952) and in hamsters by Knigge and Leathem (1956). Deane also gives details of the cytological characteristics of the granulosa cells, and the last named authors state that modified granulosa cells of pre-antrum follicles are the source of interstitial tissue in the hamster ovary. Numerous references to granulosa cells are to be found in the literature; many of these are quoted in the section on the histogenesis of the corpus luteum (p. 159) and should be consulted for their details in different forms.

Small cavities, first described by Call and Exner in 1875 in rabbit follicles, are sometimes seen in the granulosa either before or after antrum formation. They have been seen also in human follicles and those of prairie dogs, cats and whales. They have a diameter of about 30 to 50μ and contain a reticulated coagulum; sometimes a fine membrane surrounds the contents and the granulosa cells are radially arranged outside it. These cavities may either be formed from degeneration and "liquefaction of a central cell or cells, or they form as the result of secretory activity of the surrounding cells" (Brambell, 1956). It is possible, however, to suck granulosa cells from mature follicles of rabbits with a fine pipette. When cultured in a fluid medium the granulosa cells tend to grow into hollow spheres with a diameter of $50–100\mu$ (Goldby and Harrison, 1961).

The cluster of granulosa cells that surround the oocyte show evidence of dispersion at the periphery as the follicle nears maturity. Some cells show signs of degeneration (Robinson, 1918). The inner cells become columnar, radially arranged with their nuclei situated peripherally, and form the corona radiata. This appears to be present in the majority of mammals; it usually persists after ovulation until fertilization (p. 150). A corona is not formed, however, in some marsupials (Hill, 1910; Hartman, 1932b; Martínez-Esteve, 1942). The oocyte also lacks a corona at ovulation in *Ericulus* and *Elephantulus* (Strauss, 1938a; van der Horst and Gillman, 1942). The granulosa cumulus cells at the site of attachment of the oocyte to the follicle wall may form a broad-based mound or a slender stalk. The position of the cumulus on the follicle wall is generally held to be quite fortuitous (Brambell, 1956), but some consider that it lies just before ovulation in a specific position relative to the impending site of rupture. The author has found no support for Shaw's (1927) opinion that the cumulus moves round the follicle wall as ovulation approaches and as a result of some intrinsic movement in the granulosa layer.

Early in follicular development the immature oocytes are in contact with the granulosa cells. Later a jelly-like substance containing polysaccharides (Braden, 1952) appears between the plasma membrane of the oocyte and the granulosa cells. This jelly will eventually constitute the *zona pellucida* (see p. 152). Recently, Sotelo and Porter (1959) and Franchi (1960) have described long processes passing from the granulosa cells of rat follicles through the zona pellucida to mingle with the projections from the oocyte. The two sets of processes were observed to be in contact in places, but no evidence of fusion, as claimed by Kemp (1958) and Moricard (1958), was seen in electron micrographs. Both types of processes are withdrawn from the zona during maturation and fertilization. Trujillo-Cenóz and Sotelo (1959) have made similar observations in rabbit follicles and present evidence that the amorphous material of the zona pellucida is elaborated in the cytoplasm of follicle cells and later extruded into the zonal layer. Shettles (1957) describes processes of the corona radiata in living human ova that pass through the zona and enable granular fluid to be emptied into the perivitelline space.

The *follicular fluid* (or liquor folliculi) is not of consistent appearance throughout follicular growth: Robinson (1918) recognized three different kinds. A primary liquor is said to be formed by the granulosa cells to give rise to the antrum. It is secreted between them and exudes into the coalescing central cavities; it exhibits a marked reticulum. Secondary liquor is probably less viscous, and is secreted rapidly just before ovulation, possibly in the region of the cumulus. Follicular growth at this time is very rapid (Hill et al., 1935; Myers et al., 1936; Boling et al., 1941). Burr and Davies (1951) consider that secondary liquor is a transudate from blood. Tertiary liquor is formed after ovulation and plugs the cavity of the ruptured follicle. Umbaugh (1949) states that immediately after ovulation in the cow there is first an oozing of serous fluid, then a discharge of viscous, mucoid material (see also McKenzie and Terrill, 1937, concerning the ewe). Schochet (1916) concluded that follicular fluid contained proteolytic enzymes, but this has not been confirmed. Follicular fluid does possess slight thromboplastic activity (von Kaulla and Shettles, 1956). Radioactive iodine, ^{131}I, ^{131}I-γ-globulin, ^{203}Hg–mercaptomerin and ^{14}C–meprobamate pass from the blood stream into human follicular fluid (von Kaulla et al., 1958) and may be concentrated there. This property may be particularly significant if possessed by substances with mutagenic, enzyme-blocking, or radiomimetic effects. The proteins of follicular fluid have been found to be similar to those of the blood plasma (Caravaglios and Cilotti, 1957). Radioactive sulphur, as sulphate, is incorporated in the follicular mucopolysaccharide of the rabbit ovary and is transferred from granulosa cells to the follicular fluid (Zachariae, 1957).

Anovular follicles, apparently normal in structure except for the lack of an oocyte, have been described in many mammals (League and Hartman, 1925; Davis and Hall, 1950; Harrison and Matthews, 1951; Brambell, 1956). These structures do not reach maturity and seldom develop an antrum. They may have epithelial connections with the germinal epithelium, and Brambell considers that they may well be homologous with medullary cords such as described by Wilcox and Mossman (1945) in ovaries of adult shrews.

B. The theca interna

The theca differentiates about the outside of the granulosa from the surrounding stromal tissue: it is said to be induced by the growing granulosa (Dubreuil, 1957). At first it forms a concentric sheath of compressed cells; later, at the time of antrum formation, it differentiates into theca interna and theca externa (p. 146). The theca interna cells rapidly enlarge and assume a polygonal shape with vacuolated cytoplasm and vesicular nuclei. They are enmeshed in a reticular and fibrous network and the layer contains a plexus of capillaries and numerous lymphatics. The degree of development of the theca interna varies in different placental mammals, but it is always maximal just before ovulation. Mossman (1937) considered that the hypertrophied theca interna in *Geomys* near ovulation resembled an endocrine gland and called it the *thecal gland*. Similar hypertrophy of the theca interna during oestrus has been described in other mammals (Stafford et al., 1942; Harrison, 1948a, b), and Dempsey and Bassett (1943) and Deane (1952) give details of the theca interna in rats and consider it a site of steroid formation. Nishizuka (1954) states that its cells produce oestrogens. Solomons and Gatenby (1924) describe the theca interna cells of human follicles as large, stellate cells. McKay and Robinson (1947) also describe their characteristics in human ovaries and White et al. (1951) consider that a second type of cell can be distinguished in mature follicles. It has a small, dense, irregular, hyperchromatic nucleus and strikingly eosinophil cytoplasm. The authors call it a 'K cell'; its possible significance is discussed later on, p. 173. Culiner (1946) has considered the role of the thecal cell in irregularities of the baboon menstrual cycle and Shippel (1950) has reviewed the functional relationships between thecal and other ovarian cell types.

The theca interna is not always of equal thickness all round the follicle. It may show a hypertrophied region in the form of a cone projecting towards the ovarian surface (Strassman, 1941; Harrison, 1948a). The cone may play a part as a 'pathmaker' for the ascent of the growing follicle to the ovarian surface. The theca interna also thins or disappears at the site of impending rupture in mature follicles and may also be hypertrophied in the region of the cumulus (Brambell, 1956). The permeability of thecal capillaries increases before ovulation in mated rabbits (Christiansen et al., 1958). The ultrastructure and vascular supply of the theca interna and interstitial cells (see p. 155), as revealed by electron microscopy (Belt and Pease, 1956; de Groodt et al., 1957; Moricard, 1958), have recently been studied. The findings confirm the interrelationship of both tissues and indicate their essentially endocrine character (see below and Chapter 6).

The mature follicle of the marsupial Dasyurus lacks a theca interna (O'Donoghue, 1916; Hill and Gatenby, 1926), although it is present in small follicles. There is no differentiation of the theca into a cellular inner layer and a more fibrous external layer in the bats Myotis and Eptesicus (Wimsatt, 1944). The entire theca is composed of fusiform cells, but includes some larger ones that are indistinguishable from interstitial cells.

C. Follicular growth

The growth of the follicle is divided into two phases relative to that of the oocyte (Brambell, 1928, 1956; Parkes, 1931). During the first phase the oocyte grows rapidly until almost adult size, while the follicle increases only slowly in size to a diameter varying from 110μ (lesser shrew) to 300μ (pig). The size of the follicle at the end of the first phase displays only a slight tendency to increase with increasing body size in different mammals. The follicle is a solid sphere or ovoid during the first phase; the theca starts to develop and the zona pellucida is fast forming.

The first phase in at least one mammal has been considered to have two components, an initial one of slow growth of a single-layered follicle followed by a period of faster growth when the follicle is multi-layered (Matthews, 1939).

The follicle grows rapidly in size during the second phase while the oocyte increases only slightly in diameter. If $y =$ the mean diameter of the oocyte and $x =$ that of the follicle, then the two phases of growth can be expressed by the linear regression $y = a + bx$, where a and b are constants. During the second phase the follicle develops an antrum and the theca interna enlarges. The ultimate size of the follicle at the end of the second phase is directly related to body size (Parkes, 1931), and the major part of follicular growth is associated with enlargement of the follicular antrum. These statements hold good for all animals examined which have varied from the mouse to the whale (Parkes, 1931; Dempsey and Wislocki, 1941; Mackintosh, 1946; Guthrie et al., 1951; Knigge and Leathem, 1956; see also Brambell, 1956); in the Centetidae, however, no antrum is formed. By contrast, the diameter of the oocyte shows no such relationship to body size and is remarkably uniform throughout the placental mammals (Hartman, 1929).

The number of follicles which reach the end of the second phase and which ovulate varies widely in different mammals. The number that rupture is not apparently related to body size. Bats, women and elephants are usually monotocous; rodents, insectivores, some large carnivores and ungulates are polytocous. There is, however, a tendency for each species to ovulate approximately the same number of follicles at each oestrus. This holds true even if one, or part of one, ovary is removed (Lipschütz, 1925), and is known as 'the law of follicular constancy' (Lipschütz, 1928). There is a tendency for the number of follicles that rupture at oestrus within a particular species to be proportional to body weight (see Chapter 5, sect. IV, B; also Brambell and Rowlands, 1936; Brambell, 1944). It is probable that the constant number of follicles ovulating at oestrus is under the control of the anterior pituitary.

The granulosa cells of mature follicles of hedgehogs are much enlarged (Deanesly, 1934), and similar changes resembling preovulatory luteinization have been seen in mature follicles of other mammals (Harrison, 1948a, b). Such changes may well be associated with release of luteinizing hormone and could be a source of the progestins that have been detected prior to ovulation (see Chapter 6, sect. II, B and Chapter 7, sect. III, A).

IV. Interstitial cells

Mammalian interstitial cells are large and polyhedral; their nuclei are polychromatic and their cytoplasm contains lipid droplets. They were first described by Pflüger (1863), and the term 'interstitial gland' was applied collectively to them by Bouin (1902), though Tourneux (1879) had earlier noted their similarity to testicular interstitial cells. The cells undergo changes in size and in cytological characteristics during the cycle and in pregnancy. These changes are such as to suggest that they are, at least at some time, secretory elements. Interest in them has recently increased as evidence has been presented that they may secrete both oestrogens and androgens (see p. 154 and Chapter 6, sect. III). It is not yet known whether they pass through a definite

M

cycle of changes ending in degeneration, whether they persist indefinitely, or whether they dedifferentiate into connective tissue elements after their active phase has ceased (see Stafford and Mossman, 1945; Brambell, 1956).

The distribution and relative quantities of interstitial tissue in the ovaries of mammals show striking variations in different groups and even at different times in their lives. The cells are plentiful in certain Insectivora, Chiroptera, Rodentia and Carnivora, but are difficult to find in Cetacea, Artiodactyla, Perissodactyla and Primates. Some authors have divided mammals into groups according to the amount of interstitial tissue discernible, but it is now hardly possible to maintain that interstitial cells are altogether absent at all times from the ovary of any mammal.

Numerous views have been expressed on the origin of interstitial cells and almost every cell type has been implicated (Gillman, 1948). Older histologists were divided into those who supported a connective tissue, stromal or thecal origin, and those who considered that the interstitial cells arose from epithelial elements such as germinal epithelium, medullary cords, mesonephric remnants and granulosa cells (see Chapter 1; also Kingsbury, 1939 and Brambell, 1956 for reviews). A third view was put forward by O'Donoghue (1916) who considered that interstitial tissue in marsupials was composed of a definite cell type in its own right. It displays great variation in marsupials, but is present in pouch-young before any follicular apparatus has appeared. Even so it is only a matter of nomenclature as to whether one states that a cell is derived from mesenchyme or undifferentiated stroma. Other cell types, such as neural crest cells or lymphocytes, have also been implicated as precursors, but these views have received little support. In any event it is now clear that there are at least two generations of interstitial cells in many mammals.

Rennels (1951) and Dawson and McCabe (1951) find that the interstitial tissue of the rat ovary is of dual origin. A *primary* type present during the early juvenile period is closely associated with granulosa outgrowths and ingrowing cords from the germinal epithelium. Dawson and McCabe find that this primary tissue exhibits cytochemical changes suggestive of secretion as early as the 10th day of life. A *secondary* type is formed later from the theca interna of atretic follicles. Mossman (1937) considered that the theca interna of both normal, ruptured and atretic follicles was the only source of secondary interstitial tissue in adult pocket gophers. The primary type, when properly stimulated, produces large amounts of oestrogens and androgens (Rennels, 1951).

The evidence for the production of androgenic substances by ovaries of very young animals and of older ones when submitted to various experimental conditions has been reviewed by Ponse (1948, 1955). Gaarenstroom and De Jongh (1946) have postulated that a testosterone-like substance is produced in rat interstitial tissue and induces formation of antra in growing follicles. Rennels states that the two types of interstitial tissue are remarkably similar and that they may perform the same function. Claesson and Hillarp (1947) have shown that secondary interstitial tissue may well be concerned with oestrogen formation and that it and the theca interna may function independently in the ovary of the rabbit (see also Chapter 6, sect. III).

Interstitial cells of the ovaries of old black mice develop a yellowish-brown pigment which resembles that occurring in brown degeneration of mouse adrenals. This suggests an inability of the ageing cells to metabolize lipids properly (Deane and Fawcett, 1952). A somewhat similar pigment has been described in ageing corpora lutea of the monkey and sow.

The interstitial cells of the ovary of the white rat are not immediately in contact with the endothelial lining of the regional capillaries (De Groodt et al., 1957). Electron micrographs show there is an irregular perivascular subendothelial space similar to that described in many endocrine organs. The authors conclude that this is added evidence for considering the interstitial gland as an actively secreting element.

Cyclical changes in the interstitial tissue have been observed in the mole (Popoff, 1911; Matthews, 1935). During the anoestrous period the ovaries become much hypertrophied and are composed chiefly of interstitial cells and cords of epithelial cells. These occupy one portion of the ovary which is macroscopically distinguishable from another in which follicles and corpora lutea predominate. A constriction separates the two portions externally, and only the latter portion is covered with germinal epithelium. Matthews (1935) considered that the alternating peaks of activity which are shown by the two portions represent a form of intersexuality (cf. also Godet, 1949).

In certain other mammals interstitial cell development is at its maximum in prooestrus and oestrus. Certain bats, the hedgehog, some squirrels, the badger, the woodchuck, the long-tailed weasel, the Canadian porcupine and the pocket gopher (see Rasmussen, 1918; Guthrie and Jeffers, 1938a; Stafford and Mossman, 1945; Neal and Harrison, 1958) show such development.

Patzelt (1955) maintains that wild carnivores (wild cat, fox) exhibit more extensive interstitial cell development than do the domestic cat and dog and show certain characteristics. In the fox these cells also exhibit differences in winter and late spring when they are hypertrophied.

Interstitial cells in adult human ovaries have been demonstrated by several authors (see Brambell, 1956; Watzka, 1957). Bernardo-Comel

(1931) states they are sparsely distributed in the newborn, but are more easily discernible in the ovaries of children (Aschner, 1914).

Several investigators have noted the tendency of interstitial tissue to enlarge as pregnancy advances and even during lactation. In such mammals as bats (Athias, 1920), the water shrew (Price, 1953) and some New World monkeys (Dempsey, 1939; Wislocki, 1939), it becomes difficult to differentiate corpora lutea of pregnancy among the markedly luteinized interstitial tissue. Stafford and Mossman (1945) could not find any easily observable cycle in character or amount of secondary interstitial tissue in the guinea pig ovary that could be correlated with the pregnant state. They observed no degenerative changes in the cells at any stage of pregnancy and considered that they reverted to fibroblasts.

A few mammalian foetuses and neonates display a precocious hypertrophy of what can be considered primary interstitial tissue. This tissue undergoes remarkable enlargement during intra-uterine life in foetal mares (Cole et al., 1933). It appears to become maximally developed after mid-pregnancy and involutes or degenerates near term (Amoroso and Rowlands, 1951). Most foetal Pinnipedia also exhibit a similar hypertrophy of interstitial tissue, but it reaches its maximum at term and degeneration occurs during the subsequent 3 weeks (Amoroso et al., 1951; Harrison et al., 1952). Although the neonatal uterus, prostate and occasionally the utriculus masculinus show evidence of stimulation, the mammary glands do not (Harrison, 1960); abundant gonadal interstitial tissue appears cytochemically relatively inactive. The pituitary of the foetal seal late in pregnancy does, however, display precocious cellular differentiation and activity and may possibly be stimulating primary interstitial cell activity to a prolonged though slight degree.

It should be noted that it was the androgenic activity of *grafted* ovaries of guinea pigs (Lipschütz, 1932), mice (Hill, 1937) and rats (Deanesly, 1938a) that stimulated interest in the potential ambisexual activity of the ovary. All these animals possess relatively large amounts of interstitial tissue. Lipschütz found the grafts to consist eventually of luteinized epithelioid cells; Hill was unable to correlate androgenic activity with any particular cellular element, while Deanesly found it associated with extensive luteinization of the theca interna. As early as 1926, however, Parkes had shown that interstitial tissue in mice survived low doses of X-rays which destroyed all oocytes and follicles. He concluded that interstitial ovarian elements were responsible for the persistence of oestrous cycles that occurred in these animals. There would therefore appear to be impressive morphological, histochemical and experimental evidence to support the statement that interstitial tissue "enhances if it is not essential for" androgenic ovarian activity (Parkes, 1950). Such topics as histochemical characteristics, further evidence for androgenic hormone production, experimental and X-irradiation changes of interstitial tissue are also referred to in Chapters 3, 6 and 22.

V. Hilus cells

Berger (1922) observed certain cells in close relation to non-myelinated nerves and vascular spaces along the length of the human ovarian hilus and the adjacent mesovarium. He called them 'neurotropic cells' and collectively named their cell clusters the 'sympathicotropic hilus gland'. De Winiwarter (1923) and others considered them part of the chromaffin system, but Berger produced convincing evidence that they are similar to testicular Leydig cells. More recently Sternberg (1949) agreed that a point-for-point correspondence with Leydig cells can be demonstrated in terms of nuclear and cytoplasmic detail, lipids, lipochrome pigment and crystalloids of Reinke.

Hilus cells are present at birth and can be seen during the first year of life (Berger, 1945). They are difficult to find before puberty, but then reappear and persist until a decline occurs in old age. They are prominent during pregnancy and at the menopause (Sternberg, 1949). They have the cytochemical appearances of actively secreting cells, and Sternberg has produced some evidence that they are affected by chorionic gonadotrophin. Several authors therefore support the contentions that hilus cells are a characteristic component of the human ovary, that they normally have a secretory function and that they secrete androgens. Tumours and hyperplasia of ovarian hilus cells are associated with masculinization (Berger, 1942; Sternberg, 1949). Verocay (1915) and others (see Sternberg, 1949) have noted cell nests identical with ovarian hilus cells in extra-testicular sites in males. They have precisely the same relationship to non-myelinated nerves. Well-developed clusters of hilus cells are often found in relation to a prominent rete ovarii. The appearances of the rete ovarii, its development, the possibility that it is homologous with the rete testis and the changes that can occur in it are discussed by Sauramo (1954a).

VI. Vascular supply of the mammalian ovary

The main arterial supply to the ovary is from the ovarian artery which arises from the aorta below the level of the renal vessels. It passes to the ovary by the infundibulo-pelvic ligament to enter it at its mesovarian border where anastomoses occur with the uterine artery.

Before entering the ovary it is often thrown into one or more loose coils.

Andersen (1926) states that in the sow each ovarian artery divides into two branches several centimetres before reaching the hilus. At the hilus each artery divides into two to four branches. These are extremely tortuous and anastomosing ovarian veins wind about among their coils. As the arterial branches reach the follicles they break up into many smaller vessels. Most of these supply the large follicles or corpora, but there is also an irregular network throughout the remainder of the stroma. There are occasional small, non-vascular areas marking the fibrous scars of former corpora. There is a narrow non-vascular margin of germinal epithelium and underlying connective tissue, beneath which there is a complete capillary network, interrupted only where follicles or corpora reach the surface.

Primordial follicles have no special arterial supply; but when the follicle acquires an antrum it develops a wreath of capillaries in relation to the theca. When the theca is well developed there is an inner capillary plexus lying close to the outside of the membrana propria within the theca interna. This plexus communicates with an outer one in the theca externa. Venules in the theca externa communicate freely, but arterioles seldom do. No vessels enter the granulosa. A non-vascular area, the macula pellucida, develops on the protruding part of a follicle near rupture. It may be surrounded by a rosette of dilated vessels (Walton and Hammond, 1928; Markee and Hinsey, 1936). Burruano (1934), Bassett (1943) and Burr and Davies (1951) give details of the blood supply of the ovaries of rats, rabbits and other mammals and Clark (1900) gives a detailed account of that of the human ovary.

The superficial and intraparenchymal branches display spiralling in a number of mammals (Andersen, 1926; Bassett, 1943; Reynolds, 1947; Burr and Davies, 1951; Watzka, 1957), though not all vessels are coiled. In women the degree of helical spiralling of the main ovarian artery is not as great or as uniform as in the rabbit (Delson et al., 1949). Increasing degrees of spiralling are present, however, in secondary and tertiary branches; this tendency decreases after the menopause. There is evidence of increased tortuosity of ovarian vessels in foetuses and neonates, possibly as a result of oestrogenic influences in utero: it regresses after birth. Poulhès and Gaubert (1954), Sauramo (1954b) and Martini and Tonetti (1956) describe an increase in tortuosity and other variations in the ovarian arteries as age advances. Clara (1956) reviews the observations on arterio-venous anastomoses in the ovary.

The vascularization of the corpus luteum has been described by many authors. Andersen (1926) and Bassett (1943) have given extensive accounts of the process in the sow and the rat. The papers referred to in the section on the corpus luteum (VII, below) should be consulted for details in other mammals.

The lymphatic supply of the follicle and corpus luteum has been described by Poirier and Charpy (1923) in women, by Andersen (1926) in the sow, and by Wislocki and Dempsey (1939) in the monkey. Burr and Davies (1951) consider that the lymphatics must play a part in the swelling, translucency and hyperaemia that occurs in the rabbit ovary prior to ovulation.

VII. Formation and fate of the corpus luteum

The different views held in the past on the histogenesis of the corpus luteum have been reviewed several times (Marshall, 1910; Corner, 1915, 1919; Pratt, 1935; Harrison, 1948a; Brambell, 1956) and are now only of historical interest. It is generally accepted that in eutherian mammals the granulosa cells become transformed into the luteal cells of the corpus luteum. The fate of the theca interna cells is less clear, and there appear to be species differences as to whether they are incorporated as secretory elements in the corpus or whether they undergo some other fate. There is no doubt, however, that the theca interna cells have important functions before, during and just after ovulation.

A. Monotremata

The corpus luteum in *Ornithorhynchus* attains its full growth and activity during the uterine period of development of the egg (Hill and Gatenby, 1926), and signs of regression can be found as soon as that stage is completed. Three main phases occur during development of the gland.

The first phase extends from just before ovulation to the time when cleavage is completed. The corpus luteum becomes solid throughout and theca interna cells invade the luteinizing granulosa cells. Groups of theca interna cells remain at the periphery of the gland. The cells have a vacuolated cytoplasm, which becomes marked towards the end of the phase. Capillary invasion commences early, but there is no evidence of extensive intra-follicular haemorrhage (Garde, 1930). At the end of the phase a connective tissue reticulum extends throughout the gland believed by Hill and Gatenby to be formed from fibroblasts which have migrated inwards from the theca externa. Solomons and Gatenby (1924) state that the theca interna cells increase mitotically before and after ovulation, but do not hypertrophy like the granulosa cells, and do not become transformed into luteal cells. They do not form true connective tissue, neither do they become spindle-shaped. The second phase, during which the luteal cells reach the height of their cytological development, extends from the completion of cleavage up to the time of the formation of the blastocyst. The luteal cells shrink slightly towards the end of the phase; the theca interna cells have smaller nuclei and cytoplasmic vacuolation is less marked. The third phase covers a final period of retrogression. Even in the early blastocyst stage numbers of degenerating, chromophilic luteal cells are present; later they increase in number. Colloidal and granular degeneration of luteal cells is well advanced by the time the egg is laid, but vacuolation is now less obvious. Theca interna cells are not so distinct, and there is no evidence that they take on fibroblastic activity. Hill and Gatenby state that no lipid or true fat is formed in luteal cells, which is in contra-distinction to the state of affairs in the corpora lutea of eutherian mammals.

B. Marsupialia

Luteal cells in *Dasyurus viverrinus* become fully developed when the blastocysts are 6·5–7 mm in diameter and have reached the uterus. The corpus luteum is fully formed 3 days after ovulation. Sandes (1903) finds it difficult to distinguish between the parts played by the theca interna and externa. The theca interna is not well developed and forms only the vascular connective tissue of the gland. Luteal cells show some degree of vacuolation in the peripheral cytoplasm. The gland remains in its fully developed state until at least 7 weeks after the animal has started lactating. No trace of the corpus luteum remains 4 months after parturition.

The ovum of the opossum *Didelphys virginiana* reaches the uterus more rapidly than in any other mammal, and by this time (24 hours) the corpus luteum has a solid border, but still displays a central cavity (Martínez-Esteve, 1942). The gland is solid by the third and fourth cleavages. Mitotic figures are present in the luteal cells. Theca interna cells do not contribute any glandular elements to the corpus luteum. At parturition the corpus luteum shows early degenerative changes, and large vacuoles are present in the luteal cells. The stage of degeneration is reached several days earlier in pseudopregnancy. When the pouch-young leave the mother at the 3rd month no trace can usually be found of the corpora lutea of pregnancy. It is suggested that functioning corpora lutea have no connection with lactation, and that the corpora do not determine the length of the cycle.

Sharman (1955a, b) has given brief descriptions of the corpus luteum of the cycle of pregnancy and of that formed as a result of post-partum ovulation associated with lactation in *Setonix brachyurus*. He has also shown that the latter may be accompanied by delayed implantation (see Chapter 9, sect. IV, D).

C. Eutheria

1. *Insectivora*

The granulosa cells of the follicle of *Erinaceus europaeus* do not appear to become luteinized after ovulation and are shrunken in comparison with those of the ripe follicle (Deanesly, 1934). On the other hand luteinization of the granulosa commences before ovulation in *Talpa europaea* (Popoff, 1911; Matthews, 1935). Theca interna cells take part in forming the corpus, but their exact distribution is not known. The ovum of the mature follicle in *Blarina brevicauda* is surrounded by layers of granulosa cells whose size and organization cause the follicle to resemble a corpus luteum (Pearson, 1944). The corpus of pregnancy in *Sorex palustris navigator* (Conway, 1952) resembles in its phases of growth that of *Blarina*. The newly-formed corpus of *Neomys sodiens bicolor* (Price, 1953) is about 400 μ in diameter and eventually attains a size of 1mm in diameter. The corpora merge with the luteinizing interstitial tissue at the four- to eight-cell stage and later the whole ovary becomes a mass of luteinized tissue.

The development of the corpus luteum in *Elephantulus myurus* has been investigated by van der Horst and Gillman (1940, 1942, 1946). The corpus starts to develop before ovulation, and the ovum is pushed to the periphery of the follicle by the enlarging, elongated granulosa cells. The theca interna reaches its maximum development just before ovulation, and is mainly restricted to the region furthest from the surface of the developing corpus. After ovulation the theca interna cells form a central core or 'cushion' to the everted corpus luteum, and sometimes a pedicle is formed. The theca interna cells do not become theca-lutein cells and it is suggested that they become endothelial or reticular cells. A capillary network eventually forms throughout the gland, and differs from that found in many other mammals in that it does not enclose individual cells, but divides the luteal tissue into groups of cellular components, thus giving the gland a trabeculated appearance. By the early pre-polyp stage small vacuoles are present in the luteal cytoplasm, but during disintegration of the polyp or menstruation the cytoplasm loses its vacuolation and retrogressive changes commence.

The corpus luteum of pregnancy develops in the same manner as that of menstruation as far as the stage related to the dense stroma and thickened epithelial stage of the endometrium. Three periods in development of the structure can be recognized. The first extends from the time of ovulation until the embryo is 10 mm in length. There is a gradual increase in size of the corpus luteum, due solely to enlargement of individual cells. The second period terminates when the embryo is 20 mm in length, and a large fat vacuole appears and subsequently disappears from every luteal cell. During the third period, which covers the remainder of pregnancy, there is an initial increase in size of the corpus luteum, due to further enlargement of the luteal cells. Thereafter the corpus luteum decreases remarkably in size, degeneration of the luteal cells occurs, and 4 days after parturition a corpus albicans is already formed.

Van der Horst and Gillman suggest that during the second period of luteal development in pregnancy a stage of readjustment occurs. Although ovariectomies have not been performed, the fact that *Elephantulus* is liable to abort during this period tends to support this suggestion. The period of readjustment may be associated with the "stabilization of the placenta, following an extensive destruction of the decidual cells in the uterine wall, and a remarkable modification in the main arterial circulation of the placenta".

No cavity is found in the mature follicle in the Centetidae (Strauss, 1938a, b). The granulosa cells swell before ovulation and occlude the central cavity. Fertilization is said to occur while the ovum is still within the follicle, the sperm having penetrated the theca and spongy granulosa. The theca recedes at the apex of the follicle and the ovum is extruded by a swelling out of the granulosa cells. The latter then become extruded themselves, and an everted fungiform corpus luteum is formed. This is connected to the ovarian stroma by a 'Thecabecher' similar to the thecal core found in *Elephantulus*. Strauss is of the opinion that the theca interna cells form theca-lutein cells at the periphery of the early corpus luteum.

2. *Chiroptera*

The early work of van der Stricht (1901a, b, 1912) on *Nyctalus noctula* and *Plecotus aurita* has not been followed up as fully as the unusual reproductive phenomena present in bats would necessitate. Matthews (1937–8) has described the corpus luteum of the British horseshoe bats, and also some African bats (1941).

Pre-ovulatory hypertrophy of the granulosa cells is found in *Myotis lucifugus* and *Eptesicus fuscus*. Ovulation is not followed by marked folding of the follicular wall. In *Myotis*, unlike *Eptesicus*, a central cavity rarely persists after ovulation, and in most instances the corpus luteum becomes solid even before the first cleavage spindle appears in the tubal ovum. The appearances of progestational reactions in the uteri of some specimens of *Myotis*, which are about to ovulate, suggest that progesterone may be produced in the last stages before follicular rupture (Guthrie and Jeffers, 1938a, b; Wimsatt, 1944; Guthrie *et al.*, 1951). The corpus luteum of *Corynorhinus rafinesquei* reaches its maximum diameter shortly after attachment of the blastocyst (Pearson *et al.*, 1952). Immediately after attachment abundant large vacuoles appear in the corpus and give it a degenerated appearance relatively early in pregnancy. The corpus luteum of *Desmodus rotundus murinus* develops rapidly and is relatively very large, yet no mitotic figures have been observed (Wimsatt and Trapido, 1952).

3. *Carnivora*

(a) *Fissipedia*

The wall of the ruptured follicle of the cat is deeply plicated (Dawson, 1941); the folds also involve the theca interna.

The corpus luteum reaches its maximum size 10–16 days after mating (Dawson and Kosters, 1944). The corpora lutea of pregnancy start to retrogress after 20 days, those of pseudopregnancy after 28 days (Liche, 1939). Van Dyke and Li (1938), however, state that the corpus of pseudopregnancy is no longer active 20 days after ovulation.

There is local hypertrophy of the theca interna cells during oestrus and in the early stages of post-coital activity (Dawson and Friedgood, 1940). Migration of theca interna and endothelial cells into the mural granulosa occurs 48 hours after ovulation, penetrating the wall of the corpus luteum by the end of the 3rd day. The theca interna cells lose their rounded appearance after the 3rd day and resume a fibroblastic form. They migrate between the luteinizing granulosa cells and lay down collagenous tissue. Theca interna cells also remain at the periphery of the gland, but do not develop into theca-lutein cells. Vacuoles disappear from the luteal cells by the 16th day and by the 27th day there is a marked decrease in size of the gland. Luteal cells become highly vacuolated by the 50th day, and this is regarded as evidence of degeneration. These changes in the luteal cells have not been correlated with any functional change. During this period, except from the 15th–17th day, ovariectomy is invariably followed by abortion (Courrier and Gros, 1935, 1936) and thus the corpus luteum is apparently essential for the maintenance of pregnancy during this time.

The corpora lutea of lactating animals are of a bright pink colour and display increased vascularity (Dawson, 1946). The smaller vacuoles in the luteal cells disappear rapidly, but some 'giant' vacuoles persist. The functional capacity of this rejuvenated corpus luteum is not known, but it is suggested that the phenomenon is either a secondary effect from released pituitary luteotrophin or due to a general depletion of fat reserves in response to the needs of lactation. The life-span of the corpus luteum may be as long as 6–8 months from the time of mating (Dawson, 1946).

The corpora lutea of *Lynx baileyi* and *Lynx vinta* are of two types, depending on the size of the luteal cells (Duke, 1949). They appear to persist for months, and probably years, after parturition. Those of *Herpestes*, however, retrogress rapidly at the end of pregnancy (Pearson and Baldwin, 1953).

The marked pre-ovulatory folding of the granulosa layer in the mature follicle of *Vulpes fulva* causes two main types of corpus luteum to be distinguished (Pearson and Enders, 1943). The appearance of the young corpus luteum is either of an open 'lace-work' character, the folding of the mural granulosa having proceeded so rapidly that the cells are loosely arranged, or luteinization has progressed enough to give a 'compact' appearance. The early corpus luteum of the bitch shows a marked 'lace-work' appearance, but it becomes more consolidated towards the 8th day, and is compact by the 18th day (Evans and Cole, 1931; Mulligan, 1942).

The corpus luteum in *Mustela furo* reaches its greatest diameter 3–5 weeks after ovulation, and the ovaries consist almost entirely of luteal tissue (Robinson, 1918). The gland atrophies 3–4 days before the birth of the young (Hammond and Marshall, 1930). The corpora lutea of infertile cycles in *Mustela erminea* are smaller than those of pregnancy (Deanesly, 1935). The corpora of ovulation are well vascularized, but the luteal cells remain small. Both Wright (1942) and Watzka (1940) suggest that the so-called sterile matings associated with smaller corpora lutea indicate delayed implantation. Four to five stages in the development of the corpus luteum of |*Mustela vison* have been recognized (Hansson, 1947). The corpus enters an inactive phase with small luteal cells during the period of delayed implantation. The size and state of development of the corpora during the breeding season are more closely related to the length of day than to their age (Enders, 1952). The corpora lutea of *Mustela frenata* and *M. cicognani*, *Martes americana* and *M. caurina* are small and inconspicuous when associated with unimplanted blastocysts (Wright, 1942). In the martens highly vacuolated luteal cells, comparable to those of the cat in late pregnancy and to those found in the armadillo in similar circumstances, are present during the long period in which blastocysts remain unimplanted in the uterus.

The corpora lutea of pregnancy in *Meles meles* regress rapidly after parturition and a post-parturient ovulation occurs within a few weeks (Canivenc, 1957; Neal and Harrison, 1958). The corpora of the long period of delay (2 to 10 months) are poorly vascularized and appear inactive. Additional ovulations occur during the period of delay, but it is not possible, once the additional corpora have become solid, to distinguish them from those of earlier ovulations. Corpora may exhibit degenerative changes during the latter part of the delay, and in early pregnancy may contain an unusual number of leucocytes.

(b) Pinnipedia

New corpora lutea in *Callorhinus ursinus* may be lobulated or elongated ovals (Enders *et al.*, 1946), but later they become spherical. A distinct antrum, at first filled with fluid, is invaded by luteal and connective tissue. Just before whelping the luteal cells contain vacuoles, which are still prominent when the corpus luteum begins to be resorbed a few days after whelping. The gland persists for longer than a year, and takes more than 2 months after whelping to degenerate. It is unique in selectively suppressing follicular growth in the ovary in which it lies from within a few weeks of ovulation until several months after parturition during the following year. This may be due either to the relatively large size of the pinniped corpus luteum, which may be as large as the rest of the ovary, or to a sub-threshhold level of follicular stimulating hormone (FSH) induced by the growth and distortion of the pregnant uterine horn.

Harrison *et al.* (1952) and Laws (1956) find the luteal cytoplasm heavily vacuolated during the period of delay in Antarctic pinnipeds. The corpus luteum of *Phoca vitulina* is larger during lactation than at term and displays post-parturient rejuvenation (Harrison, 1960).

4. Cetacea

It is now well known that the corpora lutea of whalebone whales persist as a permanent record of the number of ovulations (Mackintosh and Wheeler, 1929; Peters, 1939; Mackintosh, 1946). Counts of the corpora can be employed as a relative measure of age (see Laws, 1958, for other references). It is, however, often difficult or impossible to differentiate between corpora lutea of pregnancy and ovulation (although Robins (1954) maintained that he could in *Megaptera*). Laws finds a mean annual increment of corpora in *Balaenoptera* of 1·4, and Chittleborough (1954) suggests the rate of accumulation in *Megaptera* is little more than one per breeding season.

For obvious reasons there is a lack of accurately timed histological material showing changes in the corpus luteum of whales. Some observations have been made on the following: *Pseudorca* (Comrie and Adam, 1937), *Megaptera* (Dempsey and Wislocki, 1941; Robins, 1954), *Globicephala* (Harrison, 1949), *Balaenoptera* (van Lennep, 1950; Laws, 1958). The blood vessels of the corpus of *Megaptera* are unusually long, and there may be a central avascular area associated with fibrosis and hyalinization. Vacuolation of luteal cells is common in active corpora of all ages. Binucleated luteal cells are common.

5. *Xenarthra*

The corpus luteum in *Dasypus novemcinctus* develops rapidly until the volume of the corpus may equal that of the rest of the ovarian tissue. The ovary appears as a small cap of cells resting on the corpus (Hamlett, 1932, 1935). During the period of delay in implantation the corpus luteum is large and fully formed, but its secretory activity is suppressed. Implantation is attended, and may even be preceded, by the appearance in the luteal cells of secretory droplets, which give the peripheral cytoplasm a vacuolated appearance. The corpus luteum enlarges and becomes highly vascular at this time. Following parturition, the corpus, which regresses from the middle of gestation, continues to degenerate during the next few months until it has been entirely replaced by connective tissue.

6. *Lagomorpha*

The earlier researches of Sobotta (1897), Honoré (1900) and Cohn (1903) on the rabbit corpus have been extended by Marshall (1925), Togari (1926), Deanesly (1930), Walton and Hammond (1928) and by cinemicrographic studies of Hill *et al.* (1935).

Ovulation occurs 10–10½ hours after copulation, and considerable haemorrhage takes place into the ruptured follicle. Theca interna cells and endothelial cells migrate in among the granulosa cells by 12 hours. The theca interna cells reach maximum development by 24 hours and rapidly lose their fat. Vacuolation of the luteal cells is apparent by the 3rd day; the cells reach their maximum development between the 5th and 8th day; but vacuolation increases until it is most marked by the 31st day. The corpus luteum is absorbed gradually after the end of pregnancy; lactation speeds up regression. The corpus luteum of pseudopregnancy shows marked vacuolation on the 18th day and thereafter appears to degenerate fairly rapidly. Bloch and Strauss (1958) find extensive luteinization of atretic follicles in *Lepus europaeus* to form a confluent corpus in pseudopregnancy. Deanesly (1930) states that when the theca interna is most prominent it contains cells with large vesicular nuclei and others of a fibroblastic nature; both contain fatty cytoplasmic granules. She maintains that the theca interna plays a part in establishing the vascular network. The theca cells disappear rapidly and by 36 hours no trace of them can be seen.

7. *Rodentia*

Apart from the mouse, guinea pig and rat little detailed histological description is available on the rodent corpus luteum. The ovary of

Citellus tridecemlineatus has been briefly described by Volker (1905), Drips (1919), and Pliske (1938). The ovary of *Marmota monax* (Rasmussen, 1918), *Sciurus carolinensis* (Deanesly and Parkes, 1933) and *Geomys bursarius* (Mossman, 1937) have all been briefly reported on.

The corpus luteum of *Cricetus auratus* (Deanesly, 1938b) and also that of *Cricetulus griseus* (Parkes, 1931) have received some attention. The ovary of *Dipodomys ordii* has been examined by Duke (1940) and that of *Ondatra zibethica* by Forbes and Enders (1940). Accessory corpora lutea, which develop from atretic follicles, appear unilaterally in the ovaries during pregnancy of *Lagidium peruanum* (Pearson, 1949) and of *Erethizon dorsatus* (Mossman and Judas, 1949). The latter authors find that the primary and accessory corpora lutea are added to by cells of the embryonic stroma of the capsule (remnants of thecal cells) turning into luteal cells. They suggest, with little evidence, that the derivation of luteal cells from stromal cells may account for the 'paraluteal' and 'theca-luteal' cells of other authors.

The classical work of Sobotta (1895, 1896) on the mouse has been followed by that of Allen (1922), Togari (1923, 1924) and Deanesly (1930). All agree that fat-laden theca interna cells proliferate actively during the first 24 hours, and invade the luteal tissue, mainly in relation to the capillaries. Bullough (1946) also finds mitoses in the granulosa cells just after ovulation. Capillaries spread to the centre of the gland by the 16th hour and the theca interna cells lose their fat. The corpus luteum reaches its maximum size 2–3 days after ovulation, and lipids are present throughout the entire gland. (Allen (1922), however, states that the corpus luteum reaches its maximum size at 10–14 days.) Theca interna cells do not form theca-luteal cells, and generally no trace of them can be found 60 hours after ovulation. Deanesly and Togari are of the opinion that the theca interna cells give rise to fibroblasts which constitute both walls of blood spaces and supporting tissue, and Deanesly suggests that these cells show affinities with the histiocytes of connective tissue.

Contrary to the observations of Long and Evans (1922), Boling (1942) finds that the average volume of the most recently formed set of corpora lutea in the rat increases rapidly between 12 and 48 hours after the beginning of heat. There is little change in volume from the 48th to the 96th hour. However, during the first 12 hours following the onset of the first heat subsequent to their formation the average volumes of the corpora lutea decrease rapidly. Vacuolation is observed in the luteal cells when the corpora lutea are $3\frac{1}{2}$ days old. Pederson (1951) strongly supports a dual origin for luteal cells from both theca interna and granulosa cells. Bassett (1949) finds an increase in the luteal cell density from the 5th to the 9th day which he believes is due to a transformation into luteal cells of small precursor cells like pre-thecal cells of growing follicles.

Weichert and Schurgast (1942) disagree with Long and Evans (1922) in that they find differences in size between the corpora of ovulation, pseudopregnancy, pregnancy, and lactation. The size is not influenced by the number of suckling young. The increase in size of the corpora in prolonged gestation is comparable to the condition in normal pregnancy, except that because of the later implantation the gestation period is lengthened and the increase in size of the corpus luteum is correspondingly delayed. This delay is in general correlated with the number of suckling young.

Changes in character and distribution of blood vessels in the corpus luteum of the albino rat have been studied by Bassett (1943). The same author (1948) also finds that in colchicine-treated albino rats there is considerable mitotic activity throughout the early pregnancy corpora lutea. During the 4th to the 7th day there is an increase in the concentration of cells, while the volume is not increasing. This suggests that there is an active proliferation of luteal cells, or some precursor cells, during the early period of luteal development. However, the late increase in volume is due to luteal cell hypertrophy.

The corpora lutea of *Cavia porcellus* have been examined by Schmidt (1942) and Stafford and Mossman (1945); they confirm the earlier work of Loeb (1906) and Sobotta (1906). After rupture of the follicle strands of elongated granulosa cells extend into the follicle on all sides, and occasionally the developing corpus becomes everted. The theca interna cells can be recognized by their granular and spindle-like appearance. Both the theca interna and granulosa cells hypertrophy and the two cell types become indistinguishable. The corpus luteum increases rapidly in size until it is 12 days old, after which time regressive changes commence (Rowlands, 1956).

8. *Proboscidea*

The ovarian cycle of *Loxodonta africana* is characterized by the occurrence of multiple ovulation (Perry, 1953). Many apparently active and histologically indistinguishable corpora are present in both ovaries at all stages of pregnancy. The corpora are replaced in mid-pregnancy by a second active set, which are formed by luteinization of all follicles with antra. Some of the larger follicles may ovulate; smaller ones do not. Luteal cells are often binucleate with heavily vacuolated cytoplasm. The corpus possesses a prominent system of channels with a well-defined lining and which are considered by Perry to be lymphatics. The corpora decline rapidly at term, with destruction of luteal cells.

9. *Artiodactyla*

The changes in the corpus luteum of the sow have been fully described by Corner (1915, 1919, 1921) and Barker (1951), in the sheep by Marshall (1904), Grant (1934), Quinlan and Maré (1931) and Warbritton (1934), in the cow by McNutt (1924), Hammond (1927), Höfliger (1948) and Asdell *et al.* (1949), and in the goat by Harrison (1948b). In the cow the structure usually shows a fluid-filled central cavity which often persists throughout its life-span. The corpus luteum is generally solid by the 8th day in sheep, sows and goats. Invasion of the granulosa by theca interna cells commences in all species so far examined between the 1st and 3rd day. Vascularization of the gland begins about the same time and nearly every cell has an endothelial coat by the 12th day. Andersen (1926) has described the blood vessels of the corpus luteum in the sow in some detail. The granulosa cells are fully luteinized by the 5th–6th day, and peripheral vacuolation of the cytoplasm of the luteal cells is found progressively from the 2nd day. The theca interna cells do not revert to fibroblasts. Solomons and Gatenby (1924) suggest that reticulum found between luteal cells is laid down by theca interna cells. Corner (1919, 1920), however, has produced evidence showing that the reticulum is in all probability laid down by endothelial cells. Corner (1948) has also investigated the distribution of the theca interna, using a technique for the demonstration of alkaline phosphatase. He finds theca interna cells, laden with phosphatase, interspersed among the granulosa cells at the 18th day of pregnancy. After this time luteal cells also acquire granules of phosphatase and recognition of theca interna cells is more difficult.

Regression of the corpus luteum in the non-pregnant sow commences at the 13th–16th day after ovulation. The degenerative process is mirrored by a marked peripheral vacuolation, cytoplasmic shrinkage, fragmentation of nuclei and subsequent disappearance of luteal cells. Corner (1921) finds numerous angular and elongated cells, with foamy cytoplasm, and a wealth of osmium-staining fatty material, which survive the degenerative process. He believes these cells to be remnants of the theca interna (see also Hammond, 1927).

In the early part of gestation the corpus luteum of pregnancy remains about the same size as that seen on the 12th–14th day. Corner (1915) has distinguished a number of stages in the life of the gland in the sow. He divides the early developmental stages into a preparatory one of 25 days, and then into two stages covering the next 15 days, in which there is a progressive appearance of vacuoles in luteal cells. From the 40th to the 75th day he finds a transitional period

N

in which the vacuoles disappear. From the 75th day onwards diverse forms of endoplasmic vacuolation occur, and regressive changes appear around the 110th day.

Höfliger (1948) finds that the corpus luteum of the cow is fully developed 9 days after ovulation. Regression of the corpus luteum of the cycle commences on the 14th day. The corpus luteum of pregnancy, which grows steadily during the first 3 months, cannot be distinguished from that of the cycle.

10. *Perissodactyla*

Küpfer (1928), Hammond and Wodzicki (1941) and Harrison (1946) find that the active stage of the corpus luteum of the mare is short compared with that of the cow and the sow, and that the maximum diameter of the fully developed gland is below that of the mature ovarian follicle (see Aitken, 1927).

Four stages have been described in the corpus luteum of pregnancy by Cole *et al.* (1931). During the first 40 days there is only one corpus luteum in the ovary. About the 40th day several follicles become fully luteinized and give rise to multiple accessory corpora lutea. Some are not true corpora lutea, but luteinized theca interna cells which remain after the granulosa cells have degenerated (Kimura and Lyons, 1937). Regression of these corpora lutea commences about the 150th day, and only minute vestiges of the glands are present during the later stages of pregnancy. Amoroso *et al.* (1948) have confirmed the observations of Kimura and Lyons (1937) that regression of the primary corpus luteum commences towards the end of the 1st month. They suggest that during the 2nd month of pregnancy a succession of follicles ovulate to form new corpora lutea.

11. *Primates other than man*

The corpus of *Macacus mulatta* has been comprehensively described by Corner *et al.* (1936), Hartman (1932a), Corner (1940, 1942, 1945), Rossman (1942) and Sturgis (1949). Prior to rupture of the follicle the granulosa cells become loosened and radially arranged. Blood vessels begin to invade the granulosa cells on the 2nd day, and reach the inner part of the corpus about the 4th day. The gland is then invaded by fibroblast-like cells which may be derived from endothelial cells. On the 1st day theca interna cells may be recognized by their position, large size, sharp outlines, vesicular nuclei and lipid-filled cytoplasm; mitoses are infrequent. However, from the 4th to the 8th day there is little to distinguish the thecal cells from the luteinizing granulosa cells. The granulosa cells so exceed the thecal cells in size by the 10th day and their vacuoles are so large and irregular that they may be clearly distinguished.

In females that do not become pregnant degeneration starts about the 13th day after ovulation. Numerous cells can be seen with many closely packed vacuoles of uniform size evenly dispersed throughout the cytoplasm ('mulberry' cells). During menstruation almost every cell shows either the 'mulberry' type of vacuolation, or possesses single 'giant' vacuoles. The volume of the corpus in non-pregnant animals increases until a few days before the beginning of menstruation and then decreases suddenly. It is suggested that the production of progesterone must cease not more than 3 days before the onset of menstruation.

The corpus luteum of pregnancy cannot be distinguished from that of the cycle of the same age until visible degeneration of the latter sets in on the 13th day. By the 24th day there is a reduction in size of the luteal cells, together with a disappearance of the lipid vacuoles. The theca interna cells retain their lipid and can be seen as clumps of cells packed into the folds of the corpus, especially at the bases of the folds. The period extending from the 19th to the 24th day is described as one of 'transition', associated with the fact that gonadotrophic substances in the urine of early pregnancy are disappearing at this time (Hamlett, 1937). There may also be a connection between the change occurring in the corpus at this time and the 'placental sign' between the 12th and 20th day (Hartman, 1929).

The corpus luteum of pregnancy after the 3rd week can be distinguished by its distinctly folded pattern, the small size of the luteal cells and absence of lipid vacuoles, the prominence of the peripheral capillary network, and the distinctness of the theca interna cells. This typical pregnancy state persists until the 146th day. Specimens obtained on the 154th and 169th day show progressively advancing signs of degeneration.

Two atypical forms of corpora have been described by Corner *et al.* (1936) and Corner (1940, 1942). Certain corpora lutea, after the period of bloom, come under some atypical influence and instead of degenerating in the usual fashion, pass into a state of prolonged existence resembling that of a corpus luteum of pregnancy of the 25th day. These forms, corpora aberrantia, are marked by folding of the walls and presence of theca interna cells about the border and at the bases of the folds. They may survive for 23 weeks and do not produce progesterone. Some corpora aberrantia may regress more rapidly than others; thus persistence of this atypical form requires a stimulus from some external source, presumably the pituitary. The suggestion that the transformation of the normal corpus luteum occurs during the earliest phase of regression is supported by the work of Rossman (1942) on the distribution of luteolipin.

Another form of corpus luteum results from luteinization of an unruptured follicle accompanied by formation of a normal corpus. This type is called an accessory corpus luteum. The cells pass through the same series of changes as the normal corpus, but early forms may be distinguished by the presence of a degenerating ovum. Accessory corpora are formed in about 17 per cent of ovulatory cycles. This form probably produces progesterone, but not in significant amounts. It appears that if a corpus luteum becomes a corpus aberrans, all accessory corpora will become corpora aberrantia accessoria.

Zuckerman and Parkes (1932) describe marked folding of the follicular wall in *Papio porcarius* and *P. hamadryas* after ovulation that gives the corpus a lobulated appearance. The luteal cells reach their maximum development after 7–8 days. Theca cells form the vascular reticular tissue. By the 13th day, when the menstrual flow commences, signs of regression are marked. By the time the next luteal phase is well established the corpus luteum of the previous phase is hardly discernible. The corpus luteum of pregnancy attains a larger size, and the luteal cells are individually larger than in the corpus of the cycle. Maximum development occurs during the 3rd week of pregnancy, but the volume of the corpus luteum, and the size of the luteal cells, falls after 4–5 weeks and remains fairly constant for at least 26 weeks. The corpus luteum disappears rapidly after parturition. Culiner (1945, 1946) finds that the theca interna cells undergo changes similar to those of luteinization, both in atretic and cystic follicles. They may give rise to theca luteal cysts and 'yellow bodies' which resemble corpus luteum cysts and corpora lutea, respectively. Culiner suggests that this precocious activity of the theca interna may be related to irregularities of the menstrual cycle. Dempsey (1940) has described the ovary of *Hylobates lar* and has observed thecal luteinization during the luteal phase like that found in *Papio* and by Säglik (1938) in the orang-utan.

12. *Man*

The paper by Meyer (1911) must still be considered the classical work on the human corpus luteum, and constitutes the fundamental statement upon which all subsequent work has been based. Since that date contributions have been made by many workers and the papers and reviews by Shaw (1925), Asdell (1928), Pratt (1935), Gillman and Stein (1941), Brewer (1942), Harrison (1948a) and Nelson and Greene (1953) should be consulted for the historical background.

Meyer found it convenient to divide the life history of the human corpus luteum into four phases, now well known as the phases of proliferation and hyperaemia, vascularization, maturity or bloom, and retrogression. Proliferation of the granulosa cells occurs during the 1st day after ovulation. In the corpus luteum of menstruation there is a gradual increase in functional activity during the first 8 days, and a peak of activity is reached by the 8th–10th day, which covers the time when the blastocyst is probably implanted. A definite reduction in activity of the corpus can be recognized by the 10th–11th day. The theca interna cells remain as definite groups of cells about the periphery of the structure and in the bases of the folds formed in the wall of the collapsed follicle. These cells have been designated the 'para-luteal' cells, or the whole group has been collectively known as the 'para-luteal' gland. Recently, White *et al.* (1951) have produced evidence of the migration of sudanophil theca interna cells into the granulosa layer of recently ruptured follicles. They call these cells 'K cells' because of their presumed high content of ketosteroids, and believe that they produce progestins. It has been suggested by Gillman and Stein (1941) that such cells represent different phases in secretory activity by thecal or granulosa cells, and Nelson and Greene (1953, 1958) consider them to be degenerating forms. At the end of the so-called stage of vascularization certain regressive changes appear in the blood vessels and both fatty degeneration and degeneration by simple atrophy take place in the luteal cells. There is a sharp increase in the amount of visible lipids and in the cholesterol esters, accompanied by a diminution of the phospholipid content. Organization accompanies this degeneration, and the whole corpus luteum is replaced by a structureless hyaline body called the corpus albicans. It is suggested that complete organization of the corpus luteum takes between 7 and 10 months. Haemorrhage may occur into the cavity of the corpus luteum during the early part of the stage of regression.

Corner Jr. (1956) finds it impossible to date the age of the corpus luteum of the cycle to within a limit smaller than one day. Capillaries invade the granulosa on day 2, and reach the cavity on day 4. Few mitoses are seen in the granulosa and theca interna before day 4, none afterwards. Haemorrhage into the cavity may occur on any day, commonly on days 2, 3 and 9, and regularly at ovulation and menstruation. Fibroblasts appear in the central cavity on day 5 and from days 3 to 6 the granulosa and theca interna are indistinguishable. Capillary dilatation reaches a peak on day 7 and thin-walled venules appear along the border of the central cavity. By day 8 the gland has reached its secretory peak, and a definite connective tissue layer lines the central cavity.

Evidence of secretory exhaustion, cell shrinkage and vacuolation occurs from days 9 to 12; so-called 'mulberry cells' appear on day 13 and degenerating nuclei from day 14. Corpora lutea later in menstruation show a variable amount of cellular degeneration which bears, however, no relation to the duration of flow. The gland collapses entirely and shows an extreme concentration of cells. The nuclei display great variation in size and structure.

Dubreuil and Rivière (1947) state that the corpus luteum secretes both progesterone and oestrogen and that the period of activity of the luteal and thecal elements is the same. They also list four main methods by which a corpus luteum may degenerate, namely, a fibrohyalin method, lipoid degeneration, rapid as well as slow necrobiosis. The authors are of the opinion that the only elements which take part in histiolytic degeneration are the epithelial cells; the remaining elements are said to dedifferentiate to the type of cell found in the ovarian stroma.

In a previous paper Dubreuil (1944) gives a list of specific characters which enable a corpus luteum of pregnancy to be differentiated from that of the cycle. An attempt to formulate such differences was previously made by Marcotty (1914).

Nelson and Greene (1958) consider that the corpus luteum of pregnancy functions only during the first 6 weeks and that it deteriorates rapidly during the 8th–16th weeks (see also Gillman and Stein, 1941). They assume that during the larger part of pregnancy the ovary acts only as an end organ responding to placental influences. It is, however, not impossible that low grade luteal, and even thecal, activity persists after the 6th week. A corpus of pregnancy may be distinguished by its greater size of structure and central cavity, by increased amount of vascular and connective tissue, by the presence of colloid, and/or calcium and of certain lipoids. Presence of calcium or colloid material, not unlike that of Call-Exner bodies, in the luteal cells is the best diagnostic characteristic. Accurate ageing of the corpora of pregnancy, other than into early (1–3 months), middle (3–6 months), and late (6–9 months), is not yet possible.

REFERENCES

Aitken, W. A. (1927). Some observations on the oestrous cycle and reproductive phenomena of the mare. *J. Amer. vet. med. Assn.* **70**, 481–491.

Alden, R. H. (1942). The periovarial sac in the albino rat. *Anat. Rec.* **83**, 421–433.

Allen, E. (1922). The oestrous cycle in the mouse. *Amer. J. Anat.* **30**, 297–371.

Allen, P., Brambell, F. W. R. and Mills, I. H. (1947). Studies on the sterility and prenatal mortality in wild rabbits. I. The reliability of estimates of prenatal mortality based on counts of corpora lutea, implantation sites and embryos. *J. exp. Biol.* **23**, 312–331.

Amoroso, E. C. and Rowlands, I. W. (1951). Hormonal effects in the pregnant mare and foetal foal. *J. Endocrin.* **7**, l–liii.

Amoroso, E. C., Hancock, J. L. and Rowlands, I. W. (1948). Ovarian activity in the pregnant mare. *Nature, Lond.* **161**, 355–356.

Amoroso, E. C., Harrison, R. J., Matthews, L. H. and Rowlands, I. W. (1951). Reproductive organs of near-term and newborn seals. *Nature, Lond.* **168**, 771–772.

Andersen, D. H. (1926). Lymphatics and blood-vessels of the ovary of the sow. *Contr. Embryol. Carneg. Instn.* **17**, 107–127.

Aschner, B. (1914). Über Morphologie und Funktion des Ovariums unter normalen und pathologischen Verhältnissen. *Arch. Gynäk.* **102**, 446–510.

Asdell, S. A. (1928). The growth and function of the corpus luteum. *Physiol. Rev.* **8**, 313–345.

Asdell, S. A., Alba, J. de, and Roberts, S. J. (1949). Studies on the estrous cycle of dairy cattle, cycle length, size of corpus luteum and endometrial changes. *Cornell Vet.* **39**, 389–402.

Athias, M. (1920). Recherches sur les cellules interstitielles de l'ovaire des cheiroptères. *Arch. Biol., Paris,* **30**, 89–212.

Barker, W. L. (1951). A cytochemical study of lipids in sows' ovaries during the estrous cycle. *Endocrinology,* **48**, 772–785.

Bassett, D. L. (1943). The changes in the vascular pattern of the ovary of the albino rat during the estrous cycle. *Amer. J. Anat.* **73**, 251–291.

Bassett, D. L. (1948). Cellular proliferation in the corpus luteum of pregnancy in the albino rat revealed by colchicine. *Anat. Rec.* **100**, 731–732.

Bassett, D. L. (1949). The lutein cell population and mitotic activity in the corpus luteum of pregnancy in the albino rat. *Anat. Rec.* **103**, 597–610.

Belt, W. D. and Pease, D. C. (1956). Mitochondrial structure in sites of steroid secretion. *J. biophys. biochem. Cytol.* **2** (Suppl.), 369–374.

Berger, L. (1922). Sur l'existence de glandes sympathicotropes dans l'ovaire et le testicule humains; leur rapports avec la glande interstitielle du testicule. *C.R. Acad. Sci., Paris,* **175**, 907–909.

Berger, L. (1942). Tumeur des cellules sympathicotropes de l'ovaire avec virilisation. *Rev. canad. Biol.* **1**, 539–566.

Berger, L. (1945). The sympathicotropic cells in the ovaries of foetuses and new borns. *Trans. roy. Soc. Can.* **39**, 23–27.

Bernardo-Comel, M. C. (1931). Intorno alle cellule interstiziali dell'ovaia di donna nel periodo fetale. *Arch. ital. Anat.* **29**, 78–108.

Bloch, S. and Strauss, F. (1958). Die weiblichen Genitalorgane von *Lepus europaeus* Pallas. *Z. Säugetierkunde,* **23**, 66–80.

Boling, J. L. (1942). Growth and regression of corpora lutea during the normal estrous cycle of the rat. *Anat. Rec.* **82**, 131–141.

Boling, J. L., Blandau, R. J., Soderwall, A. L. and Young, W. C. (1941). Growth of the Graafian follicle and the time of ovulation in the albino rat. *Anat. Rec.* **79**, 313–331.

Bouin, P. (1902). Les deux glandes à sécrétion interne de l'ovaire; la glande interstitielle et le corps jaune. *Rev. Med. Est.* **34**, 465–472.

Braden, A. W. H. (1952). Properties of the membranes of rat and rabbit eggs. *Aust. J. sci. Res.* B. **5**, 460–471.

Brambell, F. W. R. (1928). The development and morphology of the gonads of the mouse. 3. The growth of the follicles. *Proc. roy. Soc.* B. **103**, 258–272.

Brambell, F. W. R. (1944). The reproduction of the wild rabbit, *Oryctolagus cuniculus* (L). *Proc. zool. Soc. Lond.* **114**, 1–45.

Brambell, F. W. R. (1956). Ovarian changes. In "Marshall's Physiology of Reproduction" (A. S. Parkes, ed.), 3rd ed. Vol. I, pt. 1, Chap. 5. Longmans, Green & Co. London.

Brambell, F. W. R. and Rowlands, I. W. (1936). Reproduction of the bank vole (*Evotomys glareolus*, Schreber). I. The oestrous cycle of the female. *Phil. Trans.* B. **226**, 71–120.

Brewer, J. I. (1942). Studies of the human corpus luteum. Evidence for the early onset of regression of the corpus luteum of menstruation. *Amer. J. Obstet. Gynec.* **44**, 1048–1059.

Bullough, W. S. (1942). The method of growth of the follicle and corpus luteum in the mouse ovary. *J. Endocrin.* **3**, 150–156.

Bullough, W. S. (1946). Mitotic activity in the adult mouse, *Mus musculus* L. A study of its relation to the oestrous cycle in normal and abnormal conditions. *Phil. Trans.* B. **231**, 453–516.

Burr, J. H. and Davies, J. I. (1951). The vascular system of the rabbit ovary and its relationship to ovulation. *Anat. Rec.* **111**, 273–297.

Burruano, C. (1934). Contributo allo studio della vascolarizzazione dell'ovaio. *Scr. Biol. L. Castaldi*, **9**, 269–306.

Caldwell, W. H. (1887). The embryology of the Monotremata and Marsupialia. *Phil. Trans.* B. **178**, 463–486.

Call, E. L. and Exner, S. (1875). Zur Kenntniss des Graafschen Follikels und des Corpus luteum beim Kaninchen. *S.B. Akad. Wiss. Wien*, **71**, Abt. 3, 321–328.

Canivenc, R. (1957). Étude de la nidation différée du blaireau européen (*Meles meles*). *Ann. Endocr., Paris*, **18**, 716–736.

Caravaglios, R. and Cilotti, R. (1957). A study of the proteins in the follicular fluid of the cow. *J. Endocrin.* **15**, 273–278.

Chittleborough, R. G. (1954). Studies on the ovaries of the humpback whale *Megaptera nodosa* (Bonnaterre), on the West Australian coast. *Aust. J. mar. freshwater Res.* **5**, 35–63.

Christiansen, J. A., Jensen, C. E. and Zachariae, F. (1958). Studies on the mechanism of ovulation. Some remarks on the effects of depolymerization of high-polymers on the pre-ovulatory growth of follicles. *Acta endocr., Copenhagen*, **29**, 115–117.

Claesson, L. (1947). Is there any smooth musculature in the wall of the Graafian follicle? *Acta anat.* **3**, 295–311.

Claesson, L. and Hillarp, N.-Å. (1947). The formation mechanism of oestrogenic hormones. I. The presence of an oestrogen-precursor in the rabbit ovary. *Acta physiol. scand.* **13**, 115–129.

Clara, M. (1956). "Die arterio-venösen Anastomosen." 2nd ed Springer-Verlag, Vienna.

Clark, J. G. (1900). The origin, development and degeneration of the blood vessels of the human ovary. *Johns Hopk. Hosp. Rep.* **9**, 593–676.

Cohn, F. (1903). Zur Histologie und Histogenese des Corpus Luteum und des interstitiellen Ovarialgewebes. *Arch. mikr. Anat.* **62**, 745–772.

Cole, H. H., Hart, G. H., Lyons, W. R. and Catchpole, H. R. (1933). The development and hormonal content of fetal horse gonads. *Anat. Rec.* **56**, 275–293.

Cole, H. H., Howell, C. E. and Hart, G. H. (1931). The changes occurring in the ovary of the mare during pregnancy. *Anat. Rec.* **49**, 199–209.

Comrie, L. C. and Adam, A. B. (1937). The female reproductive system and corpora lutea of the false killer whale, *Pseudorca crassidens* Owen. *Trans. roy. Soc. Edinb.* **59**, 521–531.

Conway, C. H. (1952). Life history of the water shrew (*Sorex palustris navigator*). *Amer. Midland Nat.* **48**, 219–248.

Corner, G. W. (1915). The corpus luteum of pregnancy as it is in swine. *Contr. Embryol. Carneg. Instn.* **5**, 69–94.

Corner, G. W. (1919). On the origin of the corpus luteum of the sow from both granulosa and theca interna. *Amer. J. Anat.* **26**, 117–183.

Corner, G. W. (1920). On the widespread occurrence of reticular fibrils produced by capillary endothelium. *Contr. Embryol. Carneg. Instn.* **9**, 85–93.

Corner, G. W. (1921). Cyclic changes in the ovaries and uterus of the sow and their relations to the mechanism of implantation. *Contr. Embryol. Carneg. Instn.* **13**, 117–146.

Corner, G. W. (1932). Cytology of the ovum, ovary and fallopian tube. *In* "Special Cytology" (E. V. Cowdry, ed.), 2nd ed. Vol. III, p. 1568–1607. Hoeber, N.Y.

Corner, G. W. (1940). Accessory corpora lutea in the ovary of the monkey *Macaca rhesus. An. Fac. Med. Montevideo*, **25**, 553–560.

Corner, G. W. (1942). The fate of the corpora lutea and the nature of the corpora aberrantia in the rhesus monkey. *Contr. Embryol. Carneg. Instn.* **30**, 85–96.

Corner, G. W. (1945). Development, organization, and breakdown of the corpus luteum in the rhesus monkey. *Contr. Embryol. Carneg. Instn.* **31**, 117–146.

Corner, G. W. (1948). Alkaline phosphatase in the ovarian follicle and in the corpus luteum. *Contr. Embryol. Carneg. Instn.* **32**, 1–8.

Corner, G. W., Bartelmez, G. W. and Hartman, C. G. (1936). On normal and aberrant corpora lutea of the rhesus monkey. *Amer. J. Anat.* **59**, 433–457.

Corner, G. W. Jr. (1956). The histological dating of the human corpus luteum of menstruation. *Amer. J. Anat.* **98**, 377–401.

Courrier, R. and Gros, G. (1935). Contribution à l'endocrinologie de la grossesse chez la chatte. *C.R. Soc. Biol., Paris*, **120**, 5–7.

Courrier, R. and Gros, G. (1936). Dissociation foetoplacentaire réalisée par la castration chez la chatte. Action endocrinienne du placenta. *C.R. Soc. Biol., Paris*, **121**, 1517–1520.

Culiner, A. (1945). The relation of the theca cells to disturbances of the menstrual cycle. *J. Obstet. Gynaec. Brit. Emp.* **52**, 545–558.

Culiner, A. (1946). Role of the theca cell in irregularities of the baboon menstrual cycle. *S. Afr. J. med. Sci.* **11**, Biol. Suppl. 55–70.

Davis, D. E. and Hall, O. (1950). Polyovuly and anovular follicles in the wild Norway rat. *Anat. Rec.* **107**, 187–192.

Dawson, A. B. (1941). The development and morphology of the corpus luteum of the cat. *Anat. Rec.* **79**, 155–169.

Dawson, A. B. (1946). The postpartum history of the corpus luteum of the cat. *Anat. Rec.* **95**, 29–51.

Dawson, A. B. and Friedgood, H. B. (1940). Time and sequence of the preovulatory changes in the ovary of the cat after mating or mechanical stimulation of cervix uteri. *Anat. Rec.* **76**, 411–424.

Dawson, A. B. and Kosters, B. A. (1944). Preimplantation changes in the uterine mucosa of the cat. *Amer. J. Anat.* **75**, 1–37.

Dawson, A. B. and McCabe, M. (1951). The interstitial tissue of the ovary in infantile and juvenile rats. *J. Morph.* **88**, 543–571.

Deane, H. W. (1952). Histochemical observations on the ovary and oviduct of the albino rat during the estrous cycle. *Amer. J. Anat.* **91**, 363–413.

Deane, H. W. and Fawcett, D. W. (1952). Pigmented interstitial cells showing 'brown degeneration' in the ovaries of old mice. *Anat. Rec.* **113**, 239–245.

Deanesly, R. (1930). Development and vascularisation of the corpus luteum in rabbit and mouse. *Proc. roy. Soc.* B. **107**, 60–76.

Deanesly, R. (1934). The reproductive processes of certain mammals. Part VI. The reproductive cycle of the female hedgehog. *Phil. Trans.* B. **223**, 239–276.

Deanesly, R. (1935). The reproductive processes of certain mammals. Part IX. Growth and reproduction in the stoat (*Mustela erminea*). *Phil. Trans.* B. **225**, 459–492.

Deanesly, R. (1938a). The androgenic activity of ovarian grafts in castrated male rats. *Proc. roy. Soc.* B. **126**, 122–135.

Deanesly, R. (1938b). The reproductive cycle of the golden hamster. *Proc. zool. Soc. Lond.* **108**, 31–37.

Deanesly, R. and Parkes, A. S. (1933). The reproductive processes of certain mammals. Part IV. The oestrous cycle in the grey squirrel (*Sciurus carolinensis*). *Phil. Trans.* B. **222**, 47–78.

De Groodt, M., Lagasse, A. and Sebruyns, M. (1957). L'espace perivasculaire dans le tissu interstitiel de l'ovaire, vu au microscope électronique. *Bull. Micr. appl.* **7**, 101–103.

Delson, D., Lubin, S. and Reynolds, S. R. M. (1949). Vascular patterns in human ovaries. *Amer. J. Obstet. Gynec.* **57**, 842.

Dempsey, E. W. (1939). The reproductive cycle of New World monkeys. *Amer. J. Anat.* **64**, 381–398.

Dempsey, E. W. (1940). The structure of the reproductive tract in the female gibbon. *Amer. J. Anat.* **67**, 229.

Dempsey, E. W. and Bassett, D. L. (1943). Observations on the fluorescence, birefringence and histochemistry of the rat ovary during the reproductive cycle. *Endocrinology*, **33**, 384–401.

Dempsey, E. W. and Wislocki, G. B. (1941). The structure of the ovary of the humpback whale (*Megaptera nodosa*). *Anat. Rec.* **80**, 243–257.

Drips, D. (1919). Studies on the ovary of the spermophile (*Spermophilus citellus tridecemlineatus*) with special reference to the corpus luteum. *Amer. J. Anat.* **25**, 117–184.

Dubreuil, G. (1944). De quelques caractères propres des corps gestatifs de la femme. *C.R. Soc. Biol., Paris*, **138**, 699–700.

Dubreuil, G. (1957). Le déterminisme de la glande thécale de l'ovaire. Induction morphogène à partir de la granulosa folliculaire. *Acta anat.* **30**, 269–274.

Dubreuil, G. and Rivière, M. (1947). Morphologie et histologie des corps progestatifs et gestatifs (corps jaunes) de l'ovaire feminin. *Gynécologie*, **43**, 1–101.

Duke, K. L. (1940). A preliminary histological study of the ovary of the kangaroo rat, *Dipodomys ordii columbianus. Great Basin Nat.* **1**, 63–73.

Duke, K. L. (1949). Some notes on the histology of the ovary of the bobcat (Lynx) with special reference to the corpora lutea. *Anat. Rec.* **103**, 111–132.

Eckstein, P. and Zuckerman, S. (1956). Morphology of the reproductive tract. *In* "Marshall's Physiology of Reproduction" (A. S. Parkes, ed.), 3rd ed. Vol. I, pt. 1, chap. 2. Longmans, Green & Co., London.

Enders, R. K. (1952). Reproduction in the mink (*Mustela vison*). *Proc. Amer. phil. Soc.* **96**, 691–755.

Enders, R. K., Pearson, O. P. and Pearson, A. K. (1946). Certain aspects of reproduction in the fur seal. *Anat. Rec.* **94**, 214–223.

Evans, H. M. and Cole, H. H. (1931). An introduction to the study of the oestrous cycle in the dog. *Mem. Univ. Calif.* **9**, 65–118.

Flynn, T. T. and Hill, J. P. (1939). The development of the Montremata. 4. Growth of the ovarian ovum, maturation, fertilization, and early cleavage. *Trans. zool. Soc. Lond.* **24**, 445–622.

Forbes, T. R. and Enders, R. K. (1940). Observations on corpora lutea in the ovaries of Maryland muskrats collected during the winter months. *J. Wildlife Manag.* 4, 169–172.

Franchi, L. L. (1960). Electron microscopy of oocyte-follicle cell relationships in the rat ovary. *J. biophys. biochem. Cytol.* **7**, 397–398.

Gaarenstroom, J. H. and De Jongh, S. E. (1946). "A Contribution to the Knowledge of the Influence of Gonadotropine and Sex Hormones on the Gonads of Rats." Elsevier Pub. Co., N.Y.

Garde, M. L. (1930). The ovary of *Ornithorhynchus*, with special reference to follicular atresia. *J. Anat., Lond.* **64**, 422–453.

Gillman, J. (1948). The development of the gonads in man, with a consideration of the role of fetal endocrines and the histogenesis of ovarian tumors. *Contr. Embryol. Carneg. Instn.* **32**, 81–131.

Gillman, J. and Stein, H. B. (1941). The human corpus luteum of pregnancy. *J. Surg.* **72**, 129–140.

Godet, R. (1949). Recherches d'anatomie, d'embryologie normale et expérimentale sur l'appareil génital de la taupe (*Talpa europaea* L.) *Bull. biol.* **83**, 25–111.

Goldby, F. and Harrison, R. J. (1961). "Recent Advances in Anatomy", 2nd ed. Churchill, London (in Press).

Grant, R. (1934). Studies in the physiology of reproduction in the ewe. III. Gross changes in the ovary. *Trans. roy. Soc. Edinb.* **58**, 36–47.

Guthrie, M. J. and Jeffers, K. R. (1938a). A cytological study of the ovaries of the bats *Myotis lucifugus lucifugus* and *Myotis grisescens*. *J. Morph.* **62**, 523–558.

Guthrie, M. J. and Jeffers, K. R. (1938b). Growth of follicles in the ovaries of the bat *Myotis lucifugus lucifugus*. *Anat. Rec.* **71**, 477–496.

Guthrie, M. J., Jeffers, K. R. and Smith, E. W. (1951). Growth of follicles in the ovaries of the bat *Myotis grisescens*. *J. Morph.* **88**, 127–144.

Hamlett, G. W. D. (1932). The reproduction cycle in the armadillo. *Z. wiss. Zool.* **141**, 143–154.

Hamlett, G. W. D. (1935). Delayed implantation and discontinuous development in the mammals. *Quart. Rev. Biol.* **10**, 432–447.

Hamlett, G. W. D. (1937). Positive Friedman tests in the pregnant rhesus monkey, *Macaca mulatta*. *Amer. J. Physiol.* **118**, 664–666.

Hammond, J. (1927). "Physiology of Reproduction in the Cow." Cambridge University Press.

Hammond, J. and Marshall, F. H. A. (1930). Oestrus and pseudo-pregnancy in the ferret. *Proc. roy. Soc.* B. **105**, 607–629.

Hammond, J. and Wodzicki, K. (1941). Anatomical and histological changes during the oestrous cycle in the mare. *Proc. roy. Soc.* B. **130**, 1–23.

Hansson, A. (1947). The physiology of reproduction in mink (*Mustela vison* Schreb.) with special reference to delayed implantation. *Acta zool., Stockh.* **28**, 1–136.

Harrison, R. J. (1946). The early development of the corpus luteum in the mare. *J. Anat., Lond.* **80**, 160–165.

Harrison, R. J. (1948a). The development and fate of the corpus luteum in the vertebrate series. *Biol. Rev.* **23**, 296–331.

Harrison, R. J. (1948b). The changes occurring in the ovary of the goat during the oestrous cycle and in early pregnancy. *J. Anat., Lond.* **82**, 21–48.

Harrison, R. J. (1949). Observations on the female reproductive organs of the c'iang whale *Globiocephala melaena*, Traill. *J. Anat., Lond.* **83**, 238–253.

Harrison, R. J. (1960). Reproduction and reproductive organs in common seals (*Phoca vitulina*) in the Wash, East Anglia. *Mammalia*, **24**, 372–385.

Harrison, R. J. and Matthews, L. H. (1951). Sub-surface cypts in the cortex of the mammalian ovary. *Proc. zool. Soc. Lond.* **120**, 699–712.

Harrison, R. J., Matthews, L. H. and Roberts, J. M. (1952). Reproduction in some Pinnipedia. *Trans. zool. Soc. Lond.* **27**, 437–540.

Hartman, C. G. (1926). Polynuclear ova and polyovular follicles in the opossum and other mammals, with special reference to the problem of fecundity. *Amer. J. Anat.* **37**, 1–51.

Hartman, C. G. (1929). Uterine bleeding as an early sign of pregnancy in the monkey (*Macacus rhesus*) together with observations on the fertile period of the menstrual cycle. *Johns Hopk. Hosp. Bull.* **44**, 155–164.

Hartman, C. G. (1932a). Studies in the reproduction of the monkey with special reference to menstruation and pregnancy. *Contr. Embryol. Carneg. Instn.* **23**, 1–161.

Hartman, C. G. (1932b). *In* "Sex and Internal Secretions." (E. Allen, ed.). Chap. 14. Williams and Wilkins, Baltimore.

Hill, J. P. (1910). The early development of the Marsupialia, with special reference to the native cat (*Dasyurus viverrinus*). *Quart. J. micr. Sci.* **56**, 1–37.

Hill, J. P. and Gatenby, J. W. B. (1926). The corpus luteum of the Monotremata. *Proc. zool. Soc. Lond.* **47**, 715–763.

Hill, R. T. (1937). Ovaries secrete male hormones. I. Restoration of the castrate type of seminal vesicle and prostate glands to normal by grafts of ovaries in mice. *Endocrinology*, **21**, 495–502.

Hill, R. T., Allen, E. and Kramer, T. C. (1935). Cinematographic studies of rabbit ovulation. *Anat. Rec.* **63**, 239–245.

Hill, W. C. O. (1945). Notes on the dissection of two dugongs. *J. Mammal.* **26**, 153–175.

Höfliger, H. (1948). Das Ovar des Rindes in den verschiedenen Lebensperioden unter besonderer Berücksichtigung seiner funktionellen Feinstruktur. *Acta anat.* **3**, Suppl. 5, 1–196.

Honoré, C. H. (1900). Recherches sur l'ovaire du lapin. II. Recherches sur la formation du corps jaune. *Arch. Biol., Paris*, **16**, 563–599.

Jones, R. McClung. (1949). The use of vital staining in the study of the origin of germ cells in the female rat, *Mus norvegicus*. *J. Morph.* **84**, 293–326.

Kaulla, K. N. von, and Shettles, L. B. (1956). Thromboplastic activity of the human cervical mucus and ovarian follicular and seminal fluids. *Fertility and Sterility*, **7**, 166–169.

Kaulla, K. N. von, Aikawa, J. K. and Pettigrew, J. D. (1958). Concentration in the human ovarian follicular fluid of radioactive tracers and drugs circulating in the blood. *Nature, Lond.* **182**, 1238–1239.

Kellogg, M. P. (1941). The development of the periovarial sac in the white rat. *Anat. Rec.* **79**, 465–477.

Kemp, N. E. (1958). Protoplasmic bridges between oöcytes and follicle cells in vertebrates. *Anat. Rec.* **130**, 325 (Abstract).

Kent, H. A. (1959). Reduction of polyovular follicules and polynuclear ova by estradiol monobenzoate. *Anat. Rec.* **134**, 455–462.

Kimura, J. and Lyons, W. R. (1937). Progestin in the pregnant mare. *Proc. Soc. exp. Biol., N.Y.* **37**, 423–427.

Kingsbury, B. F. (1939). Atresia and the interstitial cells of the ovary. *Amer. J. Anat.* **65**, 309–331.

Knigge, K. M. and Leathem, J. H. (1956). Growth and atresia of follicles in the ovary of the hamster. *Anat. Rec.* **124**, 679–707.

Küpfer, M. (1928). The sexual cycle of female domesticated mammals. *13th and 14th Rep. Vet. Res., S. Afr.*, Pt. II, 1209 and Suppl.

Landau, R. (1938). Der ovariale und tubale Abschnitt des Genitaltraktus beim nichtgraviden und beim frühgraviden *Hemicentetes*-Weibchen. *Biomorphosis*, **1**, 228–240.

Lane, C. E. and Davis, F. R. (1939). The ovary of the adult rat. I. Changes in the growth of the follicle and in volume and mitotic activity of the granulosa and theca during the estrous cycle. *Anat. Rec.* **73**, 429–442.

Latta, J. S. and Pederson, E. S. (1944). The origin of ova and follicle cells from the germinal epithelium of the ovary of the albino rat as demonstrated by selective intra-vital staining with India ink. *Anat. Rec.* **90**, 23–35.

Laws, R. M. (1956). The elephant seal (*Mirounga leonina* Linn.). III. The physiology of reproduction. *Falkland Islands Dependencies Survey. Sci. rep.* No. 15, 1–66.

Laws, R. M. (1958). Recent investigations on fin whale ovaries. *Norweg. Whaling Gaz.* **5**, 225–254.

League, B. and Hartman, C. G. (1925). Anovular Graafian follicles in mammalian ovaries. *Anat. Rec.* **30**, 1–13.

Leckie, F. H. (1955). A study of the histochemistry of the human foetal ovary. *J. Obstet. Gynaec. Brit. Emp.* **62**, 542–547.

Liche, H. (1939). Oestrous cycle in the cat. *Nature, Lond.* **143**, 900.

Lipschütz, A. (1925). Dynamics of ovarian hypertrophy under experimental conditions. *Brit. J. exp. Biol.* **2**, 331–346.

Lipschütz, A. (1928). New developments in ovarian dynamics and the law of follicular constancy. *J. exp. Biol.* **5**, 283–291.

Lipschütz, A. (1932). Wiedervermännlichung eines kastrierten männlichen Meerschweinchens nach Eierstockverpflanzung. *Virchows Arch.* **285**, 35–45.

Loeb, L. (1906). Über die Entwickelung des Corpus luteum beim Meerschweinchen. *Anat. Anz.* **28**, 102–106.

Long, J. A. and Evans, H. M. (1922). The oestrous cycle in the rat and its associated phenomena. *Mem. Univ. Calif.* **6**, 1–148.

Mackintosh, N. A. (1946). The natural history of whalebone whales. *Biol. Rev.* **21**, 60–74.

Mackintosh, N. A. and Wheeler, J. F. G. (1929). Southern blue and fin whales. *'Discovery' Rep.* **1**, 257–540.

Marcotty, A. (1914). Ueber das Corpus luteum menstruationis und das Corpus luteum graviditatis. *Arch. Gynäk.* **103**, 63–106.

Markee, J. E. and Hinsey, J. C. (1936). Observations on ovulation in the rabbit. *Anat. Rec.* **64**, 309–319.

Marshall, F. H. A. (1904). The oestrous cycle and the formation of the corpus luteum in the sheep. *Phil. Trans.* B. **196**, 47–99.

Marshall, F. H. A. (1910). "The Physiology of Reproduction." 1st ed. Longmans, Green & Co., London.

Marshall, F. H. A. (1925). The corpus luteum. *In* "Reproduction in the Rabbit", by J. Hammond and F. H. A. Marshall, chap. IV. Edinburgh and London: Oliver and Boyd.

Martínez-Esteve, P. (1942). Observations on the histology of the opossum ovary. *Contr. Embryol. Carneg. Instn.* **30**, 17–26.

Martini, R. and Tonetti, E. (1956). Prime osservazioni sulla vascolarizzazione arteriosa dell'ovaio nelle varie età della donna. *Ateneo Parmense,* **27**, 692–708.

Matthews, L. H. (1935). The oestrous cycle and intersexuality in the female mole (*Talpa europaea* Linn.). *Proc. zool. Soc. Lond.* 347–383.

Matthews, L. H. (1937–38). 2. The female sexual cycle in the British horseshoe bats. *Trans. zool. Soc. Lond.* **23**, 224–248.

Matthews, L. H. (1939). Reproduction in the spotted hyaena *Crocuta crocuta* (Erxleben). *Phil. Trans.* B. **230**, 1–78.

Matthews, L. H. (1941). The genitalia and reproduction of some African bats. *Proc. zool. Soc. Lond.* B. **111**, 289–346.

McKay, D. G. and Robinson, D. (1947). Fluorescence, birefringence, and histochemistry of human ovary during menstrual cycle. *Endocrinology,* **41**, 378–394.

McKenzie, F. E. and Terrill, C. F. (1937). Estrus, ovulation and related phenomena in the ewe. *Res. Bull. Mo. agric. exp. Sta.* **264**, 1–88.

McNutt, G. W. (1924). The corpus luteum of the ox ovary in relation to the oestrous cycle. *J. Amer. vet. med. Ass.* **65**, 556–597.

Meyer, R. (1911). Über Corpus luteum Bildung beim Menschen. *Arch. Gynäk.* **93**, 354–404.

Moricard, R. (1958). Fonction méiogène et fonction oestrogène du follicule ovarien des mammifères (cytologie Golgienne, traceurs, microscopie électronique). *Ann. Endocr., Paris,* **19**, 943–967.

Mossman, H. W. (1937). The thecal gland and its relation to the reproductive cycle. A study of the cyclic changes in the ovary of the pocket gopher *Geomys bursarius* (Shaw). *Amer. J. Anat.* **61**, 289–319.

Mossman, H. W. (1938). The homology of the vesicular ovarian follicles of the mammalian ovary with the coelom. *Anat. Rec.* **70**, 643–655.

Mossman, H. W. and Judas, I. (1949). Accessory corpora lutea, lutein cell origin and the ovarian cycle in the Canadian porcupine. *Amer. J. Anat.* **85**, 1–40.

Mulligan, R. M. (1942). Histological studies on the canine female genital tract. *J. Morph.* **71**, 431–448.

Myers, H. I., Young, W. C. and Dempsey, E. W. (1936). Graafian follicle development throughout the reproductive cycle in the guinea-pig, with special references to changes during oestrus (sexual receptivity). *Anat. Rec.* **65**, 381–401.

Neal, E. G. and Harrison, R. J. (1958). Reproduction in the European badger (*Meles meles* L.). *Trans. zool. Soc. Lond.* **29**, 67–131.

Nelson, W. W. and Greene, R. R. (1953). The human ovary in pregnancy. *Surg. Gynec. Obstet.* **97**, 1–22.

Nelson, W. W. and Greene, R. R. (1958). Some observations on the histology of the human ovary during pregnancy. *Amer. J. Obstet. Gynec.* **76**, 66–90.

Niklaus, S. (1950). Die Kerngrösse des Follikelepithels während des Sexualzyklus beim Borstenigel. *Z. Zellforsch.* **35**, 240–264.

Nishizuka, Y. (1954). Histological studies on ovaries: mainly histochemical observations on ovarian endocrine functions. *Acta Sch. med. Univ. Kioto,* **31**, 215–257.

O'Donoghue, C. H. (1916). On the corpora lutea and interstitial tissue of the ovary in the Marsupialia. *Quart. J. micr. Sci.* **61**, 433–473.

Parkes, A. S. (1926). On the occurrence of the oestrous cycle after X-ray sterilization. I. Irradiation of mice at three weeks old. *Proc. roy. Soc.* B. **100**, 172–199.

Parkes, A. S. (1931). Reproductive processes of certain mammals. Pt. 1. Oestrous cycle of the Chinese hamster (*Cricetulus griseus* Milne-Edwards). *Proc. roy. Soc.* B. **108**, 138–149.

Parkes, A. S. (1950). Androgenic activity of the ovary. *Recent Progr. Hormone Res.* **5**, 101–114.

Patzelt, V. (1955). Über das Ovarium der Karnivoren and seine Zwischenzellen. *Z. mikr.-anat. Forsch.* **61**, 309–359.

Pearson, O. P. (1944). Reproduction in the shrew (*Blarina brevicauda* Say). *Amer. J. Anat.* **75**, 39–93.

Pearson, O. P. (1949). Reproduction of a South American rodent, the mountain viscacha. *Amer. J. Anat.* **84**, 143–173.

Pearson, O. P. and Baldwin, P. H. (1953). Reproduction and age structure of a mongoose population in Hawaii. *J. Mammal.* **34**, 436–447.

Pearson, O. P. and Enders, R. K. (1943). Ovulation, maturation and fertilization in the fox. *Anat. Rec.* **85**, 69–83.

Pearson, O. P., Koford, M. R. and Pearson, A. K. (1952). Reproduction of the lump-nosed bat (*Corynorhinus rafinesquei*) in California. *J. Mammal.* **33**, 273–320.

Pederson, E. S. (1951). Histogenesis of lutein tissue of the albino rat. *Amer. J. Anat.* **88**, 397–428.

Perry, J. S. (1953). The reproduction of the African elephant, *Loxodonta africana*. *Phil. Trans.* B. **237**, 93–149.

Peters, N. (1939). Über Grösse, Wachstum und Alter des Blauwales (*Balaenoptera musculus* L.) und Finnwales (*Balaenoptera physalus* L.). *Zool. Anz.* **127**, 193–204.

Pflüger, E. F. W. (1863). "Ueber die Eierstöcke der Säugethiere und des Menschen." Leipzig.

Pliske, E. C. (1938). The follicular cycle in the sexually mature thirteen-lined ground squirrel (*Citellus tridecemlineatus* Mitch.). *J. Morph.* **63**, 263–287.

Poirier, P. and Charpy, A. (1923). "Traité d'Anatomie Humaine." Paris.

Ponse, K. (1948). "La Différenciation du Sexe et l'Intersexualité chez les Vertébrés (Génétique et Hormones)." Rouge, Lausanne.

Ponse, K. (1955). La fonction androgène de l'ovaire chez l'animal. *IIIᵉ Réunion des Endocrinologistes de langue française.* 1955, 89–138.

Popoff, N. (1911). Le tissu interstitiel et les corps jaunes de l'ovaire. *Arch. Biol., Paris,* **26**, 483–556.

Poulhès, J. and Gaubert, J. (1954). Les artères parenchymateuses de l'ovaire. (Variations avec l'âge). *C.R. Assoc. Anat., Paris,* **82**, 880–884.

Pratt, J. P. (1935). The human corpus luteum. *Arch. Path. Lab. Med.* **19**, 380–545.

184   R. J. HARRISON

Price, M. (1953). The reproductive cycle of the water shrew, *Neomys sodiens bicolor* Shaw. *Proc. zool. Soc. Lond.* **123**, 599–621.

Quinlan, J. and Maré, G. S. (1931). The physiological changes in the ovary of the Merino sheep in South Africa and the practical application in breeding. *17th Rep. Vet. Res. S. Afr.* 663–701.

Rasmussen, A. T. (1918). Cyclic changes in the interstitial cells of the ovary and testis of the woodchuck (*Marmota monax*). *Endocrinology*, **2**, 353–404.

Rennels, E. G. (1951). Influence of hormones on the histochemistry of ovarian interstitial tissue in the immature rat. *Amer. J. Anat.* **88**, 63–107.

Reynolds, S. R. M. (1947). Adaptation of the spiral artery in the rabbit ovary to changes in the organ size after stimulation by gonadotrophins; effect of ovulation and luteinisation. *Endocrinology*, **40**, 381–387.

Reynolds, S. R. M. (1950). The vasculature of the ovary and ovarian function. *Recent Progr. Hormone Res.* **5**, 65–100.

Robins, J. P. (1954). Ovulation and pregnancy corpora lutea in the ovaries of the humpback whale. *Nature, Lond.* **173**, 201–203.

Robinson, A. (1918). The formation, rupture and closure of ovarian follicles in ferrets and ferret-polecat-hybrids and some associated phenomena. *Trans. roy. Soc. Edinb.* **52**, 302–362.

Rossman, I. (1942). On the lipin and pigment in the corpus luteum of the rhesus monkey. *Contr. Embryol. Carneg. Instn.* **30**, 97–109.

Rowlands, I. W. (1956). The corpus luteum of the guinea-pig. *Ciba Foundation Colloquia on Ageing*, **2**, 69–83.

Säglik, S. (1938). Ovaries of gorilla, chimpanzee, orang-utan and gibbon. *Contr. Embryol. Carneg. Instn.* **27**, 179–189.

Sandes, E. P. (1903). The corpus luteum of *Dasyurus viverrinus* with observations on the growth and atrophy of the Graafian follicle. *Proc. Linn. Soc. N.S.W.* **28**, 364–405.

Sauramo, H. (1954a). Development, occurrence, function and pathology of the rete ovarii. *Acta obstet. gynec. scand.* **33**, Suppl. 2, 29–46.

Sauramo, H. (1954b). The anatomy, histology, and histopathology and function of the ovarian vascular system. *Acta obstet. gynec. scand.* **33**, Suppl. 2, 113–131.

Schmidt, I. G. (1942). Mitotic proliferation in the ovary of the normal mature guinea-pig treated with colchicine. *Amer. J. Anat.* **71**, 245–270.

Schochet, S. S. (1916). A suggestion as to the process of ovulation and ovarian cyst formation. *Anat. Rec.* **10**, 447–457.

Sharman, G. B. (1955a). Studies on marsupial reproduction II. Oestrous cycle of *Setonix brachyurus*. *Aust. J. Zool.* **3**, 44–55.

Sharman, G. B. (1955b). Studies on marsupial reproduction. III. Normal and delayed pregnancy in *Setonix brachyurus*. *Aust. J. Zool.* **3**, 56–70.

Shaw, W. (1925). Formation of the corpus luteum in man. *J. Obstet. Gynaec. Brit. Emp.* **32**, 679–689.

Shaw, W. (1927). Ovulation in the human ovary: its mechanism and anomalies. *J. Obstet. Gynaec. Brit. Emp.* **34**, 469–480.

Shettles, L. B. (1957). The living human ovum. *Obstet. Gynec.* **10**, 359–365.

Shippel, S. (1950). The ovarian theca cell. *J. Obstet. Gynaec. Brit. Emp.* **57**, 362–387.

Sluiter, J. W. and Bels, L. (1951). Follicular growth and spontaneous ovulation in captive bats during the hibernation period. *Proc. kon. ned. Akad. Wet.* **54**, 585–593.

Sobotta, J. (1895). Über die Bildung des Corpus luteum bei der Maus. *Anat. Anz.* **10**, 482–490.

Sobotta, J. (1896). Über die Bildung des Corpus luteum bei der Maus. *Arch. mikr. Anat.* **47**, 261–308.

Sobotta, J. (1897). Über die Bildung des Corpus luteum beim Kaninchen. *Anat. Hefte*, **8**, 469–521.

Sobotta, J. (1906). Über die Bildung des Corpus luteum beim Meerschweinchen. *Anat. Hefte*, **32**, 89–142.

Solomons, B. and Gatenby, J. W. B. (1924). Notes on the formation, structure and physiology of the corpus luteum of man, the pig and the duck-billed platypus. *J. Obstet. Gynaec. Brit. Emp.* **31**, 580–594.

Sotelo, J. R. and Porter, K. R. (1959). An electron microscope study of the rat ovum. *J. biophys. biochem. Cytol.* **5**, 327–341.

Stafford, W. T., Collins, R. F. and Mossman, H. W. (1942). The thecal gland in the guinea-pig ovary. *Anat. Rec.* **83**, 193–207.

Stein, K. F. and Allen, E. (1942). Attempts to stimulate proliferation of the germinal epithelium of the ovary. *Anat. Rec.* **82**, 1–92.

Stafford, W. T. and Mossman, H. W. (1945). Ovarian interstitial tissue and its relation to the pregnancy cycle in the guinea-pig. *Anat. Rec.* **93**, 97–107.

Sternberg, W. H. (1949). The morphology, androgenic function, hyperplasia and tumors of the human ovarian hilus cells. *Amer. J. Path.* **25**, 493–522.

Strassman, E. O. (1941). The theca cone and its tropism toward the ovarian surface, a typical feature of growing human and mammalian follicles. *Amer. J. Obstet. Gynec.* **41**, 363–378.

Strauss, F. (1938a). Die Befruchtung und der Vorgang der Ovulation bei *Ericulus* aus der Familie der Centetiden. *Biomorphosis*, **1**, 281–312.

Strauss, F. (1938b). Die Bildung des Corpus luteum bei Centetiden. *Biomorphosis*, **1**, 489–544.

Sturgis, S. H. (1949). Rate and significance of atresia of the ovarian follicle of the rhesus monkey. *Contr. Embryol. Carneg. Instn.* **33**, 67–70.

Togari, C. (1923). On the origin of the corpus luteum of the mouse. *Aichi J. exp. Med. Nagoya*, **1**, pt. 2, 1–44.

Togari, C. (1924). On the retrogression of the corpus luteum of the mouse. *Aichi J. exp. Med. Nagoya*, **1**, pt. 4, 23–40.

Togari, C. (1926). On the corpus luteum of the rabbit. *Folia Anat. Japon.* **4**, 337–363.

Tourneaux, F. (1879). Des cellules interstitielles du testicule. *J. Anat., Paris*, **15**, 305–328.

Trujillo-Cenóz, O. and Sotelo, J. R. (1959). Relationships of the ovular surface with follicle cells and origin of the zona pellucida in rabbit oocytes. *J. biophys. biochem. Cytol.* **5**, 347–348.

Umbaugh, R. E. (1949). Superovulation and ovum transfer in cattle. *Amer. J. vet. Res.* **10**, 295–305.

Van der Horst, C. J. and Gillman, J. (1940). Ovulation and corpus luteum formation in *Elephantulus*. *S. Afr. J. med. Sci.* **5**, 73–91.

Van der Horst, C. J. and Gillman, J. (1942). The life history of the corpus luteum of menstruation in *Elephantulus*. *S. Afr. J. med. Sci.* **7**, 21–42.

Van der Horst, C. J. and Gillman, J. (1946). The corpus luteum of *Elephantulus* during pregnancy; its form and function. *S. Afr. J. med. Sci.* **11**, Biol. Suppl. 87–102.

o

Van der Stricht, O. (1901a). La rupture du follicule ovarique et l'histogenèse du corps jaune. *C.R. Ass. Anat.* (3me *Sess.*) 33.

Van der Stricht, O. (1901b). La ponte ovarique et l'histogenèse du corps jaune. *Bull. Acad. Méd. Belg.* **15**, 216–225.

Van der Stricht, O. (1912). Sur le processus de l'excrétion des glandes endocrines; le corps jaune et la glande interstitielle de l'ovaire. *Arch. Biol., Paris,* **27**, 585–722.

Van Dyke, H. B. and Li, R. C. (1938). The secretion of progesterone by the cat's ovary following the formation of corpora lutea due to the injection of anterior pituitary extract or prolan. *Chin. J. Physiol.* **13**, 213–228.

Van Lennep, E. W. (1950). Histology of the corpora lutea in blue and fin whales ovaries. *Proc. kon. ned. Akad. Wet.* **53**, 593–599.

Verocay, J. (1915). Hat Unwegsamkeit des Ductus deferens Atrophie des Hodens zur Folge? *Prag. med. Wschr.* **40**, 113–115.

Volker, O. (1905). Über die Histogenese Corporis lutei bei dem Zeisel (*Spermophilus citellus*). *Arch. Anat. Physiol., Lpz.* 301–320.

Walton, A. and Hammond, J. (1928). Observations on ovulation in the rabbit. *J. exp. Biol.* **6**, 190–204.

Warbritton, V. (1934). The cytology of the corpus luteum of the ewe. *J. Morph.* **56**, 181–202.

Watzka, M. (1940). Mikroskopisch anatomische Untersuchungen ueber die Ranzzeit und Tragdauer des Hermelins (*Putorius ermineus*). *Z. mikr.-anat. Forsch.* **48**, 359–374.

Watzka, M. (1957). Weibliche Genitalorgane. Das Ovarium. "Handbuch der mikroskopischen Anatomie." Bd. VII, Tl. 3, 1–178. Springer-Verlag.

Weichert, C. K. and Schurgast, A. W. (1942). Variations in size of the corpus luteum in the albino rat under normal and experimental conditions. *Anat. Rec.* **83**, 321–334.

White, R. F., Hertig, A. T., Rock, J. and Adams, E. C. (1951). Histological and histochemical observations on the corpus luteum of human pregnancy with special reference to corpora lutea associated with early normal and abnormal ova. *Contr. Embryol. Carneg. Instn.* **34**, 55–74.

Wilcox, D. E. and Mossman, H. W. (1945). The common occurrence of "testis" cords in the ovaries of a shrew (*Sorex vagrans* Baird). *Anat. Rec.* **92**, 183–195.

Wimsatt, W. A. (1944). Growth of the ovarian follicle and ovulation in *Myotis lucifugus lucifugus*. *Amer. J. Anat.* **74**, 129–174.

Wimsatt, W. A. and Kallen, F. C. (1957). The unique maturation response of the Graafian follicles of hibernating bats and the question of its significance. *Anat. Rec.* **129**, 115–131.

Wimsatt, W. A. and Trapido, H. (1952). Reproduction and the female reproductive cycle in the tropical American vampire bat, *Desmodus rotundus murinus*. *Amer. J. Anat.* **91**, 415–446.

Wimsatt, W. A. and Waldo, C. M. (1945). The normal occurrence of a peritoneal opening in the bursa ovarii of the mouse. *Anat. Rec.* **93**, 47–57.

Winiwarter, H. de. (1923). À propos des cellules sympathicotropes de l'ovaire humain. *C.R. Soc. Biol., Paris,* **89**, 830–833.

Wislocki, G. B. (1939). Observations on twinning in marmosets. *Amer. J. Anat.* **64**, 445–483.

Wislocki, G. B. and Dempsey, E. W. (1939). Remarks on the lymphatics of the reproductive tract of the female rhesus monkey (*Macaca mulatta*). *Anat. Rec.* **75**, 341–363.

Wotton, R. M. and Village, P. A. (1951). The transfer function of certain cells in the wall of the Graafian follicle as revealed by their reaction to previously stained fat in the cat. *Anat. Rec.* **110**, 121–127.

Wright, P. L. (1942). Delayed implantation in the long-tailed weasel (*Mustela frenata*), the short-tailed weasel (*M. cicognani*) and the marten (*Martes americana*). *Anat. Rec.* **83**, 341–353.

Zachariae, F. (1957). Studies on the mechanism of ovulation; autoradiographic investigation on the uptake of radioactive sulphate (^{35}S) into the ovarian follicular mucopolysaccharides. *Acta endocr., Copenhagen,* **26**, 215–224.

Zuckerman, S. (1951). The number of oocytes in the mature ovary. *Recent Progr. Hormone Res.* **6**, 63–109.

Zuckerman, S. and Parkes, A. S. (1932). The menstrual cycle of the primates. Part V. The cycle of the baboon. *Proc. zool. Soc. Lond.* 138–191.

CHAPTER 3

OVARIAN HISTOCHEMISTRY

F. JACOBY

I. Introduction

The complex and dynamic morphology of the ovary poses a special problem with regard to the presentation of histochemical data. Doubtless, innumerable chemical processes are involved in these morphological changes. It is tempting to gather together the available histochemical findings for each type of ovarian tissue or structure and to knit them into a comprehensive story. This would, however, result in a highly speculative account. It cannot be too strongly emphasized that compared with the number of chemical reactions occurring in ovarian tissues, the number of chemical substances or chemical groups whose presence can be visualized and localized by histo- and/or cytochemical methods is very limited indeed. Therefore, any attempt at constructing from so few histochemical building stones a chain of chemical connections is not only hazardous, but possibly misleading and certainly premature.

With these considerations in mind, it was decided to take in turn each individual substance or group of related substances, as revealed by histochemical methods; to map out their distribution and localization throughout the ovary and to place them, wherever possible, in a rational physiological context. It is felt that this approach will yield a clearer and less repetitive review.

The substances or groups of substances to be discussed, all of them organic chemical compounds, are: the nucleic acids, lipids, glycogen,

189

saliva-resistant PAS-positive material ('mucopolysaccharides'), ascorbic acid, various enzymes and pigments. Autoradiography, although related to some of the foregoing, will be treated in a special section. Reference to localization of inorganic material as revealed by microincineration has been omitted. The existing, relatively scanty information on this subject referring to the ovary has been given by Hintzsche (1956).

To correlate the histochemical findings with physiological data will not always be possible or advisable, either for lack of adequate knowledge, or because of the existence of widely divergent results. Histochemistry, in its modern form, is still a young branch of biology, little explored in depth and as yet limited in application. It is only one aspect of the very intricate field of cellular chemistry and metabolism. It may be compared to an opaque coloured glass window, through which one tries to look into the chemical furnace of the cell; and it must always be realized that the result of many histochemical reactions is as static as a stain. Only in conjunction with a time scale does it show its superiority over the latter. Yet, in one respect, it is becoming an indispensable tool in the physiological study of cells and tissues, that is, in its capacity of localizing chemical substances. This localization is as a rule superior to a chemical determination on a tissue homogenate, though quantitatively, in most instances, inferior. Other advantages of histochemical methods will become apparent in the succeeding pages.

No claim of completeness is made: neither in respect of chemical substances for the visualization of which histochemical tests exist, as very often a reference to the ovary is merely incidental and superficial when a new technique has been tried out and applied to numerous tissues in a general survey; nor with regard to the literature on the ovary throughout the animal kingdom. It was found necessary to restrict the survey almost entirely to the mammalian ovary. In keeping with the new impetus which histochemistry has received during the last two decades—Gomori's paper (1939) on the histochemical demonstration of alkaline phosphatase can be said to have acted like a catalyst—the bulk of the literature reviewed in this chapter is drawn from this recent period.

Comments on methods and technical procedures, on their validity and specificity could not, for obvious reasons, be omitted altogether, but they have been condensed to a minimum. Readers seeking detailed information on these and connected aspects are referred to the comprehensive and admirable presentations of the subject given both in monographs (Lison, 1936, 1953; Gomori, 1952a; Pearse, 1953, 1960) and several reviews (e.g. Pearse, 1954; Hale, 1957).

II. Review of histochemical findings

A. Nucleic acids

The methods of identifying nucleic acids (DNA and RNA) at the microscopic level are so well known that only a brief reference to them is necessary. Ultraviolet (UV) absorption at 2600 Å identifies the presence of the purine or pyrimidine base; the Feulgen reaction reveals the sugar moiety, but only deoxyribose, and hence is specific for DNA only. The acid component is revealed by basophilia, i.e. affinity for basic dyes at suitable pH. This staining becomes significant only in conjunction with specific extraction or depolymerization methods; e.g. treatment with ribonuclease will abolish basophilia due to RNA. The names of Caspersson and Brachet are foremost in connection with the design and application of these methods and their physiological interpretation (for summaries see Caspersson, 1950; Brachet, 1950, 1957). In more recent years autoradiography has also been used in conjunction with NA metabolism; for instance, the incorporation of ^{32}P (see p. 226) or other labelled nucleic acid precursors into RNA has been studied. On a cytological level it was found that nucleolar RNA is metabolically much more active than cytoplasmic RNA (see Brachet, 1957). A pertinent observation on the nucleoli of mouse oocytes was made by Odeblad and Magnusson (1954). (See also Polvani, 1959.)

The recognition of the role of both nucleolar and cytoplasmic RNA in protein synthesis has been one of the most fruitful concepts of modern biology; and the evidence for its reality, gathered from numerous branches of biology by observation and experiment, is very convincing. Much has been contributed to it by work with oocytes and ova of lower vertebrates or invertebrates. Hence, it is of particular interest to look at the mammalian ovary in this light.

The histochemical localization of nucleic acids in the ovary is best considered under the following headings: (1) their general distribution, and (2) the special cases of (a) the growing and (b) the fully grown, unfertilized oocyte.

1. General distribution of nucleic acids

In this context DNA is of restricted interest as, fundamentally, it occurs only in nuclei and in them in approximately constant amounts, but cytoplasmic RNA, as will be seen, varies greatly in space and time.

The germinal epithelium of developing rat ovaries was found rich in RNA by Vincent and Dornfeld (1948) and that of developing chick embryo gonads by Smith and Harley (1956). The latter workers record also a high RNA content of the gonadal primordial germ cells, whilst human primordial germ cells contain only a moderate amount of RNA, localized mainly peripherally in the cytoplasm (McKay *et al.*, 1953). Appreciable amounts of RNA were also found in egg cords and granulosa cells in the ovaries of the foetal horse (Davies *et al.*, 1957) and in rat oogonia and oocytes (Ishida, 1952).

During the formation of the tunica albuginea and interfollicular stroma the connective tissue cells show intense basophilia (due to RNA; Vincent and Dornfeld, 1948).

The germinal epithelium in adult rats contains only small amounts of RNA and primordial follicles mere traces (Deane, 1952).

The epithelial cells of growing follicles are particularly rich in cytoplasmic RNA (Vincent and Dornfeld, 1948; Dalcq, 1950; Deane, 1952; Hedberg, 1953; Buño and Hekimian, 1955). Here, intense cellular multiplication takes place and new protoplasm is being built up continuously. Besides, the cells are instrumental in the formation of the liquor folliculi which also contains some protein component. The granulosa cells retain their high content of cytoplasmic RNA during the first few days after ovulation when they grow in size (and possibly also in number) to become transformed into the granulosa lutein cells (Deane, 1952). Thereafter, when they begin to function as steroid-producing cells, basophilia wanes; and little RNA is found in mature corpora lutea, thecal and interstitial cells.

2. Nucleic acids and the growing oocyte

Vincent and Dornfeld (1948), using Feulgen stain and RN-ase-controlled basophilia on rat ovaries, suggested a lack of synthesis of DNA in the nucleus of the growing oocyte; the nucleoli became progressively more basophil, and a perinuclear basophil area (RNA) appeared in the cytoplasm which the authors interpreted as a sign of rapid protein synthesis (Fig. 1). More extensive and partly quantitative studies were made by Alfert (1950). He determined the DNA content of mouse oocytes by means of photometric analysis on Feulgen-stained material. The amount of nuclear DNA was found constant from the smallest primordial oocyte to large primary oocytes, in spite of an increase of the nuclear volume from 400 to 600 μ^3; but the amount of nuclear protein (measured by means of Millon's reaction) increased parallel with the increase in nuclear volume, so that the nuclear protein concentration remains constant during growth of the primary oocyte. There is thus no evidence that DNA is involved in the building up of this protein, but RNA—in keeping with Caspersson's theory—may well be involved. Cytoplasmic basophilia, due to RNA, is pronounced in early growing oocytes, but reduced in fully grown oocytes. Similarly, young oocytes have one or more nucleoli which stain strongly with Azure A, but the fully grown oocyte has a Feulgen-positive shell around a non-stainable nucleolar area. The latter observation was confirmed by Flax (1951) and Dalcq (1953b) and is also borne out by Austin and Braden's study (1953) with the UV-absorption method on fully-grown *living* oocytes isolated from rat ovaries. Strongest absorption was seen in the region immediately surrounding the nucleolus, which itself showed surprisingly little absorption.

Ishida (1952) found the amount of cytoplasmic RNA of oocytes of primary follicles in *young* rats considerably greater than in adult rats.

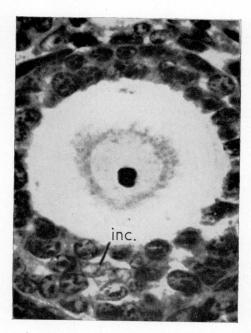

FIG. 1. Oocyte from ovary of 18-day-old rat showing intense basophilia of nucleolus and basophil perinuclear area in cytoplasm. Methylene blue; *inc*: metachromatic inclusion. (Reproduced by permission from Vincent and Dornfield, 1948.)

With the growth of follicle and oocyte a reduction in cytoplasmic RNA occurred in the young rats, whilst in adults the moderate RNA content of the growing oocyte appeared to remain fairly constant as shown by an estimation of stained material.

Hedberg (1953) investigated qualitatively and quantitatively sections of oocytes from human primary, growing and mature Graafian follicles by X-ray-microradiography and UV-absorption. He found that the quite remarkable increase in the protein fraction during the

P

growth of the oocyte from the earliest stage to that at the time of antrum formation was not paralleled by an increase in cytoplasmic RNA. Indeed, the RNA fraction remained practically constant, and its concentration was generally low. The latter point has been observed also by Dalcq (1955). Hedberg tried to reconcile this discrepancy between protein synthesis and the surprisingly low RNA concentration of the growing human oocyte by suggesting that perhaps the RNA-rich follicular epithelial cells bear the brunt of protein synthesis and that they, in some way, transfer the protein to the oocyte.

Thus, there appears to be a lack of uniformity amongst different species as regards the RNA-'linked' mechanism of protein increase in the growing oocyte. Amount and concentration of cytoplasmic RNA seem to vary with species as well as with age. In some instances it is said to increase with growth of the oocyte, in others to decrease, and in yet others to remain constant. However, the contradictions may be more apparent than real. It is unlikely that RNA is actually used up in the process of protein synthesis; and the rate of turnover may be a more important factor. There is a remarkable similarity in size of fully grown mammalian oocytes, but the time during which the final size is reached varies greatly in different species. It is conceivable that if this size is to be attained within a short time, larger amounts of RNA are necessary than when the growth period is more protracted.

Agreement seems to exist on the very high nucleolar RNA content during the growth period of the oocyte, and, equally, on its disappearance prior to maturation.

3. *RNA and the morphogenetic organization of the mammalian oocyte*

Dalcq and his co-workers (Dalcq, 1950; Jones-Seaton, 1950; Dalcq and van Egmond, 1953; de Geeter, 1954), searching for visible proof of a morphogenetic organization in unfertilized mammalian oocytes, have claimed that such an organization is indicated by an unequal distribution of cytoplasmic RNA. They found that there is a large subcortical area of greater basophilia which corresponds to the presumptive dorsal region of the ovum, destined to form the main part of the embryo. Although centrifugation would shift much of the basophil granules towards the centrifugal pole, there remained some more homogeneous basophil material close to the 'dorsal' region. Also, the follicular epithelial cells bordering on this region were larger and more basophil than the remaining follicular epithelial cells. Such features of asymmetry and gradient in follicles and oocytes were described for the rat, mouse, guinea pig, rabbit, cat, dog, mole and primates, including man, but they were more obvious in some of these species than in others.

These observations on a gradient in RNA content in unfertilized mammalian oocytes have not yet been generally confirmed, in contrast to the accepted gradient (in ova) which becomes manifest *after* fertilization. Indeed, some workers have emphasized the homogeneous or uniformly granular appearance of the whole of the oocyte cytoplasm and the lack of evidence of polarity (Hamilton, 1944, for human ova; Hamilton and Day, 1945, for horse ova). Austin and Braden (1953), using the UV-absorption method on fully-grown *living* oocytes isolated from rat ovaries, noted that the cytoplasm showed a fairly strong, evenly distributed absorption; and Hedberg (1953) also concluded that the cytoplasm of human ovarian oocytes is uniformly granular. None of the various methods he used furnished any evidence for polarity or gradients within the cytoplasm, but misleading artifacts can and do arise. Dalcq and his co-workers (Dalcq, 1953a; Dalcq and van Egmond, 1953) have been very careful in excluding artifacts; in view of the fundamental importance of this work, their results deserve the closest attention.

B. Lipids

1. *Lipids at sites of presumed steroid hormone production*

In turning to the distribution, localization and varying accumulations of lipids or fatty substances in the ovary, we enter a very controversial and complex field. Yet it is precisely the behaviour of this group of substances within the ovarian tissues which has particularly attracted the histochemist in recent years. Great efforts have been made to reveal the presence and changing quantities of oestrogenic hormones in various tissues of the ovary, and, thereby, (a) to identify the elements that are responsible for the formation of these compounds, and (b) to find visible evidence, at these sites, for the ebb and flow of hormone production and secretion.

The histochemistry of the organs which are now known to produce steroid hormones (adrenal, ovary, testis, placenta) dates back well over 60 years. The presence, in certain cells of these organs, of sudanophil, birefringent, acetone-soluble lipids with properties different from those of ordinary fat has long been known to histologists, and extraction methods revealed these droplets to consist of cholesterol esters, phospholipids, triglycerides and fatty acids. The ovarian interstitial gland of rodents and the corpora lutea, strikingly filled with such droplets, have long been linked with hormone formation and secretion. The subsequent isolation and synthesis of the steroid compounds is exciting history within living memory. As a consequence, methods used by the organic chemist for characterizing steroid compounds were applied,

directly or with modifications, to the appropriate organs, first, by
Bennett (1940) to the adrenal cortex and, subsequently, by Dempsey
and Bassett (1943) to rat ovaries. Testing the lipid droplets for a
variety of physical (optical) and histochemical properties, such as
birefringence before and after digitonin precipitation, fluorescence in
UV light, phenyl-hydrazone formation (indicative of carbonyl groups),
colour reaction after treatment with concentrated sulphuric acid
(typically given by unsaturated steroids), sudanophilia and acetone-
solubility, these workers concluded that the lipids contained a mixture
of cholesterol and ketosteroid hormone.

These reactions, varying in combinations, can be demonstrated,
as far as the ovary is concerned, in theca interna cells of growing
follicles, corpus luteum cells, cells of the interstitial gland (where this
occurs) and also in the so-called 'hilus' cells (supposed to be androgen
producers). Yet the high hopes that the actual hormone(s) were
being visualized in this way were soon shattered when it was shown
that lipid aldehydes, known as plasmals (or other aut-oxidation products of unsaturated fatty acid esters of cholesterol) rather than ketosteroids were responsible for the phenyl-hydrazine reaction (Gomori,
1942, 1952a; Albert and Leblond, 1946; Claesson and Hillarp, 1947c;
Boscott et al., 1948; Boscott and Mandl, 1949). Feulgen's plasmal
Schiff-reaction (specific for aldehydes: Verne, 1929) was shown to
parallel the hydrazine carbonyl reaction. Whether it is a true plasmal
reaction or a pseudo-plasmal reaction (Cain, 1950; Hack, 1952; Deane
and Seligman, 1953) is of subordinate importance. Also, the later introduced so-called Ashbel-Seligman carbonyl reaction (1949) is not by
itself specific for ketosteroids (Gomori, 1952b). A full discussion of this
continuing controversy (e.g. Deane and Andrews, 1953; de Groodt,
1957), is beyond the scope of this chapter, and the interested reader
is referred to the comprehensive accounts of Cain (1950), Gomori
(1952a, b), Deane and Seligman (1953) and Deane (1958).

There is, then, no histochemical method as yet which conclusively
demonstrates ketosteroid hormones (in passing it should be recalled
that oestradiol is not a keto-type of steroid). The set of tests which is
now frequently being applied to steroid hormone-producing tissues
reveals not a single substance but various lipid substances. They may be
mixtures; one may be, and often probably is, the vehicle for another,
so that several are revealed at the same site. An additional important
point is that often some pretreatment (oxidation or hydrolysis) is
necessary for obtaining a positive reaction. For instance, there may be
little birefringence in a freshly frozen section, more on standing, and
more still if a formol-fixed frozen section is used (e.g. Yoffey and
Baxter, 1947). Similarly, the carbonyl reaction is entirely negative on

fresh tissues and becomes positive only after various pretreatments. All this has to be kept in mind in the evaluation of these histochemical methods and in interpreting the results obtained with them on ovarian tissues at different functional stages. However, it must be emphasized that the simultaneous presence of these different lipids in the same tissue is, to a large extent, not fortuitous but indicative of, and conditioned by, the specific steroid metabolic processes occurring therein. Hence, the so-called 'battery' of histochemical reactions revealing these lipid substances is by no means without value. Even for sudanophilia alone—the least specific test—it was found that the presence of fine sudanophil granules indicates high hormone activity, (i.e. hormone secretion), and accumulation of coarse granules low activity (i.e. storage or even degeneration) (Skowron and Keller,

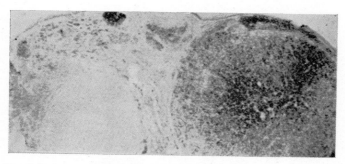

Fig. 2. Rat ovary, in early dioestrus: Schultz reaction. Part of a first-generation corpus luteum on the left, a second-generation corpus on the right. The young corpus contains no cholesterol-like substances; the older one shows a positive reaction. (Reproduced from Deane and Barker, 1952.)

1934; Corner *et al.*, 1945). The test for birefringent material—at best of spheroid crystals showing a Maltese cross—combined with the Schultz test has been of particular value in demonstrating the presence or absence of cholesterol (Fig. 2) (or unsaturated steroids in general). The carbonyl and Schiff reactions, though often displaying the said tissues in a striking manner (e.g. Fig. 3), seem to be of less value than was originally thought for assessing different functional states and will, therefore, receive only passing attention. Meaning and significance of autofluorescence are not yet at all clear and will be discussed separately below (p. 205).

With these points in mind we will now review the more important contributions made in recent years to the 'lipid' histochemistry of the ovary in relation to steroid hormone formation and release. Some of the work is descriptive, revealing changing histochemical pictures with changing physiological states; other work is experimental, probing into the mechanism of these changes. Rational interpretation of either aspect would be impossible without the accumulated knowledge of modern reproductive physiology.

Dempsey and Bassett (1943) concluded from their work on the rat that it is the theca interna cells which produce the oestrogenic hormone and not the granulosa cells, because the latter did not give any of the various 'steroid' reactions. They found crystalline and granular, acetone-soluble birefringent material present in the theca interna of follicles from the time near antrum formation and increasing with the

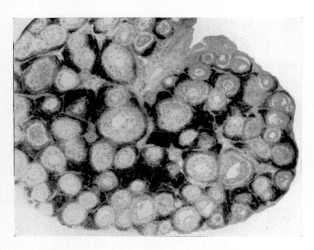

Fig. 3. Ovary of a 19-day-old rat to show interstitial tissue as revealed by the Schiff plasmal reaction. (Reproduced by permission from Dawson and McCabe, 1951.)

growth of the follicle up to the time just prior to ovulation. Subsequently, birefringence declined in the theca and was also negligible in young corpora lutea up to about 48 hours; then birefringent material accumulated in the granulosa lutein cells, but apparently varying in amount with age of the corpus luteum, indicating fluctuations in function. The results of the sulphuric acid test were similar to those of birefringence, whilst sudanophilia was more erratic. Much 'steroid' material was found also in older corpora lutea, atretic follicles and interstitial cells. That present in degenerating cells was thought to represent biologically inactive end-products of steroid metabolism.

Everett (1945), studying the corpora lutea of the cycle in rats, noticed a large accumulation of cholesterol, during oestrus, in the next youngest set of corpora lutea. He suggested that cholesterol serves as a precursor of progesterone. For storage to occur a special ratio of circulating luteinizing hormone (LH)/luteotrophic hormone (LTH) was found to be all-important. In corpora lutea of gestation and lactation (rat, guinea pig) no sign of cholesterol storage (negative Schultz test; no bire-fringence) is seen (Everett, 1947; Claesson and Hillarp, 1948), pre-sumably because they are in a state of active progesterone secretion. This agrees with earlier observations made by Corner (1932) on the non-birefringence of the lipids in functional corpora lutea of the sow, and with the subsequent observations of Dawson and Velardo (1955) on rat corpora lutea during pseudopregnancy. However, Everett (1947) showed that experimental intervention could reproduce storage (see also below, p. 202).

Deane's (1952) more extensive studies covering a succession of con-trolled oestrous cycles in rats brought out some points of special interest: (1) the three structures, theca interna, corpora lutea (i.e. of previous cycles) and interstitial cells, all show evidence of secretion (reduction of Schultz test and of birefringence) in the immediate preovulatory period; (2) the lipids of large vesicular follicles becoming atretic at the time of ovulation give the full range of 'steroid' tests, suggesting a luteinizing response to gonadotrophic stimulation; whilst follicles becoming atretic at other times of the cycle show merely accumulation of coarse lipid material.

Histochemical evidence indicating that the theca interna represents the predominant site of oestrogen production and the only one in the growing follicle was obtained for a number of species. Dempsey (1948) lists the rhesus monkey, cat, sow and woman; it also applies to the cow (Höfliger, 1948) and hamster (Knigge and Leathem, 1956). In the latter species the development of the theca interna, and with it the manifestation of the various lipid reactions, are very much delayed when compared with corresponding stages in the rat.

More detailed observations on the lipids of human ovaries during the menstrual cycle were made by McKay and Robinson (1947). The 'steroid' tests were found positive in the theca interna cells of larger growing follicles, negative in the granulosa cells, but in young corpora lutea positive in both. At the height of corpus luteum activity there was a decrease in fine sudanophil granules in the granulosa lutein cells, whilst the coarser sudanophil droplets in the theca interna were less affected. Similarly, birefringence was only slight in granulosa lutein cells at that time, but much more marked in theca interna cells. These and additional results with other tests are fundamentally con-sistent with the view that in the growing follicle the theca produces the oestrogenic hormone, and that later theca and granulosa lutein cells may both produce oestrogen and progesterone. This conclusion needs some amplification and comment. It is known that progesterone secretion starts prior to ovulation, hence it should, at that time, on histochemical grounds, be linked to theca cell activity only; in young corpora lutea either of the two cell populations may well be responsible for the production and secretion of both hormones. However, at the height of corpus luteum activity the histochemical evidence points to the granulosa lutein cells as actively secreting, whilst the theca cells show signs of storage or inactivity. This would be in keeping with the fact that, at any rate in women, the theca interna cells, remaining outside the glandular part of the corpus, gradually regress to a 'fibro-blastic' condition (cf. also Chapter 6).

Degenerating corpora lutea show coarse sudanophil droplets and often an increase in birefringent crystals, material regarded as biologically inactive degradation products.

White *et al.* (1951) in their histochemical description of human gestational corpora lutea have drawn attention to a special type of cell, supposedly of thecal origin, which appears scattered amongst the granulosa lutein cells. These cells ('K'-cells) showed an acetone-fast uniform, non-granular sudanophilia (Sudan black B). This alone makes it appear unlikely that they contain steroid material. Other lipid tests were, by present standards, similarly equivocal. There is thus little foundation for the suggestion that these cells might be the progesterone producers in the corpus luteum. Whether these 'K' cells correspond to the 'dark' granulosa lutein cells mentioned by Gillman and Stein (1941) or to those described by Leckie (1954) as occurring predominantly in corpora lutea and containing a lipo-mucoprotein material, cannot, on the available evidence, be decided. Gillman and Stein, in their investigation of human gestational corpora lutea, noted the almost complete absence of visible cholesterol throughout pregnancy.

In this connection the earlier work of Skowron and Keller (1934) on rabbits' gestational corpora lutea is of interest. They found fine sudanophil granules to be present in the granulosa lutein cells throughout gestation, indicating continuous secretory activity, which conforms with the well-known fact that in this species a functional corpus luteum is indispensable almost up to the end of pregnancy (see also Chapter 9). Absence of birefringence and a negative Schultz test confirm this notion (Claesson and Hillarp, 1948).

The lipid tests performed on sows' ovaries (Barker, 1951; Deane and Barker, 1952), though generally falling into line, have yielded a few points of special interest. (1) There is a definite sudanophilia with occasional birefringence in the basal cell layer of the membrana granulosa of normal growing follicles, which diminishes towards ovulation (Fig. 4a and b). The authors believe that triglycerides are responsible for this reaction, all other 'steroid' tests being negative. (2) In the lutein cells of young corpora lutea there is, apart from stainable lipid droplets and granules, an acetone-insoluble general background stain obtained with Sudan black B and with carbonyl reagents, indicating the presence of phospholipids* (see also p. 233). (3) The 'steroid' and other lipid material which accumulates in involuting corpora lutea (and also in the interstitial tissue) of the sow becomes increasingly acetone-insoluble in contrast to that of the involuting corpora lutea of rats. Lastly, it seems certain that in the sow theca interna cells insinuate themselves into the glandular cell population of the corpus

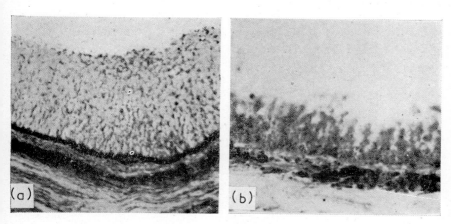

FIG. 4. Sow ovary during dioestrus and prooestrus. Sudan black B. (a) Dioestrus, lipid droplets in theca interna cells and in basal layer of granulosa. (b) Prooestrus, the theca interna is broader than in (a), and its cells are heavily laden with small lipid droplets. Small amounts of lipid are present in the granulosa. (Reproduced by permission from Deane and Barker, 1952.)

luteum (Corner 1944, 1948). They can be traced there, for some time, by virtue of their strong alkaline phosphatase reaction (see p. 221); later, they are no longer identifiable. A 'dual' cell population exists, but there is as yet no histochemical evidence that this has resulted, in this species, in a division of labour with regard to the production of the different steroid hormones.

* The distribution, in rat ovaries, of phospholipids as revealed by Baker's method has been studied by Buño and Hekimian (1955) and Buño (1957). Phospholipids were demonstrated in the theca interna of growing and mature follicles and in the most external layer of the membrana granulosa. In very young corpora lutea they are more abundant than the lipids stainable with Sudan black B. Their quantity, at a maximum when the corpus luteum is fully mature, may well be connected with an increase in mitochondria (see also pp. 226 and 233).

Deane and Fawcett (1956) analysed histochemically luteomata and granulosa cell tumours that had resulted from intrasplenic ovarian transplants in gonadectomized rats. It is interesting to note that in such tumours evidence for oestrogen production, on the basis of the various 'lipid' tests, was found to rest exclusively with theca cells and not the granulosa cells.

The idea of cholesterol being a precursor substance of oestrogenic hormones, already mentioned in connection with the work of Everett (1945), was developed in a series of histochemical studies by Claesson and his colleagues (Claesson and Hillarp, 1947a, b, 1948; Claesson *et al.*, 1948; Aldman *et al.*, 1949a, b).

In 1947, Claesson and Hillarp histochemically demonstrated the presence of a sterol of the cholesterol type in the interstitial gland and theca interna of the rabbit ovary. They found the amount of this sterol to vary in relation to sexual phases: during oestrus, pregnancy (after day 2) and pseudopregnancy large amounts were present, in immature ovaries or during anoestrus very little or none. Chemical extraction methods showed that most of the sterol was present as a biologically inactive ester. After coitus or injection of gonadotrophin the sterol was mobilized from these cells in the ovary parallel with signs of production and secretion of active oestrogenic hormone (Figs. 5a–d). Reduction of cholesterol of the interstitial gland was also found in association with post-partum oestrus. These results strongly suggested that the histochemically detectable sterol is the precursor of the oestrogenic hormones formed in the rabbit ovary. Application of the same methods to ovaries of the rat and guinea pig (Claesson and Hillarp, 1947b, 1948) yielded essentially similar but less consistent and striking results. Sterol storage in the interstitial tissue of the rat was found variable, but usually elevated at prooestrus and metoestrus and high throughout pregnancy and during lactation; in the theca interna it was high only in preovulatory follicles and in pregnancy up to day 16, and then practically zero until day 20 when re-accumulation occurred, i.e. 1–2 days before parturition. Coitus or graded gonadotrophic stimulation were shown to mobilize oestrogen-precursor from both interstitial and theca interna cells of preovulatory follicles. In the guinea pig, no sign of storage was ever seen in the theca interna; in the interstitial cells small amounts were present throughout the cycle, more during the last third of pregnancy and during lactation. Such species differences are worthy of note.

Further analysis of the storage mechanism of oestrogen-precursor in the interstitial tissue of the rat ovary (Aldman *et al.*, 1949a, b; Claesson, 1954a) revealed that *intense* gonadotrophic stimulation results in depletion of the store, while *low-level* gonadotrophic stimulation,

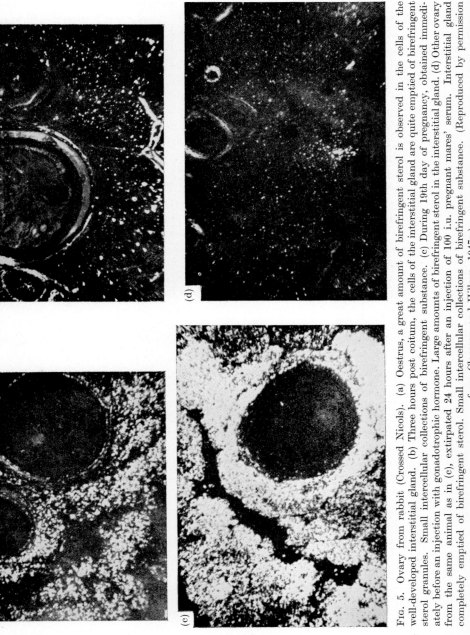

FIG. 5. Ovary from rabbit (Crossed Nicols). (a) Oestrus, a great amount of birefringent sterol is observed in the cells of the well-developed interstitial gland. (b) Three hours post coitum, the cells of the interstitial gland are quite emptied of birefringent sterol granules. Small intercellular collections of birefringent substance. (c) During 19th day of pregnancy, obtained immediately before an injection with gonadotrophic hormone. Large amounts of birefringent sterol in the interstitial gland. (d) Other ovary from the same animal as in (c), extirpated 24 hours after an injection of 100 i.u. pregnant mares' serum. Interstitial gland completely emptied of birefringent sterol. Small intercellular collections of birefringent substance. (Reproduced by permission from Claesson and Hillarp, 1947a.)

with an adequate FSH/LH ratio, will lead to storage of precursor and inhibit its transformation into active hormone.

More detailed and combined with quantitative biochemical analysis is Claesson's work (1954b, c) on the interstitial gland of rabbits. Under certain conditions this occupies a large volume in the ovary and is therefore, after excision of corpora lutea and puncture of large follicles, very suitable for biochemical work. Such work had shown previously (Claesson et al., 1948, 1953) that subsequent to gonadotrophic stimulation there is a marked decrease in esterified cholesterol and fatty acids and a great increase in phospholipids, whilst the amount of acetalphospholipids remained unchanged. Claesson then probed the intracellular localization, before and after gonadotrophic stimulation, of the lipid fractions by a variety of methods (cytological, histochemical, microbiochemical). Granules giving the Schultz reaction were found not to be identical with the Sudan-black granules, as many of the latter persisted after stimulation, whilst the Schultz reaction was already much reduced after 3 hours, and later became almost negative. Strongly birefringent acetone-soluble crystalline lipids also disappeared after stimulation. The intensities of both the Schultz reaction and birefringence were paralleled by quantitative cholesterol estimations. Fresh teased 'living' cells, obtained from ovaries before stimulation, were seen to be loaded with granules, and there was strong birefringence. After stimulation, there was a progressive decrease in the birefringence and size of granules, but not in their numbers; only one fraction of the isolated granules showed marked birefringence. Analysis of the lipid extracted from these granules strongly suggested that the double refraction was due mainly to cholesterol ester. The increased phospholipid was largely concentrated in the general cytoplasmic fraction and was thought to be due to newly formed mitochondria.

The 'precursor' hypothesis is also supported by studies on the lipid histochemistry of the ovarian interstitial tissue of infantile and prepubertal rats (Rennels, 1949, 1951; Dawson and McCabe, 1951; Falck, 1953). Interstitial tissue of a primary type (from granulosa cell cords) and of a secondary type (from the theca of atretic follicles) can be distinguished. The various 'lipid' reactions are first negative in this tissue until approximately day 9 after birth. Then cholesterol storage begins, that is, at a time when the ovarian interstitial cells are still unresponsive to gonadotrophic stimulation. But after about day 12 such artificial stimulation will mobilize cholesterol from the interstitial cells and oestrogenic effects become apparent. Thus the biochemical system necessary for the conversion of cholesterol into oestrogenic hormone, which is incomplete up to a certain age, can be brought into play by injections of chorionic gonadotrophin. Histochemically,

Schultz-positive and birefringent material was found much reduced, whilst the Schiff test (plasmalogen) was little affected and sudanophilia not at all.

In contrast to this the interstitial cells of horse foetal gonads, which are well known for their remarkable hypertrophy, seem to contain lipid material of a different sort. Davies et al. (1957), who applied a great number of tests to these cells, concluded that there are probably two different lipids present, one of which is in combination with carbohydrate and protein. In some respects this material resembles that found by Leckie (1954, 1955) in human foetal and adult ovaries.

Further sites of presumed steroid hormone production are the clusters of epithelioid cells lying in close vicinity to blood vessels and nerve bundles in the hilar region of the ovary. They are known as 'hilus' cells and are considered to be equivalent to the Leydig (interstitial) cells, with which they share all cytological and cytochemical properties, including the occasional presence of Reinke's crystals which, according to Sternberg (1949), are probably protein in nature. They always contain lipid granules and droplets to a varying extent. Watzka and Eschler (1933) observed them in sow ovaries, especially from pregnant animals, but most available data concern human females. They are present in the foetus, absent (or difficult to find) during childhood, reappear at puberty and are prominent during pregnancy and at the time of the menopause. These fluctuations suggest functional activities. Cases of virilism have been associated with the presence of small tumours of these cells. Thus, for reasons of both morphology and pathology, most workers ascribe to them an androgenic function (cf. also Chapters 2 C and 6). This idea is supported by histochemical findings (Sternberg, 1949; Bartolomei, 1954; Dhom, 1955). All the tests which were supposed to characterize ketosteroids have given positive results in these cells. This issue could possibly be decided, if there was a specific histochemical test for male sex hormone.

2. Note on autofluorescence

Pure crystals of oestrogenic hormone(s), when treated with sulphuric acid, give a characteristic intense light-greenish fluorescence. By means of the same highly specific fluorescence, Bierry and Gouzon (1936) were able to detect oestrogen in chloroform extracts of pregnancy urine. It was a logical step to apply the technique of demonstrating autofluorescence in UV light to ovarian sections, but the results obtained by different workers have been very divergent and the interpretation of the phenomenon is fraught with difficulties. With one exception (Burkl and Kellner, 1954; see p. 206), all studies seem to have been done on formol-fixed frozen sections, but formalin, according to some authors, affects the outcome of the reaction profoundly; length of fixation may also be of importance. On the other hand, *unfixed* unsaturated fats and fatty acids become increasingly fluorescent on oxidation (Gomori, 1952a). An additional complication arises from the fact that vitamin A gives a similar green fluorescence which is, however, destroyed by the UV radiation, and hence is fleeting. In most accounts it is not mentioned whether the observed fluorescence was labile or stable (e.g. Dempsey and Bassett, 1943; McKay and Robinson, 1947; Deane, 1952).

Ragins and Popper (1942) observed fading fluorescence on formol-fixed frozen sections of human ovaries. They found it linked to lipid substances (acetone-soluble) and to show fluctuations with age and phases of the cycle; the main sites were the theca interna and granulosa lutein cells. Though the speed of fading was variable, the authors concluded that, essentially, the bulk of the greenish fluorescence seen was due to vitamin A. Dempsey and Bassett (1943), observing (? stable) fluorescence in rat ovaries, did not subscribe to this view, but thought it more likely that the fluorescence was due to steroids, possibly the actual hormones. Claesson and Hillarp (1947a) observed a UV-labile (hence vitamin A) bluish-green fluorescence in frozen sections of rat ovaries, provided these had been fixed in formalin for only a few hours; after longer fixation the fluorescence was no longer obtained. Rockenschaub (1951a, b, 1954), on the other hand, saw in formol-fixed frozen sections of rodent and especially human material autofluorescence which did not disappear after 30 min. exposure to UV radiation. In growing follicles it was present only in the theca but, after ovulation, both in theca and granulosa lutein cells. In the human ovary the fluorescence of the latter cells comes to an end 12 days after ovulation. Rockenschaub concluded that the phenomenon is due to the various steroid hormones. As evidence for secretion he noted greenish fluorescence in capillaries either of the theca of mature follicles or of mature corpora lutea. He derived supporting evidence for his interpretation from observations on the placenta where only the plasmodiotrophoblast (steroid hormone-producer) showed fluorescence, but not the cytotrophoblast.

Burkl and Kellner (1954) tried to reproduce, in *unfixed* sections of rat ovaries, the fluorescence characteristic for crystals of pure oestrogenic hormone. They eventually succeeded, but only with sections that first had been dried for 24 hours. They found that 3 hours after gonadotrophic stimulation there was a transitory increase in fluorescence in interstitial cells, theca interna cells of large follicles and also in 'lumina' (? antra). The latter point is of special interest. The high oestrogen content of the follicular fluid is well known, yet none of the histochemical tests, supposedly indicative of steroid hormones, has ever been seen to give a positive reaction in the liquor. The authors conclude that the interstitial and theca cells produce, under gonado-trophic stimulation, oestrogenic hormone from a precursor, and that the hormone is soon released into the circulation.

As already suggested, the differences in results and interpretation make it practically impossible to draw any valid conclusion from these various studies. Perhaps quantitative UV-absorption spectrography, performed under standardized conditions, might offer prospects of success, but technical difficulties are likely to be great.

3. *Lipids at other ovarian sites*

In comparison with the histochemical work focused, in recent years, on the presumed sites of steroid hormone production, studies concerned with lipids present at other sites in the ovary have been scanty. Yet some of the latter fatty substances are of no minor biological impor-tance. Foremost amongst these is the yolk material of the oocyte. The amount of this varies greatly with different species, probably connected with the varying needs for food store (see Corner, 1932). For example, sow and horse oocytes build up a large amount of yolk, those of the cat and bitch somewhat less, whilst in the mouse, rat, ape and man the amount of yolk material is negligible. The mode of yolk formation is not yet definitely known. In young oocytes mitochon-dria and Golgi material aggregate at a certain stage at one side of the nucleus forming the so-called vitellogenic zone or Balbiani's yolk nucleus. Here the first yolk droplets are formed; then mitochondria and Golgi material disperse and further yolk granules (gradually becoming globules) appear in the general cytoplasm, fairly uniformly distributed. Recent histochemical studies relevant to this manner of yolk formation were made by Ortmann (1955) for the bitch and by Guraya (1957) for the pigeon. On the other hand, it has been claimed, on the basis of sections stained for lipids, that fat may reach the oocytes via the cumulus cells and their processes through the zona pellucida (Wotton and Village, 1951). Ortmann, using Sudan black B, found the germinal epithelium free from fat, but the cells of the epithelial (? Pflüger's) tubes—a characteristic feature of the bitch's ovarian cortex—contained coarse lipid droplets, mainly in the infranuclear region. Primordial oocytes which lie in the deep parts of these tubes also have coarse sudanophil droplets. These disappear when the 'yolk nucleus' begins to form. Oocytes, especially of primordial follicles, are also rich in phospholipids as revealed by Baker's method (Buño, 1957).

C. Carbohydrates

1. *Glycogen*

Considering the length of time for which a reliable test for glycogen in the form of Best's carmine stain (saliva controlled) has been known, the data available appear meagre and, in particular, cover only a very limited number of species. Of these the rat has been studied more frequently (Togari, 1927; Brandenburg, 1938; Wislocki *et al.*, 1947; Harter, 1948; Deane, 1951, 1952; Ishida, 1952) than other species. In recent times, the PAS reaction (also saliva controlled) is being preferentially used.

Human primordial germ cells, whilst migrating to the gonad primordium, were found to contain glycogen (McKay *et al.*, 1953, 1955; Hertig *et al.*, 1958). Some divergent observations were made concerning the glycogen content of rat oogonia which, according to Brandenburg (1938), are present up to day 5 after birth and in a state of active multiplication. He found them free of glycogen. It may be that the high metabolic activity connected with this cellular proliferation does not permit accumulation of glycogen. Ishida (1952), however, noticed abundant glycogen in oogonia and in oocytes of immature rats. Sundberg (1924), when studying human embryos, found much glycogen in oogonia, but less in early oocytes.

Most workers agree that in primordial oocytes and especially in growing ones glycogen is usually present. This holds certainly for the rat where, according to Harter (1948), "the normally developing ovum is the only cell (sc. in ovary) containing appreciable amounts of glycogen." For the mouse, Goldmann (1912) reported accumulation of glycogen confined to the oocytes of growing and maturing follicles, and Moss *et al.* (1954) made similar observations on growing oocytes of the cow, the glycogen content increasing with the size of the Graafian follicle. In hibernating bats, too, some glycogen is present in growing, but much less in immature oocytes (Nakano, 1928). Little was seen in rabbits' oocytes (Togari, 1927; Foraker *et al.*, 1955) and none in those of guinea pigs (Togari, 1927), which again makes it impossible to generalize on this point.

The oocytes of atretic follicles frequently show glycogen (rabbit, mouse, rat, guinea pig: Togari, 1927), sometimes in the form of coarse clumps (mouse: Goldmann, 1912; bat: Nakano, 1928; rat: Deane, 1951, 1952). The granulosa cells, normally free of glycogen in the rat, mouse, rabbit and guinea pig, also tend, at the beginning of atresia, to show glycogen deposits, especially in the cumulus oöphorus. This glycogen accumulation in atresia, especially in granulosa cells, may well be an indication of the waning vitality of the cells concerned. Indeed,

Deane (1951) has interpreted it as an early sign of atresia, a symptom preceding karyorrhexis, and thus of diagnostic value. In contrast to this, Moss *et al.* (1954) observed in the cow normally a fair amount of glycogen in the cumulus cells and some in the membrana granulosa, but none in atretic follicles.

Small amounts of glycogen occur transitorily in theca interna cells of the rabbit, mouse, rat and guinea pig, both in normal and atretic follicles (Togari, 1927).

Few observations exist on the glycogen content of corpora lutea and the interstitial gland or tissue. None was found in the rat, but in certain bats glycogen was detected in the granulosa lutein cells of older

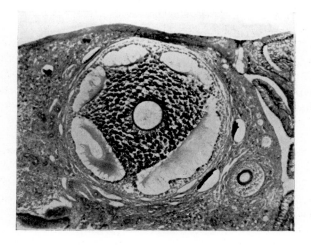

Fig. 6. A mature 'follicle of hibernation' in the bat, *Myotis lucifugus lucifugus*, showing the abundance and distribution of glycogen in the cells of the discus proligerus and its connecting retinacula. Bauer-Feulgen stain. (Reproduced by permission from Wimsatt and Kallen, 1957.)

corpora lutea of pregnancy (Wimsatt and Kallen, 1957). Also, in the mouse and rabbit, glycogen appears increasingly in corpora lutea during the first part of pregnancy and again at the time of regression (Togari, 1927; Kondo, 1936); it is also conspicuous in the rabbit's interstitial gland during pregnancy. The latter finding is of interest in view of Hökfelt's (1951) biochemical work on the glycogen content of this tissue in pregnant rabbits following gonadotrophic stimulation. He found a rapid fall of glycogen within 3 hours, and the low level was maintained for about 24 hours.

Q

The most remarkable and striking phenomenon, however, as far as localization of ovarian glycogen is concerned, occurs in the maturing follicle of hibernating bats. This was apparently first discovered by Nakano (1928) in *Vespertilio abramus*, fell into oblivion and was re-discovered and investigated in greater detail by Wimsatt (1949) and Wimsatt and Kallen (1957) in *Myotis lucifugus lucifugus* as well as in seven other species of hibernating bats. Nakano, using Best's carmine, found that there was so much glycogen in the follicular epithelial cells of larger follicles (approx. 400μ diameter) that "in the stained prepara-tion one could see the follicle with the unaided eye as a red roundish body" (transl.). Follicles in this condition are present only during hiber-nation, so that later Wimsatt and Kallen refer to them as "follicles of hibernation". It is the cumulus which is predominantly affected (Fig. 6) and which on account of the massive intracellular glycogen load assumes huge dimensions, leaving only a crescentic space for the liquor. The largest amount of glycogen is in the cells surrounding the oocyte so that a gradient is suggested, perhaps connected with the peri-pheral thecal blood supply. These follicles persist for 5–7 months in this preovulatory state—a phenomenon unique amongst mammals—and Wimsatt and Kallen consider this chemical specialization as an "adaptation to meet the energy requirements of the ovum-follicle complex during the prolonged period of dormancy, when the general metabolism of the hibernating animal is drastically reduced." Survival and subsequent full maturation of follicles depend on it. A parallel is found in the uterus where—if fertile copulation has occurred—sperms survive during hibernation with their heads attached to the glycogen-laden uterine epithelium (Nakano, 1928). Non-hibernating bats do not show this specialization of the cumulus (Wimsatt, 1944).

2. 'Mucopolysaccharides'

(a) General considerations

The still incompletely understood group of substances known as mucopolysaccharides and/or carbohydrate-protein complexes has a wide distribution. All give a more or less pronounced saliva-resistant PAS reaction. Some of them are strongly acidic and may or may not occur as esters of sulphuric acid. These are usually loosely combined with protein. Others, the so-called neutral mucopolysaccharides, are generally found in firm combination with protein (the gonadotrophic hormones or their precursors are examples of this kind). But it is important to realize that mixtures of the various, somewhat arbitrarily defined mucopolysaccharides also occur, and this fact may well account for apparently inconsistent or divergent histochemical reactions. Acid mucopolysaccharides are further characterized by giving a strong,

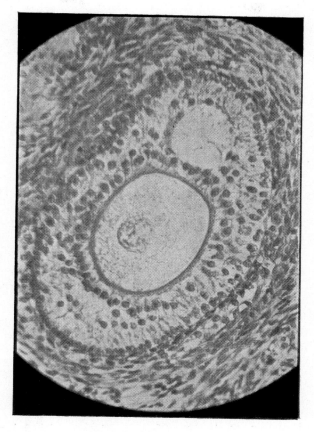

Fig. 7. Cat ovary. PAS reaction (saliva-controlled), to show positive reaction of zona pellucida and liquor folliculi.

[facing page 210.

3. OVARIAN HISTOCHEMISTRY 211

so-called γ-metachromasia, whilst muco-proteins or neutral mucopoly-saccharides may or may not show a metachromasia of the β-type, i.e. a less complete colour change towards red. Although the strongest and alcohol-fast metachromasia is given by sulphated mucopolysacch-arides, sulphation is no longer considered a prerequisite for the meta-chromatic reaction. It seems that the degree of dye-polymerization, dye and substrate concentrations, are of equal or even greater impor-tance (Michaelis and Granick, 1945; Michaelis, 1947; Zachariae and Jensen, 1958); much uncertainty, however, still surrounds the mech-anism, significance and interpretation of metachromasia.

In the following account PAS-positive material always refers to material stainable by the periodic acid-Schiff (PAS) reaction even after incubation with saliva or malt diastase. In the majority of the in-vestigations reviewed the PAS reaction was performed, and in a few unspecified instances Bauer's reaction.

Minute PAS-positive granules have been seen in the germinal epithelium (Harter, 1948) and in primary oocytes (Leblond, 1950) of the rat, but the extra-gonadal primordial germ cells, in man, were found devoid of any saliva-resistant PAS-reactive material (McKay et al., 1953). PAS-positive material was found in the general ovarian stroma, in connection with the fibres of the theca interna and of corpora lutea (Moss et al., 1954) and particularly in the cortical stroma (Leblond, 1950; Moog and Wenger, 1952; Moss et al., 1954). It is perhaps not unreasonable to suggest that the mucopolysaccharides present in the stroma may be involved in the little understood and probably very complex mechanism of ovulation. Besides a rise of intrafollicular pressure (for a possible mechanism see Zachariae and Jensen, 1958), proteinase activity acting on collagen, special localized vascular conditions, depolymerization of mucoid substances and viscosity changes may all play an important part.

(b) *Zona pellucida*

This structure gives consistently a positive PAS reaction (e.g. in the mouse, rat, rabbit, cat, bat, cow, sheep and sow; see Fig. 7), which, according to Harter (1948), Chang and Hunt (1956), Hadek (1958) and others, is not affected by hyaluronidase. Da Silva Sasso (1959), however, found in rabbit ovaries that after 18 hours incubation with hyaluronidase the intensity of the PAS reaction and of some other staining tests was much reduced or staining abolished altogether. Hence he concluded that the zona pellucida contains hyaluronic acid in addition to other acid mucopolysaccharides. Of various proteolytic enzymes trypsin has been found the most active in dissolving the zona, especially of hamster eggs (Braden, 1952; Chang and Hunt, 1956).

Much higher enzyme concentrations and longer incubation periods were needed for rat and rabbit eggs; yet in these last two species additional sperms often penetrate into the perivitelline space, though not in the hamster. Braden (1952) also demonstrated protein histochemically, and concluded that the zona (in the rat and rabbit) consists of a polysaccharide-protein complex, a neutral or weakly acid mucoprotein, the type of protein differing in the two species. The zona in the rat dissociates at pH 5, while that of the rabbit requires greater acidity; H_2O_2 removes the zona in both species.

Metachromasia of the zona seems to vary amongst the different species. In the rat it is absent, but occurs in the sow, cat and sheep, and is weak and alcohol-labile in the rabbit (Braden, 1952). Hyaluronidase does not affect the metachromasia of the zona pellucida in the sow (Wislocki et al., 1947), but was found to weaken it in the rabbit (da Silva Sasso, 1959). Thus it seems that the mucopolysaccharides or polysaccharide-mucoproteins of the zona in the cat, sheep and sow have a composition or concentration different from that in the rat; they may, indeed, differ from species to species. Harter, who was the first to discover that the PAS-reactive material of the zona was most readily soluble at an acid pH, suggested that this property might be connected with the process of sperm penetration, as it is known that actively motile sperms create an acid environment around themselves. Braden, however, thinks that the presence of H_2O_2, known to be formed by sperms, may be a more important factor for sperm penetration than acidity. The presence of the mucopolysaccharides as such, being a viscous material, may be instrumental in sperm adhesion (Leblond, 1950).

(c) *Liquor folliculi*

The positive PAS reaction of this material is another consistent finding for all species studied, and there is no doubt that more than one mucopolysaccharide is present in this fluid, one being hyaluronic acid. The liquor shows varying degrees of metachromasia (Wislocki et al., 1947; Dempsey et al., 1947; Palla, 1947; Vincent and Dornfeld, 1948; Deane, 1952; Braden, 1952; Vimeux, 1952; Halmi and Davies, 1953; Davies et al., 1957; Hadek, 1958; Zachariae and Jensen, 1958). Palla noted that in immature follicles the metachromatic material was present in network distribution, but was diffuse in mature follicles. In general, the metachromatic staining of the liquor becomes weaker in the preovulatory phase (e.g. Buño and Hekimian, 1955), probably due to hydration. Treatment with hyaluronidase abolishes the metachromasia of the liquor but not the PAS reaction (Wislocki et al., 1947; Harter, 1948; Braden, 1952; Buño and Hekimian, 1955; Hadek, 1958;

Zachariae and Jensen, 1958). On the other hand, Odeblad (1952d) reported that in the follicular fluid of rabbits the degree of metachromasia parallels the intensity of ^{35}S autoradiography (see p. 229). This indicates that sulphated polysaccharides are additional constituents of follicular fluid, at least in this species; Vimeux (1952), finding that drops of liquor folliculi would prolong clotting time, also suggested the presence of heparin. Recently, Jensen and Zachariae (1958) have isolated a chondroitin sulphuric acid and hyaluronic acid from the liquor of bovine Graafian follicles. They found that the molecular weight of the mucopolysaccharides decreases with maturation of the follicles and that the preovulatory follicle contains a thermolabile, non-dialyzable substance capable of degrading the isolated acid mucopolysaccharides (see also Zachariae, 1959).

The matrix of the cumulus in rabbits and rats was found to give a strong γ-metachromasia, also removable by hyaluronidase (Braden, 1952).

In discussing the mucopolysaccharides of the liquor reference must also be made to the granulosa cells. Harter (1948) found in the follicular epithelial cells of rats small PAS-positive granules and intercellular PAS-positive cement material, both readily extractable by buffers and removable by hyaluronidase. This enzyme is present in high concentration in sperms; hence its physiological function, as suggested by Austin (1948), may well be to help the sperm to traverse the layer of cumulus cells and thus to reach the ovum. In the cells around the antrum, Harter found larger PAS-positive granules, less readily extractable and not removed by hyaluronidase. Furthermore, there was a general increase in the larger PAS granules prior to ovulation, the time when much follicular fluid is formed. Harter concluded that the small PAS granules are related to the formation of intercellular cementing material and the large ones are precursors of liquor folliculi. The latter view is consistent with Odeblad and Boström's (1953) observations on the distribution of ^{35}S in Graafian follicles of rabbits at different times after administration of the isotope (see p. 229).

These observations also shed light on the problem of the formation of the zona pellucida. Harter thinks that it is probably formed from the ovum rather than from the follicular epithelial cells since at the time the zona makes its appearance the follicular epithelial cells do not yet contain any PAS-positive granules; this contention, however, is not supported by electron microscopy.

In addition, mucopolysaccharides (PAS-positive material) are found in the following sites: the basement membrane of follicles (largely removable by hyaluronidase); Call-Exner bodies, which are probably mere variants of accumulated liquor, though they have been said to contain glycogen (Smith and Ketteringham, 1938); the glassy membrane of atretic follicles (Moss *et al.*, 1954); the cytoplasm of atretic oocytes, where it is of a quality different from that occurring in normal oocytes (Harter, 1948) and certain spherical inclusions in some lutein cells in the cow (Moss *et al.*). The latter may be similar to the lipo-mucoprotein (PAS-positive) material observed and described, as already mentioned, by Leckie (1954, 1955); this, however, was not confined to intra- and extracellular sites in corpora lutea, but occurred also as globules between granulosa cells.

3. *Ascorbic acid*

The depletion of the adrenal cortex of ascorbic acid is used as a method of assay for adrenocorticotrophic hormone (ACTH). This and many other observations, clinical and experimental, have led to the assumption of a close connection between ascorbic acid and adrenal steroid hormone metabolism, though little is known of the nature of this relationship. As a corollary the distribution, content and localiza- tion of ascorbic acid in the ovary have been investigated, histochemically and biochemically, both as such and in relation to changing ovarian states. Ascorbic acid reduces silver nitrate in acid solution. In the histochemical test black granules are precipitated at sites where ascorbic acid is concentrated. The specificity of the test seems high, localization only approximate.

Gough and Zilva (1933) were probably the first to report a positive reaction given by corpora lutea in ovaries of women, cows, guinea pigs and rats. Giroud *et al.* (1934) and Giroud and Leblond (1935) found silver granules in interstitial cells and in corpora lutea, both cyclic and gestational ones, of the rat, rabbit, guinea pig, hedgehog, cat and cow. They emphasized the variability in the amount of granules, which they thought indicative of functional fluctuations. Höfliger (1948) mentions an increase in vitamin C in the growing corpus luteum of the cycle in the cow. Hoch-Ligeti and Bourne (1948), studying rat ovaries during oestrous cycles, found a dense deposition of granules in the peripheral cytoplasm of oocytes, subsequently confirmed by Deane (1952). The germinal epithelium showed an increased number of granules at metoestrus; the largest accumulation of granules, however, occurred, also at metoestrus, in the membrana granulosa, i.e. at the time of its transformation into lutein tissue. No cyclic variations with respect to ascorbic acid content were seen in the corpora lutea. Deane (1952) mentions as the main sites of ascorbic acid granules, in rats' ovaries, the theca interna cells, lutein cells, interstitial cells and the granulosa cells of large follicles becoming atretic at the time of ovulation; the parallelism between this localization and that of lipid droplets is unlikely to be fortuitous.

Miller and Everett (1948) discovered that injection of LH into pregnant rats causes an increased concentration of ascorbic acid in the corpora lutea at the same time as cholesterol accumulates (Schultz test becoming strongly positive). If, in addition to LH, an excess dose of LTH is given, ascorbic acid concentration is lowered more rapidly than that of cholesterol; this parallels the situation in the adrenal cortex following ACTH stimulation. Claesson *et al.* (1949) and Hökfelt (1950) made somewhat similar observations (only biochemical) on the ascorbic acid content of the interstitial gland and of gestational corpora lutea in rabbits following gonadotrophic stimulation. It is worth mentioning that the concentration of ascorbic acid in the unstimulated interstitial gland was found to be about fifty times as high as that of blood.

D. Enzymes*

1. *Steroid-3β-ol-dehydrogenase*

Of the various enzymes whose presence in tissue sections can be visualized, one, steroid-3β-ol-dehydrogenase, has to be singled out because of its direct involvement in steroid hormone synthesis; its demonstration, by a very complex microscopic histochemical method, has recently been described by Wattenberg (1958). As far as the ovary is concerned—the enzyme is present also in testis, adrenal cortex and placenta—Wattenberg found it to be localized intracellularly in corpora lutea (granulosa lutein cells) of man and rat and in the interstitial cells of rat and rabbit. The histochemical localization is in agreement with quantitative biochemical data. Of all steroids used as substrates only dehydro*epi*androsterone and pregnenolone gave positive results; hence the reaction appears highly specific. The important inference is that—apart from the corpus luteum—the interstitial cells are shown to be capable of progesterone synthesis, or, more precisely, the terminal step of this synthesis.

2. *Alkaline phosphomonoesterase*

Some of the histochemical work on alkaline phosphatase (AP) done with Gomori's calcium-cobalt-sulphide method suffers from the effects of overlong incubation periods which are apt to result in diffusion artifacts (Jacoby and Martin, 1949; Martin and Jacoby, 1949; Cleland, 1950, and others). Intense nuclear reactions, particularly suspicious in this respect, have been repeatedly reported for various ovarian tissues. This has made assessment of AP activity often difficult and

* For a recent account of the histo-enzymology of the ovary, see Arvy (1960).

some selection necessary. Obviously, some of the work will have to be repeated with shorter incubation times and controlled by the azo-dye method, which is practically free from the drawback of diffusion. Some workers have used a variety of substrates, but the results have not differed sufficiently to warrant special reference.

(a) *AP of primordial germ cells*

The histochemical demonstration of AP will probably be linked for ever with the hypothesis, and its proof, of the extra-gonadal origin of the primordial germ cells in mammals. It is true that, with standard histological methods, careful examination of normal embryonic material and of material that had resulted from experimental intervention in ontogenesis (Everett, 1943) had already produced much evidence in favour of this hypothesis; and the path of migration of the primordial germ cells from the yolk sac endoderm, where they were first seen, to the mesoderm of the genital ridge had been repeatedly described (for a review of the literature see Chapter 1; also Witschi, 1948). Distribution and size of certain cells were the main criteria, which, however, were not generally agreed upon and, indeed, were open to argument.

In 1950 Baxter, using Gomori's method on a 10 mm human embryo, noticed that the very cells having the above criteria of primordial germ cells gave a very strong cytoplasmic and nuclear AP reaction. At that stage they were seen in the dorsal mesentery and the mesoderm on the medial aspect of each mesonephros. McKay *et al.* (1953) investigated a whole series of human embryos, ranging in size from 5–35 mm, by the azo-dye technique. The high cytoplasmic AP activity of the primordial germ cells was in this way clearly demonstrated and their path of migration revealed. At the 23 mm stage most of these AP-positive primordial germ cells had arrived in the gonad (Fig. 8). This agrees with a description by Rossi *et al.* (1951a) of an obviously Gomori-'overstained' undifferentiated gonad of a human embryo of the same length. This contained large round cells with an AP reaction both in cytoplasm and nucleus and small cells showing merely a 'reacting' nuclear membrane. Later, Rossi and Reale (1957) described the presence of AP-positive extra-gonadal primordial germ cells in a 4·5 mm human embryo. Chiquoine (1954) studied fifty mouse embryos (from day 6–12 post coitum) in serial sections stained by Gomori's method and confirmed the migratory route of the primordial germ cells; he also obtained total germ cell counts and so was able to demonstrate the increase in germ cell population. McAlpine (1955) made corresponding observations on the rat.

These studies, using the AP reaction as a ready marker of primordial germ cells, go a long way in supporting the view of the extra-gonadal origin and migration of the primordial germ cells. Further evidence, practically amounting to definite proof, has come from genetic experiments on sterility-producing mutations in certain strains of mice (Mintz and Russell, 1955, 1957; Mintz, 1957a, b, c). Parents heterozygous to the mutation were mated and all litters, 8–12 days of age, serially sectioned and stained by the azo-dye method for AP. Total

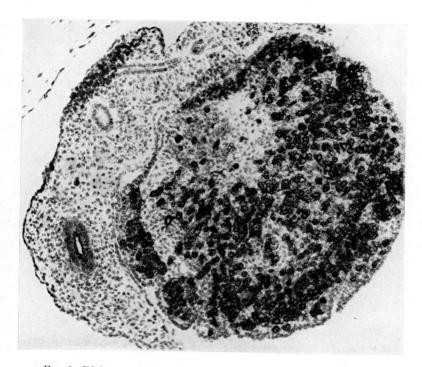

Fig. 8. Right ovary of a 35 mm female human embryo. The gonads of this embryo contain most of the germ cells. Alpha naphthyl alkaline phosphatase. (Reproduced by permission from McKay et al., 1953.)

counts of AP-positive cells (presumably primordial germ cells) were made and their locations recorded (Fig. 9). In approximately 25 per cent of embryos, the expected ratio of defective homozygotes, the number of AP-positive cells was radically reduced and their migration retarded. The eventual result in these homozygotes is sterile gonads. In one series, cases with complete absence of primordial germ cells were observed. In the normal offspring the germ cells were followed through later stages. AP activity was retained in gonia during their intragonadal multiplication phase and in oocytes in the early prophase stages of meiosis (see also Borghese, 1956).

As already referred to, the AP reaction is confined to the cytoplasm of the primordial germ cells and is more pronounced at their extreme periphery, if such precise intracellular localization is permissible. The significance of the enzyme's high concentration in this, as in many other sites, is, however, at present obscure. As mentioned, such cells are also rich in glycogen (p. 208) and RNA (p. 191), and thus everything

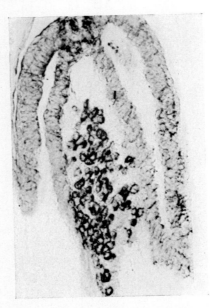

Fig. 9. Normal mouse embryo of 9 days. Azo-dye method for demonstration of alkaline phosphatase. Many germ cells in region of mid-gut (note cytoplasmic AP reaction). (Reproduced by permission from Mintz and Russell, 1957.)

points to a state of great metabolic activity, in which phosphomonoesterases very likely play an important role.

Attempts by Chiquoine and Rothenberg (1957) to reproduce the above results in *Amblystoma* and in chick embryos were unsuccessful, because of a too generalized AP reaction which did not permit selective staining of the primordial germ cells which, in these species, apparently have a low AP concentration. The authors incline to relate this difference to different migratory activity of the primordial germ cells. This is high and definite in mammals, but less clear-cut in chick embryos where the transport of the primordial germ cells to the gonad regions takes place via the blood-vascular system (Willier, 1950; Simon, 1957a, b; see also Chapter 1).

In this connection it is worth noting that Smith and Harley (1956) found the germ cells in gonads of 16–21 day chick embryos AP-negative. This strongly contrasts with the findings in gonads of rat and mouse embryos of comparable ages (McAlpine, 1955; Borghese, 1956; Mintz, 1957b). Borghese emphasizes particularly that in embryonic ovaries of mice only oogonia are AP-positive, but all somatic cells negative.

(b) AP at other ovarian sites

In a human ovary at term Rossi et al. (1951b) found no AP activity in primordial follicles and oocytes, considerable activity in the endothelium of capillaries and arterioles, especially in the theca, and slight activity in some growing or vesicular follicles, but this latter statement can be accepted only with reserve because of the nuclear reaction. The zona pellucida was reported as AP-positive—a rare finding. Corner (1948) noticed it in the rhesus monkey, Moss et al. (1954) in the Graafian follicles of the sow, though not invariably, and Wimsatt (1949) in Myotis, but in other species of bat the zonae were AP-negative.

Absence of AP activity was consistently reported for the germinal epithelium, oocytes and liquor folliculi of adult ovaries.

Positive capillary reactions are frequently encountered in a number of species, particularly in the rat (Gomori, 1941; Jacoby, 1947), so that their occurrence in the theca interna and in the corpus luteum does not necessarily indicate any specialization of these structures with regard to AP activity. Such reactions, especially referring to the corpus luteum, have, however, been frequently reported, e.g. in man (Corner, 1948; Ober, 1950; White et al., 1951; Genesi, 1953); sow (Corner, 1948); bat (Wimsatt, 1949); rat (Deane, 1952; Verne and Hébert, 1952b; Ford and Hirschman, 1955; Buño and Hekimian, 1955; Deane and Fawcett, 1956; Knigge and Leathem, 1956; cf. Fig. 10a); mouse (Moog and Wenger, 1952); cow (Moss et al., 1954); goat (Finocchio et al., 1956); and hamster (Knigge and Leathem, 1956). This, occasionally marked, vascular reaction is apt to cause diffusion artifacts, and thus statements concerning AP activity of theca and granulosa lutein cells have to be accepted with some caution. With this reservation, a simplified Table (Table I) has been compiled which shows the rather variable results of AP tests applied to the large follicles and corpora lutea of different species; Figs. 10–11 serve to illustrate this point.

With the exception of that in rabbits, the theca of large follicles of all the species represented is AP-positive, sometimes very strongly so (e.g. in the sheep: Hadek, 1958; cf. Fig. 11). In view of the fact that

220 F. JACOBY

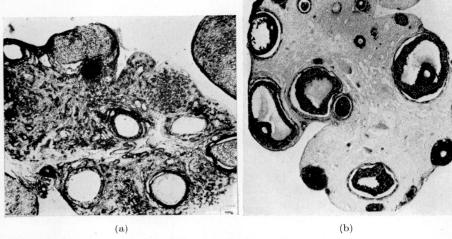

(a) (b)

Fig. 10. Rat and hamster ovary; fixed in cold 80 per cent alcohol and stained for alkaline phosphatase. (a) Rat. The ovarian stroma, endothelium of blood vessels, and theca interna exhibit AP activity, while the granulosa cells are negative. (b) Hamster. Moderate enzyme activity is present in the theca interna, while the stroma is negative. Intense enzyme activity in the granulosa cells is in contrast to that seen in the rat. (Reproduced by permission from Knigge and Leathem, 1956.)

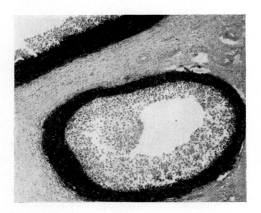

Fig. 11. Sheep ovary. Strong alkaline (non-specific glycero-) phosphatase reaction in the theca interna of Graafian follicles. (Reproduced by permission from Hadek, 1958.)

the granulosa cells are negative in most species, the intense AP reaction of the membrana granulosa in the hamster is worthy of note (Fig. 10b). After ovulation there is, in some instances, a reversal of the AP distribution as between granulosa and theca lutein cells. Intracellular localization has been emphasized by Corner, Knigge and Leathem and by Hadek.

TABLE I

Alkaline phosphatase reaction in Graafian follicles and in corpora lutea of different species

Species	Large Graafian follicles		Corpora lutea	
	Granulosa cells	Theca interna	Granulosa lutein cells	Theca interna
Human	−	+ *	−	+, later −
Sow	−	+	−, later +	+
Cow	−	+ *	+, later ± *	+ *
Sheep	−	+ +	+, later −	+ +
Goat	−	+	−	(+)*
Mouse	−	+ *		+
Rat	−	+ *	+, later − *	−
Bat	−	+		−
Bitch	±	+	−	(+), later −
Guinea pig	(+)	+ +	+ +	+
Rabbit	+	−	+ *	± *
Rhesus monkey	+	+	+ +	+, later −
Hamster	+ +	+ *	(+)	

− = No reaction;   + = definite reaction;
± = occasional positive reaction;   + + = strong reaction;
+) = weak reaction;   * = at least some of the reaction is given by stroma and/or blood vessels.

The theca of corpora lutea in women, the rhesus monkey and bitch is AP-positive for only a short time after ovulation. In the sow, Corner (1948) was able to follow theca interna cells—'labelled' by the AP reaction—invading the granulosa lutein cell layer which is devoid of AP activity and remains so almost up to the 7th week of pregnancy. Then AP appears in the granulosa lutein cells, and the two cell types can no longer be distinguished. In the guinea pig AP activity seems to increase in the granulosa cells after ovulation. In the cow, corpora lutea of early pregnancy, in contrast to those of the cycle, lack AP activity (Moss *et al.*, 1956).

The 'K'-cells of human corpora lutea described by White *et al.* (1951; see also p. 200) were found temporarily AP-positive in both 'cyclic' and gestational corpora lutea. The latter in their entirety were reported as heavily positive by Genesi (1953).

The distribution of AP as set out in the table for follicles refers to normal, more or less mature follicles. Younger follicles or atretic follicles may show a reverse or otherwise different distribution. For instance, in the cow, primary follicles show more AP activity in the granulosa than in the theca (Moss et al., 1954). During atresia, in the rat, Deane (1951, 1952) found that the granulosa cells, normally AP-negative and strongly basophil, become AP-positive, and that this reaction parallels the accumulation of lipids in this layer. Again, Knigge and Leathem (1956) demonstrated, by means of the azo-dye method, a shift of AP activity to the theca in atretic follicles of the hamster, while Moss et al. (1954) recorded AP-positive clumps in atretic ova of the cow.

Interstitial cell tubules derived from the theca have been described as AP-positive in the cow (Moss et al.).

The presence of AP on fibres (? reticulin) of theca and/or corpora lutea in the mouse and hamster has been specially commented upon by Moog and Wenger (1952). Moss et al. (1954) noted the same in the theca of preovulatory follicles in the cow. It can also be seen in the rat (Deane, 1952; Jacoby, unpublished studies) and goat (Finocchio et al., 1956). This links up with other observations which have been made on high AP concentrations in relation to fibre formation (see Bradfield, 1950).

Lastly, Dhom and Mende (1956), in human ovaries, found AP activity consistently displayed by the so-called 'hilus' cells (see p. 205), and its intensity inversely related to the lipid content of these cells, suggesting a connection with fluctuations in hormone production.

The speculations which have been attached to the roles of phosphatases, especially of AP, are too general to serve any useful purpose and merely mask our complete ignorance. It is to be hoped that their demonstration, in high concentration, in particular sites and at particular times will stimulate micro-biochemical research which may eventually succeed in solving the problems set by the presence of these enzymes. At present, we have to be content not only with mapping out their distribution in space and time, but with using each of them as a 'stain' which—as shown—has proved its great worth in the identification of cell types.

3. Non-specific esterases

The distribution and localization of these enzymes in adult mammalian ovaries have been investigated by a number of workers, but the histochemical techniques used varied widely, especially with regard to fixatives and substrates employed. It seems that the esterases which attack long-chain molecules such as 'Tweens' are preserved after acetone fixation, but esterase activity, demonstrable on fresh frozen sections with short-chain esters of naphthol or naphthol AS, is largely destroyed by acetone fixation (Hunter and Kneiske, 1957). Hence the literature contains divergent results, even when similar techniques were used by different workers—quite apart from variations due to species differences. More precise techniques permitting reproducibility will have to be designed before reliance can be placed on the occurrence and distribution of these enzymes.

Nevertheless, the following observations, drawn from existing data, are worth recording.

Entirely negative results were obtained with human adult ovaries (Gomori, 1946; Chessick, 1953). Human primordial germ cells were also found negative (McKay et al., 1953), but germ cells in chick embryos gave a definite response (Smith and Harley, 1956). Positive reactions were also reported for the germinal epithelium in the rat (Barrnett, 1952), guinea pig (Grieten, 1955), hamster (Knigge and Leathem, 1956) and chick embryo (Smith and Harley, 1956).

Little esterase activity was found in primary follicles (Marc Quen, 1950; Barrnett, 1952), considerably more in secondary (antra-containing) follicles, where it was localized at the periphery of and in between the granulosa cells (Marc Quen, 1950; Hunter and Kneiske, 1957; see Fig. 12a), though the reliability of this localization is doubtful.

Corpora lutea have been found esterase-positive in the dog, rabbit, guinea pig, rat and mouse (Gomori, 1946; Marc Quen, 1950; Barrnett, 1952; Verne and Hébert, 1952a, b; Ishida, 1954; Grieten, 1955; Buño and Hekimian, 1955; Hunter and Kneiske, 1957). The reaction product is granular and confined mainly to the cytoplasm of the granulosa lutein cells (Fig. 12b). Activity in the theca was noted by Ishida. A moderate, sometimes even a marked reaction has also been obtained in interstitial cells and the interstitial gland of the rat, guinea pig and rabbit, respectively (Fig. 13).

The reactivity in corpora lutea and interstitial cells was obtained with both 'Tweens' and short-chain esters (indoxyl acetate, α-naphthol acetate) as substrates, which suggests that in these locations at least two different esterases are present.

As a curiosity it may be added that connective tissue cells, probably of the macrophage type—sometimes found scattered in the stroma, sometimes aggregated around the periphery of a corpus luteum—gave a particularly strong esterase reaction which was not abolished by acetone fixation (Nachlas and Seligman, 1949; Hunter and Kneiske, 1957).

224 F. JACOBY

The most important and reliable outcome of these fragmentary investigations on esterases is their occurrence in corpora lutea.

On the basis of histochemical studies, Verne and Hébert gained the impression that esterase activity of the corpora lutea paralleled their functional activity and suggested that the enzyme plays an important role in the elaboration of progesterone. They do not say precisely how they visualize the action of an esterase in this process, but the idea is supported by other data pointing to a relationship between esterase and

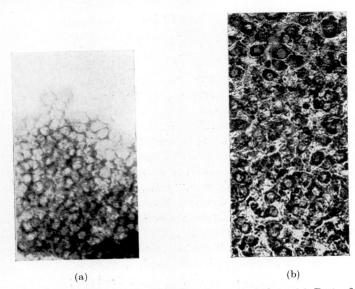

(a)   (b)

Fig. 12. Rat ovary. Non-specific esterase reaction. (a) Part of secondary follicle. The cells of the granulosa layer are surrounded by intensely reactive material with some reactivity probably in the cell membrane. (b) Corpus luteum. The reaction in the lutein cells is confined to the cytoplasm. (Reproduced by permission from Hunter and Kneiske, 1957.)

gonadal hormone metabolism. It would be interesting to compare histo- and biochemical estimations of esterase activity on excised corpora lutea of known ages.

4. Other enzymes

Other enzymes whose presence and localization in ovaries have been demonstrated histochemically are *succinic dehydrogenase* (rat: Padykula, 1952; rabbit: Foraker and Denham, 1952; Foraker *et al.*, 1955; woman: Foraker *et al.*, 1953; bitch: Nachlas *et al.*, 1957b); *β-glucuronidase* (rat: Friedenwald and Becker, 1948; Seligman *et al.*, 1954; Fishman and Baker, 1956); *amylophosphorylase* (woman: Takeuchi *et al.*, 1955); *leucine-aminopeptidase* (guinea pig: Nachlas *et al.*, 1957a); and *TPN and DPN diaphorase* (mouse: Merklin, 1958). In the last instance highest activity was recorded in corpora lutea on day 6 of pregnancy. It is of interest to note that intense amylophosphorylase activity was found in arterial walls, none in follicles. This could be construed as additional indirect evidence against the existence of smooth muscle fibres around follicles.

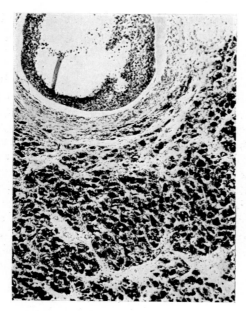

FIG. 13. Rabbit ovary. Marked esterase activity in interstitial gland cells. Naphthol AS technique. (Reproduced by permission from Chessick, 1953.)

Succinic dehydrogenase activity deserves some special comments. Histochemically, the corpora lutea of rats showed varying degrees of activity, gestational ones more than those of the cycle. This agrees with the earlier biochemical work on this enzyme by Meyer *et al.* (1945, 1947) who, using excised homogenized corpora lutea, demonstrated that SDH-activity can be used as a criterion of luteal activity. Foraker and Denham (1952) and Foraker *et al.* (1953, 1955) extended the histochemical work on this enzyme to rabbit and human ovaries. They confirmed the high activity in corpora lutea (mainly in the granulosa lutein cells) and, in the rabbit, observed it also in the interstitial gland. In addition, they recorded fair SDH-activity in granulosa and theca

R

interna cells of developing follicles, and correlated the pattern of distribution of this enzyme with both presumed sites of hormone production and places of cellular proliferation.

E. Autoradiography

This technique has, in recent years, come into use as a means of localizing experimentally administered radioactive isotopes in histological sections. The application of this method to the mammalian ovary has so far been limited to only a few elements, mainly ^{32}P and ^{35}S. The following results throw further light on the dynamic events in the ovary.

1. *Uptake of* ^{32}P

Leblond *et al.* (1948) determined the sites of newly-formed DNA by means of autoradiography, after injections of ^{32}P as phosphate into female rats. The technical design of the experiments was such that all P-containing compounds, except DNA, were largely removed. In general, high activity was recorded over places of high mitotic activity. In the ovary the authors found 24 hours after intravenous injection of ^{32}P a strong reaction limited to the granulosa of some follicles. The lack of reaction in other large follicles was explained as being due to either beginning atresia or the attainment of full maturity.

These results were confirmed, considerably amplified and extended to other species (rabbit, guinea pig, mouse) by Odeblad and his coworkers (Odeblad, 1951, 1952a, b; Block *et al.*, 1953; Englund and Odeblad, 1953; Nati and Odeblad, 1955), by Gothié (1954a) and Petersohn (1958).

There was little reaction over primordial follicles, but normal growing follicles showed some and Graafian follicles considerable radioactivity, especially in the granulosa but also in the theca interna, whilst atretic follicles contained only small amounts of ^{32}P. Normal oocytes of Graafian follicles showed very little ^{32}P, and least was present in follicular fluid. The difference in ^{32}P uptake between normal and atretic follicles was studied in greater detail by Block *et al.* (1953). Normal Graafian follicles ('stage 3') were clearly distinguishable on that basis from atretic ones, but normal primordial and ripening follicles did not differ greatly from atretic ones of the same stages. Growing corpora lutea showed considerable uptake of ^{32}P (Fig. 14), regressing ones little (Odeblad, 1952a). The massive incorporation of ^{32}P corresponds in time to the period of growth and specific endocrine function of the corpus luteum. Though much of the ^{32}P revealed is nucleic acid (DNA *and* RNA) and protein-phosphorus, there is additional evidence that phospholipids (see p. 201) are also involved in the high uptake of ^{32}P

(Odeblad, 1952d; Englund and Odeblad, 1953; Petersohn, 1958). In some of these studies, histology, autoradiography, and quantitative photometric records have been carefully related (Fig. 15).

The interstitial gland showed moderate uptake of ^{32}P both in untreated rabbits and in rabbits given human chorionic gonadotrophin,

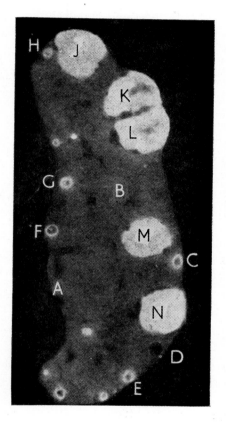

Fig. 14. Rabbit ovary. Autoradiograph after injection of ^{32}P (6 hours before death). White areas indicate high ^{32}P concentrations. J-N: corpora lutea; C, E–H: healthy follicles; D: probably atretic follicle; B: interstitial gland. (Reproduced by permission from Odeblad, 1952a.)

but increased uptake following combined administration of human chorionic gonadotrophin and pregnant mares' serum. By comparing birefringence and ^{32}P uptake, it was found that a high degree of birefringence (phase of storage of oestrogen-precursor; 'secretory rest') was associated with a low incorporation of ^{32}P, whilst an interstitial

gland, almost depleted of birefringent material (phase of hormone release) would show strong ^{32}P activity (Odeblad, 1952b). It seems then
that the transformation of cholesterol into the active oestrogenic
hormone and its release involves a high turnover of phosphorous
compounds.

It is perhaps strange that the oocyte showed so little or hardly any
^{32}P activity, but it should be recalled that the unfertilized sea urchin

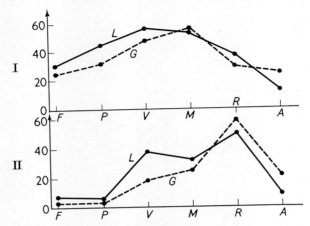

Fig. 15. Results of a quantitative autoradiographic study with ^{32}P
of artificially induced corpora lutea in the rabbit: I, periphery (the
lutein zone); II, centre. Ordinates: number of ^{32}P atoms per 1000 μ^3,
provided that 1 mC/kg was given to the animal. Abscissae: stage of
development (F = Graafian follicle, P = stage of proliferation,
V = stage of vascularization, M = stage of maturity, R = stage of
regression, A = corpus albicans stage). L indicates the curves
obtained by photometer recording. G indicates the curves obtained by
grain counting. Each point of the curve is the mean of 4–8 observations. (Reproduced by permission from Englund and Odeblad, 1953.)

egg, in contrast to the fertilized one, permits hardly any labelled ortho-
phosphate to enter (Lindberg, 1950). Perhaps this applies also to the
mammalian oocyte.

Thus ^{32}P activity is found highest over growing (proliferating and
enlarging) and over actively hormone-secreting cells, and is related to
NA- and phospholipid metabolism.

2. Uptake of ^{35}S

Uptake of ^{35}S by ovarian structures, mainly of rabbits, was also
investigated by Odeblad (1952c, d, e), Boström and Odeblad (1952),
Odeblad and Boström (1953), Gothié (1954a, b), Nati and Odeblad
(1955) and by Zachariae (1957) after injection of ^{35}S as sulphate. None

or very little was found in primary oocytes at any stage; some, variable in extent, was present in granulosa cells of larger follicles, but very large amounts in follicular fluid (Fig. 16). With regard to corpora lutea, practically no ^{35}S was found in lutein cells, moderate amounts in the connective tissue of mature corpora lutea and large amounts in that of old ones. As it is known that S as sulphate ion is not used for amino acid synthesis it is perhaps not surprising that no evidence was obtained for its incorporation into the growing oocyte*. On the other hand, ^{35}S as sulphate enters readily into esterified mucopolysaccharides; hence the strong reaction given by liquor folliculi. Also the radio-activity recorded for the connective tissue of corpora lutea may be

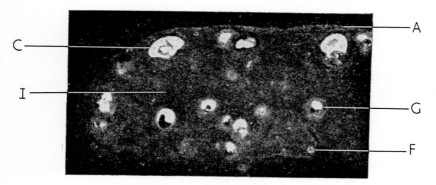

Fig. 16. Rabbit ovary. Autoradiograph to show uptake of ^{35}S. *I*: interstitial gland; *C*: liquor folliculi; *G*: granulosa layer; *F*: small follicle with central oocyte; *A*: tunica albuginea. (Reproduced by permission from Boström and Odeblad, 1952.)

due to the ground matrix material associated with collagen. Meta-chromasia given by liquor folliculi to varying degrees correlates well with this ^{35}S activity (see p. 213), although Dempsey *et al.* (1947), found the liquor only very weakly, if at all, acid.

Interestingly, there was no evidence of ^{35}S activity over the zona pellucida of ovarian oocytes, in spite of the fact that this structure (as mentioned before, p. 211) gives a strong saliva-resistant PAS reaction and occasionally shows metachromasia, but when an ovum (fertilized or not) passes through the uterine tube, its zona pellucida concentrates ^{35}S-containing substances strongly, at least in rabbits (Gothié, 1958).

Further, more dynamic insight into the process of liquor formation was obtained when Odeblad and Boström (1953) followed the sequence of events in the uptake of ^{35}S in Graafian follicles of rabbits by examin-ing sections for maximal radioactive localization at different times

* For incorporation of ^{35}S-methionine, however, see Greenwald and Everett (1959).

(from hours to weeks) after the injection of ^{35}S. They found that at 16 hours there was a peak of radioactivity in theca and, more markedly, in granulosa cells, and only at 48 hours in the liquor folliculi (Fig. 17). This suggests that it is the granulosa cells which incorporate ^{35}S into an organic compound of the mucopolysaccharide type before it is secreted into the follicular fluid (see p. 213). The amount of ^{35}S in the liquor was reduced to half its maximum value in about one week.

Similar observations on the shift with time of ^{35}S in antrum-containing follicles of rabbits were made by Gothié (1954a, b) and Zachariae (1957). Moricard and Gothié (1955) noted in fully mature follicles, following simultaneous coitus or gonadotrophin injection and administration of ^{35}S, a remarkable accumulation of the isotope in cumulus

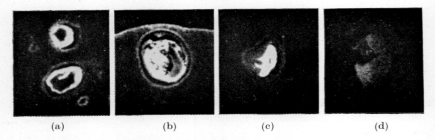

(a)   (b)   (c)   (d)

FIG. 17. Typical autoradiographs of rabbit ovaries: (a) 2 hours; (b) 16 hours; (c) 48 hours and (d) 384 hours after injection of ^{35}S. In (a) small amounts of ^{35}S in the theca and granulosa and hardly any in the liquor. In (b) maximum amounts of ^{35}S in the theca and granulosa, but the liquor still contains only a moderate amount. In (c) the contents of ^{35}S in the theca and granulosa have decreased and the liquor shows maximum incorporation. In (d) the amounts of ^{35}S in the theca, granulosa and liquor are small but still highest in the liquor. (Reproduced by permission from Odeblad and Boström, 1953.)

cells and in the vicinity of the zona pellucida. They interpreted this as evidence for the role of the liquor mediating between gonadotrophin, secretory activity of cumulus cells and the termination of the first maturation division. Zachariae (1957), in similar experiments, found very little or no ^{35}S in the liquor of the rapidly enlarging follicle, from which he concluded that the rapid preovulatory increase in follicular size is not due to a further release of sulphated mucopolysaccharides from the granulosa cells (cf. also Peckham and Kiekhofer, 1959).

Attempts to trace hormones by means of isotopes to their target organs are intriguing. It is therefore worth mentioning that Sonenberg et al. (1951) followed the radioactivity in female rats subsequent to administration of ^{131}I-labelled prolactin. They found in one case a significant concentration in corpora lutea and in another in follicular fluid.

F. Pigments

Haemorrhages occur not infrequently in ovaries, though they vary in extent with the species. Hence blood pigments, especially haemosiderin, can often be found and identified by the usual histochemical methods. Of greater interest, however, are some non-haematogenous pigments. Not to mention these would, incidentally, amount to avoiding the issue of the term 'luteum'. This term was, with justification, first applied to the involuting brick-red 'corpora' of cows' ovaries. As a general term it is a misnomer as has been repeatedly stated, but perhaps most emphatically by Dubreuil (1950). It is probably carotene stored in the granulosa lutein cells which is responsible for the yellow-orange colour which characterizes the corpus luteum of some species, notably that of the cow. Carotene is not present in corpora lutea of rodents, the cat, bitch, sheep and sow (Corner, 1932). Whether it is present in cyclic human corpora lutea and in those of late pregnancy is not yet decided, but it is certain that the human corpus luteum of early pregnancy has very little pigment and is rather greyish in colour.

The pigment accumulating in regressing corpora lutea of the rhesus monkey was studied in some detail by Rossman (1942). He suggested the name 'luteolipin' in preference to Ciaccio's term 'chromolipoid', in order to differentiate it from carotenoids which have also been called chromolipoids. In contrast to most lipids and also to carotene, luteolipin resists extraction with fat solvents and remains stainable with Sudan III even in paraffin sections. It gives a saliva-resistant Bauer reaction. In old corpora lutea it is the predominant cytoplasmic component of the regressing lutein cells, but it also occurs in fair amounts in macrophages. Rossman did not find luteolipin in corpora lutea of sow, sheep and cow; it is also absent from those of goats (Harrison, 1948), but is said to be present in bitch's corpora lutea.

Reagan (1950) described a pale yellow-brownish globular pigment, ceroid, occurring within macrophages at the periphery of involuting corpora lutea and in the interstitial tissue of human ovaries. The pigment was found to be acid-fast, iron-free, stainable with Sudan in paraffin sections, silver-reducing and giving a marked fluorescence of a brownish hue. Reagan refers to it as a lipo-protein complex resulting from disintegration products of lutein cells.

A pigment, somewhat similar to ceroid though not identical with it, was noticed by Fekete (1946) in ovarian interstitial cells of old mice. It was subsequently characterized histochemically in greater detail by Deane and Fawcett (1952). They found it to be acetone-insoluble, sudanophil, to give a positive Schultz test, a positive chromic acid-Schiff reaction and a yellowish-white fluorescence. They suggested that the appearance of this pigment is due to the ageing cells being unable to metabolize lipids which in consequence become gradually transformed into insoluble complexes.

The pigment masses observed by Hadek (1958) within macrophages in corpora albicantia of the sheep seem to be of a similar nature.

III. Concluding remarks

The application of modern histochemical methods to the mammalian ovary has yielded both interesting and illuminating, as well as some unexpected results. Outstanding amongst the latter is the identification of the mammalian primordial germ cells based on their high alkaline phosphatase activity. This discovery has not only resulted in a solution of the long-standing problem of the migration of these cells from extra-gonadal regions into the gonadal folds, but has been successfully applied to the morphological analysis of genetic experiments. Other histochemical methods, particularly those connected with the demonstration of 'lipid' substances, greatly facilitate the recognition and identification of various ovarian structures and cell groups, such as the theca interna, atretic follicles, interstitial cells and different generations of corpora lutea.

Impressive efforts have been made in attempts to elucidate the mode of formation of the steroid hormones. Although the main aim, the visualization, by histochemical means, of these hormones, has apparently not yet been achieved, many relevant data have been accumulated. The main cellular sites of steroid hormone-production are no longer conjectural, but it seems that in all three sites (theca interna, corpora lutea and interstitial cells) both oestrogen and progesterone are being produced*; much evidence also exists that cholesterol serves as precursor substance for both. Gonadotrophic stimulation will mobilize some or all of the cholesterol with corresponding signs of sex-hormone activity. The work of Wattenberg (1958) marks the beginning of a new line of histochemical attack on this problem, and indeed of a direct approach to the mechanism of hormone synthesis. An extension of this work to cyclic phenomena may well be fruitful. It is conceivable that gonadotrophic hormones act on such 'intermediate' enzyme systems and, depending on their own relative proportions, may activate, at certain times, an enzyme system that serves oestrogen formation and, at others, systems that result in the conversion of cholesterol into both oestrogen and progesterone. (It should be mentioned that so far no

* Recent work by Falck (1959), however, suggests that some synergistic action of granulosa cell tissue is necessary.

reference to the site of relaxin production seems to have been made in histochemical work). The increase in succinic dehydrogenase in growing and actively functioning corpora lutea is another instance of enzyme-hormone relationship. Meyer and McShan (1950a, b) have suggested that this enzyme may be involved in the development of the necessary energy for the specific cell function: synthesis and secretion of hormone. This enzyme is mainly, if not exclusively, localized in mitochondria. There is perhaps a link here to the phospholipid staining of lutein cells of young corpora lutea, as reported by Barker (1951) and Buño (1957) (see p. 201).

Any discussion of the localization of alkaline phosphatase in the ovary (see p. 215 ff., above) is handicapped by the conspicuous lack of precise knowledge about the part played by this enzyme in general or specific cellular metabolic processes, as it may reasonably be involved in many chains of reactions. Another complication arises in relation to biochemical data. For instance, Meyer and McShan (1950a, b) found considerably increased AP activity in tissue homogenates of growing and functioning corpora lutea of rats. The interpretation of this biochemical finding in terms of functional activity of the lutein cells is made difficult by the fact that, histochemically, AP in these corpora is predominantly localized in the vascular tissue. This shows the importance of histochemical studies as a necessary adjunct to, and ally of, biochemical work. With regard to the possible role of AP in this situation, it may be instrumental, as suggested for other sites of high AP activity, in the rapid transfer of substances across cell membranes, in this instance from blood to lutein cells via the endothelium and vice versa. In some instances, however, AP has been stated to be present within the lutein cells, and here its role may be more intimately related to the specific metabolism of these cells (Stafford et al., 1947; see also Pinkerton, 1959).

The presence of AP in actively differentiating organs during embryogenesis has been repeatedly reported (see Borghese, 1957) and its close association with RNA and/or glycogen emphasized. The cyclically differentiating ovarian structures offer a parallel, but the association with RNA is not close and that with glycogen even less. The possible roles assigned to AP are highly speculative but plausible; amongst them is its hydrolytic action in breaking down organic phosphoric compounds, thus making available the building stones for the synthesis of complex substances such as nucleic acids and glucoproteins or mucopolysaccharides. Another is the formation of fibrous proteins. In such processes the enzyme may even become adsorbed on, or fixed to, the newly formed material. In this way the AP reaction of reticular fibres (e.g. in the theca) may be brought about. The same could hold

s

for the zona pellucida, but it is the exception rather than the rule to find this structure AP-positive. This could be due to different concentrations of enzyme existing in different species. Since large amounts of enzyme are lost in paraffin-embedded material, it might be useful to repeat the work with AP-negative zonae pellucidae on frozen sections.

The existence of local 'inductors' and 'organizers' has been postulated not only for the differentiation of the gonads (e.g. Witschi, 1951), but also for that of the cyclic ovarian structures (e.g. Dubreuil, 1950). Nothing is known chemically, let alone histochemically, about these factors. This is only one of many gaps that exist in the histochemical picture which this survey has tried to present. In this jig-saw puzzle many of the discovered pieces are still lying about isolated, only few are linked together. Much patient work is needed before even the outlines of an overall meaningful picture will take shape.

New histochemical methods are being constantly invented and described. They will have to be applied with care and discrimination in *ad hoc* studies to the ovary in all its phases of activity, if further progress is to be made. Sometimes the histochemist by discovering high concentrations of a substance in a particular location may give a hint or lead to the biochemist, sometimes their roles will be reversed. In any case, close co-operation between both is essential; in addition, the 'pure' histologist, with his own technical equipment, may be required to act in a mediating role.

REFERENCES

Albert, S. and Leblond, C. P. (1946). Distribution of Feulgen and 2:4-dinitrophenylhydrazine reactions in normal, castrated, adrenalectomised, and hormonally-treated rats. *Endocrinology*, **39**, 386–400.

Aldman, B., Claesson, L., Hillarp, N.-Å. and Odeblad, E. (1949a). Studies on the storage mechanism of the oestrogen-precursor. *Acta endocr., Copenhagen*, **2**, 24–32.

Aldman, B., Claesson, L., Hillarp, N.-Å. and Odeblad, E. (1949b). Studies on the storage of the oestrogen-precursor in the interstitial gland of the ovary of rats treated with oestradiol benzoate and progesterone. *Acta anat.* **8**, 92–95.

Alfert, M. (1950). Cytochemical study of oögenesis and cleavage in the mouse. *J. cell. comp. Physiol.* **36**, 381–409.

Arvy, L. (1960). Contribution to the histoenzymology of the ovary. *Z. Zellforsch.* **51**, 406–420.

Ashbel, R. and Seligman, A. M. (1949). A new reagent for the histochemical demonstration of active carbonyl groups. A new method for staining ketonic steroids. *Endocrinology*, **44**, 565–583.

Austin, C. R. (1948). Function of hyaluronidase in fertilization. *Nature, Lond.* **162**, 63.

Austin, C. R. and Braden, A. W. H. (1953). The distribution of nucleic acids in rat eggs in fertilization and early segmentation. 1. Studies on living eggs by ultraviolet microscopy. *Aust. J. exp. Biol. med. Sci.* **6**, 324–333.

Barker, W. L. (1951). A cytochemical study of lipids in sows' ovaries during the estrous cycle. *Endocrinology*, **48**, 772–785.

Barrnett, R. J. (1952). The distribution of esterolytic activity in the tissues of the albino rat as demonstrated with indoxyl acetate. *Anat. Rec.* **114**, 577–599.

Bartolomei, G. (1954). Ricerche istochimice sulle cellule dell'ilo ovarico. *Atti Soc. med.-chir. Padova*, **31**, 162–168.

Baxter, J. S. (1950). Alkaline phosphatase in primordial germ cells in a 10 mm human embryo. *Int. Anat. Congr., Oxford*, (Abstr.) 17–18.

Bennett, H. S. (1940). The life-history and secretion of the cells of the adrenal cortex of the cat. *Amer. J. Anat.* **67**, 151–227.

Bierry, H. and Gouzon, B. (1936). La détection spectrale de l'hormone oestrogène dans l'urine de la femme enceinte. *C.R. Acad. Sci., Paris*, **202**, 686–687.

Block, E., Magnusson, G. and Odeblad, E. (1953). A study of normal and atretic follicles with autoradiography. *Acta obstet. gynec. scand.* **32**, 1–6.

Borghese, E. (1956). La fosfatasi alcalina nelle gonadi del *Mus musculus* normale e dell' anemico W/W. *Symp. genetica et biologica Ital.* **5**, 131–140.

Borghese, E. (1957). Recent histochemical results of studies on embryos of some birds and mammals. *Int. Rev. Cytol.* **6**, 289–341.

Boscott, R. J. and Mandl, A. M. (1949). The histochemical demonstration of ketosteroids in adrenal tissue. *J. Endocrin.* **6**, 132–136.

Boscott, R. J., Mandl, A. M., Danielli, J. F. and Shoppee, C. W. (1948). Cytochemical demonstration of ketosteroids. *Nature, Lond.* **162**, 572.

Boström, H. and Odeblad, E. (1952). Autoradiographic observations on the uptake of S^{35} in the genital organs of the female rat and rabbit after injection of labelled sodium sulfate. *Acta endocr., Copenhagen*, **10**, 89–96.

Brachet, J. (1950). "Chemical Embryology." (Transl. by L. G. Barth.) Interscience Publ. Inc., New York.

Brachet, J. (1957). "Biochemical Cytology." Academic Press Inc., New York.

Braden, A. W. H. (1952). Properties of the membranes of the rat and rabbit eggs. *Aust. J. sci. Res.* **5**, 460–471.

Bradfield, J. R. G. (1950). The localization of enzymes in cells. *Biol. Rev.* **25**, 113–157.

Brandenburg, W. (1938). Das Glykogen im Eierstock der Ratte. *Z. mikr.-anat. Forsch.* **43**, 581–594.

Buño, W. (1957). Étude histochimique des phospholipides dans l'ovaire. *C.R. Ass. Anat.* **43**, 842–847.

Buño, W. L. and Hekimian, L. (1955). Estudio histoquímico del ovario de la rata en relación con el cielo estral, la gestación y la lactación. *An. Fac. Med. Montevideo*, **40**, 42–62.

Burkl, W. and Kellner, G. (1954). Über die Entstehung der Zwischenzellen im Rattenovar und ihre Bedeutung im Rahmen der Oestrogenproduktion. *Z. Zellforsch.* **40**, 361–378.

Cain, A. J. (1950). The histochemistry of lipoids in animals. *Biol. Rev.* **25**, 73–112.

Caspersson, T. O. (1950). "Cell Growth and Cell Function." W. W. Norton & Company Inc., New York.

Chang, M. C. and Hunt, D. M. (1956). Effects of proteolytic enzymes on the zona pellucida of fertilized and unfertilized mammalian eggs. *Exp. Cell Res.* **11**, 497–499.

Chessick, R. D. (1953). Histochemical study of the distribution of esterases. *J. Histochem. Cytochem.* **1**, 471–485.

Chiquoine, A. D. (1954). The identification, origin, and migration of the primordial germ cells in the mouse embryo. *Anat. Rec.* **118**, 135–145.

Chiquoine, A. D. and Rothenberg, E. J. (1957). A note on alkaline phosphatase activity of germ cells in *Amblystoma* and chick embryos. *Anat. Rec.* **127**, 31–35.

Claesson, L. (1954a). Effect of N-methylethylphenyl-barbituric acid (Prominal) on the cholesterol content in the ovarian interstitial gland of the rat. *Acta physiol. scand.* **31**, Suppl. 113, 1–10.

Claesson, L. (1954b). Quantitative relationship between gonadotrophic stimulation and lipid changes in the interstitial gland of the rabbit ovary. *Acta physiol. scand.* **31**, Suppl. 113, 23–51.

Claesson, L. (1954c). The intracellular localization of the esterified cholesterol in the living interstitial gland cell of the rabbit ovary. *Acta physiol. scand.* **31**, Suppl. 113, 53–78.

Claesson, L. and Hillarp, N.-Å. (1947a). The formation mechanism of oestrogenic hormones. I. The presence of an oestrogen precursor in the rabbit ovary. *Acta physiol. scand.* **13**, 115–129.

Claesson, L. and Hillarp, N.-Å. (1947b). The formation mechanism of oestrogenic hormones. II. The presence of the oestrogen-precursor in the ovaries of rats and guinea-pigs. *Acta physiol. scand.* **14**, 102–119.

Claesson, L. and Hillarp, N.-Å. (1947c). Critical remarks on the histochemical reactions for ketosteroids. *Acta anat.* **3**, 109–114.

Claesson, L. and Hillarp, N.-Å. (1948). Sterol content of the interstitial gland and corpora lutea of the rat, guinea-pig and rabbit ovary during pregnancy, parturition and lactation. *Acta anat.* **5**, 301–305.

Claesson, L., Diczfalusy, E., Hillarp, N.-Å. and Högberg, B. (1948). The formation mechanism of estrogenic hormones. Lipids of the pregnant rabbit ovary, and their changes on gonadotrophic stimulation. *Acta physiol. scand.* **16**, 183–200.

Claesson, L., Hillarp, N.-Å., Högberg, B. and Hökfelt, B. (1949). Changes in the ascorbic acid content in the interstitial gland of the rabbit ovary following gonadotrophic stimulation. *Acta endocr., Copenhagen*, **2**, 249–256.

Claesson, L., Hillarp, N.-Å. and Högberg, B. (1953). Lipid changes in the interstitial gland of the rabbit ovary at oestrogen formation. *Acta physiol. scand.* **29**, 329–339.

Cleland, K. W. (1950). A study of the alkaline phosphatase reaction in tissue sections. Part II. The histological and cytological validity. *Proc. Linn. Soc., N.S.W.* **75**, 54–69.

Corner, G. W. (1932). Cytology of the ovum, ovary and Fallopian tube. *In* "Special Cytology" (E. V. Cowdry, ed.), Vol. III, pp. 1567–1607. P. B. Hoeber, Inc., New York.

Corner, G. W. (1944). Alkaline phosphatase in the ovarian follicles and corpora lutea. *Science*, **100**, 270–271.

Corner, G. W. (1948). Alkaline phosphatase in ovarian follicle and corpus luteum. *Contr. Embryol. Carneg. Instn.* **32**, 1–8.

Corner, G. W., Hartman, C. G. and Bartelmez, G. W. (1945). Development, organization, and breakdown of the corpus luteum in the rhesus monkey. *Contr. Embryol. Carneg. Instn.* **31**, 117–146.

Dalcq, A. M. (1950). The morphogenetic organization of the oöcyte and follicle in some mammals, including man. *Int. Anat. Congr., Oxford*, (Abstr.) 49–50.

Dalcq, A. (1953a). Fixation de l'oeuf des mammifères et répartition, dans celui-ci, des acides ribonucléiques. *C.R. Soc. Biol., Paris*, **147**, 1259–1261.

Dalcq, A. (1953b). Fixation de l'oeuf des mammifères. Détection de l'acide desoxyribonucléique et relation de celui-ci avec les chromosomes. *C.R. Soc. Biol., Paris*, **147**, 1261–1263.

Dalcq, A. M. (1955). Processes of synthesis during early development of rodents' eggs and embryos. *Studies on Fertility*, **7**, 113–122.

Dalcq, A. and van Egmond, M. (1953). Effets de la centrifugation sur l'oöcyte de trois mammifères. *Arch. Biol., Paris*, **64**, 311–397.

Davies, J., Dempsey, E. W. and Wislocki, G. B. (1957). Histochemical observations on the fetal ovary and testis of the horse. *J. Histochem. Cytochem.* **5**, 584–590.

Dawson, A. B. and McCabe, M. (1951). The interstitial tissue of the ovary in infantile and juvenile rats. *J. Morph.* **88**, 543–571.

Dawson, A. B. and Velardo, J. T. (1955). A histochemical study of lipids of the corpora lutea of the rat during pseudopregnancy. *Amer. J. Anat.* **97**, 303–319.

Deane, H. W. (1951). Histochemical characteristics of atretic follicles in the rats' ovaries. *Anat. Rec.* **111**, 504–505. (Abstr.)

Deane, H. W. (1952). Histochemical observations on the ovary and oviduct of the albino rat during the estrous cycle. *Amer. J. Anat.* **91**, 363–413.

Deane, H. W. (1958). Intracellular lipides: their detection and significance. *In* "Frontiers in Cytology" (S. L. Palay, ed.), pp. 227–263. Yale University Press.

Deane, H. W. and Andrews, J. S. (1953). A comparison of the staining of lipid droplets in the mouse ovary by the Schiff reaction and by the Ashbel-Seligman carbonyl reaction. *J. Histochem. Cytochem.* **1**, 283–295.

Deane, H. W. and Barker, W. L. (1952). A cytochemical study of lipids in the ovaries of the rat and sow during the oestrous cycle. *In* "Testis, Ovary, Eggs and Sperm" (E. T. Engle, ed.), pp. 176–195. C. C. Thomas, Springfield, Ill.

Deane, H. W. and Fawcett, D. W. (1952). Pigmented interstitial cells showing "brown degeneration" in the ovaries of old mice. *Anat. Rec.* **113**, 239–245.

Deane, H. W. and Fawcett, D. W. (1956). Histochemical characteristics of intrasplenic ovarian transplants in gonadectomised rats. *J. nat. Cancer Inst.* **17**, 541–567.

Deane, H. W. and Seligman, A. M. (1953). Evaluation of procedures for the cytological localization of ketosteroids. *Vitam. & Horm.* **11**, 173–204.

Dempsey, E. W. (1948). The chemical cytology of endocrine glands. *Recent Progr. Hormone Res.* **3**, 127–157.

Dempsey, E. W. and Bassett, D. L. (1943). Observations on the fluorescence, birefringence, and histochemistry of the rat ovary during the reproductive cycle. *Endocrinology*, **33**, 384–401.

Dempsey, E. W., Bunting, H., Singer, M. and Wislocki, G. B. (1947). Dye-binding capacity and other chemo-histological properties of mammalian mucopolysaccharides. *Anat. Rec.* **98**, 417–429.

Dhom, G. (1955). Morphologische, quantitative und histochemische Studien zur Funktion der Hiluszellen des Ovars. *Z. Geburtsh. Gynäk.* **142**, 182–228; 289–313.

Dhom, G. and Mende, H. J. (1956). Die alkalische Phosphatase in den Hiluszellen des Ovars. *Virchow's Arch.* **328**, 337–346.

Dubreuil, G. (1950). Les glandes endocrines de l'ovaire féminin. Leur variabilité, leur variations d'après des observations morphologiques personnelles. *Gynéc. Obstét.* **49**, 137–154; 282–292.

Englund, S. and Odeblad, E. (1953). An autoradiographic study with radio-active phosphorus of artificial corpora lutea in the rabbit. *Acta obstet. gynec. scand.* **32**, 13–23.

Everett, J. W. (1945). Microscopically demonstrable lipins of cyclic corpora lutea in rat. *Amer. J. Anat.* **77**, 293–323.

Everett, J. W. (1947). Hormonal factors responsible for cholesterol deposition in corpus luteum of rat. *Endocrinology,* **41**, 364–377.

Everett, N. B. (1943). Observational and experimental evidences relating to the origin and differentiation of the definite germ cells in mice. *J. exp. Zool.* **92**, 49–91.

Falck, B. (1953). Occurrence of cholesterol and formation of oestrogen in the infantile rat ovary. *Acta endocr., Copenhagen,* **12**, 115–122.

Falck, B. (1959). Site of production of oestrogen in the ovary of the rat. *Nature, Lond.* **184**, 1082.

Fekete, E. (1946). Comparative study of ovaries of virgin mice of the dba and C57 black strains. *Cancer Res.* **6**, 263–269.

Finocchio, F., Lombardo, N. and Lo Sardo, G. (1956). Attività fosfomonoestera-sica alcalina e PAS reattività nel corpo luteo estrale della capra. *Boll. Soc. ital. Biol. sper.* **32**, 1382–1385.

Fishman, W. H. and Baker, J. R. (1956). Cellular localization of β-glucuronidase in rat tissues. *J. Histochem. Cytochem.* **4**, 570–587.

Flax, M. H. (1951). Pentose nucleic acids and proteins during oögenesis and early development of the mouse. *Anat. Rec.* **111**, 465. (Abstr.)

Foraker, A. G. and Denham, S. W. (1952). Neotetrazolium in determination of succinic dehydrogenase activity in the ovary. *Proc. Soc. exp. Biol., N.Y.* **80**, 132–134.

Foraker, A. G., Celi, P. A. and Denham, S. W. (1953). Dehydrogenase activity. 1. In the ovary. *Obstet. & Gynec.* **2**, 407–413.

Foraker, A. G., Denham, S. W. and Mitchell, D. D. (1955). Succinic dehydro-genase and endogenous reductase activity in the rabbit ovary in pregnancy. *J. Obstet. Gynaec., Brit. Emp.* **62**, 447–451.

Ford, D. H. and Hirschman, A. (1955). Alkaline phosphatase activity in the ovaries of immature and maturing albino rats. *Anat. Rec.* **121**, 531–544.

Friedenwald, J. S. and Becker, B. (1948). The histochemical localization of glucuronidase. *J. cell. comp. Physiol.* **31**, 303–309.

Geeter, L. de. (1954). Études sur la structure de l'oeuf vierge et les premiers stades du développement chez le cobaye et le lapin. *Arch. Biol., Paris,* **65**, 363–436.

Genesi, M. (1953). Rilievi istotopografici sulla distribuzione della fosfatasi alcalina. Attività enzimatica dell' ovario, dell' utero e delle formazioni annes-siali parovariche umane in condizione normali e patologiche. *Minerva ginec., Torino,* **5**, 302–313.

Gillman, J. and Stein, H. B. (1941). Human corpus luteum of pregnancy. *Surg. Gynec. Obstet.* **72**, 129–149.

Giroud, A. and Leblond, C. P. (1935). Localisations électives de l'acide ascor-bique ou vitamine C. *Arch. Anat. micr. Morph. exp.* **31**, 111–142.

Giroud, A., Leblond, C. P. and Giroux, M. (1934). La vitamine C dans l'ovaire et de corps jaune. *C.R. Acad. Sci., Paris,* **198**, 850–851.

Goldmann, E. E. (1912). Die äussere und innere Secretion des gesunden und kranken Organismus im Lichte der "Vitalen Färbung". *Beitr. klin. Chir.* **78**, 1–108.

Gomori, G. (1939). Microtechnical demonstration of phosphatase in tissue sections. *Proc. Soc. exp. Biol., N.Y.* **42**, 23–26.

Gomori, G. (1941). The distribution of phosphatase in normal organs and tissues. *J. cell. comp. Physiol.* **17**, 71–83.

Gomori, G. (1942). Histochemical reactions for lipid aldehydes and ketones. *Proc. Soc. exp. Biol., N.Y.* **51**, 133–134.

Gomori, G. (1946). Distribution of lipase in the tissues under normal and under pathologic conditions. *Arch. Path.* **41**, 121–129.

Gomori, G. (1952a). "Microscopic Histochemistry." The University of Chicago Press.

Gomori, G. (1952b). The histochemistry of lipid carbonyl compounds. *J. Lab. clin. Med.* **39**, 649–659.

Gothié, S. (1954a). Étude comparée de la répartition du P^{32} et du S^{35} dans l'organisme de lapine, spécialement dans l'ovaire. *C.R. Soc. Biol., Paris*, **148**, 1210–1213.

Gothié, S. (1954b). La réponse folliculaire et ovulaire; emploi des traceurs dans l'étude de la gonadotrophine choriale. *Ann. Endocr., Paris*, **15**, 579–584.

Gothié, S. (1958). Contribution à l'étude de la membrane pellucide de l'oeuf de lapine à l'aide du ^{35}S. *J. Physiol., Paris*, **50**, 293–294.

Gough, J. and Zilva, S. S. (1933). The silver nitrate staining reaction for ascorbic acid in the adrenal, pituitary and ovary of various species of animals. *Biochem. J.* **27**, 1279–1286.

Greenwald, G. S. and Everett, N. B. (1959). The incorporation of S^{35} methionine by the uterus and ova of the mouse. *Anat. Rec.* **134**, 171–184.

Grieten, J. (1955). Les cholinestérases dans l'ovaire. *C.R. Soc. Biol., Paris*, **149**, 826–828.

Groodt, M. de. (1957). Confirmation expérimentale d'une corrélation entre la positivité de la réaction d'Ashbel et Seligman et l'activité des cellules interstitielles de l'ovaire. *Scalpel, Brux.* **110**, 900–905.

Guraya, S. S. (1957). Histochemical studies of lipids in oöcytes. 1. Lipids in the oögenesis of *Columba livia*. *Quart. J. micr. Sci.* **98**, 407–423.

Hack, M. H. (1952). A new histochemical technique for lipides applied to plasmal. *Anat. Rec.* **112**, 275–301.

Hadek, R. (1958). Morphological and histochemical study on the ovary of the sheep. *Amer. J. Vet. Res.* **19**, 873–881.

Hale, A. J. (1957). The histochemistry of polysaccharides. *Int. Rev. Cytol.* **6**, 194–264.

Halmi, N. S. and Davies, J. (1953). Comparison of aldehyde fuchsin staining, metachromasia and periodic-acid-Schiff reactivity of various tissues. *J. Histochem. Cytochem.* **1**, 447–459.

Hamilton, W. J. (1944). Phases of maturation and fertilization in human ova. *J. Anat., Lond.* **78**, 1–4.

Hamilton, W. J. and Day, F. T. (1945). Cleavage stages of the ova of the horse, with notes on ovulation. *J. Anat., Lond.* **79**, 127–130.

Harrison, R. J. (1948). The changes occurring in the ovary of the goat during the oestrous cycle and in early pregnancy. *J. Anat., Lond.* **82**, 21–48.

Harter, B. T. (1948). Glycogen and carbohydrate-protein complexes in the ovary of the white rat during the oestrous cycle. *Anat. Rec.* **102**, 349–367.

Hedberg, E. (1953). The chemical composition of the human ovarian oöcyte. *Acta endocr., Copenhagen*, **14**, Suppl. 15, 1–89.

240   F. JACOBY

Hertig, A. T., Adams, E. C., McKay, D. G., Rock, J., Mulligan, W. J. and Menkin, M. F. (1958). A thirteen-day human ovum studied histochemically. *Amer. J. Obstet. Gynec.* **76**, 1025–1040.

Hintzsche, E. (1956). "Das Aschenbild tierischer Gewebe und Organe", pp. 97–100. Springer Verlag, Berlin.

Hoch-Ligeti, C. and Bourne, G. H. (1948). Changes in concentration and histological distribution of ascorbic acid in ovaries, adrenals, and livers of rats during oestrous cycles. *Brit. J. exp. Path.* **29**, 400–407.

Höfliger, H. (1948). Das Ovar des Rindes in den verschiedenen Lebensperioden unter besonderer Berücksichtigung seiner funktionellen Feinstruktur. *Acta anat.* Suppl. 5, 1–196.

Hökfelt, B. (1950). Changes in the ascorbic acid content of the corpus luteum of pregnancy in the rabbit after gonadotrophic stimulation. *Acta physiol. scand.* **20**, 172–179.

Hökfelt, B. (1951). Changes in the glycogen content of the interstitial gland of the pregnant rabbit ovary following gonadotrophic stimulation. *Acta physiol. scand.* **22**, 231–237.

Hunter, R. L. and Kneiske, K. M. (1957). Quantitative study of non-specific esterase in the rat ovary. *J. Histochem. Cytochem.* **5**, 154–158.

Ishida, K. (1952). Histochemical studies of rat ova with special reference to glycogen of them after ovulation. *Tohoku J. agric. Res.* **3**, 39–49.

Ishida, K. (1954). Histochemical studies of lipase in rat ovaries with special reference to that in normal and atretic ova. *Tohoku J. agric. Res.* **4**, 133–139.

Jacoby, F. (1947). Use of the phosphatase reaction in a method of demonstrating bile capillaries in rats. *J. Physiol.* **106**, 33P.

Jacoby, F. and Martin, B. F. (1949). The histochemical test for alkaline phosphatase. *Nature, Lond.* **163**, 875.

Jensen, C. E. and Zachariae, F. (1958). Studies on the mechanism of ovulation. Isolation and analysis of acid mucopolysaccharides in bovine follicular fluid. *Acta endocr., Copenhagen,* **27**, 356–368.

Jones-Seaton, A. (1950). Étude de l'organisation cytoplasmique de l'oeuf des rongeurs, principalement quant à la basophilie ribonucléique. *Arch. Biol., Paris,* **61**, 291–444.

Knigge, K. M. and Leathem, J. H. (1956). Growth and atresia of follicles in the ovary of the hamster. *Anat. Rec.* **124**, 679–698.

Kondo, Jotaro. (1936). *Mitt. jap. Ges. Gynäk.* **31**. (Ref. *Ber. Biol.* **41**).

Leblond, C. P. (1950). Distribution of periodic acid-reactive carbohydrates in adult rat. *Amer. J. Anat.* **86**, 1–49.

Leblond, C. P., Stevens, C. E. and Bogoroch, R. (1948). Histological localization of newly-formed DNA. *Science,* **108**, 531.

Leckie, F. H. (1954). A histochemical study of the human ovary; preliminary report. *J. Obstet. Gynaec., Brit. Emp.* **61**, 772–776.

Leckie, F. H. (1955). A study of the histochemistry of the human foetal ovary. *J. Obstet. Gynaec., Brit. Emp.* **62**, 542–547.

Lindberg, O. (1950). On surface reactions in the sea urchin egg. *Exp. Cell Res.* **1**, 105–114.

Lison, L. (1936). "Histochimie Animale." Gauthier-Villars, Paris.

Lison, L. (1953). "Histochimie et Cytochimie Animales." Gauthier-Villars, Paris.

Marc Quen, J. (1950). Lipase activity in the ovary of the laboratory mouse. *Anat. Rec.* **106**, 281. (Abstr.)

Martin, B. F. and Jacoby, F. (1949). Diffusion phenomenon complicating the histochemical reaction for alkaline phosphatase. *J. Anat., Lond.* **83**, 351–363.

McAlpine, R. J. (1955). Alkaline glycerophosphatase in the developing adrenal, gonads, and reproductive tract of the white rat. *Anat. Rec.* **121**, 407–408. (Abstr.)

McKay, D. G., Hertig, A. T., Adams, E. C. and Danziger, S. (1953). Histochemical observations on the germ cells of human embryos. *Anat. Rec.* **117**, 201–219.

McKay, D. G., Adams, E. C., Hertig, A. T. and Danziger, S. (1955). Histochemical horizons in human embryos. 1. Five mm embryo. *Anat. Rec.* **122**, 125–144.

McKay, D. G. and Robinson, D. (1947). Observations on the fluorescence, birefringence, and histochemistry of the human ovary during the menstrual cycle. *Endocrinology*, **41**, 378–394.

Merklin, R. J. (1958). TPN and DPN diaphorase in the pregnant mouse. *Anat. Rec.* **130**, 338. (Abstr.)

Meyer, R. K. and McShan, W. H. (1950a). Enzymes in the ovarian tissues of rats. *In* "Menstruation and its Disorders" (E. T. Engle, ed.), pp. 62–94. C. C. Thomas, Springfield, Ill.

Meyer, R. K. and McShan, W. H. (1950b). Hormone-enzyme relationship. *Recent Progr. Hormone Res.* **5**, 465–512.

Meyer, R. K., McShan, W. H. and Erway, W. F. (1945). Succinic dehydrogenase activity of ovarian and lutein tissue. *Endocrinology*, **37**, 431–436.

Meyer, R. K., Soukup, S. W., McShan, W. H. and Biddulph, C. (1947). Succinic dehydrogenase in rat ovarian tissues during pregnancy and lactation. *Endocrinology*, **41**, 35–44.

Michaelis, L. (1947). The nature of the interaction of nucleic acids and nuclei with basic dyestuffs. *Cold Spr. Harb. Symp. quant. Biol.* **12**, 131–142.

Michaelis, L. and Granick, S. (1945). Metachromasy of basic dyestuffs. *J. Amer. chem. Soc.* **67**, 1212–1219.

Miller, D. C. and Everett, J. W. (1948). Ascorbic acid concentration and cholesterol storage in corpora lutea of pregnant rats under experimental conditions. *Endocrinology*, **42**, 421–423.

Mintz, B. (1957a). Germ cell origin and history in the mouse: genetic and histochemical evidence. *Anat. Rec.* **127**, 335–336. (Abstr.)

Mintz, B. (1957b). Interaction between two allelic series modifying primordial germ cell development in the mouse embryo. *Anat. Rec.* **128**, 591. (Abstr.)

Mintz, B. (1957c). Embryological development of primordial germ cells in the mouse; influence of a new mutation, Wj. *J. Embryol. exp. Morph.* **5**, 396–403.

Mintz, B. and Russell, E. S. (1955). Developmental modifications of primordial germ cells, induced by the W-series genes in the mouse embryo. *Anat. Rec.* **122**, 443. (Abstr.)

Mintz, B. and Russell, E. S. (1957). Gene-induced embryological modifications of primordial germ cells in the mouse. *J. exp. Zool.* **134**, 207–237.

Moog, F. and Wenger, E. L. (1952). The occurrence of a neutral mucopolysaccharide at sites of high alkaline phosphatase activity. *Amer. J. Anat.* **90**, 339–378.

Moricard, R. and Gothié, S. (1955). Étude de la répartition en S[35] dans les cellules folliculaires périovocytaires au cours de l'ovogenèse et de la terminaison de la première mitose maturation chez la lapine adulte. *C.R. Soc. Biol., Paris*, **149**, 1918–1922.

Moss, S., Wrenn, T. R. and Sykes, J. F. (1954). Some histological and histochemical observations of the bovine ovary during the estrous cycle. *Anat. Rec.* **120**, 409–433.

Moss, S., Sykes, J. F. and Wrenn, T. R. (1956). Some observations on the bovine corpus luteum and endometrium during early stages of pregnancy. *Amer. J. vet. Res.* **17**, 607–614.

Nachlas, M. M. and Seligman, A. M. (1949). The comparative distribution of esterase in the tissues of five mammals by a histochemical technique. *Anat. Rec.* **105**, 677–687.

Nachlas, M. M., Crawford, D. T. and Seligman, A. M. (1957a). The histochemical demonstration of leucine-aminopeptidase. *J. Histochem. Cytochem.* **5**, 264–278.

Nachlas, M. M., Tsou, K.-C., de Souza, E., Cheng, Ch. and Seligman, A. M. (1957b). Cytochemical demonstration of succinic dehydrogenase by the use of a new p-nitrophenyl substrated ditetrazole. *J. Histochem. Cytochem.* **5**, 420–436.

Nakano, O. (1928). Über die Verteilung des Glykogens bei den zyklischen Veränderungen in den Geschlechtsorganen der Fledermaus, und über die Nahrungsaufnahme der Spermien in den weiblichen Geschlechtswegen. *Fol. anat. japon.* **6**, 777–828.

Nati, G. and Odeblad, E. (1955). Observations on the uptake of radiophosphate and radiosulphate in the mouse ovary under some hormonal conditions. *Acta endocr., Copenhagen*, **19**, 43–48.

Ober, K. G. (1950). Die wechselnde Aktivität der alkalischen Phosphatase im Endometrium und Ovar während des menstruellen Cyclus sowie im Myometrium unter der Geburt. Eine histochemische Darstellung. *Klin. Wschr.* **28**, 9–16.

Odeblad, E. (1951). Unfertilized rabbit ova in P^{32}-autoradiography. *Exp. Cell Res.* **2**, 574–576.

Odeblad, E. (1952a). Contributions to the theory and technique of quantitative autoradiography with P^{32} with special reference to the granulosa tissue of the Graafian follicles in the rabbit. *Acta radiol., Stockh.* Suppl. 93.

Odeblad, E. (1952b). Autoradiography with P^{32} of the rabbit ovary. *Acta obstet. gynec. scand.* **31**, 63–73.

Odeblad, E. (1952c). Unfertilized rabbit ova in S^{35}-autoradiography. *Exp. Cell Res.* **3**, 694–695.

Odeblad, E. (1952d). A biophysical study on the follicular fluid of the rabbit. *Acta endocr., Copenhagen*, **11**, 269–274.

Odeblad, E. (1952e). Autoradiographic observations with S^{35} on the corpus luteum of the rabbit. *Acta endocr., Copenhagen*, **11**, 306–310.

Odeblad, E. and Boström, H. (1953). A time-picture relation study with autoradiography on the uptake of labelled sulphate in the Graafian follicles of the rabbit. *Acta radiol., Stockh.* **39**, 137–140.

Odeblad, E. and Magnusson, G. (1954). An autoradiographic study on the intracellular accumulation of radioactive phosphate in the egg cell of the mouse. *Acta endocr., Copenhagen*, **17**, 290–293.

Ortmann, R. (1955). Zur Darstellung der Gesamtlipoide an Pflügerschen Schläuchen und Oözyten im Hundeovar. *Morph. Jb.* **95**, 142–150.

Padykula, H. A. (1952). The localization of succinic dehydrogenase in tissue sections of the rat. *Amer. J. Anat.* **91**, 107–146.

Palla, V. (1947). Richerche istochimiche sulla pseudomucina del "liquor folliculi". *Arch. ital. Anat.* **52**, 246–257.

Pearse, A. G. Everson. (1953). "Histochemistry." J. & A. Churchill Ltd., London; ditto 2nd edition (1960).

Pearse, A. G. Everson. (1954). Azo dye methods in enzyme histochemistry. *Int. Rev. Cytol.* **3**, 329–358.

Peckham, B. and Kiekhofer, W. (1959). The movement of tritium labelled water in the human ovarian follicle. *Amer. J. Obstet. Gynec.* **78**, 1012–1019.

Petersohn, K. L. (1958). Autoradiographische Untersuchungen über die Lokalisation von P^{32} im Ovar von Kaninchen und Meerschweinchen. *Geburtsh. u. Frauenh.* **18**, 1399–1408.

Pinkerton, J. H. (1959). Oestrogen production in the immature human ovary (observations based upon histochemical studies). *J. Obstet Gynaec., Brit. Emp.* **6**, 820–822.

Polvani, F. (1959). Metabolismo nucleoproteico dell' ovaio e dell' utero—studio con adenina -8 -^{14}C. *Riv. istochim.* **5**, 193–207.

Ragins, A. B. and Popper, H. (1942). Variation of vitamin-A fluorescence in cyclic changes of ovary. *Arch. Path. (Lab. Med.)* **34**, 647–662.

Reagan, J. W. (1950). Ceroid pigment in the human ovary. *Amer. J. Obstet. Gynec.* **59**, 433–436.

Rennels, E. G. (1949). Some factors influencing the cholesterol content of the interstitial tissue of the immature rat. *Anat. Rec.* **105**, 520. (Abstr.)

Rennels, E. G. (1951). Influence of hormones on the histochemistry of ovarian interstitial tissue in the immature rat. *Amer. J. Anat.* **88**, 63–107.

Rockenschaub, A. (1951a). Die Eigenfluoreszenz in Follikeln und Gelbkörpern. *Zbl. ges. Gynäk. Geburtsh.* **73**, 1206–1212.

Rockenschaub, A. (1951b). Eigenfluoreszenz und Hormonbildung in Theca und Granulosa. *Mikroskopie*, **6**, 304–306.

Rockenschaub, A. (1954). Zur Frage der hormonellen Steuerung des menstruellen Zyklus. I. Eigenfluoreszenz und Steroidhormonabgabe im Eierstock. *Zbl. ges. Gynäk. Geburtsh.* **76**, 1329–1338.

Rossi, F., Pescetto, G. and Reale, E. (1951a). La localizzazione istochimica della fosfatasi alcalina e le sue variazioni nel corso della sviluppo prenatale dell' uomo. *Z. Anat. EntwGesch.* **115**, 500–528.

Rossi, F., Pescetto, G. and Reale, E. (1951b). La localizzazione della fosfatasi alcalina ed il suo tasso nell' embrione umano di 9 mm. *Z. Anat. EntwGesch.* **116**, 190–201.

Rossi, F. and Reale, E. (1957). The somite stage of human development studied with the histochemical reaction for the demonstration of alkaline glycerophosphatase. *Acta anat.* **30**, 656–681.

Rossman, I. (1942). On the lipin and pigment in the corpus luteum of the rhesus monkey. *Contr. Embryol. Carneg. Instn.* **30**, 97–109.

Seligman, A. M., Tsou, K.-C., Rutenburg, S. H. and Cohen, R. B. (1954). Histochemical demonstration of β-d-glucuronidase with a synthetic substrate. *J. Histochem. Cytochem.* **2**, 209–229.

Silva Sasso, W. da. (1959). Existence of hyaluronic acid at the zona pellucida of the rabbit's ovum. *Acta anat.* **36**, 352–357.

Simon, D. (1957a). Sur la localisation des cellules germinales primordiales chez l'embryon de poulet et leur mode de migration vers les ébauches gonadiques. *C.R. Acad. Sci., Paris*, **244**, 1541–1543.

Simon, D. (1957b). La migration des cellules germinales de l'embryon de poulet vers les ébauches gonadiques: preuves expérimentales. *C.R. Soc. Biol., Paris*, **151**, 1576–1580.

Skowron, S. and Keller, T. (1934). Die histologischen Veränderungen der Fett-substanzen des gelben Körpers beim Kaninchen während und nach der Schwangerschaft, nebst allgemeinen Bemerkungen über die Fettverteilung im Eierstock. *Z. Zellforsch.* **21**, 425–440.

Smith, A. G. and Harley, C. M. (1956). Histochemical identification of chicken gonadal cells in tissue culture. *Arch. Path.* **62**, 497–504.

Smith, J. T. and Ketteringham, R. C. (1938). Rupture of the Graafian follicles. *Amer. J. Obstet. Gynec.* **36**, 453–460.

Sonenberg, M., Money, W. L., Keston, A. S., Fitzgerald, P. J. and Godwin, J. T. (1951). Localization of radioactivity after administration of labelled prolactin preparations to the female rat. *Endocrinology*, **49**, 709–719.

Stafford, R. O., McShan, W. H. and Meyer, R. K. (1947). Acid and alkaline phosphatases in rat ovarian tissues during pregnancy and lactation. *Endocrinology*, **41**, 45–54.

Sternberg, W. H. (1949). The morphology, androgenic function, hyperplasia, and tumours of the human hilus cells. *Amer. J. Path.* **25**, 493–521.

Sundberg, C. (1924). Das Glycogen in menschlichen Embryonen von 15, 27 und 40 mm. *Z. ges. Anat.* **73**, 168–246.

Takeuchi, T., Higashi, K. and Watanuki, S. (1955). Distribution of amylophosphorylase in various tissues of human and mammalian organs. *J. Histochem. Cytochem.* **3**, 485–491.

Togari, Ch. (1927). On the appearance of glycogen in the female reproductive glands of rodents with special reference to their histology. *Fol. anat. japon.* **5**, 429–489.

Verne, J. (1929). Étude histochimique des substances aldéhydiques formées au cours du métabolisme des corps gras. *Ann. Physiol. Physiochim. biol.* **5**, 245–267.

Verne, J. and Hébert, S. (1952a). Étude cytochimique de l'activité estérasique dans les glandes endocrines hormonogènes. *Ann. Endocr., Paris*, **13**, 659–663.

Verne, J. and Hébert, S. (1952b). Les activités phosphatasiques et estérasiques dans les follicules e tles corps jaunes de l'ovaire de la rate blanche. *C.R. Soc. Biol., Paris*, **146**, 390–391.

Vimeux, J. (1952). Metachromasie du liquide folliculaire. *C.R. Soc. Biol., Paris*, **146**, 1918–1919.

Vincent, W. S. and Dornfeld, E. J. (1948). Localization and role of nucleic acids in the developing rat ovary. *Amer. J. Anat.* **83**, 437–469.

Wattenberg, L. W. (1958). Microscopic histochemical demonstration of steroid-3β-ol dehydrogenase in tissue sections. *J. Histochem. Cytochem.* **6**, 225–232.

Watzka, M. and Eschler, J. (1933). Extraglanduläre Zwischenzellen im Eierstockhilus des Schweines. *Z. mikr.-anat. Forsch.* **34**, 238.

White, R. F., Hertig, A. T., Rock, J. and Adams, E. C. (1951). Histologic and histochemical observations on the corpus luteum of human pregnancy with special reference to corpora lutea associated with early normal and abnormal ova. *Contr. Embryol. Carneg. Instn.* **34**, 55-74.

Willier, B. H. (1950). Sterile gonads and the problem of the origin of germ cells in the chick embryo. *Arch. Anat. micr. Morph. exp.* **39**, 269–273.

Wimsatt, W. A. (1944). Growth of the ovarian follicle and ovulation in *Myotis lucifugus lucifugus*. *Amer. J. Anat.* **74**, 129–173.

Wimsatt, W. A. (1949). Glycogen, polysaccharide complexes and alkaline phosphatase in the ovary of the bat during hibernation and pregnancy. *Anat. Rec.* **103**, 564–565. (Abstr.)

Wimsatt, W. A. and Kallen, F. C. (1957). The unique maturation response of the Graafian follicles of hibernating vespertilionid bats and the question of its significance. *Anat. Rec.* **129**, 115–131.

Wislocki, G. B., Bunting, H. and Dempsey, E. W. (1947). Metachromasia in mammalian tissues and its relationship to mucopolysaccharides. *Amer. J. Anat.* **81**, 1–31.

Witschi, E. (1948). Migration of the germ cells of human embryos from the yolk sac to the primitive gonadal folds. *Contr. Embryol. Carneg. Instn.* **32**, 67–80.

Witschi, E. (1951). Embryogenesis of the adrenal and the reproductive glands. *Recent Progr. Hormone Res.* **6**, 1–27.

Wotton, R. M. and Village, P. A. (1951). The transfer function of certain cells in the wall of the Graafian follicle as revealed by their reaction to previously stained fat in the cat. *Anat. Rec.* **110**, 121–127.

Yoffey, J. M. and Baxter, J. S. (1947). The formation of birefringent crystals in the suprarenal cortex. *J. Anat., Lond.* **81**, 335–342.

Zachariae, F. (1957). Studies on the mechanism of ovulation. Autoradiographic investigations on the uptake of radioactive sulphate (^{35}S) into the ovarian follicular mucopolysaccharides. *Acta endocr., Copenhagen*, **26**, 215–223.

Zachariae, F. (1959). Acid mucopolysaccharides in the female genital system and their role in the mechanism of ovulation. *Acta endocr., Copenhagen*, **33**, Suppl. 46, 1–64.

Zachariae, F. and Jensen, C. E. (1958). Studies on the mechanism of ovulation. Histochemical and physico-chemical investigations on genuine follicular fluids. *Acta endocr., Copenhagen*, **27**, 343–355.

CHAPTER 4

ATRESIA

D. L. INGRAM

I. Introduction

For the purposes of the present review, atresia will be considered as representing the process or processes whereby oocytes are lost from the ovary other than by ovulation. Atresia is a degenerative process, the duration of which is unknown. Its early stages are difficult to diagnose histologically, particularly in primordial oocytes. Advanced stages in medium-sized and large follicles, in contrast, are easy to recognize. Most of the early studies of atresia were restricted to the morphology of follicles at late stages of atresia; more recent experiments are concerned with the detection of the earliest stages.

The observation that the human ovary contains some 500,000 oocytes at birth and becomes depleted of germ cells at the menopause underlines the important part that atresia plays in the life-history of the ovary. Of the 500,000 oocytes which are said to be present at birth, only some 400 will ovulate in the course of 30 years' reproductive life; the remaining 99·9 per cent of the original 'stock' are destined to

undergo atresia at various stages in their development. Similarly, in
the rat, the number of oocytes decreases from 40,000 at birth to about
10,000 at the age of 3 weeks, even before the first ovulation takes
place. Degeneration of oocytes in the ovary of lower vertebrates has
also been reported (Bonnet, 1899; Pearl and Boring, 1918; Garde, 1930;
Matthews, 1950; Brambell, 1956), but the extent to which it is responsible for fluctuations in the population of germ cells is unknown since
numerical studies are not available.

II. Morphology of atretic oocytes
A. Atresia of medium-sized and large follicles

Changes which occur during atresia of medium-sized and large
follicles (oocytes surrounded by two or more layers of granulosa cells)
affect both the oocyte and the granulosa cells. Opinions differ as to
the site of the earliest changes. Clark (1923) believes they are first
seen in the oocyte, whereas others (e.g. Asami, 1920) maintain that
the granulosa cells are the first to be affected. In any event, it is agreed
that the earliest changes are rapidly followed by signs of degeneration
in other parts of the follicle.

1. *Atretic changes in the oocyte*

The nucleus of the oocytes in normal medium-sized or large follicles
is large and surrounded by a smooth nuclear membrane. When an
oocyte becomes atretic, nuclear changes may consistently be seen.
Sometimes pyknosis of the nucleus, or fragmentation of the nucleus
associated with the breakdown of the nuclear membrane, may be
observed (Stockard and Papanicolaou, 1917; Garde, 1930).

Atresia may also be associated with the beginning of maturation
division. The first polar body may be formed as in the normal pre-
ovulatory maturation, but the second division may be inhibited and
degenerative changes appear (Branca, 1925). Sometimes the nucleus
divides into several fragments, possibly by amitotic divisions, with the
formation of a syncytium. It has also been reported that divisions which
closely resemble the early stages of embryonic development may occur
in some follicles, with the result that structures like the neural tube
and foetal placenta are formed parthenogenetically. This type of development has been extensively studied by Loeb (1901, 1905, 1911,
1930, 1932) who concluded that 10 per cent of the ovaries of 6-months-
old guinea pigs show signs that parthenogenesis had taken place.
The observations of Schottlaender (1891), van der Stricht (1901),
Newman (1913), Sansom (1920) and Branca (1925) support Loeb's
conclusions. Bonnet (1899), on the other hand, believes that no parthenogenesis occurs in fish, amphibians, reptiles or mammals, and that

the divisions are signs of degeneration. In this conclusion, Bonnet is supported by the observations of Balfour (1880), Athias (1909), Addison (1916), Stockard and Papanicolaou (1917), Engle (1927) and Kampmeier (1929). The literature on this subject has been fully reviewed by Branca (1925), Athias (1929) and Pincus (1936). Pincus points out that much depends on what is meant by the term 'parthenogenesis': "If by parthenogenesis is meant the development of a mature individual from an unfertilized egg then it is at once certain that parthenogenesis does not take place in mammalian ovaries. If, on the other hand, a cleavage of the ovum with an equatorial division of the chromosomes is the criterion then there is some evidence that occasionally parthenogenesis occurs in ovarian eggs." For a further discussion of this problem, the reader is referred to Pincus's (1936) monograph.

Cytoplasmic changes in the course of atresia have also been described. The presence of crystalloid bodies has been reported for the mouse by Mertens (1895), Chappellier (1909), Brambell (1927), Engle (1927) and Gresson (1933); similar bodies were observed in the opossum (Martínez-Esteve, 1942). Black crystals in atretic oocytes of the monkey have been observed by Pollak (1926); the crystals were cylindrical in shape, between 3 and 9μ long, and occurred in medium-sized follicles in groups of as many as thirteen.

The distribution of the mitochondria and Golgi apparatus and the presence of granules (Asami, 1920; Kampmeier, 1929) appears to be different in atretic oocytes (Gresson, 1933). Mitochondria aggregate into masses up to the time when maturation division sets in even if fragmentation has also occurred. The distribution of the Golgi bodies becomes uneven.

Other features of the atretic oocyte are fatty degeneration (Clark, 1923; Gresson, 1933), vacuolation of the yolk (Kampmeier, 1929; Allen et al., 1930), breakdown of the nuclear and cell membranes (Kramer et al., 1933; Harrison, 1948) and shrinkage and hyalinization of the zona pellucida (Hedberg, 1953) which persists for a long time and frequently is the last part of the follicle to disappear (Benthin, 1911; Asami, 1920; Clark, 1923; Harrison, 1948).

2. Atretic changes in the granulosa cells

Mitotic divisions are absent from granulosa cells of atretic follicles. The suggestion that atypical divisions may occur has been made by Pinho (1923). The granulosa cells may well become sudanophil (Deane and Andrews, 1953), indicating that fatty degeneration is taking place (see also Schottlaender, 1891, 1893; Benthin, 1911; Asami, 1920; Martínez-Esteve, 1942).

T

Atresia may also be recognized by chromatolysis of the granulosa cells and pyknosis of the nuclei, leading to the degeneration of the whole follicular epithelium (van der Stricht, 1901; Allen, 1904; Asami, 1920; Pinho, 1923; Hammond, 1925; Engle, 1927; Brambell, 1927; Kramer et al., 1933; Deanesly, 1935; Krafta, 1939; and Matthews, 1941). The degenerated granulosa cells become detached from the follicular wall and float into the antrum. The liquor folliculi may become gelatinous and cloudy, the cumulus oöphorus also degenerates, and the oocyte floats freely in the antrum (Allen et al., 1930).

While the granulosa cells are undergoing degeneration, the zona pellucida is invaded by cells which are believed to assist in the removal of the oocyte (Stevens, 1904; Sansom, 1920; Kampmeier, 1929). Some authors believe that these cells are modified granulosa cells (van der Stricht, 1901; Pinho, 1923; Branca, 1925; Garde, 1930), while others regard them as leucocytes or connective tissue cells (Newman, 1913; Stockard and Papanicolaou, 1917). The function of these cells is uncertain as is their phagocytic activity (Clark, 1923).

A further sign of early atresia is the formation of a hyaline band between the membrana granulosa and the theca interna (Kampmeier, 1929). In some cases connective tissue cells invade the follicle from the theca and grow inwards between the granulosa cells, thus ultimately obliterating the antrum (Schottlaender, 1891, 1893; Marshall, 1904; Stevens, 1904; Cohn, 1909; Asami, 1920; Winiwarter, 1923; Hammond, 1925; Brambell, 1927; Kramer et al., 1933).

Hypertrophy of the theca interna, influenced by luteinizing hormone, may also take place. The enlarged cells grow into the membrana granulosa, and in some follicles this process may result in the formation of a small group of interstitial-like cells, whereas in others a nodule of tissue similar to a small corpus luteum is formed (Schottlaender, 1891, 1893; van der Stricht, 1901; Cohn, 1909; Benthin, 1911; Salazar, 1922a, b; Winiwarter, 1923; Zuckerman and Parkes, 1932; Deanesly, 1935; Pincus and Enzmann, 1937; Matthews, 1941). Luteinization of follicular constituents may also take place in follicles whose membrana granulosa does not degenerate completely before the thecal cells undergo hypertrophy (Brambell, 1956). Luteinization of a follicle which retains its oocyte results in the formation of a corpus luteum atreticum. The view that the corpus luteum atreticum is composed of both thecal and granulosa cells is held by Săglik (1938) and Pederson (1951). Luteinization of the granulosa is especially marked in animals treated with pituitary hormones (Engle and Smith, 1929). Brambell (1956) is careful to draw attention to the fact that all the corpora lutea which contain the remains of an oocyte are not derived from atretic follicles. In some instances the oocyte may fail to be extruded from the follicle at the time of ovulation, and a true corpus luteum is formed with an ovum at its centre (see also Sobotta, 1896).

Atresia may also be associated with the formation of cysts which may attain a considerable size; they are lined by a single layer of epithelium, and their cavity is filled with a watery fluid. Such cysts often develop when the ovary is stimulated by a high titre of gonadotrophin. They have been observed after subtotal ovariectomy (Lipschütz and Voss, 1925) and during pregnancy (van der Horst and Gillman, 1945). They have also been described in the ovaries of prepubertal girls (Felix, 1912).

Follicles are also known to become haemorrhagic cysts (Heape, 1905; Hammond, 1925; Hill and White, 1933) as a result of bleeding from capillaries supplying the granulosa cells. The follicle becomes dark-brown and ultimately is resorbed. Haemorrhagic follicles have been particularly frequently observed in the unmated rabbit.

B. Atresia of primordial oocytes

The changes which occur during atresia of primordial oocytes (surrounded by a single layer of granulosa cells) are less well documented than corresponding changes for larger follicles. The nuclei of atretic primordial oocytes of the rabbit are said to contain masses of dense granules (Pincus and Enzmann, 1937). Brambell (1927) described a series of stages in 'direct degeneration' of oocytes in the mouse. Recent quantitative studies have shown that the criteria used for differentiating normal from atretic primordial oocytes are largely subjective (Green, Mandl and Jones; personal communications). The principal feature by which atretic oocytes have been differentiated from normal ones is the crinkled appearance of the nuclear membrane (Fig. 1). A secondary and less readily defined criterion is the appearance of unevenly distributed chromatin. Since both these criteria may be influenced by the type of fixative used (Ingram, unpublished data), it is clear that direct comparisons can only be made between tissues subjected to identical histological procedures. Moreover, it is known that individual observers vary in their ability to make consistent replicate counts on the same tissue. It is therefore evident that classifications of oocytes into normal and atretic represent only best estimates and are not absolute values.

The proportion of primordial oocytes to the total population which are believed to be atretic varies between about 60–70 per cent in the rat and 50 per cent in the mouse. If the assumption is made that atresia occurs continuously through life, then it is clear that the number affected afresh during one particular oestrous cycle is likely to be very small. An approximate calculation based on the counts of oocytes of

young and very old animals (Mandl and Shelton, 1959) suggests that
the percentage of the total population undergoing atresia during any
particular oestrous cycle is of the order of about 1 per cent. Since the
estimated proportion of oocytes judged to be atretic is very high
(Mandl and Zuckerman, 1950), the implication is that atretic oocytes
remain histologically recognizable for long periods before they disappear. In view of the difficulty of making a precise diagnosis of atretic

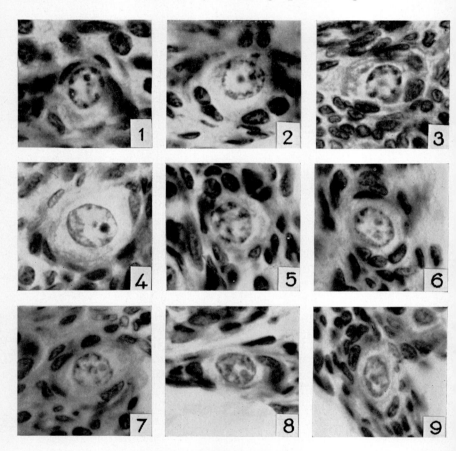

FIG. 1. Normal and atretic primordial oocytes (rat). The oocytes
shown in *1, 2* and *3* would be regarded as normal. Those in *4, 5* and *6*
have some of the characteristics of atresia but might, nevertheless, be
regarded as normal by some workers. The oocytes in *7, 8* and *9* are
all atretic. Because of the high magnification used in the photographs
(× 1,500) the nucleolus is not in focus in all instances; the sections are,
however, all cut through the middle of the oocyte. When examining
oocytes through the microscope, it is always necessary to manipulate
the fine adjustment.

primordial oocytes, it may be prudent to measure atresia by the rate at which the total number of oocytes decreases minus the estimated number which ovulates.

C. Histochemistry

Histochemical studies have helped to elucidate some of the changes which take place in large follicles undergoing atresia, but they have added nothing to the existing knowledge about atresia of primordial oocytes (see also Chapter 3). In a study of the distribution of ^{32}P in the rabbit ovary, Odeblad (1951, 1952) showed that primordial oocytes take up no more phosphorus than does the connective tissue; medium-sized follicles contain relatively large amounts, and the highest concentration is found in Graafian follicles. In the normal follicle, the phosphorus was concentrated in the granulosa cells and a considerable amount was present in the theca interna; in contrast, little was detected in either the ovum or the follicular fluid. Further studies by Block et al. (1953) showed that in atretic medium-sized follicles the density of radiophosphorus was high in about one third and low in about two thirds of the instances. Atretic Graafian follicles consistently contained very little phosphorus in comparison with normal structures of the same size. The low density of ^{32}P in atretic follicles is correlated with the low incidence of mitoses after the onset of atresia.

In parallel with the loss of phosphorus from atretic follicles, granulosa cells appear to acquire an intense phosphatase reaction (Deane, 1951, 1952) which is normally present only in 'dendritic-like processes' (Moog and Wenger, 1952). Subsequently ribonuclease-resistant basophilic granules which, according to Deane, correspond to the Feulgen-positive globules observed in atretic follicles by Vincent and Dornfeld (1948), become apparent. It is believed they represent desoxyribonucleic acid from pyknotic or fragmented nuclei.

While glycogen is usually absent from granulosa cells, it appears in the cumulus oöphorus of the atretic follicle (Deane, 1951, 1952). Ascorbic acid, lipid droplets and esterase activity appear at the same time (Deane and Andrews, 1953). Deane also states that atresia at the time of ovulation differs from that occurring at other stages of the cycle; in ovaries removed 3–12 hours after ovulation granulosa cells display a positive Schultz reaction for cholesterol and a positive Ashbel-Seligman carbonyl reaction, and they contain birefringent crystals. These changes indicate that steroids may be elaborated but, as Deane observes, it is doubtful whether they are liberated into the blood stream since close vascular relations are not established.

A differential distribution of argyrophilic substances in the cytoplasm of oocytes in normal and atretic follicles has also been reported

(Dawson, 1952), the concentration being greater in atretic follicles. Dawson believes that this difference becomes apparent before degenerative changes take place in the granulosa cells. This method of early diagnosis is however only applicable to the larger follicles and is restricted to the prepubertal animal.

Hedberg (1953) studied the chemical composition of the oocyte by means of X-ray microradiography and spectrography of ultra-violet light absorption. Early stages of atresia in primordial oocytes could not however be detected by these means. In Graafian follicles, the first sign of atresia was a slight shrinkage of the oocyte in relation to the follicle which was not, however, associated with any changes in the nucleus or cytoplasm. Measurements revealed that as the volume of the atretic oocyte decreases, its total dry weight/unit volume increases as compared with the normal. Atresia was also associated with an increase in the amount of protein/unit volume of tissue, a change which is most probably related to the shrinkage of the cell.

Histochemical studies thus suggest that the first change which occurs in Graafian follicles relates to the ovum itself (change in distribution of argyrophilic granules; shrinkage of the oocyte) but that it is followed rapidly by changes in the granulosa cells (increase in phosphatase activity; decrease of phosphorus uptake; breakdown of nuclei). There is also some evidence to suggest that steroid hormones or their precursors are elaborated in the atretic follicle, although it is doubtful whether they enter the circulation. (The reader is again referred to Chapter 3, sect. II, B.)

III. Factors which influence atresia

A. Age

It is generally agreed that large numbers of oocytes are degenerating in the ovaries of very young animals. The suggestion has even been made that all oocytes formed during embryonic life disappear from the ovary and are replaced by proliferations from the germinal epithelium (see review by Everett 1945; see also Chapter 1, sect. II, I).

The majority of oocytes formed during foetal life in the cat are said to degenerate between 45 and 68 days after birth and to be replaced by newly-formed germ cells before puberty (Winiwarter and Sainmont, 1909). Similar findings for other species are reported by Rubaschkin (1912), Kingery (1917), Swezy (1929), Hargitt (1930) and Swezy and Evans (1930). In contrast, Kingsbury (1913, 1938) believes that whereas large numbers of oocytes degenerate in the ovary of the prepubertal cat, no neoformation of germ cells occurs. The numbers of oocytes were not counted in any of these studies, and the conclusion that all germ cells undergo atresia is based only on the examination of selected sections. If degeneration and neoformation take place simultaneously (see Swezy, 1929; Hargitt, 1930), then it would be necessary to differentiate between oocytes formed in foetal life and those formed later. The above observations therefore do no more than suggest that large numbers of oocytes become atretic during prepubertal life.

Estimates of the number of oocytes in the ovary at different ages, however, provide some measure of the rate of atresia. The figures given for the human are somewhat inconsistent. Simkins (1932) suggested that the number of oocytes falls from 300,000 at birth to 20,000 at 14 years. According to Block (1952), the number of oocytes in girls aged 6–9 years is about 484,000, falling to 155,000 at 18–24 years and 8,300 at 40–44 years. Block's estimates for individual counts were very variable, partly due perhaps to genetic differences between the subjects.

Such information as is available for the dog suggests that the number of oocytes drops from about 700,000 at birth to 350,000 at puberty; this initial rapid decrease is followed by a slower decline to 35,000 at 5 years and 500 at 10 years (Schotterer, 1928). Desaive's (1941) figures for the rabbit are based on only seven animals, but they are consistent with the view that the most severe depletion occurs before puberty.

The only species apart from man which have been studied adequately are the rat, the mouse and the monkey, though estimates for the latter relate only to the adult. The relationship between age and the size of the oocyte population in the rat has been studied by Arai (1920a), Slater and Dornfeld (1945), Mandl and Zuckerman (1951b), and Mandl and Shelton (1959). These studies show that the number of oocytes falls from about 40,000 at birth to about 8,000 at puberty 40–45 days later. During the following 3 years, only 6,000 to 7,000 more oocytes are lost. Since the decline in the number of germ cells is largely due to atresia, it follows that the number of oocytes which become atretic per unit time varies with age. The latter value expressed as a percentage of the total number of oocytes, on the other hand, is fairly constant.

Jones's (1957) comprehensive study of the germ cell populations in four different strains of mice showed that (i) the general pattern of the decline in the number of oocytes is similar to that observed in the rat, and (ii) differences in the decline of oocyte numbers exist between some of the strains. The latter observation underlines the profound effect of genetic factors on the rate of atresia, and the importance of carefully controlling experiments.

Estimates of the proportion of oocytes considered atretic vary between 70 per cent in the rat (Mandl and Zuckerman, 1950), 50 per

cent in four pure strains of mice and 36 per cent for the hybrids of
CBA × A (Jones, 1957). No differences in the proportion were observed
in rats of different ages, but in the mouse there was a tendency for old
animals of one strain (RIII) to have a higher proportion of atretic
oocytes. No atretic oocytes were found in the neonatal mouse, such cells
first appearing a few days after birth and their proportion rising to 50
per cent a little before or at sexual maturity (Jones, 1957). Corresponding
observations on the rat have not as yet been made.

Since the decline in the number of oocytes in different strains of mice
varies, while the proportion diagnosed as atretic is roughly constant,
the implication is that oocytes remain in the ovary after becoming
atretic for a period of time which varies between the strains. A second
implication which derives from Jones's observations is that the time
taken for an oocyte to become atretic and disappear from the ovary
varies with age. The rapid depletion in the population of germ cells
during the first few days after birth indicates that an oocyte may become atretic and disappear within a week or less. In the adult, on the
other hand, the atretic oocyte must remain in the ovary for long periods.
Such conclusions are of necessity based on the assumption that neoformation of oocytes does not occur after birth (see Chapter 1, sect. II, I).

B. Reproductive cycle

It is widely held that waves of atresia affect the number of medium-
sized and large follicles in phase with the oestrous cycle. Thus Lane
and Davis (1939) showed that the total number of medium-sized
and large follicles varies in phase with the oestrous cycle, follicles with a
diameter of 200–300μ being destined either to undergo maturation or
to become atretic. Boling et al. (1941) concluded that atretic changes in
large follicles of the rat first become obvious on the 3rd day of the
cycle. Similarly, Engle (1927) showed that in the mouse, the number of
atretic follicles with or without antra surrounded by six or more layers
of granulosa cells rises before ovulation and reaches a peak in early
dioestrus. These follicles then presumably disappear rapidly, since
their number falls to its lowest on the following day. In the guinea pig,
the number of large atretic follicles increases from the 8th day of the
cycle and reaches its maximum at the time of ovulation on the 16th
day (Myers et al., 1936). Harman and Kirgis (1938) also concluded
that the number of atretic follicles was lowest during the first few days
of the cycle. In the rabbit, a species which does not experience oestrous
cycles but which remains in heat for long periods, large follicles become
atretic at all times (Asami, 1920). The percentage of oocytes with two
to four layers of granulosa cells believed to be atretic is said to be
constant at about 62 per cent (Pincus and Enzmann, 1937). It is

estimated from successive photographs of the same ovary that each follicle persists for 7–10 days before being replaced (Hill and White, 1933). Thus in the rabbit the process of growth and atresia occur side by side and each atretic follicle may be replaced immediately by a healthy one throughout heat.

Similar variations in the number of atretic follicles have been observed in the mare (Hammond and Wodzicki, 1941) and the goat (Harrison, 1948). Follicles which do not ovulate during oestrus are said to undergo atresia in the cat (Liche, 1939) and the sow (Allen et al., 1925). In the baboon, a wave of follicular growth occurs at the beginning of a cycle and ends in the ovulation of only one ovum, the remaining follicles becoming atretic; the luteal phase of the menstrual cycle is not accompanied by waves of growth or atresia (Zuckerman and Parkes, 1932).

In the bat (*Myotis*), follicles of all sizes become atretic during autumn and winter; from October to February, most of the atretic follicles are 124–163μ in diameter, but from February onwards atresia affects the smaller follicles (84–123μ in diameter), while the number of large atretic follicles decreases (Guthrie and Jeffers, 1938).

Cyclical variations in the number of atretic primordial oocytes are the subject of considerable controversy. From a qualitative study based on rats, guinea pigs, dogs, cats, monkeys and some human material, Evans and Swezy (1931) concluded that all oocytes, including primary ones, become atretic at oestrus, the sole surviving follicles being those that are ovulated. They postulated at the same time that neoformation of oocytes occurred at the beginning of each cycle. Similarly, Schwarz et al. (1949) reported that all oocytes in the human ovary become atretic in each menstrual cycle. These studies take no account of the variations in the number of oocytes which occur with age and therefore have little validity (Zuckerman, 1951, 1956; see also Chapter 1).

The only systematic studies of the total numbers of normal and atretic oocytes are those for the monkey (Green and Zuckerman, 1951, 1954), the rat (Mandl and Zuckerman, 1950, 1951a, b; Mandl et al., 1952) and the mouse (Jones, 1957). In the monkey, the total numbers of oocytes did not vary significantly in phase with the cycle, but there was a tendency for the number of medium-sized and large follicles diagnosed as normal to fluctuate. The greatest number of normal follicles with antra were seen in the middle of the menstrual cycle (Green and Zuckerman, 1951, 1954). In the rat, the total numbers of oocytes were also shown not to vary significantly at different stages of the cycle. Mandl and Zuckerman (1950) point out that "estimations of atretic oocytes at various stages of the cycle are subject to considerable variation since the diagnosis of atresia depends on qualitative judgement".

U

Subject to this limitation, the data "suggest that the rate of degeneration does not vary systematically with the phases of the rat vaginal cycle". In contrast, Mandl and Zuckerman (1952) confirmed the earlier conclusion that medium-sized and large follicles vary in phase with the oestrous cycle; "while the numbers are too small to permit of statistical analysis, the figures suggest that the process of atresia is most marked in 250–349 μ follicles between the onset of oestrus and ovulation when the highest number of degenerating 350–449 μ follicles is also observed." Jones (1957) was also unable to find systematic fluctuations in the proportion of atretic oocytes. Such quantitative studies as have been made, therefore, contradict Evans and Swezy's (1931) statement that atresia affects all the oocytes in the ovary at each reproductive cycle. At the same time, the possibility that very small changes not readily detected by the methods used may occur cannot be eliminated.

C. Pregnancy and lactation

Qualitative studies suggest that growth and atresia of follicles continue during pregnancy (Asami, 1920; Evans and Swezy, 1931), but the rates of atresia were not compared with those in non-pregnant animals. Harrison (1948) suggests that in the goat a phase of atresia sets in between the 20th and 42nd day of pregnancy and continues until the 60th day when all medium-sized and large follicles are atretic. Lactating monkeys show a larger number of atretic follicles which had become hyalinized than do normal animals (Zuckerman, 1931).

The only quantitative study reported relates to the mouse (Engle, 1927). The number of atretic follicles with more than six layers of granulosa cells was lower during the first $4\frac{1}{2}$ days of pregnancy than in non-pregnant animals, and tended to decline further. The incidence of atresia must however increase again, since in the last few days before parturition the number of atretic follicles is similar to that of the non-pregnant animal shortly before ovulation. An initial decline in the incidence of atresia is also believed to occur during pseudopregnancy.

The formation of corpora lutea atretica appears to be common during pregnancy and has been described for the baboon, the elephant, the bank vole and the mare between the 40th and 150th day of pregnancy (see Seitz, 1905a, b, 1906; Cole et al., 1931; Zuckerman and Parkes, 1932; Brambell and Rowlands, 1936; Perry, 1953).

From the limited amount of quantitative information available, it would seem that the incidence of atresia among medium-sized and large follicles may be modified by pregnancy. No information is available about the effect of either pregnancy or lactation on the atresia of primordial oocytes.

D. Hypophysectomy

It has been reported repeatedly that the number of oocytes is greater in hypophysectomized than in normal animals. Swezy (1933) suggested that the rate of oogenesis increases after hypophysectomy.* The effect of age on the number of oocytes was not, however, taken into account and the number of oocytes was estimated in only one ovary. In a similar study, Paesi (1949) estimated the numbers of oocytes surrounded by one or more layers of cuboidal granulosa cells in four rats whose right ovary was removed at the time of hypophysectomy and used as control for the left which was removed at autopsy 8 days later. The numbers were higher for the left ovaries. This study also is open to criticism since primordial oocytes, which make up 90 per cent of the total population (Green et al., 1951) were not included.

Burkl and Kellner (1954) also found that the number of oocytes was slightly higher in hypophysectomized than in control rats, and interpreted these observations as confirming the belief of Swezy and Paesi that neoformation of oocytes increases following the removal of the pituitary.

In a quantitative re-investigation of the effect of hypophysectomy on the rate of decline in the total number of oocytes, Ingram (1953) showed that in the rat (i) the population of oocytes falls after hypophysectomy as it does in the intact animal but that the rate of decline is slower, and (ii) the number of medium-sized and large follicles is very much lower in the hypophysectomized animals. The simplest explanation seems to be that after hypophysectomy oocytes are no longer lost by atresia or by ovulation of large follicles. If this hypothesis is correct, the difference in the total number of oocytes in the hypophysectomized and control animals (minus the estimated number which would ovulate) provides an estimate of the number of oocytes lost by atresia of medium-sized and large follicles. The estimate is that between 70 and 200 days of age 1,000 medium and large-sized follicles are lost. The slope of the regression line for the hypophysectomized animals gives information about the atresia of primordial oocytes (since very few, if any, medium-sized follicles are formed). The tentative estimate is that 2,000 oocytes become atretic between 70 and 200 days of age.

Jones's (1957) preliminary study suggests that in the mouse also, the number of oocytes decreases more slowly with age following hypophysectomy. In her view, the proportion of atretic primordial oocytes declines after the removal of the pituitary.

* See also Chapter 1, sect. II, I.

E. Unilateral ovariectomy

Unilateral ovariectomy is followed by compensatory hypertrophy of the remaining ovary which ovulates about the same number of ova as do both ovaries of a normal animal. It is of interest therefore to discover whether the increased number of ovulations is associated with a decreased incidence of atresia in growing follicles, or whether a larger number of follicles develop.

In a series of studies which led to the formulation of 'the law of follicular constancy', Lipschütz (1925, 1928) and Lipschütz and Voss (1925) found that 5–16 months after subtotal ovariectomy, the total number of oocytes present in the hypertrophied fragments was greatly reduced by comparison with the number expected in an equal volume of tissue from a normal animal. Similar results were obtained in a second experiment in which the whole of one ovary and part of the other was removed in one group of animals, while in a second the ovaries were left *in situ* but one ovary was cut into two. Cats subjected to subtotal ovariectomy had very few oocytes left by comparison with the number found in a corresponding fragment of the controls. In a further experiment on rabbits, it was found that following the removal of one ovary and part of the second, the number of oocytes in the remaining fragment was smaller than in a bisected ovary of control animals; the number of large follicles, in contrast, was the same as in both ovaries of a normal animal.

In the unilaterally ovariectomized rat, the number of oocytes in the remaining ovary was found to be only about 4 per cent less than in the single ovary of a normal rat up to 7 weeks after operation (Arai, 1920b). The number of ova ovulated, however, was the same as in both ovaries of the unoperated animal. Mandl and Zuckerman (1951a) confirmed Arai's observations and showed that the number of large follicles in the unilaterally spayed rat is about twice that found in the single ovary of controls; in each instance, about half of the follicles were atretic. In a further experiment, it was shown that the rate of loss of oocytes increased inversely with the amount of ovarian tissue left in the body (Mandl *et al.*, 1952). In unilaterally spayed animals the number of oocytes lost per unit time was nevertheless less than that lost from both ovaries of a normal animal.

These observations imply that the removal of one ovary may influence the rate of atresia in the other. In view of the difficulty of making consistent diagnoses of atresia, it is impossible to draw any firm conclusions. It seems probable, however, that since the rate at which oocytes are lost in the unilaterally spayed animal is less than that from both ovaries of a normal animal, the rate at which oocytes become atretic decreases in the former.

F. Hormones

Since the effects of endogenous hormones have already been discussed (pp. 256–258), only those of exogenous hormones will be considered.

The degeneration of medium-sized and large follicles after the administration of oestrogen into intact animals (Noble, 1938) is probably mediated by an indirect effect *via* the pituitary. The direct action of oestrogen, on the other hand, appears to be the prevention of follicular degeneration. Thus Pencharz (1940) and Williams (1940, 1944a, b) found that the injection of large amounts of oestrogen into immature rats immediately after hypophysectomy inhibits involution of the ovaries, due to the persistence of large numbers of medium-sized follicles. The ovaries of animals injected immediately after hypophysectomy contain large numbers of follicles greater than 200μ in diameter (Williams, 1940, 1944a, b). If the animals were left for 1 month after the removal of the pituitary before oestrogen was administered, very few medium-sized follicles were found in the experimental animals and none in the controls. Similar results have also been obtained by Ingram (1959a) on adult animals. The amount of oestrogen required to promote follicular growth by direct action is high (1 mg stilboestrol/day).

Androgens administered into intact female rats appear to stimulate follicular growth initially, but long-term treatments are associated with depression of growth and ovulation (Starkey and Leathem, 1938). These effects are probably mediated *via* the pituitary, since testosterone propionate given to immature hypophysectomized animals did not maintain ovarian weight (Pencharz, 1940).

The likelihood that sex hormones influence the number of atretic follicles at the first stage of maturation division, which occur more commonly in immature than postpubertal animals, was investigated by Ingram (1959b). It was found that 5 days after injection of either pregnant mares' serum or oestrogen immature animals possessed fewer follicles containing dividing oocytes than did the litter-mate controls. The animals which had received gonadotrophin developed corpora lutea and cystic follicles. The most probable explanation is that when exogenous gonadotrophin is administered, those follicles which have begun to divide undergo luteinization to form corpora lutea, and are thus omitted from the counts. In the normal immature animal, luteinization is rare and follicles which have begun to divide remain in the ovary as atretic follicles. The reduction in the number of dividing oocytes in the oestrogen-treated animals was accompanied by the appearance of patches of interstitial tissue similar in shape and size to large follicles. It would appear most probable therefore that atretic follicles had become obliterated by the ingrowth of the theca interna as described by Rennels (1951).

G. Nutrition

Very little information is available about the effect of nutrition on the rate of atresia. Menschik (1948) reported that after prolonged treatment with vitamin E, there was an increase in the number of atretic oocytes. Although some attempt was made to count the number of oocytes in selected sections, total numbers are not given and no definite conclusion may be drawn from the report.

Vitamin B deficiency appears to be associated with an impairment in reproductive capacity (Findlay, 1921; Richter *et al.*, 1938) and an increase in the number of atretic follicles (Parkes, 1928). These effects may have been mediated by the pituitary since the ovaries of vitamin B-deficient animals are able to respond to exogenous gonadotrophin (Marrian and Parkes, 1929).

The feeding of extra food to sheep (flushing) may lead to an increase in the number of ova ovulated (Clark, 1934), but it is not known whether this is due to the development of more follicles or a reduction in atresia. In either event it is most probably related to hypophysial secretion of gonadotrophin. In contrast, starvation of mice leads to ovarian atrophy and the appearance of 'deficiency cells'; oestrous cycles cease but the ability to respond to exogenous gonadotrophin is maintained (Mulinos *et al.*, 1939).

It is most probable that any dietary or other factor which interrupts the occurrence of regular oestrous cycles *via* its effect on the pituitary* will also cause atresia of medium-sized and large follicles. The rate at which the total number of oocytes declines with age may therefore also be affected. In the light of present knowledge, however, there is no evidence to suggest that nutrition has any direct effect on atresia.

H. Ischaemia and grafting†

Ischaemia and transplantation lead to the degeneration of a large number of oocytes, those cells which survive the treatment being capable, however, of remaining in the ovary and undergoing normal development. Oocytes have been observed 2–3 years after grafting in the guinea pig (Pettinari, 1928), $14\frac{1}{2}$ months in the rat (Marshall and Jolly, 1907) and 1 year in the monkey (Mandl and Zuckerman, 1949). The number of germ cells which survive represent only a small fraction of the number present at the time of transplantation (cf. Mandl and Zuckerman, 1949; Green and Zuckerman, 1954). It has also been shown that the percentage of oocytes that is lost after transplantation of mouse ovaries is very variable and perhaps partly dependent on the site to which the graft is transferred (Jones, 1957). Small pieces of tissue tend to lose a smaller percentage of oocytes than do large pieces.

* See also Chapter 18, sect. II.
† See also Chapter 21, sect. IV and V, and Chapter 1, sect II, I.

The loss of germ cells varies between 20 and 80 per cent according to the site and size of the transplant.

In a further quantitative study, Green *et al.* (1956) counted the number of oocytes in (1) unfrozen tissue which had not been grafted, (2) frozen tissue which had been grafted, and (3) slices of tissue which had been grafted but not frozen. The experiment was undertaken to test the hypothesis that new oocytes are formed in ovarian grafts of tissue subjected to very low temperatures (Parkes and Smith, 1953). The results showed that about half the oocytes were lost when the tissue was grafted but not frozen. Freezing the tissue before transplantation caused a decrease to 10 per cent. A reduction in the number of oocytes is thus brought about by both the freezing procedure and transplantation itself.

In vitro studies of ovarian tissue reported hitherto are only qualitative (Martinovitch, 1937, 1938; Gaillard, 1950; Ingram, 1956). Most of the oocytes appear to survive when the tissue is removed from embryos; explants from adult ovaries usually become necrotic because the large and medium-sized follicles soon degenerate (Ingram, 1956). The latter observation conforms with Lipschütz's (1924) statement that in grafts atresia was accelerated in "those follicles which have already attained a certain size at the time when transplantation was performed".

The observations mentioned above suggest that any process in which the ovarian blood supply is interrupted rapidly results in atresia of germ cells even when the ovary is grafted back into the capsule (Jones, 1957). This conclusion is also supported by Butcher's (1932) observation that all oocytes are destroyed a week following the placing of permanent ligatures on the hilar vessels of the rat ovary. Butcher's observation that half the animals used possessed oocytes 30 days after ligaturing is probably due to the fact that a small proportion of the oocytes do survive until revascularization takes place (Martinovitch, 1935). Experiments on the rabbit ovary revealed that the number of oocytes that are destroyed by ischaemia is related to the time for which the ligatures remained on the hilar vessels (Martinovitch, 1934). Total occlusion of the blood supply for 72 hours killed all the oocytes, but if some blood was allowed to pass, some oocytes survived and developed even if the ligature was left permanently in place.

The evidence thus indicates that oocytes, particularly those that have begun development, are very sensitive to ischaemia, possibly due to deprivation of oxygen and gonadotrophin.

I. X-irradiation

The number of oocytes in ovaries exposed to X-irradiation decreases rapidly, and the changes which take place at the cellular level are fully discussed elsewhere (see Chapter 22, sect. II). It is generally agreed that the degenerative changes following irradiation are not strictly analogous to those occurring spontaneously during atresia (see Zuckerman, 1956; cf. Van-Eck, 1956; Mandl, 1959), and that no conclusions about the life-span of the atretic oocyte may be drawn from irradiation studies.

IV. Conclusions

A. Causal factors

It is evident that many experimental procedures which affect the rate of atresia also involve some alteration in the supply of gonadotrophin. The withdrawal of this hormone following hypophysectomy results in the atresia of those follicles that have reached an advanced stage of development. In contrast, an excess of FSH may lead to the formation of cystic follicles, while a high titre of LH results in the formation of corpora lutea atretica. Since atresia of medium-sized and large follicles is thus partly related either directly or indirectly to the supply of gonadotrophin, the possibility arises that the variation which occurs in the atresia of these follicles in the course of the oestrous cycle is also controlled by the pituitary. The vascularity of individual follicles may also participate, those follicles provided with a relatively poor blood supply (and hence a low level of gonadotrophin) probably being the first to become atretic.

The fact that the rate of atresia of growing follicles rises at oestrus suggests that oestrogen may be the causal factor. On the other hand, oestrogen promotes the growth of follicles in hypophysectomized animals, and it seems probable that the effect of this hormone in the intact animal is an indirect one *via* the pituitary.

The mechanism of atresia following ischaemia and irradiation appears to differ from that which occurs spontaneously. A few oocytes may become atretic from ischaemia because, for instance, of the pressure of a nearby growing follicle, and a few may degenerate as the result of natural background irradiation. The cause for the rapid decline in the total number of oocytes, especially during early postnatal life, must however be attributed to some cause or causes which are as yet completely unknown.

B. Duration of atresia

All attempts to determine the time taken for an oocyte to become atretic and disappear from the ovary are based on certain premises which may be unjustified. For instance, the view of Swezy and Evans (1931) that all oocytes become atretic at each oestrous cycle was closely linked with the thesis that neoformation of oocytes continues through-out life. Similarly, Van-Eck's (1956) method of estimating the time for which an atretic oocyte survives was based on the unwarranted assumption that post-irradiation atresia is identical to natural atresia. The view advanced above (see p. 256) that a primordial oocyte may become atretic and disappear within 1 week during early postnatal life is based on the assumption that none of the oocytes are atretic at birth. Sturgis's (1949) estimate that in the monkey, follicles which become atretic at the time of ovulation persist for 5 weeks, is based on the premise that the cytological changes in the luteal cells of atretic follicles occur at the same speed as they do in the formation of the normal corpus luteum.

A better understanding of the whole problem is hampered by the fact that (i) atresia is difficult to diagnose with certainty, especially in the case of primordial oocytes, and (ii) that it is impossible to view the same oocyte at different stages of development or atresia. While it is possible that the first difficulty may be overcome by the use of special histological techniques, the second problem is almost insur-mountable. The use of tissue culture and phase contrast microscopy may enable the observer to follow the process of atresia, but there can be no guarantee that the process will be the same under experimental as under natural conditions.

It may be concluded that whereas the disappearance of oocytes in early postnatal life may be measured in days, atretic oocytes may remain in the ovaries of the adult for periods of months or even years.

C. Consequences and significance of atresia

Two questions arise from the preceding discussion: has atresia any essential function; and does it have any consequences, either advan-tageous or disadvantageous, to the animal?

In answer to the first question, it has been postulated that the amount of hormone produced by follicles destined to ovulate is insufficient to stimulate the reproductive tract, additional hormone being derived from atretic medium-sized and large follicles. This hypothesis, however, is based on the assumption that the amount of hormone produced by those follicles that ovulate is insufficient, and that atretic follicles are capable of producing hormone.

The only function that has been ascribed to atresia of primordial oocytes is that it may serve as a selective process in which only the 'fittest' survive. This view is unacceptable since there is no evidence that those qualities which allow an oocyte to survive are associated with those characteristics which favour the survival of the animal as a whole.

The result of atresia throughout life is that old animals have a much reduced 'stock' of oocytes. In man and certain strains of mice (Thung *et al.*, 1956), the population of oocytes is completely exhausted long before the average expectation of life has been reached. It has been suggested that the reduction in the supply of oocytes is one of the factors which influence the decline in fertility in old age (Zuckerman, 1955), a decrease in litter-size occurring both when the oocyte population is reduced naturally in old age (Ingram *et al.*, 1958) or experimentally by means of X-rays (Ingram, 1958). In the latter study, it was also found that fewer medium-sized follicles were present in ovaries containing a depleted number of primordial oocytes. A decrease in fertility may therefore be a consequence of a high rate of atresia or lack of growing follicles; other factors however undoubtedly play their part in senile sterility.

In conclusion, it must be stressed that all too little is known about factors influencing the onset of atresia. Two problems in particular need to be investigated: one is to establish the precise morphological changes which occur when a primordial oocyte becomes atretic; the second is to obtain more information about the effects of a depleted supply of oocytes on fertility and the length of reproductive life.

REFERENCES

Addison, W. H. F. (1916). Fragmentation of the ovum within the Graafian follicle. *Proc. path. Soc., Philad.* **37**, 1.
Allen, B. M. (1904). The embryonic development of the ovary and of the testis of mammals. *Amer. J. Anat.* **3**, 89–146.
Allen, E., Kountz, W. B. and Francis, B. F. (1925). Selective elimination of ova in the adult ovary. *Amer. J. Anat.* **34**, 445–465.
· Allen, E., Pratt, J. P., Newell, Q. U. and Bland, L. J. (1930). Human ova from large follicles; including a search for maturation divisions and observations on atresia. *Amer. J. Anat.* **46**, 1–43.
Arai, H. (1920a). On the post-natal development of the ovary (albino rat), with especial reference to the number of ova. *Amer. J. Anat.* **27**, 405–462.
Arai, H. (1920b). On the cause of the hypertrophy of the surviving ovary after semispaying (albino rat) and on the number of ova in it. *Amer. J. Anat.* **28**, 59–79.
· Asami, G. (1920). Observations on the follicular atresia in the rabbit ovary *Anat. Rec.* **18**, 323–344.
Athias, M. (1909). Les phénomènes de division de l'ovule dans les follicules de Graaf en voie d'atrésie chez le lérot (*Eliomys quercinus* L.). *Anat. Anz.* **34** 1–23.
Athias, M. (1929). Les phénomènes de division de l'oocyte au cours de l'atrésie folliculaire chez les mammifères. *Arch. Anat. micr.* **25**, 405–425.
Balfour, F.M. (1880). "A Treatise on Comparative Embryology." Vol. 1. Macmillan & Co.

Benthin, W. (1911). Ueber Follikelatresie in Säugetierovarien. *Arch. Gynaek.* **94**, 599–636.

Block, E. (1952). Quantitative morphological investigations of the follicular system in women. Variations at different ages. *Acta anat.* **14**, 108–123.

Block, E., Magnusson, G. and Odeblad, E. (1953). A study of normal and atretic follicles with autoradiography. *Acta obstet. gynec. scand.* **32**, 1–6.

Boling, J. L., Blandau, R. J., Soderwall, A. L. and Young, W. C. (1941). The growth of the Graafian follicle and the time of ovulation in the albino rat. *Anat. Rec.* **79**, 313–331.

Bonnet, R. (1899). Giebt es bei Wirbeltieren Parthenogenesis? *Ergebn. Anat. EntwGesch.* **9**, 820–870.

Brambell, F. W. R. (1927). The development and morphology of the gonads of the mouse. The morphogenesis of the indifferent gonad, and of the ovary. *Proc. roy. Soc. B.* **101**, 391–408.

Brambell, F. W. R. (1956). Ovarian changes. *In* "Marshall's Physiology of Reproduction" (A. S. Parkes, ed.). Vol. I, pt. 1. Longmans, Green & Co., London.

Brambell, F. W. R. and Rowlands, I. W. (1936). Reproduction of the bank vole. 1. The oestrous cycle of the female. *Phil. Trans. B.* **226**, 71–98.

Branca, A. (1925). L'oocyte atrésique et son involution. *Arch. Biol., Paris,* **35**, 325–440.

Burkl, W. and Kellner, G. (1954). Hypophysektomie und postnatale Oogenese bei Ratten. *Acta anat.* **23**, 49–57.

Butcher, E. O. (1932). Regeneration in ligated ovaries and transplanted ovarian fragments of the white rat (*Mus norvegicus albinus*). *Anat. Rec.* **54**, 87–104.

Chappellier, A. (1909). Follicules pluriovulaires et dégénérescence ovulaire chez la souris blanche. *C.R. Soc. Biol., Paris,* **66**, 543–545.

• Clark, E. B. (1923). Observations on the ova and ovaries of the guinea pig, *Cavia cobaya. Anat. Rec.* **25**, 313–331.

Clark, R. T. (1934). Studies on the physiology of reproduction in sheep. *Anat. Rec.* **60**, 125–135.

Cohn, F. (1909). Ueber das Corpus luteum und den atretischen Follikel des Menschen und deren cystische Derivate. *Arch. Gynaek.* **87**, 367–444.

Cole, H. H., Howell, C. E. and Hart, G. H. (1931). The changes in the ovary of the mare during pregnancy. *Anat. Rec.* **49**, 199–210.

Dawson, A. B. (1952). Argyrophilic inclusions in the cytoplasm of the ova of the rat in normal and atretic follicles. *Anat. Rec.* **112**, 37–59.

Deane, H. W. (1951). Histochemical characteristics of atretic follicles in rats. *Anat. Rec.* **111**, 504–505.

Deane, H. W. (1952). Histochemical observations on the ovary and oviduct of the albino rat during the oestrous cycle. *Amer. J. Anat.* **91**, 363–414.

Deane, H. W. and Andrews, J. S. (1953). A comparison of the staining of lipid droplets in the mouse ovary by the Schiff reaction and by the Ashbel-Seligman carbonyl reaction. *J. Histochem.* **1**, 283–295.

Deanesly, R. (1935). The reproductive processes of certain mammals. Growth and reproduction in the stoat (*Mustela erminea*). *Phil. Trans. B.* **225**, 459–492.

Desaive, P. (1941). Contribution radio-biologique à la démonstration de la fixité, dans l'ovaire de la lapine adulte, des sources du développement follicu-laire. *Acta brev. neerl. Physiol.* **4**, 10–30.

Engle, E. T. (1927). A quantitative study of follicular atresia in the mouse. *Amer. J. Anat.* **39**, 187–203.

Engle, E. T. and Smith, P. E. (1929). The origin of the corpus luteum in the rat as indicated by studies upon luteinization of the cystic follicle. *Anat. Rec.* **43**, 239–246.

Evans, H. M. and Swezy, O. (1931). Ovogenesis and the normal follicular cycle in adult mammalia. *Mem. Univ. Calif.* **9**, 119–225.

Everett, N. B. (1945). The present status of the germ-cell problem in vertebrates. *Biol. Rev.* **20**, 45–55.

Felix, W. (1912). Degeneration of follicles in young girls, sometimes cystic degeneration. *In* "Manual of Human Embryology" (F. Keibel and F. P. Mall, eds.) Vol. 2, p. 752. J. B. Lippincott Co., Philadelphia.

Findlay, G. M. (1921). An experimental study of avian beriberi. *J. Path. Bact.* **24**, 175–191.

Gaillard, P. J. (1950). Sex cell formation in explants of the foetal human ovarian cortex. I & II. *Proc. Acad. Sci. Amst.* **53**, Nos. 8 and 9, pp. 3–30.

Garde, M. L. (1930). The ovary of *Ornithorhynchus*, with special reference to follicular atresia. *J. Anat., Lond.* **64**, 422–453.

Green, S. H. and Zuckerman, S. (1951). The number of oocytes in the mature rhesus monkey (*Macaca mulatta*). *J. Endocrin.* **7**, 194–202.

Green, S. H. and Zuckerman, S. (1954). Further observations on oocyte numbers in mature rhesus monkeys (*Macaca mulatta*). *J. Endocrin.* **10**, 284–290.

Green, S. H., Mandl, A. M. and Zuckerman, S. (1951). The proportion of ovarian follicles in different stages of development in rats and monkeys. *J. Anat., Lond.* **85**, 325–329.

Green, S. H., Smith, A. U. and Zuckerman, S. (1956). The numbers of oocytes in ovarian autografts after freezing and thawing. *J. Endocrin.* **13**, 330–334.

Gresson, R. A. R. (1933). A study of the cytoplasmic inclusions and nucleolar phenomena during oogenesis of the mouse. *Quart. J. micr. Sci.* **75**, 697–722.

Guthrie, M. J. and Jeffers, K. R. (1938). Growth of follicles in the ovaries of the bat, *Myotis lucifugus lucifugus*. *Anat. Rec.* **71**, 477–496.

Hammond, J. (1925). "Reproduction in the Rabbit." Oliver & Boyd, Edinburgh.

Hammond, J. and Wodzicki, K. (1941). Anatomical and histological changes during the oestrous cycle in the mare. *Proc. roy. Soc.* B. **130**, 1–23.

Hargitt, G. T. (1930). The formation of the sex glands and germ cells of mammals. *J. Morph.* **49**, 277–321.

Harman, M. T. and Kirgis, H. D. (1938). The development and atresia of the Graafian follicle and the division of intra-ovarian ova in the guinea-pig. *Amer. J. Anat.* **63**, 79–100.

Harrison, R. J. (1948). The changes occurring in the ovary of the goat during the oestrous cycle and in early pregnancy. *J. Anat., Lond.* **82**, 21–48.

Heape, W. (1905). Ovulation and degeneration of ova in the rabbit. *Proc. roy. Soc.* B. **76**, 260–268.

Hedberg, E. (1953). The chemical composition of the human ovarian oocyte. *Acta endocr., Copenhagen*, **14**, Suppl. 15, 1–89.

Hill, M. and White, W. E. (1933). The growth and regression of follicles in the oestrous rabbit. *J. Physiol.* **80**, 174–178.

Horst, C. J. van der, and Gillman, J. (1945). The behaviour of the Graafian follicle of *Elephantulus* during pregnancy with special reference to the hormonal regulation of ovarian activity. *S. Afr. J. med. Sci. Suppl.* **10**, 1–14.

Ingram, D. L. (1953). The effect of hypophysectomy on the number of oocytes in the adult albino rat. *J. Endocrin.* **9**, 307–311.

Ingram, D. L. (1956). Observations on the ovary cultured *in vitro*. *J. Endocrin.* **14**, 155–159.

Ingram, D. L. (1958). Fertility and oocyte numbers after X-irradiation of the ovary. *J. Endocrin.* **17**, 81–90.

Ingram, D. L. (1959a). The effect of oestrogen on the atresia of ovarian follicles. *J. Endocrin.* **19**, 123–125.

Ingram, D. L. (1959b). The effect of gonadotrophins and oestrogen on ovarian atresia in the immature rat. *J. Endocrin.* **19**, 117–122.

Ingram, D. L., Mandl, A. M. and Zuckerman, S. (1958). The influence of age on litter-size. *J. Endocrin.* **17**, 280–285.

Jones, E. C. (1957). "The ageing ovary." Thesis. University of Birmingham.

Kampmeier, O. F. (1929). On the problem of "parthenogenesis" in the mammalian ovary. *Amer. J. Anat.* **43**, 45–64.

Kingery, H. M. (1917). Oogenesis in the white mouse. *J. Morph.* **30**, 261–316.

Kingsbury, B. F. (1913). The morphogenesis of the mammalian ovary: *Felis domestica*. *Amer. J. Anat.* **15**, 345–387.

Kingsbury, B. F. (1938). The post-partum formation of egg cells in the cat. *J. Morph.* **63**, 397–413.

Krafta, J. (1939). Parthenogenic cleavage in the human ovary. *Anat. Rec.* **75**, 19–21.

Kramer, M. M., Harman, M. T. and Brill, A. K. (1933). Disturbances of reproduction and ovarian changes in the guinea pig in relation to vitamin C deficiency. *Amer. J. Physiol.* **106**, 611–622.

Lane, C. E. and Davis, F. R. (1939). The ovary of the adult rat. 1. Changes in growth of the follicle and in volume and mitotic activity of the granulosa and theca during the oestrous cycle. *Anat. Rec.* **73**, 429–442.

Liche, H. (1939). Oestrous cycle in the cat. *Nature, Lond.* **143**, 900.

Lipschütz, A. (1924). "The Internal Secretion of the Sex Glands." Heffer & Sons, Cambridge.

Lipschütz, A. (1925). Dynamics of ovarian hypertrophy under experimental conditions. *Brit. J. exp. Biol.* **2**, 331–346.

Lipschütz, A. (1928). New developments in ovarian dynamics and the law of follicular constancy. *Brit. J. exp. Biol.* **5**, 283–291.

Lipschütz, A. and Voss, H. E. V. (1925). Further developments on the dynamics of ovarian hypertrophy. *Brit. J. exp. Biol.* **3**, 35–41.

Loeb, L. (1901). On progressive changes in the ova in mammalian ovaries. *J. med. Res.* **6**, 39–46.

Loeb, L. (1905). Über hypertrophische Vorgänge bei der Follikelatresie nebst Bemerkungen über die Oocyten in den Marksträngen und über Teilungserscheinungen am Ei im Ovarium des Meerschweinchens. *Arch. mikr. Anat.* **65**, 728–753.

Loeb, L. (1911). The parthenogenetic development of ova in the mammalian ovary and the origin of ovarian teratoma and chorio-epitheliomata. *J. Amer. med. Ass.* **56**, 1327.

Loeb, L. (1930). Parthenogenetic development of eggs in the ovary of the guinea pig. *Proc. Soc. exp. Biol., N.Y.* **27**, 213–416.

Loeb, L. (1932). The parthenogenetic development of eggs in the ovary of the guinea pig. *Anat. Rec.* **51**, 373–408.

Mandl, A. M. (1959). A quantitative study of the sensitivity of oocytes to X-irradiation. *Proc. roy. Soc.* B. **150**, 53–71.

Mandl, A. M. and Shelton, M. (1959). A quantitative study of oocytes in young and old nulliparous laboratory rats. *J. Endocrin.* **18**, 444–450.

Mandl, A. M. and Zuckerman, S. (1949). Ovarian autografts in monkeys. *J. Anat., Lond.* **83**, 315–324.

Mandl, A. M. and Zuckerman, S. (1950). The numbers of normal and atretic ova in the mature rat. *J. Endocrin.* **6**, 426–435.

Mandl, A. M. and Zuckerman, S. (1951a). Numbers of normal and atretic oocytes in unilaterally spayed rats. *J. Endocrin.* **7**, 112–119.

Mandl, A. M. and Zuckerman, S. (1951b). The relation of age to numbers of oocytes. *J. Endocrin.* **7**, 190–193.

Mandl, A. M. and Zuckerman, S. (1952). Cyclical changes in the number of medium and large follicles in the adult rat ovary. *J. Endocrin.* **8**, 341–346.

Mandl, A. M., Zuckerman, S. and Patterson, H. D. (1952). The number of oocytes in ovarian fragments after compensatory hypertrophy. *J. Endocrin.* **8**, 347–356.

Marrian, G. F. and Parkes, A. S. (1929). The effect of anterior pituitary preparations administered during dietary anoestrus. *Proc. roy. Soc.* B. **105**, 248–258.

Marshall, F. H. A. (1904). The oestrous cycle in the common ferret. *Quart. J. micr. Sci.* **48**, 323–345.

Marshall, F. H. A. and Jolly, W. A. (1907). Results of removal and transplantation of the ovaries. *Trans. roy. Soc. Edinb.* **45**, 589–599.

Martínez-Esteve, P. (1942). Observations on the histology of the opossum ovary. *Contr. Embryol. Carneg. Instn.* **30**, 17–26.

Martinovitch, P. N. (1934). La ligature temporaire des ovaires de la lapine et le problème de l'ovogenèse postnatale chez cet animal. *C.R. Soc. Biol., Paris,* **116**, 1294–1297.

Martinovitch, P. N. (1935). La ligature permanente des ovaires des rats blancs et le problème de la formation post-natale des cellules germinatives chez cet animal; expériences effectuées sur des ovaires décapsulés. *C.R. Soc. Biol., Paris,* **118**, 349–351.

Martinovitch, P. N. (1937). Development *in vitro* of the mammalian gonad. *Nature, Lond.* **139**, 413.

Martinovitch, P. N. (1938). The development *in vitro* of the mammalian gonad: ovary and ovogenesis. *Proc. roy. Soc.* B. **125**, 232–249.

Matthews, L. H. (1941). Reproduction in the spotted hyaena *Crocuta crocuta*. *Phil. Trans.* B. **230**, 1–78.

Matthews, L. H. (1950). Reproduction in the basking shark *Cetorrhinus maximus* (Gunner). *Phil. Trans.* B. **234**, 247–316.

Menschik, Z. (1948). The influence of vitamin E on ovarian structures in mice. *Quart. J. exp. Physiol.* **34**, 97–113.

Mertens, H. (1895). Recherches sur la signification du corps vitellin de Balbiani dans l'ovule de mammifères et des oiseaux. *Arch. Biol., Paris,* **13**, 389.

Moog, F. and Wenger, E. L. (1952). The occurrence of a neutral mucopolysaccharide at sites of high alkaline phosphatase activity. *Amer. J. Anat.* **90**, 339–377.

Mulinos, M. G., Pomerantz, L., Smelser, J. and Kurzrok, R. (1939). Estrusinhibiting effects of inanition. *Proc. Soc. exp. Biol., N.Y.* **40**, 79–83.

Myers, H. I., Young, W. C. and Dempsey, E. W. (1936). Graafian follicle development throughout the reproductive cycle in the guinea pig with special reference to changes during oestrus (sexual receptivity). *Anat. Rec.* **65**, 381–402.

Newman, H. H. (1913). Parthenogenetic cleavage of the armadillo ovum. *Biol. Bull., Wood's Hole*, **25**, 58–78.

Noble, R. L. (1938). Effect of synthetic oestrogenic substances on the body-growth and endocrine organs of the rat. *Lancet*, **235**, 192–195.

Odeblad, E. (1951). Autoradiography with ^{32}P of the rabbit ovary. *Acta obstet. gynec. scand.* **31**, 63–73.

Odeblad, E. (1952). Contributions to the theory and technique of quantitative autoradiography with ^{32}P with special reference to the granulosa tissue of the graafian follicles in the rabbit. *Acta radiol., Stockh.* **93**, Suppl., 1–123.

Paesi, F. J. A. (1949). Hypophysectomy and oocyte numbers. *Acta endocr., Copenhagen*, **3**, 89–104.

Parkes, A. S. (1928). The nature of the anoestrous condition resulting from vitamin B deficiency. *Quart. J. exp. Physiol.* **18**, 397–401.

Parkes, A. S. and Smith, A. U. (1953). Regeneration of rat ovarian tissue grafted after exposure to low temperatures. *Proc. roy. Soc.* B. **140**, 455–470.

Pearl, R. and Boring, A. M. (1918). Sex studies: the corpus luteum in the ovary of the domestic fowl. *Amer. J. Anat.* **23**, 1–35.

Pederson, E. S. (1951). Histogenesis of lutein tissue of the albino rat. *Amer. J. Anat.* **88**, 397–428.

Pencharz, R. I. (1940). Effect of oestrogens and androgens alone and in combination with chorionic gonadotrophin on the ovary of the hypophysectomized rat. *Science*, **91**, 554.

Perry, J. S. (1953). The reproduction of the African elephant *Loxodonta africana*. *Phil. Trans.* B. **237**, 93–149.

Pettinari, V. (1928). "Greffe Ovarienne et Action Endocrine de l'Ovaire." Gaston Doin, Paris.

Pincus, G. (1936). "The Eggs of Mammals." Macmillan, New York.

Pincus, G. and Enzmann, E. V. (1937). The growth, maturation and atresia of ovarian eggs in the rabbit. *J. Morph.* **61**, 351–383.

Pollak, W. (1926). Über Kristalloide in Eizellen von *Macacus rhesus*. *Anat. Anz.* **61**, 202–204.

Rennels, E. G. (1951). The influence of hormones on the histochemistry of ovarian interstitial tissue in the immature rat. *Amer. J. Anat.* **88**, 63–108.

Richter, C. P., Holt, L. E., Barelare, B. and Hawkes, C. D. (1938). Changes in fat, carbohydrate and protein appetite in vitamin B deficiency. *Amer. J. Physiol.* **124**, 596–602.

Rubaschkin, W. (1912). Zur Lehre von der Keimbahn bei Säugetieren. Über die Entwicklung der Keimdrüsen. *Anat. Hefte*, **46**, 345–411.

Săglik, S. (1938). Ovaries of gorilla, chimpanzee, orang-utan and gibbon. *Contr. Embryol. Carneg. Instn.* **27**, 179–189.

Salazar, A. L. (1922a). Sur l'existence de faux corps jaunes autonomes dans la glande interstitielle de la lapine. *Anat. Rec.* **23**, 189–193.

Salazar, A. L. (1922b). Sur la forme de dégénérescence des follicules anovulaires de Regaud et d'autres reliquats provenant des cordons ovigènes de l'ovaire de la lapine. *Anat. Rec.* **24**, 79–83.

Sansom, G. S. (1920). Parthenogenesis in the water vole *Microtus amphibius*. *J. Anat., Lond.* **55**, 68–77.

Schotterer, A. (1928). Beitrag zur Feststellung der Eianzahl in verschiedenen Altersperioden bei der Hündin. *Anat. Anz.* **65**, 177–192.

Schottlaender, J. (1891). Beitrag zur Kenntnis der Follikelatresie nebst einigen Bemerkungen über die unveränderten Follikel in den Eierstöcken der Säugetiere. *Arch. mikr. Anat.* **37,** 192–238.

Schottlaender, J. (1893). Ueber den Graaf'schen Follikel, seine Enstehung beim Menschen und seine Schicksale bei Menschen und Säugetieren. *Arch. mikr. Anat.* **41,** 219–294.

Schwarz, O. H., Young, C. C. and Crouse, J. C. (1949). Ovogenesis in the adult human ovary. *Amer. J. Obstet. Gynec.* **58,** 54–64.

Seitz, L. (1905a). Zur Frage der Luteinzellenwucherung in atretischen Follikeln während der Schwangerschaft. *Zbl. Gynäk.* **29,** 578–585.

Seitz, L. (1905b). Die Luteinzellenwucherung in atretischen Follikeln, eine physiologische Erscheinung während der Schwangerschaft. *Zbl. Gynäk.* **29,** 257–263.

Seitz, L. (1906). Die Follikelatresie während der Schwangerschaft insbesondere die Hypertrophie und Hyperplasie der Theca interna Zellen (Thecaluteinzellen) und ihre Beziehungen zur Corpus Luteum Bildung. *Arch. Gynaek.* **77,** 203–356.

Simkins, C. S. (1932). The development of the human ovary from birth to sexual maturity. *Amer. J. Anat.* **51,** 465–493.

Slater, D. W. and Dornfeld, E. J. (1945). Quantitative aspects of growth and oocyte production in the early prepubertal rat ovary. *Amer. J. Anat.* **76,** 253–276.

Sobotta, J. (1896). Über die Bildung des Corpus luteum bei der Maus. *Arch. mikr. Anat.* **47,** 261–308.

Starkey, W. F. and Leathem, J. H. (1938). Gonadotrophic action of testosterone propionate on the immature mouse ovary. *Proc. Soc. exp. Biol., N.Y.* **39,** 218–220.

Stevens, T. G. (1904). The fate of the ovum and Graafian follicle in pre-menstrual life. *J. Obstet. Gynaec., Brit. Emp.* **5,** 1–12.

• Stockard, C. R. and Papanicolaou, G. N. (1917). The existence of a typical oestrous cycle in the guinea pig with a study of its histological and physiological changes. *Amer. J. Anat.* **22,** 225–283.

Stricht, O. van der (1901). Deuxième demonstration d'atrésie ovulaire et d'atresia folliculaire. *Verh. anat. Ges., Jena,* **15,** 208–210.

Sturgis, S. H. (1949). Rate and significance of atresia of the ovarian follicle of the rhesus monkey. *Contr. Embryol. Carneg. Instn.* **33,** 67–80.

Swezy, O. (1929). Ovarian chromosome cycle in mixed rat strain. *J. Morph.* **48,** 445–469.

Swezy, O. (1933). "Ovogenesis and its Relation to Hypophysis." Science Press, Lancaster, Pennsylvania.

Swezy, O. and Evans, H. M. (1930). The human ovarian germ cells. *J. Morph.* **49,** 543–577.

Thung, P. J., Boot, L. M. and Mühlbock, O. (1956). Senile changes in the oestrous cycle in and ovarian structure in some inbred strains of mice. *Acta endocr., Copenhagen,* **28,** 8–32.

Van-Eck, G. J. V. (1956). Neo-ovogenesis in the adult monkey. *Anat. Rec.* **125,** 207–224.

Velloso, A. de Pinho (1923). Atrésie de l'épithélium folliculaire ovarique chez les mammifères. *C.R. Soc. Biol., Paris,* **88,** 830–833.

Vincent, W. S. and Dornfeld, E. J. (1948). Localization and role of nucleic acids in the developing rat ovary. *Amer. J. Anat.* **83,** 437–470.

Williams, P. C. (1940). Effect of stilboestrol on the ovaries of hypophysecto-mized rats. *Nature, Lond.* **145**, 338.

Williams, P. C. (1944a). Ovarian response after hypophysectomy to oestrogen treatment. *J. Endocrin.* **4**, 131–136.

Williams, P. C. (1944b). Ovarian stimulation by oestrogens: effects in immature hypophysectomized rats. *Proc. roy. Soc.* B. **132**, 189–199.

Winiwarter, H. de (1923). Les débuts de l'atrésie folliculaire. *C.R. Soc. Biol., Paris,* **89**, 960–962.

Winiwarter, H. de and Sainmont, G. (1909). Nouvelles recherches sur l'oogenèse et l'organogenèse de l'ovaire des mammifères (chat). *Arch. Biol., Paris,* **24**, 1–142.

Zuckerman, S. (1931). The menstrual cycle of the primates. Part IV. Observa-tions on the lactation period. *Proc. zool. Soc. Lond.* 593–602.

Zuckerman, S. (1951). The number of oocytes in the mature ovary. *Recent Progr. Hormone Res.* **6**, 63–109.

Zuckerman, S. (1955). Fecundity in relation to oocyte numbers. *Proc. Vth Int. Conf. on Planned Parenthood, Tokyo,* pp. 197–200.

Zuckerman, S. (1956). The regenerative capacity of ovarian tissue. *Ciba Foun-dation Coll. Ageing,* **2**, 31–58.

Zuckerman, S. and Parkes, A. S. (1932). The menstrual cycle of the primates, Part V. The cycle of the baboon. *Proc. zool. Soc. Lond.* 139–191.

CHAPTER 5

THE OVARIAN CYCLE IN VERTEBRATES

J. S. PERRY AND I. W. ROWLANDS

I. Introduction

The cyclical nature of breeding activity is one of the most prominent features of reproduction in vertebrates. A very large number of species breed only once a year, but always at a constant time in each successive year. In others, including many mammals, breeding occurs at more frequent intervals, but whether they breed without rest or for only a certain part of the year, the interval between successive broods or litters is relatively constant and is characteristic of the species concerned.

The breeding rhythm is well known to be controlled from without by a series of external factors which initiate ovarian activity through the intermediation of the anterior pituitary gland. A cycle of events is established within the ovary, comprising the growth of a determinate number of follicles, leading to the periodic release of an equivalent number of ova, followed by changes in the spent follicle which vary in accordance with the phylogenetic position of the species. This ovarian cycle is concerned not only with the supply of fertile eggs but, in very diverse ways, with the well-being of the products of conception. In reference to mammals, the two terms 'follicular phase' and 'luteal phase' have come into common usage to describe the two parts of the ovarian cycle separated by ovulation. It is often convenient, however, to define the cycle in terms of the ovulation-interval, but when this is done, it should be borne in mind that the interval comprises the luteal phase of one cycle and the follicular phase of the next. The sequence of the two phases is frequently obscured by the rapidity of events and by overlap between the end of the luteal phase and the beginning of the follicular phase of the next cycle.

Only a proportion of the follicles which grow eventually ovulate, the majority being destined to degenerate before they mature. 'Waves' of follicular growth, atresia* and regression commonly occur before puberty and recur at intervals throughout adult life. The products of such atresia are more or less transient. In mammals, they may survive for a time as apparently active corpora lutea, or they may be more rapidly incorporated into the ovarian stroma or even, according to some authorities, contribute to the interstitial tissue and so perhaps assume a cyclic secretory function.

The physiology of reproduction has been more fully investigated in mammals than in other vertebrates, and here the phenomena of the oestrous cycle so dominate the picture that it is common to think of oestrus—the period of sexual receptivity on the part of the female—rather than ovulation, as being the central event of the cycle, and of the oestrous cycle as if it were synonymous with the ovarian cycle. Events in the oestrous cycle are of course associated with, and largely controlled by, changes in the ovary, but these effects are manifested in the accessory sex organs. Little is known, or can be conjectured, about the evolution of the oestrous cycle, but it may be regarded as an adaptation associated with internal fertilization.

II. The cycle in non-mammalian vertebrates†

A. Cyclostomes

The lampreys have only one breeding season; they spawn in the spring in which they become mature, and then immediately die. Their eggs are small, in contrast to those of *Myxine* and the hagfishes, which are enclosed in an elaborate egg-case and are about 25 mm long. There is no oviduct in the cyclostomes, and the egg-capsule is produced by the ovary. This feature of their reproduction presupposes an activity of the follicle which is rarely encountered in other vertebrates. The

* See Chapter 4.
† For a description of the structure of the ovary in these groups of animals, the reader is referred to Chapter 2B.

eggs are shed into the coelom and escape to the exterior by an opening in the body wall. They are fertilized externally, spermatozoa reaching the egg by a pore, the micropyle, in the egg-capsule.

Lyngnes (1936) found well-developed corpora lutea in *Myxine*, formed in both ruptured and atretic follicles. He drew attention to their resemblance to the corpora lutea of ovulation and atresia in mammals.

B. Elasmobranchs

Information concerning the ovarian cycle in this class is largely confined to studies of the reproduction of a few species, including the smooth dogfish, *Mustelus canis* (Hisaw and Abramowitz, 1937), the spiny dogfish, *Squalus acanthias* (Hisaw and Albert, 1947), the dogfish *Scylliorhinus canicula* (Metten, 1941), the Indian ray, *Rhinobatus granulatus* (Samuel, 1943), and the basking shark, *Cetorhinus maximus* (Matthews, 1950), all of which are viviparous species. It is abundantly clear that these species differ with respect to the periodicity of breeding, but have at least one salient feature in common in that the ovaries contain large numbers of corpora lutea. A large proportion of these structures arise from the atresia of unripe follicles. These, as well as the corpora lutea of ovulation, persist for long periods and are associated with internal fertilization, which is general in the elasmobranchs.

It is apparent that follicular development and ovulation may proceed in the presence of large corpora lutea. In *Scylliorhinus*, Metten found that the uterus always contained four to six pairs of embryos, each pair being at a different stage of development. The interval between ovulations is therefore much shorter than the gestation period. *Mustelus canis* breeds once a year and gives birth to about sixteen young after a pregnancy of about 10 months. At the time of parturition, in spring, the ovaries contain sixteen to twenty large follicles and ova which have developed during the latter half of gestation. Their maturation follows and ovulation occurs in June and July. *Squalus acanthias* was estimated to have a gestation period of 20 to 22 months. Ovulation occurs shortly after parturition and at the same time another oocyte begins to grow, so that follicular development occupies 2 years. The corpora lutea of ovulation persist for about 18 months.

The most detailed histological study of the ovary of any of the above species is that of Samuel for *Rhinobatus*, but unfortunately it was made on only a single specimen. The ovary, however, contained more than twenty corpora lutea in varying stages of development. Matthews has calculated that the ovary of the basking shark contains at least six million ova exceeding 0·5 mm in diameter, together with very numerous corpora lutea, most of the latter having arisen by direct transformation of atretic follicles. Only the larger corpora lutea were considered to have resulted from ovulation; evidently they do not inhibit follicular maturation, at least in the non-pregnant fish.

C. Teleosts

The order Teleostei is very large and comprises some 20,000 living species, the majority of which exhibit a well-defined sexual periodicity under the control of external factors and associated with migratory habits; the salmon and the eel are renowned for the long journeys that they make. Their breeding habits range from the continuous production of free-swimming young in *Brachyraphis episcopi* (Turner, 1938) to the deposition of a single batch of eggs once in the lifetime of the individual in *Oncorhynchus* (Hoar, 1955). Although internal fertilization, viviparity and complex mating and parental behaviour occur in a number of teleostean species, there is no close homology between these and the equivalent phenomena in the higher vertebrates. This is a reflection of the morphological differences between the ovary and oviducts of teleosts and those of elasmobranchs, Amphibia and Amniota (see Chapter 2B, sect. III, C; also Hoar, 1957). The oviducts of teleosts appear to serve only a mechanical function, and although the growth of the oviduct of the bitterling to form a protruding ovipositor is believed by Bretschneider and Duyvené de Wit (1947) to be a response to an ovarian hormone, 'oviductin', it occurs before ovulation and has no gestational significance.

1. *Oviparous forms*

The great majority of teleosts are oviparous and shed large numbers of ova which are fertilized externally. The main function of the follicle is the transfer of material to the oocytes during vitellogenesis. It may also play a part in the formation of the zona pellucida, and those eggs which are furnished with processes for attachment to weeds and stones derive them from the follicle wall and not from the oviduct (Champy and Gley, 1923). The ovarian cycle usually follows a single rhythm associated with a restricted breeding season rigidly controlled by external stimuli (Bullough, 1939, 1940). Vivien (1939) has described the cycle of follicular development in *Gobius paganellus*, in which the oocytes grew from a diameter of 100 to 120μ in July to 600 to 630μ by the following May before spawning took place. The rate of development of oocytes into mature ova was found by Hann (1927) to be similar in the freshwater teleost *Cottus bairdii*, but in this species the complete cycle of oogenesis occupied 2 years. Yolk first appears in the ovum of the goldfish when it reaches a diameter of about 150μ (Beach, 1959): vitellogenesis extends through 4 or 5 months and the

mature ovum is about 500μ in diameter. Ling (1958), in a comprehensive study of the garfish *Reporhamphus melanochir* in Australian
waters, described the occurrence of cycles of growth and regression of
ova in the immature fish which closely parallel those of the adult during
the spawning season, as was similarly shown for the young hake by
Hickling (1935). The adult garfish has a spawning season lasting from
September to March. Throughout this season the ovaries contain eggs
in all stages of growth, which implies the existence of a succession of
follicular cycles during spring and summer. Cyclical activity appears
to be in abeyance during autumn and winter.

Hypertrophy of the follicular epithelium to form 'luteal' tissue after
ovulation or after resorption of ova has been shown to occur in some
of these oviparous fishes. Craig-Bennett (1931) has reported the occurrence of a short-lived corpus luteum of ovulation in the stickleback,
but it is doubtful if it has any functional activity. The cyclical production of corpora lutea from unruptured follicles, the 'pre-ovulatory'
corpora lutea, has been described by Bretschneider and Duyvené de Wit
(1947) in the bitterling, and post-ovulatory hypertrophy of the follicle
of *Fundulus heteroclitus* (Matthews, 1938) results in the formation of a
structure which closely resembles a corpus luteum and lasts for 5 to
6 months. Bowers (1954) has described the occurrence of corpora
lutea in ovaries containing mature ova during the protracted spawning
season of the European whiting, and similar structures, abundant
towards the end of the spawning season, were reported by Ling (1959)
in the garfish, but were not studied in detail. The hypertrophy of the
zona granulosa of the goldfish, which was found to occur in immature,
maturing and mature follicles at all times of the year (Beach, 1959), was
associated with the degeneration of the egg and the resorption of yolk.

There is an oestrous cycle in the sense that the behaviour of males
and females is co-ordinated in various ways which tend to synchronize
the release of ova and spermatozoa. In this type of reproductive cycle
the follicular epithelium appears not to assume an endocrine role;
oestrogens are found in fish ovaries but the site of their formation has
not been identified (see Dean and Chester Jones, 1959).

2. *Viviparous forms*

Only a comparatively small number of teleosts give birth to living
young. They have been studied in considerable detail, and because the
ovary is involved in the mechanism of gestation the investigations have
provided much information about the ovarian cycle. Fertilization is
always intra-follicular so that ovulation and the formation of a corpul
luteum do not occur, and gestation is not associated with a lutea
phase in the ovarian cycle. Any changes of this nature occur before

fertilization, e.g. the 'pre-ovulatory' corpora lutea which, it is claimed, control the mating behaviour of *Lebistes* (Jaski, 1939; Bretschneider and Duyvené de Wit, 1947). The follicle assumes the novel function of a 'uterus' and follicular rupture is the equivalent of parturition.

Two trends of evolution are discernible in viviparous teleosts, namely, the elaboration of varying degrees of placental complexity on the one hand, and of superfoetation on the other. The guppy, *Lebistes*, shows little change from an oviparous condition save for the retention of the developing eggs in the follicle and, for a little time, in the ovarian cavity, when the ruptured follicle functions as a 'calyx nutriciens' and secretes an embryotrophe. At the other extreme, in *Heterandria formosa*, there is very little yolk; a placenta is developed from the somatopleure of the pericardial sac, which is enormously expanded to cover the fore-end of the embryo, and in which an extensive portal capillary network is closely applied to the epithelium of the follicle wall (Fraser and Renton, 1940; Amoroso, 1952).

The second of the evolutionary trends referred to above involves the progressive reduction of the retarding effect which pregnancy generally has upon the maturation of oocytes. In some of the Poeciliidae (classification of Berg, 1947) the delay is shortened, and species can be arranged in order of progressively shorter intervals between broods. Thus Turner (1937) describes a series beginning with the *"Gambusia* type" in which only small oocytes are found in the ovary after the expulsion of a brood. Some of them grow rapidly and are fertilized 8 days later. In the *"Lebistes* type" some growth of oocytes occurs during pregnancy. Fertilization follows very closely upon parturition in *Quintana atrizona*, and it precedes parturition in some species, resulting in superfoetation. This is so extreme in *Heterandria formosa* at the height of the breeding season that six or more broods may be developing in the ovary at the same time.

The most extreme degree of superfoetation therefore occurs in a genus in which there is little or no accumulation of yolk, so that oocyte maturation does not involve a prolonged period of vitellogenesis. In other viviparous teleosts, however, a small yolk-sac is associated, not with an efficient placenta but with development in the ovarian cavity into which embryotrophic material is secreted. A large yolk sac is often associated with intra-follicular gestation and a placental connection of which the function is mainly respiratory.

D. Amphibians

1. *The breeding habit*

The reproductive processes of amphibians tend to be relatively simple, as pointed out by Smith (1955), because they do not generally involve either the production of cleidoic eggs or the viviparous habit, and the majority return to water to breed. A few, however, like the salamander (Wilder, 1917) and some tree frogs (Bhaduri, 1932), are wholly terrestrial. Fertilization is internal in the salamander in which, as in some anurans and at least one gymnophionian (Amoroso, 1952), the eggs are retained in the oviduct where the embryos develop. Two anurans, *Pipa dorsigera* and *Nototrema marsupiatum*, exhibit a curious pseudo-placentation, the embryos developing in pouches on the back of the female. Nothing, however, is known of the controlling mechanism of the extensive modifications and complex behaviour patterns which are involved, or of the ovarian cycle of these animals.

The breeding season is rigidly controlled by external factors; in the majority of species spawning occurs once a year in spring.

2. *Follicular maturation*

Smith (1955) states that the cyclical changes in the ovary can be divided into three phases: (a) ovarian growth, (b) ovulation, and (c) ovarian regression. As in the fishes, the ovaries increase greatly in weight during the period of egg-growth, and there is a corresponding decrease after ovulation. The period of growth extends over many months before spawning, in sharp contrast to the rapid loss of weight after ovulation. Smith describes the course of events in *Rana temporaria* as a typical species. Intra-follicular development of the egg occupies 3 years and proceeds in three annual stages: (i) primary germ cells change by repeated division during the winter into a number of 'cell nests', (ii) in the following summer young follicles develop from these cell nests while (iii) young follicles formed in the previous summer mature and prepare for ovulation.

3. *The corpus luteum*

During the process of vitellogenesis, some of the larger follicles undergo degeneration leading to the formation of the so-called 'pre-ovulatory' corpora lutea which are a prominent feature of the ovaries of many amphibians. This follicular change is considered by Bretschneider and Duyvené de Wit (1947) to be evoked in response to a gonadotrophic stimulus from the pituitary gland, but Smith points out that this view cannot be accepted unequivocally, for this type of change is brought about as a result of hypophysectomy (Tuchmann-Duplessis, 1945, quoted by Smith, 1955). It is possible, however, that the fully-formed pre-ovulatory corpora lutea respond to pituitary gonadotrophin by secreting a sex hormone which influences the oviduct.

Ovulation is followed by luteinization of the follicular epithelium, but there is no evidence that the corpora lutea so formed have any function.

The probability that pre-ovulatory corpora lutea are of greater importance than those of ovulation in amphibians is strengthened by the fact that the major function of the oviduct is to secrete a mucoid substance around the eggs during their passage to the exterior. Oviducal activity must therefore be initiated before ovulation takes place.

E. Reptiles

1. *The breeding habit*

Most species breed in spring or summer and experience a single ovarian cycle annually. There are notable exceptions to this common pattern, and the general habit of the species is not always related to its distribution. Thus the two genera of Saharan lizards *Acanthodactylus* and *Uromastyx* occupy similar habitats in the same locality, but the former breeds twice and the latter only once in the summer months (Kehl, 1944). Similarly, the viviparous lizard *Lygosoma quoyi* of Australia breeds once a year, whereas the oviparous species *Amphibolurus muricatus*, of similar distribution, breeds twice annually, with an interval of 6 to 7 weeks between the ovulations (Weekes, 1934). Further, tropical snakes of the genera *Dryophylax* and *Tomodon* have eggs in the oviducts at almost all seasons (Valle and Souza, 1942), but several species of tropical sea-snakes ovulate only once a year (Bergman, 1943; Samuel, 1944). Conversely, variation of the breeding habit within a species, in accordance with the environment, appears to occur in the turtle *Pseudemys scripta* (Cagle, 1944) and in the rattlesnake *Crotalus viridis* (Rahn, 1942).

2. *Growth of oocyte and follicle*

The rate of growth of the ovum and follicle varies considerably. The ovum is always macrolecithal and the amount of yolk is roughly proportional to the size of the animal. Follicular development and vitellogenesis were described in detail by Boyd (1941) for the New Zealand gecko, *Hoplodactylus maculatus*. Large flask-shaped cells, often packed with fat-globules, are a feature of the follicular epithelium surrounding oocytes 1·25 mm in diameter. By the end of vitellogenesis the mature egg is 6 to 8 mm in diameter and the greatly attenuated follicular epithelium is reduced to a single layer of small cells. The theca is differentiated into internal and external layers late in the development of the oocyte, but the two layers are probably not homologous with the theca interna and externa of mammals (Weekes, 1934; Miller, 1948).

A sudden increase in ovarian size before ovulation suggests that yolk-formation is very rapid in many species. In the horned toad,

Phrynosoma solare (Blount, 1929), the ovary grows from 50 cu. mm during hibernation to 100 cu. mm at the beginning of June, and then increases to 3600 cu. mm by mid-July, with follicles 7 to 10 mm in diameter. The ripe follicles rupture before the end of July and the ovary reverts almost immediately to its winter size. A similar rapid growth of ova occurs in the Indian lizard *Hemidactylus flaviviridis* (Dutta, 1946), in *Lacerta agilis* (Regamey, 1935) and in four viviparous Javanese sea-snakes described by Bergman (1943).

Vitellogenesis occupies 2 to 3 months in *Acanthodactylus* and *Uromastyx* (Kehl, 1944, see above); in the former species it is more rapid in the second than in the first of the two breeding cycles. The Steppe tortoise *Testudo horsfieldi* lays a total of twelve to sixteen eggs in three or four clutches (Sergeev, 1941), but it is not clear how long each clutch takes to mature. Follicular development and yolk formation begin soon after the breeding season in the lizard *Sceloporus* (Woodbury and Woodbury, 1945) and in the box turtle *Terrapene carolina* (Altland, 1951); in the former they are retarded or halted during winter hibernation and completed by rapid growth in spring, whereas in the latter two to eight eggs accumulate large quantities of yolk during the later months of the year.

Miller (1948) found that in *Xantusia vigilis* the process of follicular maturation occupies a period of 3 years. During the young animal's first spring and summer some ten to twenty follicles reach a diameter of about 0·1 mm. By the end of the first year of life five to ten follicles in each ovary have reached 0·5 to 0·6 mm. During the second year these follicles undergo further attrition and only two to four survive; by May or June of the following year each ovary contains two or three follicles of 1·5 mm, only one of which proceeds to maturity. Its final growth to a diameter of 6·5 mm is very rapid. The process is initiated annually, so that one ovum (rarely two) matures in each ovary and is ovulated in each year of life from the third onwards. Thus Miller was able to recognize distinct sets of follicles in the ovaries of this lizard at all stages of the cycle. A similar classification of follicles has also been made in two viviparous snakes, *Thamnophis radix* (Cieslak, 1945) and *T. sirtalis* (Bragdon, 1952), and in *Pseudemys scripta* (Cagle, 1944).

3. *The corpus luteum*

A well-defined corpus luteum is formed after ovulation in many reptiles, but its occurrence is not clearly related to the reproductive habit. The corpora lutea are smaller than the follicles from which they are derived, although they are large in relation to body weight by comparison with mammals. Thus in *Enhydrina schistosa* (Samuel,

1944) the fully mature egg is 70 mm long but the corpus luteum is only 15 mm in diameter, and is stated to be the largest so far described in a reptile. Ovulation of the macrolecithal ovum involves greater follicular trauma than is usual in mammals. This may have some bearing on the observation that in members of several genera of snakes the follicular epithelium becomes completely detached at ovulation. It is not lost, however, but regains its contact with the theca within 3 days (Bragdon, 1952). The luteal elements are stated to be formed exclusively from the cells of the membrana granulosa in most species, although the participation of the theca interna has been described in *Lacerta agilis* (Hett, 1924) and *Terrapene carolina* (Altland, 1951).

It would seem that in oviparous species the persistence of the corpus luteum is not necessarily related to the interval between ovulation and egg-laying. In *Amphibolorus muricatus* the corpus luteum persists in an apparently active state for 3 weeks, and its regression is complete at the time of lay 2 weeks later (Weekes, 1934). In two species, *Hemidactylus flaviviridis* (Dutta, 1946) and *Terrapene carolina* (Altland, 1951), the corpora lutea usually remain active, as determined by histological examination, until the eggs are laid, but regression sets in immediately afterwards. Their early regression in some specimens of *T. carolina* suggests that events in the oviduct are not closely dependent upon the condition of the corpora lutea, at least in the stages immediately before the eggs are laid.

Among the viviparous reptiles, gestation ranges from 9 weeks in some species of *Thamnophis* (Cieslak, 1945; Bragdon, 1952) to 5 months in several genera of sea-snakes (Bergman, 1943), and in the majority the corpora lutea persist throughout pregnancy. It is difficult to evaluate their functional activity, but oöphorectomy has shown them to be necessary for embryonic survival in early pregnancy in five species of snakes (Clausen, 1935, 1940), and Porto (1941) has reported that extracts of the corpora lutea of two other species exerted a progestational effect on the uterus of the oestrogenized rabbit.

The growth of follicles is inhibited during gestation and throughout the following winter and spring in *Thamnophis radix* (Cieslak, 1945) and the corpora lutea are recognizable for the whole of this period. In contrast, it has been shown that regression of the corpora lutea occurs before the end of pregnancy in *Lygosoma quoyi* (Weekes, 1934) and *Xantusia vigilis* (Miller, 1951), in both of which gestation lasts 3 to $3\frac{1}{2}$ months.

F. Birds

Many birds rear only one brood per annum, many rear two, some rear several, and a few species breed almost continuously throughout the year. In some species the second clutch of eggs is laid before the first is hatched, but in most there is an interval between broods.

1. *Clutch size*

Counts of eggs in large numbers of nests have been recorded for many species (see Davis, 1955) and it is evident that the clutch-size is generally constant within narrow limits. Marshall (1936) quotes several cases of a bird laying many more than the normal number of eggs when each egg was withdrawn as it was laid. Witschi (1935), for instance, found that a house sparrow, which normally lays four or five eggs in a clutch, may lay up to fifty eggs, including as many as nineteen on successive days, when they are removed daily. It appears that such a series is brought to an end when the ovary has been emptied of all oocytes which are, at that time, capable of developing to maturity. The case of the domestic hen is, of course, unique. The habit of broodiness has been partially suppressed and a hen may lay regularly for many months with only brief interruptions. In wild birds, when the clutch is complete, broodiness is induced by the action of pituitary hormones (see Folley, 1952). Witschi's experiments show that these hormones are released in response to an external stimulus which is probably tactile (Marshall, 1936).

2. *Follicular development*

Brambell (1925) has described the formation of follicles in the hen. They were present in the ovary of the 4-day-old chick, and contained oocytes 34 to 70μ in diameter. The cells of the follicular epithelium, which at first are few in number and flattened in shape, rapidly divide, become cubical, and form a continuous layer. Between the 3rd and 6th weeks after hatching many of the follicles begin to grow rapidly, but they become atretic before they are more than about 400μ in diameter. Further follicles are eliminated in later life and only a small proportion of those that are present in the ovary at sexual maturity survive to ovulate. Stieve (1919) counted between 24,500 and 26,000 follicles in the ovary of a jackdaw at 6 months; as this bird lays five to six eggs per annum it can be calculated that not more than 0·01 per cent of these oocytes are likely to be ovulated.

An oocyte which is destined to survive to ovulation in the hen grows slowly to about 6 mm in diameter and then suddenly begins to grow about twenty-five times as rapidly, with the change in the nature of the yolk deposited (Riddle, 1911, 1916). A comparable change in the growth-rate, corresponding to the rapid deposition of almost the whole of the yolk in the days immediately preceding ovulation, appears to be characteristic of birds in general. It has been analysed in the pigeon by

Bartelmez (1912) and in the starling by Bissonnette and Zujko (1936). According to Bartelmez the final growth phase is not initiated in the pigeon in the absence of copulation or an equivalent stimulus, and little yolk is deposited in oocytes which are not destined to ovulate.

Bissonnette and Zujko recorded the sizes of the fourteen largest follicles in starlings killed between December and April. The range of diameter of these follicles was 0·40 to 0·54 mm in December, 0·99 to 1·83 mm in mid-March, and 0·94 to 9·08 mm on 20 April, just before ovulation. Calculation showed that there was a period of 108 days of slow growth when the diameter of the largest follicle increased by an average of 0·009 mm per day, followed by 26 days of rapid growth at an average of 0·285 mm per day. The average daily increase in volume between 7 December and 3 April, calculated from the same data, was approximately 0·027 cu. mm per day, whereas the corresponding figure for the last interval recorded (10–20 April) was 37·5 cu. mm per day. Rapid yolk deposition begins in the largest oocyte when it reaches a diameter of about 2 mm and by the time it is ovulated four or five others will have entered upon the rapid growth phase. The starling usually lays four to six eggs (Davis, 1955) and more oocytes enter upon the final growth phase, and begin to accumulate yolk, than are normally destined to mature and ovulate.

3. *The discharged follicle*

The discharged follicle has not been shown to have any function in birds comparable with that of prolonging the retention of eggs in the oviduct, as it does in mammals. On the contrary, it would seem that follicular rupture is itself controlled by a neural stimulus evoked by oviposition, for it is characteristic of birds that each egg is laid before the next is ovulated, and the oviduct holds only one egg at a time (Huston and Nalbandov, 1953).

III. The cycle in monotremes

The extant species, the platypus and the spiny ant-eater, have one annual breeding season in the spring; the former usually lays two eggs and the latter only one.

The growth of the follicle and oocyte, and the formation of the corpus luteum, have been described by Hill and Gatenby (1926), Garde (1930) and Flynn and Hill (1939). The interesting affinities of the group are strikingly illustrated by the peculiarities of the ovarian cycle. The oocyte is macrolecithal, but the follicular epithelium reaches its maximum development at the time of ovulation and so differs from that of reptiles and birds, and resembles that of the higher mammals. Immediately before ovulation the follicle wall secretes a fluid which surrounds the oocyte and which must be regarded as homologous with the fluid that fills the antrum in the Graafian follicle of marsupial and placental mammals. Furthermore, the monotremes are oviparous and lay a cleidoic egg, and the parallel with the sauropsids, more especially the reptiles, extends to the morphology of the ovary and reproductive tract (Eckstein and Zuckerman, 1956), but the spent follicle gives rise to a corpus luteum of unmistakably mammalian character. It is not known whether the corpus luteum has an endocrine function, but it has been shown that the intra-uterine phase of embryonic development is between 12 and 28 days (see Asdell, 1946) and the endometrial glands apparently secrete a nutritive substance, which is absorbed by the oocyte for some time before the outer shell is applied to the developing egg (Hill, 1933, 1941). The corpus luteum reaches its maximum size during this period and begins to regress before the eggs are laid. Incubation of the eggs is associated with parental behaviour analogous to that of birds, the mother being warm-blooded, but the monotremes are unique in that incubation is followed by lactation similar to that of the higher mammals.

IV. The cycle in marsupial and eutherian mammals

A. The initiation of the cycle

1. *Follicular proliferations*

The ovarian cortex is established before birth and contains large numbers of oocytes, each surrounded by a primordial follicle. Some of the earlier-formed follicles are involved in one or several waves of growth and proliferation before or soon after birth, but they degenerate before puberty. From the few detailed accounts that are available, it is probable that these events are governed by an intrinsic rhythm which is constant for any given species. Thus in the mouse (Brambell, 1927) there is a wave of development about 6 days after birth and many of the follicles have acquired traces of an antrum by the 14th day. These follicles reach their maximum size, about 0·3 mm diameter, at about 3 weeks, and the ovary at this time is as large as that of the adult. The oocytes and follicles then degenerate and nearly all have disappeared by the 28th day. From this time on, the mouse ovary always contains a number of follicles of various sizes; the largest surviving at 28 days will continue to grow and eventually ovulate at about 56 days. In the guinea pig, Bookhout (1945) distinguished two waves of follicular development during embryonic life and three others before puberty, the last of which gave rise to follicles destined to mature and ovulate.

Follicular development up to the stage of antrum formation occurs in late foetal stages in the cow and sheep, and to an unusual extent in the late foetal and neonatal stages in the giraffe (see Kellas *et al.*, 1958). In the giraffe, these large follicles do not undergo the usual process of atresia, but give rise to large numbers of corpus luteum-like structures which are "solid, spherical bodies, well vascularized, and surrounded by a theca externa".

Puberty seems to mark the end of the period of rhythmic production of new follicles, for at this stage and throughout reproductive life the ovary always contains follicles in various stages of growth. The rhythm now becomes one of follicular maturation and ovulation rather than one which involves the growth of groups of follicles from the primordial stage.

2. *Ovulation and oestrus*

The establishment of the ovulatory rhythm and its integration with the oestrous cycle occupies a period between the first onset of reproductive activity and the attainment of sexual maturity. There is good reason to suppose that in many mammals, ovulation and oestrus are not synchronized immediately at puberty. Thus the ovaries of many wild species, e.g. the hedgehog (Deanesly, 1934), the bank-vole (Brambell and Rowlands, 1936), and the elephant (Perry, 1953), when examined at the onset of the first or a subsequent breeding season, contained several sets of corpora lutea although there was no evidence that mating had occurred. It has been inferred that these animals had ovulated once or several times without a synchronous oestrus, as sheep are known to do at the onset of the breeding season (Grant, 1934a), a phenomenon known as 'silent heat'. Further evidence that ovulation and oestrus may only gradually come into phase is provided by the observations of Mirskaia and Crew (1930) on the breeding of mice.

The menstrual cycles in man (see Ashley-Montagu, 1946) and the rhesus monkey (Hartman, 1938; Smith and Rubenstein, 1940) during adolescence are rarely accompanied by ovulation and this condition may persist for 1 to 2 years before ovulation becomes a regular event.

3. *Hormonal factors*

The ovarian cycle during adult reproductive life is controlled by reciprocal hormonal action between the ovary and the anterior pituitary gland (see Chapter 7, sect. III). In early life it seems probable that a gonadotrophin (FSH) is present in the pituitary gland before the ovary has acquired the capacity to respond to it. In the rat, for instance, Clark (1935) found that the pituitary gland contains some FSH at birth, but the ovaries first become sensitive to exogenous gonadotrophin between the 4th and 10th days after birth (Price and Ortiz, 1944). The ovaries of the hamster are similar to those of the rat in this respect (Ortiz, 1947), and no ovarian response was elicited in the mouse until about the 12th day (Pfeiffer and Hooker, 1942). Thus it would appear that the formation of follicles in the medullary cords of the mouse, described by Brambell (1927), occurs before the ovary becomes sensitive to gonadotrophin, at least to that of exogenous origin. The first cortical proliferation in the mouse may also be independent of pituitary secretion, but Pfeiffer and Hooker observed follicular stimulation and oestrogen secretion in mice treated with serum gonadotrophin (PMS) between the 15th and 35th days, and the early part of this period coincides with that during which Brambell observed very extensive follicular development. The follicles regressed without ovulation or luteinization, presumably because of a deficiency of luteinizing hormone (LH). Smithberg and Runner (1956) have shown that treatment with exogenous FSH and LH can lead to ovulation and oestrus in mice at 30 to 35 days and progesterone, administered after mating, enabled these mice to maintain gestation and to suckle their young.

Lauson et al. (1939), extending Clark's work on the rat, have shown that the amount of gonadotrophin in the pituitary gland rises to a concentration many times that in the adult gland by the 3rd week after birth, and it may be that follicular proliferations in the ovarian cortex before puberty are stimulated by pituitary hormones produced at this time. Lane (1935) showed that follicular development reached a peak in the immature rat between the 35th and 40th days, after which it decreased until puberty. Lauson and his colleagues, however, interpreted their own results as an indication that gonadotrophin accumulates within the anterior pituitary gland until the ovary begins to 'consume' it. They showed that in their animals the growth of follicles for the first ovulation at puberty began about the time that the gonadotrophin-content of the pituitary gland began to fall. The difficulty of relating the hormone-content of a gland to its rate of secretion has to be borne in mind in all estimations of this kind.

B. Characteristics of the follicle and corpus luteum

1. *The Graafian follicle**

The distinctive feature of the ovarian follicle of the marsupial and eutherian mammals is the large central cavity or antrum, filled with a

* See also Chapter 1, sect. II, I and Chapter 2C, sect. III.

Y

clear fluid in which the egg is suspended. The term Graafian follicle is properly applied only to this structure. In most eutherian mammals the antrum first appears when the follicle reaches a diameter two to three times that of the contained oocyte.

The great reduction in the amount of yolk, and hence in the size, of the mammalian egg as compared with that of birds and reptiles, is not accompanied by a proportionate reduction in the size of the follicle, since the fluid-filled antrum in effect replaces the yolk-mass. The arrangement of the follicular tissue as a relatively thin wall surrounding the large antrum is probably necessary to bring the membrana granulosa, which is avascular, into maximum contact with the highly vascular theca interna. Brambell (1928, 1956) and Parkes (1931 b) showed that the mammalian egg is almost fully grown at a very early stage in the development of the follicle, before the appearance of the antrum. For this reason the quantitative relationship between the egg and the follicle is diphasic in all species so far investigated. The size of the mature follicle is constant for the species and bears a close relation to average body weight. The eggs, on the other hand, vary little in size and such variation as exists, appears to be quite unrelated to body size. The eggs of marsupials are only slightly larger than those of eutherian mammals (see Pincus, 1936).

2. *The corpus luteum*

The mean maximum size of the corpus luteum in successive cycles is constant, but is less closely related to body weight than is that of the follicle. It depends mainly upon the number of granulosa cells left in the ruptured follicle and the degree to which they hypertrophy. In some species the latter is determined by the physiological state, so that the ultimate size of the corpus luteum is greater in pregnant than in unmated animals. These include the hamster (Deanesly, 1938), guinea pig (Rowlands, 1956) and pig (Corner, 1921). In the rat (Long and Evans, 1922) and mouse (Deanesly, 1930) a characteristic degree of luteal hypertrophy is associated with each of four different physiological states: (a) the unmated animal, (b) pseudopregnancy, (c) pregnancy and (d) lactation. In each case the size of the whole gland is directly proportional to that of the individual luteal cells.

As a general rule, the corpus luteum is larger than the follicle from which it is derived. An exception is the mare, where a very large follicle, up to 7 cm in diameter, gives rise to a corpus luteum of about 3 cm. In some species, e.g. the grey squirrel (Deanesly and Parkes, 1933), the hedgehog (Deanesly, 1934) and baboon (Zuckerman and Parkes, 1932), the corpus luteum of pregnancy attains a volume only slightly greater than that of the mature follicle, the ratio being less than 1·2 : 1 in all of them. The corresponding ratio in the stoat (Deanesly, 1935) is about 7·8 : 1, and in the bank-vole (Brambell and Rowlands, 1936) about 10·6 : 1 (see also Chapters 2C, 6 and 9).

C. The cycle of the unmated animal

The 'basic' ovarian cycle, in which pregnancy and lactation are not involved, is rarely encountered in wild mammals because oestrus almost always leads to coitus and pregnancy. Our knowledge of the cycle is therefore limited to a small number of domesticated species, and in none is it possible to observe the continuous changes taking place in an individual. Continuity can only be inferred from data derived from a considerable number of animals killed at different stages of the cycle; Mandl and Zuckerman (1952) have emphasized the limitations that are imposed by this fact.

Three types of cycle may be distinguished, based on differences in degree rather than in kind (see Eckstein and Zuckerman, 1955). The classification depends on whether or not ovulation requires the stimulus of coitus and, in the event of its being spontaneous, whether the resulting corpus luteum is active or inactive. Examples of the three types of cycle are described below (see also Chapter 6, sect. II.A).

1. *Ovulation dependent on mating*

This type of cycle was shown to occur in the ferret by Marshall (1904) and in the rabbit by Heape (1905). Other examples include the mink (Hansson, 1947), the ground-squirrel (Foster, 1934), the short-tailed shrew (Pearson, 1944), and, probably, the American opossum, *Didelphis azarae* (Martínez-Esteve, 1937), the European weasel (Deanesly, 1944), the domestic cat (see Eckstein and Zuckerman, 1956), and the American mole, *Scalopus aquaticus* (Conaway, 1959).

The domestic rabbit breeds more or less regularly throughout the year, although the wild rabbit has a well-defined breeding season (Brambell, 1944). Photographic records of the ovaries of individual rabbits, repeated at intervals, showed that the location of mature follicles changed completely within 14, or even 7 days (Hill and White, 1934). It is clear, therefore, that successive groups of follicles mature and degenerate. These results were confirmed almost simultaneously by Smelser *et al.* (1934), who emphasized the continuous nature of follicle production, proceeding at a rate comparable with that of the regression of mature follicles, so that the total number capable of ovulation is kept nearly constant.

The ferret has a well-defined breeding season in spring and summer. The ovarian follicles rarely exceed 250μ in diameter during anoestrus (Hammond and Marshall, 1930; Hill and Parkes, 1933), and Robinson

(1918) states that successive sets of follicles are produced, the size attained by each set increasing with the approach of the breeding season. Those produced in January reach a diameter of 460 to 650μ, and by March the ovaries contain mature follicles of 1·2 to 1·4 mm. Follicular growth continues throughout the 2- to 3-week period of pro-oestrus, and maturation occurs during the 30-hour interval between coitus and ovulation. Hammond and Marshall considered that the mature follicles remain in an ovulable condition until the end of the breeding season if mating does not occur. Rowlands (unpublished) has observed, however, a gradual recession of oestrous symptoms in unmated ferrets, associated with luteinization of the cells of the membrana granulosa of the mature follicles and the production of luteal cysts.

The domestic cat usually has two main breeding seasons which vary somewhat according to locality and climatic conditions. Oestrus occurs at intervals of about 14 days during these periods (Scott and Lloyd-Jacob, 1955). From researches such as those of Manwell and Wickens (1928) and Gros (1936), it is evident that corpora lutea are not produced. If mating is prevented, the mature follicles appear to regress; thus successive waves of follicular maturation and regression occur as in the rabbit (above) but at more widely spaced intervals, so that the female is not maintained in continuous oestrus.

2. *Spontaneous ovulation with inactive corpora lutea*

It is now well-established that the corpus luteum of the rat, the mouse and possibly many other small rodents, is relatively inactive. This probably accounts for the very short interval of 4 to 6 days between ovulations in the mouse (Allen, 1922; Parkes, 1928), rat (Long and Evans, 1922; Mandl, 1951), Chinese hamster (Parkes, 1931a) and Syrian hamster (Deanesly, 1938).

Medium-sized follicles, 300 to 500μ in diameter, are present at all times during the oestrous cycle of the mouse (Brambell and Parkes, 1927) and of the rat (Lane and Davis, 1939; Mandl and Zuckerman, 1952), and form a reserve from which a number are periodically selected for further growth and maturation. Mandl and Zuckerman showed that in the unmated rat the modal size of follicles, among those over 350μ, was progressively greater in animals killed at successive stages of the cycle from metoestrus until the next oestrus. These data appear likely to represent successive stages in the growth of the same follicles rather than the growth of successive sets of follicles, each regressing before the next set enlarges. If so, it may be concluded that a considerable proportion of the follicles that embark upon the final growth phase undergo atresia at various stages of growth, and that the surviving follicles grow at a fairly constant rate from a diameter of about 350μ beginning soon after ovulation. The onset of this final growth phase is evidently not inhibited by the newly-formed corpora lutea of ovulation. The final growth phase of the follicle in the mouse, on the other hand, appears to begin about 3 days after the preceding ovulation (Brambell and Parkes, 1927).

In the hamsters, the corpora lutea of ovulation regress so rapidly after a growth period of 2 to 3 days that they are almost unrecognizable by the time ovulation has recurred. They regress more slowly in the mouse (see Fig. 1) and rat, so that the ovaries of unmated adults normally contain three to five sets of corpora lutea in different stages of

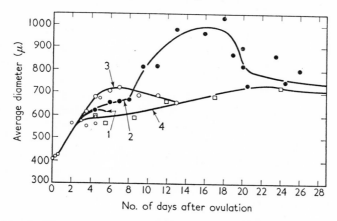

FIG. 1. The growth and regression of the corpora lutea of the mouse during the dioestrous cycle (1), pregnancy (2), pseudopregnancy (3), and lactation (4). (Reproduced by permission from Deanesly, 1930.)

development and regression. They do not induce progestational changes in the endometrium, and traumatic stimulation of the uterine wall does not evoke a decidual reaction.

3. Spontaneous ovulation with functional corpora lutea

The simplest type of cycle within this group is that which occurs in monoestrous species such as the dog. Follicles are very small during anoestrus and the follicular phase is associated with pro-oestrus which lasts about 10 days (Evans and Cole, 1931). Ovulation is followed by a pseudopregnancy lasting about 2 months, and the corpus luteum persists for most of this time (Marshall and Halnan, 1917).

The presence of a functional corpus luteum in polyoestrous animals is associated with a longer interval between successive ovulations than that described for the rat and mouse. In primates, the follicular phase is clearly separated from the preceding luteal phase by a period of menstruation midway between ovulations. One of the most detailed studies is that of Zuckerman and Parkes (1932) on the baboon. Follicles of 800 to 1000μ in diameter are present at all times in the young adult. After menstruation, further growth is initiated in a group of a dozen or more follicles, only one of which eventually matures. The process occupies about 14 days, and the mature follicle reaches a diameter of 6 mm. The corpus luteum is fully grown by about the 7th day after ovulation, when its size is similar to that of the mature follicle. Regression quickly sets in and the corpus luteum is greatly reduced in size by the 13th day. The end of the luteal phase is marked by the recurrence of menstruation.

In other mammals there occurs a considerable degree of overlap between a new follicular phase and the luteal phase of the preceding cycle. For example, developing follicles may be traced through two cycles in the cow before they ovulate (Hammond, 1927). The domestic ungulates have been extensively studied and accounts of the ovarian cycle have been given for the pig (Corner, 1921), cow (Hammond, 1927; Höfliger, 1948), sheep (Grant, 1934b; Hadek, 1958), goat (Harrison, 1948) and horse (Hammond and Wodzicki, 1941).

The cycle continues throughout the year in the pig, but it may cease in the cow (Hammond, 1927) and in the horse (Burkhardt, 1947) in unfavourable conditions. In the sheep and the goat, cyclical oestrous activity is confined to autumn and winter although some ovarian activity may persist throughout anoestrus (Watson, 1952). The interval between successive ovulations is 16 days in the sheep and 21 days in the others. All except the horse have a prominent luteal phase; the corpus luteum reaches its maximum size in about 8 days, and regresses 3 or 4 days before the next ovulation. The horse has a shorter luteal phase and a correspondingly longer follicular phase, with which is associated a very large Graafian follicle, reaching a maximum diameter of 7 cm (Day, 1939), and a long period of oestrus lasting about 6 days.

A more complex type of ovarian cycle is found in the guinea pig, and it has been interpreted in various ways. The cycle lasts 16 to 18 days without any seasonal variation. Loeb (1911) observed atresia in most of the vesicular follicles remaining after ovulation. A wave of follicular growth occurred 5 to 6 days later and by the 10th day after ovulation a small number of follicles exhibited the cytological changes characteristic of maturity. He stated that these follicles degenerated and the definitive follicular phase began immediately afterwards, culminating in ovulation 6 or 7 days later. Myers et al. (1936), on the other hand, stated that follicles began to grow 2 or 3 days after ovulation and grew steadily until the onset of oestrus, when they enlarged more rapidly and ovulated about 10 hours later. In a series of animals examined by Rowlands (Fig. 2) follicular changes during the 10 days following ovulation closely resembled those described by Loeb. However, the occurrence of fully mature follicles, together with others in various stages of atresia, on every subsequent day, suggests that there is a succession of short cycles of follicular maturation and atresia, beginning on the 6th day after ovulation. Only those follicles which enter upon the pre-ovulatory changes during oestrus do so in an endocrine environment which permits their ovulation.

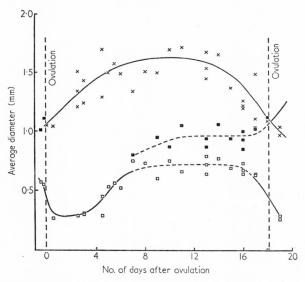

FIG. 2.   The growth and regression of the corpora lutea, and follicular development and maturation in unmated guinea pigs.
×—×, the corpora lutea, □—□, the twelve largest follicles during the 7 days following ovulation, ■—■, follicles undergoing pre-ovulatory changes from the 8th day after ovulation, and □---□, the twelve largest follicles not exhibiting the above changes.

Loeb (1911) described the corpora lutea as being fully developed, histologically, by the 6th day after ovulation, regressive changes appearing in the luteal cells 4 days later. This suggests that the abortive follicular phase which he described coincides with the active luteal phase of the cycle. Measurements of the corpus luteum of ovulation show that it continues to increase in size for 10 to 12 days, but its progesterone-content is found to have dropped from 16·2 μg/g on the 6th day to 7·7 μg/g on the 12th day (Rowlands and Short, 1959). This is a striking confirmation of Loeb's conclusion, which was based entirely on histological criteria.

D. The cycle after sterile mating

Mating with a vasectomized male results in the formation of a functional corpus luteum, and a condition of pseudopregnancy, in animals that do not ovulate spontaneously and in those in which the corpus luteum of ovulation is inactive. On the other hand, sterile mating does not prolong the luteal phase of the cycle of animals that have a functional corpus luteum in the unmated condition.

The corpora lutea of pseudopregnancy persist as long as those of pregnancy in the ferret (Hammond and Marshall, 1930) and mink (Enders, 1952), but in the rabbit (Bouin and Ancel, 1909a; Hammond, 1925) and cat (Gros, 1935; Liche, 1939) they are of shorter duration than those of pregnancy. Large follicles are present in these animals throughout pseudopregnancy, and Hammond (1925) has recorded that some rabbits will mate from the 2nd day onwards, but ovulation is not induced. When large and medium-sized follicles were destroyed in pseudopregnant rabbits (Klein and Mayer, 1942; Klein, 1946) they were replaced by others. These facts indicate that the corpus luteum of pseudopregnancy inhibits ovulation but does not otherwise interfere with follicular development.

A diagram showing the growth of the corpus luteum of the mouse during pseudopregnancy and in other physiological conditions, given by Deanesly (1930), is reproduced in Fig. 1. The corpora lutea of pseudopregnancy reach their maximum size by about the 7th day and then slowly regress. Their growth is accounted for by hypertrophy of the individual luteal cells. The effect of sterile mating in the rat was described by Long and Evans (1922) and further data are provided by Weichert and Schurgast (1942). The corpora lutea are said to grow at the same rate as those of gestation for 4 to 5 days, when they reach a diameter of 1·5 mm, which they maintain throughout pseudopregnancy.

A unique type of ovarian cycle, in which the follicular phase is unusually long, is found in many species of bats. These include the common pipistrelle (Courrier, 1922), the British horseshoe bats (Matthews, 1937), and the North American species *Myotis lucifugus* (Guthrie and Jeffers, 1938b; Wimsatt, 1944), *M. grisescens* (Guthrie and Jeffers, 1938a), *Eptesicus fuscus* (Wimsatt, 1944), and *Corynorhinus rafinesquei* (Pearson *et al.*, 1952). As a general rule, these species copulate just before hibernation, but fertilization does not occur until spring; in some animals this requires a further mating. In the autumn there is present in one ovary a single vesicular follicle about 450μ in diameter which remains almost unchanged until the resumption of normal metabolic activity in the following spring. It then rapidly matures and ovulates within 24 hours. The follicular phase therefore lasts for about 8 to 9 months. The high fertility rate precludes observation of the luteal phase in the non-pregnant bat, but it must in any case be short in comparison with the follicular phase.

E. The cycle in pregnancy*

1. *The corpus luteum*

The life-span of the corpus luteum of eutherian mammals during pregnancy is lengthened by the endocrine activity of the placenta, but in marsupials, which have no allantoic placenta, it is not prolonged and the normal periodicity of oestrus and ovulation is not disturbed. It is difficult to assess the functional life of the corpus luteum in relation to its anatomical persistence. It persists throughout gestation in the majority of species, but there is much histological and experimental evidence to suggest that its function may decline long beforehand, as in the primates. In other species, however, such as the horse (Kimura and Lyons, 1937) and *Nycteris luteola*, an African bat (Matthews, 1941), the corpus luteum disappears completely very early in gestation; in the horse, however, it is replaced very soon by short-lived accessory corpora lutea.

As stated above (see p. 290) there is no constant relation between the maximum size attained by the corpora lutea in non-pregnant and pregnant animals of different species. Quantitative studies have also shown species differences in the growth-rate of the corpus luteum in relation to the stage of gestation. Rowlands (1956) showed that the corpus luteum grows at about the same rate in pregnant and unmated guinea pigs. In the latter, however, it begins to regress on the 12th day, after reaching a volume of 2·35 cu. mm, whereas the corpus luteum of pregnancy continues to grow without interruption for another 7 or 8 days, attains a volume of 3·14 cu. mm, and remains unchanged until parturition. The cessation of luteal growth about the 20th day coincides with the establishment of the allanto-chorionic placenta. This contrasts with the course of events in the rat (Long and Evans, 1922) and the mouse (Deanesly, 1930) in which luteal growth is halted after the first 3 or 4 days, and is suddenly resumed when the placenta is established, about the 8th day in the mouse and the 10th to 12th day in the rat. Stimulation of the corpus luteum at this time is probably related to the secretion of luteotrophin by the placenta (Astwood and Greep, 1938).

There is evidence that in species where implantation is delayed, growth of the corpus luteum ceases while the blastocysts are free in the

* See also Chapter 9.

uterine lumen and recommences at the time of implantation. Morphological and cytological differences in the corpus luteum before and after implantation have been described in the badger (Harrison and Neal, 1956, 1959; Canivenc, 1957) and in certain seals (Harrison et al., 1952). In the armadillo, however, it has been shown (Talmage et al., 1954) that the corpus luteum grows rapidly during the pre-implantation stage and is not histologically dissimilar after implantation.

2. Accessory corpora lutea

The sporadic occurrence of accessory corpora lutea during pregnancy has been described in the rhesus monkey (Corner, 1940), Canadian porcupine (Mossman and Judas, 1949) and wild Norway rat (Hall, 1952). In the mountain viscacha (Pearson, 1949) they are formed regularly from the 40th day and as many as twelve accumulate by the end of gestation (100 days). Accessory corpora lutea are also formed regularly in the horse (Cole et al., 1931; Rowlands, 1949) from successive ovulations of follicles, one or more at a time, over a period of 2 to 3 months starting with the regression of the primary corpus luteum. They are also formed, at the beginning and again half-way through pregnancy, in the elephant (Perry, 1951, 1953). During the period of delay in implantation in the mink (Hansson, 1947; Enders, 1952) and badger (Harrison and Neal, 1959) one or more follicles ovulate and give rise to corpora lutea, and in the former the ova sometimes become fertilized and implanted, so that these corpora lutea also become corpora lutea of pregnancy.

3. The follicular cycle

The cyclical production of follicles at intervals corresponding to the length of the oestrous cycle has been shown to occur in the pregnant rat (Swezy and Evans, 1930) and guinea pig (Evans and Swezy, 1931; Bujard, 1952). Loeb (1911) and Rowlands (1956) observed follicular development in pregnant guinea pigs at all times after the 10th day, similar to that in the latter half of the cycle in the unmated animal.

Very great species differences occur in respect to follicle production during pregnancy. Thus very large numbers of follicles are produced in three distinct phases in Elephantulus (van der Horst and Gillman, 1945), and Brambell (1953) found almost fully grown follicles in the common shrew at all except the earliest stages of pregnancy. At the other extreme is the vampire bat, in which Wimsatt and Trapido (1952) failed to find vesicular follicles at any time during gestation. Williams et al. (1956) observed a significant increase in the number and size of follicles in sheep during early pregnancy, but in later stages, follicle number remained constant while follicle size decreased.

The fate of follicles formed in post-implantation stages of pregnancy is also extremely variable. They may ovulate as in the horse and elephant, and in the European hare, as suggested by Hediger's (1950) observations on superfoetation. The luteinization of follicles that undergo atresia, as described by Swezy and Evans (1930) in the rat, is of fairly widespread occurrence and has been described in a number of species, including the ferret (Robinson, 1918), grey squirrel (Deanesly and Parkes, 1933), hedgehog (Deanesly, 1934) and rabbit (Halliday, 1959). Atretic corpora lutea, composed of both thecal and granulosa elements, contribute to the mass of luteal tissue which, in the water-shrew, almost entirely fills the ovary by mid-pregnancy (Price, 1953).

4. *Interstitial tissue*

Ovarian interstitial tissue is conspicuous in some species, but its function remains unknown. Its prominence in the rabbit, ferret and cat has given rise to the suggestion that it exerts an inhibitory effect on ovulation which is only overcome by the stimulus of coitus in these species (Bouin and Ancel, 1909b; Hammond, 1925; Liche, 1939).

The amount and appearance of this tissue varies at different stages of the reproductive cycle in different species. Interstitial cells are largely derived from thecal elements; an increase in their size and number is frequent in late pregnancy, as for example in the rabbit (Fetzer *et al.*, 1958), and is associated with increased follicular atresia (see Brambell, 1956). Harrison and Neal (1956) have observed increased activity in the interstitial cells of the badger during the delay in implantation and have suggested that they may have an important function in causing the delay. In some bats (Guthrie and Jeffers, 1938a; Pearson *et al.*, 1952) maximum activity occurs during lactation, and in the mole the tissue enlarges to a remarkable degree during winter anoestrus (Matthews, 1935; see also Chapter 2C).

The massive enlargement of the foetal gonads of the horse and some other species during late pregnancy is caused entirely by hypertrophy of the interstitial tissue, but is not accompanied by similar changes in the maternal ovaries (Cole *et al.*, 1933; Amoroso and Rowlands, 1951; Harrison *et al.*, 1952; Perry, 1953).

F. The cycle in lactation*

Lactation has a marked inhibitory effect on cyclical ovarian activity and oestrus in all but a few mammals; ovarian quiescence may be regarded as a contributory factor in the promotion of maternal behaviour.† The guinea pig provides an exception to the general rule in

* See also Chapter 9, sect. II, and V.

† See also Chapter 20, sect. II, B.

that the normal ovarian cycle is resumed after parturition whether or not the litter is suckled. Oestrus and ovulation occur regularly 7 to 10 days after parturition in the mare, which is normally mated at this, the 'foal heat'. The cow is usually mated 3 to 7 weeks after calving, suggesting that ovarian activity is resumed after the lapse of one or two cycles. Oestrus without ovulation often occurs a few days after parturition in the sow (Warnick *et al.*, 1950) and ovulation is inhibited for about 8 weeks unless the young are removed, when the cycle is resumed very promptly (Heitman and Cole, 1956). Chittleborough (1958) has noted the occurrence of a post-partum ovulation in a small proportion of humpback whales in which pregnancy and lactation were concurrent. In the majority of individuals, however, ovulation did not occur after parturition or during lactation, but the loss of a calf after birth was followed by early resumption of the cycle. Lactation not only inhibits the follicular cycle but involves a considerable degree of ovarian involution in the sheep (Grant, 1934b), rabbit (Hammond, 1925) and baboon (Zuckerman and Parkes, 1932).

When ovulation occurs in the immediate post-partum period, as for example in many rodents, a luteal phase may persist thoughout lactation and cyclical activity is not resumed until after the litter is weaned. The maintenance of lactation anoestrus is not mediated through the corpora lutea of lactation, at least in the rat (McKeown and Zuckerman, 1938). In the mouse, as seen in Fig. 1, the so-called corpora lutea of lactation become as large as those of pseudopregnancy (Deanesly, 1930). They grow more slowly than those of any other physiological state, and hypertrophy of the luteal cells, leading to increase in size of the corpora lutea, does not occur until the 11th day of lactation (Greenwald, 1958). Up to this time the corpora lutea of lactation are smaller than the regressing corpora lutea of pregnancy. Greenwald found that the average size of the largest follicles (about 350μ in diameter) remained constant throughout lactation in some mice, although larger follicles (up to 450μ) were found in others after the 12th day.

When conception results from copulation at the post-partum oestrus, implantation is commonly delayed and the life of the corpus luteum is prolonged accordingly. It develops into a gland indistinguishable from that of pregnancy unaccompanied by lactation. It has been shown in the bank-vole (Brambell and Rowlands, 1936) that implantation after a period of delay associated with lactation was accompanied by renewed growth of the corpus luteum. This was at a stage of pregnancy quite distinct from that associated with renewed luteal growth in the rat and mouse which, as shown above, accompanied placentation.

An even more striking effect of lactation on the corpus luteum of pregnancy occurs in some marsupials, and has been described in detail by Sharman (1955a and b). In *Setonix brachyurus* and *Protemnodon eugenii*, as in other marsupials, the duration of the corpus luteum of pregnancy in the non-lactating animal is equal to that of the corpus luteum of the normal cycle. When conception occurs at the onset of lactation, i.e. at the post-partum oestrus, the corpus luteum remains small and its growth is inhibited for as long as the young are suckled. After they have emerged from the pouch, it undergoes further development and implantation occurs. From this time onwards the corpus luteum resembles that of pregnancy in the absence of lactation. It is clear, therefore, that in these marsupials the post-implantation stages of pregnancy cannot take place concurrently with lactation.

REFERENCES

Allen, E. (1922). The oestrous cycle in the mouse. *Amer. J. Anat.* **30**, 297–371.

Altland, P. D. (1951). Observations on the structure of the reproductive organs of the box turtle. *J. Morph.* **89**, 599–621.

Amoroso, E. C. (1952). *In* "Marshall's Physiology of Reproduction" (A. S. Parkes, ed.), Vol. 2., p. 127. Longmans, Green & Co., London.

Amoroso, E. C. and Rowlands, I. W. (1951). Hormonal effects in the pregnant mare and foetal foal. *J. Endocrin.* **7**, 1–liii.

Asdell, S. A. (1946). "Patterns of Mammalian Reproduction," p. 39. Comstock Publ. Co. Inc., Ithaca, N.Y.

Ashley-Montagu, M. F. (1946). "Adolescent Sterility." Charles C. Thomas, Springfield, Ill.

Astwood, E. B. and Greep, R. O. (1938). A corpus luteum-stimulating substance in the rat placenta. *Proc. Soc. exp. Biol., N.Y.* **38**, 713–716.

Bartelmez, G. W. (1912). The bilaterality of the pigeon's egg. A study in egg organisation from the first growth period of the oocyte to the beginning of cleavage. *J. Morph.* **23**, 269–329.

Beach, A. W. (1959). Seasonal changes in the cytology of the ovary and of the pituitary gland of the goldfish. *Canad. J. Zool.* **37**, 615–625.

Berg, L. S. (1947). "Classification of Fishes both Recent and Fossil." J. W. Edwards, Ann Arbor, Michigan.

Bergman, A. M. (1943). The breeding habits of sea snakes. *Copeia*, 1943, 156–160.

Bhaduri, J. L. (1932). Observations on the urino-genital system of the tree-frogs of the genus *Rhacophorus* Kuhl with remarks on their breeding habits. *Anat. Anz.* **74**, 336–343.

Bissonnette, T. H. and Zujko, A. J. (1936). Normal progressive changes in the ovary of the starling (*Sturnus vulgaris*) from December to April. *Auk*, **53**, 31–50.

Blount, R. F. (1929). Seasonal cycles of the interstitial cells in the testis of the horned toad (*Phrynosoma solare*), seasonal variation in the number and morphology of the interstitial cells and the volume of the interstitial tissue. *J. Morph.* **48**, 317–343.

Bookhout, C. G. (1945). The development of the guinea-pig ovary from sexual differentiation to maturity. *J. Morph.* **77**, 233–263.

Bouin, P. and Ancel, P. (1909a). Sur la fonction du corps jaune. Action du corps jaune vrai sur l'utérus. (Deuxième note préliminaire). *C.R. Soc. Biol., Paris*, **66**, 505–507.

Bouin, P. and Ancel, P. (1909b). Sur les homologies et la signification des glandes à sécrétion interne de l'ovaire. (Première note). *C.R. Soc. Biol., Paris*, **67**, 464–466.

Bowers, A. B. (1954). Breeding and growth of whiting (*Gadus merlangus* L.) in Isle of Man waters. *J. Mar. biol. Ass., U.K.* **33**, 97–123.

Boyd, M. M. M. (1941). The structure of the ovary and the formation of the corpus luteum in *Hoplodactylus maculatus* Gray. *Quart. J. micr. Sci.* **82**, 337–376.

Bragdon, D. E. (1952). Corpus luteum formation and follicular atresia in the common garter snake, *Thamnophis sirtalis*. *J. Morph.* **91**, 413–445.

Brambell, F. W. R. (1925). The oogenesis of the fowl (*Gallus bankiva*). *Phil. Trans.* B. **214**, 113–151.

Brambell, F. W. R. (1927). The development and morphology of the gonads of the mouse. 1. The morphogenesis of the indifferent gonad and of the ovary. *Proc. roy. Soc.* B. **101**, 391–409.

Brambell, F. W. R. (1928). The development and morphology of the gonads of the mouse. 3. The growth of the follicles. *Proc. roy. Soc.* B. **103**, 258–272.

Brambell, F. W. R. (1935). Reproduction in the common shrew (*Sorex araneus* Linnaeus). 1. The oestrous cycle of the female. *Phil. Trans.* B. **225**, 1–49.

Brambell, F. W. R. (1944). The reproduction of the wild rabbit, *Oryctolagus cuniculus* (L). *Proc. zool. Soc. Lond.* **114**, 1–45.

Brambell, F. W. R. (1956). *In* "Marshall's Physiology of Reproduction" (A. S. Parkes, ed.), Vol. 1, Pt. 1. Chap. 5. Longmans, Green & Co., London.

Brambell, F. W. R. and Parkes, A. S. (1927). The normal ovarian cycle in relation to oestrus production. *Quart. J. exp. Physiol.* **18**, 185–198.

Brambell, F. W. R. and Rowlands, I. W. (1936). Reproduction of the bank vole (*Evotomys glareolus*, Schreber). 1. The oestrous cycle of the female. *Phil. Trans.* B. **226**, 71–97.

Bretschneider, L. H. and Duyvené de Wit, J. J. (1947). "Sexual Endocrinology of Non-mammalian Vertebrates." Elsevier, Amsterdam.

Bujard, E. (1952). Le cycle oestral n'est pas effacé dans l'ovaire de cobaye gravide. *Arch. Anat., Strasbourg*, **34**, 89–94.

Bullough, W. S. (1939). A study of the reproductive cycle of the minnow in relation to the environment. *Proc. zool. Soc. Lond.* A. **109**, 79–102.

Bullough, W. S. (1940). The effect of the reduction of light in spring on the breeding season of the minnow (*Phoxinus laevis*, Linn.). *Proc. zool. Soc. Lond.* A. **110**, 149–157.

Burkhardt, J. (1947). Anoestrus in the mare and its treatment with oestrogen. *Vet. Rec.* **59**, 341–342.

Cagle, F. R. (1944). Sexual maturity in the female of the turtle *Pseudemys scripta elegans*. *Copeia*, 1944, 149–152.

Canivenc, R. (1957). Etude de la nidation différée du blaireau européen (*Meles meles*). *Ann. Endocr., Paris*, **18**, 716–736.

Champy, C. and Gley, P. (1923). Observations cytologiques sur les ovocytes des poissons et de quelques autres vertébrés. *Arch. Anat. micr.* **19**, 241–308.

Chittleborough, R. G. (1958). The breeding cycle of the female humpback whale *Megaptera nodosa* (Bonnaterre). *Aust. J. Mar. Freshw. Res.* **9**, 1–18.

Cieslak, E. S. (1945). Relations between the reproductive cycle and the pituitary gland in the snake *Thamnophis radix*. *Physiol. Zoöl.* **18**, 299–329

Clark, H. M. (1935). A prepubertal reversal of the sex difference in the gonado-tropic hormone content of the pituitary gland of the rat. *Anat. Rec.* **61**, 175–192.

Clausen, H. J. (1935). The effects of ovariotomy and hypophysectomy on par-turition in snakes. *Anat. Rec.* **64**, Suppl., 88.

Clausen, H. J. (1940). Studies on the effect of ovariotomy and hypophysectomy on gestation in snakes. *Endocrinology*, **27**, 700–704.

Cole, H. H., Howell, C. E. and Hart, G. H. (1931). The changes occurring in the ovary of the mare during pregnancy. *Anat. Rec.* **49**, 199–208.

Cole, H. H., Hart, G. H., Lyons, W. R. and Catchpole, H. R. (1933). The development and hormonal content of fetal horse gonads. *Anat. Rec.* **56**, 275–293.

Conaway, C. H. (1959). The reproductive cycle of the eastern mole. *J. Mammal.* **40**, 180–194.

Corner, G. W. (1921). Cyclic changes in the ovaries and uterus of the sow and their relation to the mechanism of implantation. *Contr. Embryol. Carneg. Instn.* **13**, 119–146.

Corner, G. W. (1940). Accessory corpora lutea in the ovary of the monkey *Macaca rhesus*. *An. Fac. Med., Montevideo*, **25**, 553–560.

Courrier, R. (1922). Le cycle génital de la femelle chez certains mammifères hibernants. *C.R. Soc. Biol., Paris*, **87**, 1365–1367.

Craig-Bennett, A. (1931). The reproductive cycle of the three-spined stickle-back, *Gasterosteus aculeatus*, Linn. *Phil. Trans.* B. **219**, 197–279.

Davis, D. E. (1955). *In* "Recent Studies in Avian Biology" (A. Wolfson, ed.). p. 264. Univ. Illinois Press, Urbana.

Day, F. T. (1939). Sterility in the mare associated with irregularities of the oestrous cycle. *Vet. Rec.* **51**, 1113–1126.

Dean, F. D. and Chester Jones, I. (1959). Sex steroids in the lungfish (*Protopterus annectens* Owen). *J. Endocrin.* **18**, 366–371.

Deanesly, R. (1930). The corpora lutea of the mouse, with special reference to fat accumulation during the oestrous cycle. *Proc. roy. Soc.* B. **106**, 578–595.

Deanesly, R. (1934). The reproductive processes of certain mammals. Part VI. The reproductive cycle of the female hedgehog. *Phil. Trans.* B. **223**, 239–276.

Deanesly, R. (1935). The reproductive processes of certain mammals. Part IX. Growth and reproduction in the stoat (*Mustela erminea*). *Phil. Trans.* B. **225**, 459–492.

Deanesly, R. (1938). The reproductive cycle of the golden hamster (*Cricetus auratus*). *Proc. zool. Soc. Lond.* A. **108**, 31–37.

Deanesly, R. (1944). The reproductive cycle of the female weasel (*Mustela nivalis*). *Proc. zool. Soc. Lond.* **114**, 339–349.

Deanesly, R. and Parkes, A. S. (1933). The reproductive processes of certain mammals. Part IV. The oestrous cycle of the grey squirrel (*Sciurus caroli-nensis*). *Phil. Trans.* B. **222**, 47–78.

Dutta, S. K. (1946). Studies of the sexual cycle in the lizard *Hemidactylus flaviviridis* (Ruppel). *Allahabad Univ. Stud. (Zool.)* Sept., pt. 1, 57–153.

Eckstein, P. and Zuckerman, S. (1955). Reproduction in mammals. *Mem. Soc. Endocrin.* No. 4, 114–127.

Eckstein, P. and Zuckerman, S. (1956). *In* "Marshall's Physiology of Reproduc-tion" (A. S. Parkes, ed.), Vol. 1, Pt. 1, Chap. 2 and Chap. 4. Longmans, Green & Co., London.

304   J. S. PERRY AND I. W. ROWLANDS

Enders, R. K. (1952). Reproduction in the mink (*Mustela vison*). *Proc. Amer. phil. Soc.* **96**, 691–755.

Evans, H. M. and Cole, H. H. (1931). An introduction to the study of the oestrous cycle in the dog. *Mem. Univ. Calif.* **9**, 65–118.

Evans, H. M. and Swezy, O. (1931). Ovogenesis and the normal follicular cycle in the adult Mammalia. *Mem. Univ. Calif.* **9**, 119–224.

Fetzer, S., Ring, W. and Berndt, R. (1958). Das Verhalten der ovariellen Zwischenzellen des Kaninchens während der Gestation. *Naturwissenschaften*, **45**, 347.

Flynn, T. T. and Hill, J. P. (1939). The development of the Monotremata. 4. Growth of the ovarian ovum, maturation, fertilization, and early cleavage. *Trans. zool. Soc. Lond.* **24**, 445–622.

Folley, S. J. (1952). *In* "Marshall's Physiology of Reproduction" (A. S. Parkes, ed.), Vol. 2, p. 572. Longmans, Green & Co., London.

Foster, M. A. (1934). The reproductive cycle in the female ground-squirrel *Citellus tridecemlineatus* M. *Amer. J. Anat.* **54**, 487–511.

Fraser, E. A. and Renton, R. M. (1940). Observations on the breeding and development of the viviparous fish *Heterandria formosa*. *Quart. J. micr. Sci.* **81**, 479–520.

Garde, M. L. (1930). The ovary of *Ornithorhynchus*, with special reference to follicular atresia. *J. Anat., Lond.* **64**, 422–453.

Grant, R. (1934a). Studies on the physiology of reproduction in the ewe. Part 1. The symptoms, periodicity and duration of oestrus. *Trans. roy. Soc. Edinb.* **58**, 1–15.

Grant, R. (1934b). Studies on the physiology of reproduction in the ewe. Part III. Gross changes in the ovaries. *Trans. roy. Soc. Edinb.* **58**, 36–47.

Greenwald, G. S. (1958). A histological study of the reproductive tract of the lactating mouse. *J. Endocrin.* **17**, 17–23.

Gros, G. (1935). Evolution de la muqueuse utérine chez la chatte. *C.R. Soc. Biol., Paris*, **118**, 1575–1578.

Gros, G. (1936). Contribution à l'endocrinologie sexuelle. Le cycle génital de la chatte. (Quoted by Eckstein and Zuckerman, 1956).

Guthrie, M. J. and Jeffers, K. R. (1938a). A cytological study of the ovaries of the bats *Myotis lucifugus lucifugus* and *Myotis grisescens*. *J. Morph.* **62**, 523–557.

Guthrie, M. J. and Jeffers, K. R. (1938b). Growth of follicles in the ovaries of the bat *Myotis lucifugus lucifugus*. *Anat. Rec.* **71**, 477–496.

Hadek, R. (1958). Morphological and histochemical study on the ovary of the sheep. *Amer. J. vet. Res.* **19**, 873–881.

Hall, O. (1952). Accessory corpora lutea in the wild Norway rat. *Texas Rep. Biol. Med.* **10**, 32–38.

Halliday, R. (1959). The occurrence of corpora lutea atretica in the ovaries of pregnant domestic rabbits. *J. Endocrin.* **19**, 10–15.

Hammond, J. (1925). "Reproduction in the Rabbit", pp. 65–88. Oliver & Boyd, Edinburgh.

Hammond, J. (1927). "The Physiology of Reproduction in the Cow." Cambridge University Press.

Hammond, J. and Marshall, F. H. A. (1930). Oestrus and pseudo-pregnancy in the ferret. *Proc. roy. Soc.* B. **105**, 607–630.

Hammond, J. and Wodzicki, K. (1941). Anatomical and histological changes during the oestrous cycle in the mare. *Proc. roy. Soc.* B. **130**, 1–23.

Hann, H. W. (1927). The history of the germ-cells of *Cottus bairdii* Girard. *J. Morph.* **43**, 427–480.

Hansson, A. (1947). The physiology of reproduction in the mink (*Mustela vison*, Schreb.) with special reference to delayed implantation. *Acta zool., Stockh.* **28**, 1–136.

Harrison, R. J. (1948). The changes occurring in the ovary of the goat during the estrous cycle and in early pregnancy. *J. Anat., Lond.* **82**, 21–48.

Harrison, R. J. and Neal, E. G. (1956). Ovulation during delayed implantation and other reproductive phenomena in the badger (*Meles meles* L.). *Nature, Lond.* **177**, 977–979.

Harrison, R. J. and Neal, E. G. (1959). Delayed implantation in the badger (*Meles meles* L.). *Mem. Soc. Endocrin.* No. 6, 19–25.

Harrison, R. J., Matthews, L. H. and Roberts, J. M. (1952). Reproduction in some Pinnipedia. *Trans. zool. Soc. Lond.* **27**, 437–540.

Hartman, C. G. (1938). Menstruation without ovulation ("pseudomenstruation"): incidence and treatment, with special reference to the rhesus monkey. *In* "Les Hormones Sexuelles" (L. Brouha, ed.), pp. 103–118. Hermann, Paris.

Heape, W. (1905). Ovulation and degeneration of ova in the rabbit. *Proc. roy. Soc.* B. **76**, 260–268.

Hediger, H. (1950). "Wild Animals in Captivity", tr. G. Sircom. Butterworth & Co., London.

Heitman, H. Jnr. and Cole, H. H. (1956). Further studies in the induction of estrus in lactating sows with equine gonadotrophin. *J. Anim. Sci.* **15**, 970–977.

Hett, J. (1924). Das Corpus luteum der Zauneidechse (*Lacerta agilis*). *Z. mikr.-anat. Forsch.* **1**, 41–84.

Hickling, C. F. (1935). Seasonal changes in the ovary of the immature hake (*Merluccius merluccius* L.). *J. Mar. biol. Ass. U.K.* **20**, 443–462.

Hill, C. J. (1933). The development of Monotremata. Part I. The histology of the oviduct during gestation. *Trans. zool. Soc. Lond.* **21**, 413–443.

Hill, C. J. (1941). The development of the Monotremata. Part V. Further observations on the histology and the secretory activities of the oviduct prior to and during gestation. *Trans. zool. Soc. Lond.* **25**, 1–31.

Hill, J. P. and Gatenby, J. W. B. (1926). The corpus luteum of the Monotremata. *Proc. zool. Soc. Lond.* pp. 715–763.

Hill, M. and Parkes, A. S. (1933). Studies on the hypophysectomized ferret. IV. Comparison of the reproductive organs during anoestrus and after hypophysectomy. *Proc. roy. Soc.* B. **113**, 530–536.

Hill, M. and White, W. E. (1934). The growth and regression of follicles in the oestrous rabbit. *J. Physiol.* **80**, 174–178.

Hisaw, F. L. and Abramowitz, A. A. (1937). The physiology of reproduction in the dogfish, *Mustelus canis. Rep. Wood's Hole oceangr. Instn.* pp. 21–22.

Hisaw, F. L. and Albert, A. (1947). Observations on the reproduction of the spiny dogfish *Squalus acanthias. Biol. Bull., Wood's Hole*, **92**, 187–199.

Hoar, W. S. (1955). Reproduction in teleost fish. *Mem. Soc. Endocrin.* No. 4, 5–22.

Hoar, W. S. (1957). *In* "The Physiology of Fishes" (M. E. Brown, ed.), p. 287. Academic Press, New York.

Höfliger, H. (1948). Das Ovar des Rindes in den verschiedenen Lebensperioden unter besonderer Berücksichtigung seiner funktionellen Feinstruktur. *Acta anat.* Suppl. 5, 1–196.

z

Horst, C. J. van der, and Gillman, J. (1945). The behaviour of the Graafian follicle of *Elephantulus* during pregnancy, with special reference to the hormonal regulation of ovarian activity. *S. Afr. J. med. Sci.* **10**, Biol. Suppl., 1–14.

Huston, T. M. and Nalbandov, A. V. (1953). Neurohumoral control of the pituitary in the fowl. *Endocrinology*, **52**, 149–156.

Jaski, C. J. (1939). Ein Oestruszyklus bei *Lebistes reticulatus* (Peters). *Proc. Acad. Sci., Amst.* **42**, 20–207.

Kehl, R. (1944). Etude de quelques problèmes d'endocrinologie génitale chez certains reptiles du Sud-Algérian. *Rev. canad. Biol.* **3**, 131–219.

Kellas, L. M., van Lennep, E. W. and Amoroso, E. C. (1958). Ovaries of some foetal and prepubertal giraffes (*Giraffa camelopardalis* Linnaeus). *Nature, Lond.* **181**, 487–488.

Kimura, J. and Lyons, W. R. (1937). Progestin in the pregnant mare. *Proc. Soc. exp. Biol., N.Y.* **37**, 423–427.

Klein, M. (1946). Oestrogen level and ovarian-hypophysial relationship during pseudo-pregnancy and pregnancy in the rabbit. *J. Endocrin.* **5**, xxv–xxvii.

Klein, M. and Mayer, G. (1942). Réactions ovariennes à la stimulation localisée des follicules de de Graaf. *Arch. Phys. biol.* **16**, Suppl. 5, 57–59.

Lane, C. E. (1935). The follicular apparatus of the ovary of the immature rat and some of the factors which influence it. *Anat. Rec.* **61**, 141–153.

Lane, C. E. and Davis, F. R. (1939). The ovary of the adult rat. I. Changes in the growth of the follicle and in volume and mitotic activity of the granulosa and theca during the estrous cycle. *Anat. Rec.* **73**, 429–442.

Lauson, H. D., Golden, J. B. and Sevringhaus, E. L. (1939). The gonadotrophic content of the hypophysis throughout the life-cycle of the normal female rat. *Amer. J. Physiol.* **125**, 396–404.

Liche, H. (1939). Oestrous cycle in the cat. *Nature, Lond.* **143**, 900.

Ling, J. K. (1958). The sea garfish, *Reporhamphus melanochir* (Cuvier & Valenciennes) (Hemiramphidae), in South Australia: breeding, age determination, and growth rate. *Aust. J. Mar. Freshw. Res.* **9**, 60–110.

Loeb, L. (1911). The cyclical changes in the ovary of the guinea-pig. *J. Morph.* **22**, 37–70.

Long, J. A. and Evans, H. M. (1922). The oestrous cycle in the rat and its associated phenomena. *Mem. Univ. Calif.* **6**, 1–148.

Lyngnes, R. (1936). Rückbildung der ovulierten und nicht ovulierten Follikel im Ovarium der *Myxine glutinosa* L. Skr. norske VidenskAkad., Oslo, I. Mat. Naturv. Kl. No. 4, 1–116.

Mandl, A. M. (1951). The phases of the oestrous cycle in the adult white rat. *J. exp. Biol.* **28**, 576–584.

Mandl, A. M. and Zuckerman, S. (1952). Cyclical changes in the number of medium and large follicles in the adult rat ovary. *J. Endocrin.* **8**, 341–346.

Manwell, E. J. and Wickens, P. G. (1928). The mechanisms of ovulation and implantation in the domestic cat. *Anat. Rec.* **38**, (Abstr.), 54.

Marshall, F. H. A. (1904). The oestrous cycle in the common ferret. *Quart. J. micr. Sci.* **48**, 323–345.

Marshall, F. H. A. (1936). The Croonian lecture; sexual periodicity and the causes which determine it. *Phil. Trans.* B. **226**, 423–456.

Marshall, F. H. A. and Halnan, E. T. (1917). On the post-oestrous changes occurring in the generative organs and mammary glands of the non-pregnant dog. *Proc. roy. Soc.* B. **89**, 546–559.

Martínez-Esteve, P. (1937). Le cycle sexuel vaginal chez le marsupial *Didelphys azarae*. *C.R. Soc. Biol., Paris*, **124**, 502–504.

Matthews, L. H. (1935). The oestrous cycle and intersexuality in the female mole (*Talpa europaea* Linn.). *Proc. zool. Soc. Lond.* pp. 347–382.

Matthews, L. H. (1937). The female sexual cycle in the British horseshoe bats. *Trans. zool. Soc. Lond.* **23**, 224–266.

Matthews, L. H. (1941). Notes on the genitalia and reproduction of some African bats. *Proc. zool. Soc. Lond.* B. **111**, 289–346.

Matthews, L. H. (1950). Reproduction in the basking shark *Cetorhinus maximus* (Gunner). *Phil. Trans.* B. **234**, 247–316.

Matthews, S. A. (1938). The seasonal cycle in the gonads of *Fundulus*. *Biol. Bull., Wood's Hole*, **75**, 66–74.

McKeown, T. and Zuckerman, S. (1938). The suppression of oestrus in the rat during pregnancy and lactation. *Proc. roy. Soc.* B. **124**, 464–475.

Metten, H. (1941). Studies on the reproduction of the dogfish. *Phil. Trans.* B. **230**, 217–238.

Miller, M. R. (1948). The seasonal histological changes occurring in the ovary, corpus luteum and testis of the viviparous lizard *Xantusia vigilis*. *Univ. Calif. Publ. Zool.* **47**, 197–223.

Miller, M. R. (1951). Some aspects of the life history of the Yucca night lizard *Xantusia vigilis*. *Copeia*, 1951, 114–120.

Mirskaia, L. and Crew, F. A. E. (1930). Maturity in the female mouse. *Proc. roy. Soc., Edinb.* **50**, 179–186.

Mossman, H. W. and Judas, I. (1949). Accessory corpora lutea, lutein cell origin, and the ovarian cycle in the Canadian porcupine. *Amer. J. Anat.* **85**, 1–39.

Myers, H. I., Young, W. C. and Dempsey, E. W. (1936). Graafian follicle development throughout the reproductive cycle in the guinea-pig, with especial reference to changes during oestrus (sexual receptivity). *Anat. Rec.* **65**, 381–401.

Ortiz, E. (1947). The postnatal development of the reproductive system of the golden hamster (*Cricetus auratus*) and its reactivity to hormones. *Physiol. Zoöl.* **20**, 45–66.

Parkes, A. S. (1928). The length of the oestrous cycle in the unmated normal mouse: records of one thousand cycles. *Brit. J. exp. Biol.* **5**, 371–377.

Parkes, A. S. (1931a). The reproductive processes of certain mammals. Part I. The oestrous cycle of the Chinese hamster (*Cricetulus griseus*). *Proc. roy. Soc.* B. **108**, 138–147.

Parkes, A. S. (1931b). The reproductive processes of certain mammals. II. The size of the Graafian follicle at ovulation. *Proc. roy. Soc.* B. **109**, 185–196.

Pearson, O. P. (1944). Reproduction in the shrew (*Blarina brevicauda*, Say). *Amer. J. Anat.* **75**, 39–93.

Pearson, O. P. (1949). Reproduction of a South American rodent, the mountain viscacha. *Amer. J. Anat.* **84**, 143–173.

Pearson, O. P., Koford, M. R. and Pearson, A. K. (1952). Reproduction of the lump-nosed bat (*Corynorhinus rafinesquei*) in California. *J. Mammal.* **33**, 273–320.

Perry, J. S. (1951). Reproduction of the African elephant, *Loxodonta africana*. *J. Endocrin.* **7**, liii–lv.

Perry, J. S. (1953). The reproduction of the African elephant, *Loxodonta africana*. *Phil. Trans.* B. **237**, 93–149.

Pfeiffer, C. A. and Hooker, C. W. (1942). Early and late effects of daily treatment with pregnant mare serum upon the ovary of mice of the A strain. *Anat. Rec.* **84**, 311–329.

Pincus, G. (1936). "The Eggs of Mammals", p. 40. The Macmillan Company, New York.

Porto, A. (1941). Sôbre a presença de progesterona no corpo amarelo de serpentes ovovivíparas. *Mem. Inst. Butantan*, **15**, 27–30.

Price, D. and Ortiz, E. (1944). The relation of age to reactivity in the reproductive system of the rat. *Endocrinology*, **34**, 215–239.

Price, M. (1953). The reproductive cycle of the water shrew *Neomys fodiens bicolor* Shaw. *Proc. zool. Soc. Lond.* **123**, 599–621.

Rahn, H. (1942). The reproductive cycle of the prairie rattler. *Copeia*, 1942, 233–240.

Regamey, J. (1935). Les caractères sexuels du lézard (*Lacerta agilis* L.). *Rev. suisse Zool.* **42**, 87–168.

Riddle, O. (1911). On the formation, significance and chemistry of the white and yellow yolk of ova. *J. Morph.* **22**, 455–491.

Riddle, O. (1916). Studies on the physiology of reproduction in birds. 1. The occurrence and measurement of a sudden change in the rate of growth of avian ova. *Amer. J. Physiol.* **41**, 387–396.

Robinson, A. (1918). The formation, rupture, and closure of ovarian follicles in ferrets and ferret-polecat hybrids, and some associated phenomena. *Trans. roy. Soc. Edinb.* **52**, 303–362.

Rowlands, I. W. (1949). Serum gonadotrophin and ovarian activity in the pregnant mare. *J. Endocrin.* **6**, 184–191.

Rowlands, I. W. (1956). The corpus luteum of the guinea-pig. *Ciba Foundation Coll. Ageing*, **2**, 69–83.

Rowlands, I. W. and Short, R. V. (1959). The progesterone content of the guinea-pig corpus luteum during the reproductive cycle and after hysterectomy. *J. Endocrin.* **19**, 81–86.

Samuel, M. (1943). Studies on the corpus luteum in *Rhinobatis granulatus* Cuv. *Proc. Indian Acad. Sci.* B. **18**, 133–157.

Samuel, M. (1944). Studies on the corpus luteum in *Enhydrina schistosa* (Daudin) and *Hydrophis cyanocinctus* (Daudin) of the Madras coast. *Proc. Indian Acad. Sci.* B. **20**, 143–174.

Scott, P. P. and Lloyd-Jacob, M. A. (1955). Some interesting features in the reproductive cycle of the cat. *Stud. Fertil.* **7**, 123–129.

Sergeev, A. M. (1941). On the biology of reproduction in the steppe tortoise (*Testudo horsfieldi* Gray). *Zool. Zh.* **20**, 118–134.

Sharman, G. B. (1955a). Studies on marsupial reproduction. III. Normal and delayed pregnancy in *Setonix brachyurus*. *Aust. J. Zool.* **3**, 56–70.

Sharman, G. B. (1955b). Studies on marsupial reproduction. IV. Delayed birth in *Protemnodon eugenii*. *Aust. J. Zool.* **3**, 156–161.

Smelser, G. K., Walton, A. and Whetham, E. O. (1934). The effect of light on ovarian activity in the rabbit. *J. exp. Biol.* **11**, 352–363.

Smith, C. L. (1955). Reproduction in female Amphibia. *Mem. Soc. Endocrin.* No. 4, 39–55.

Smith, R. M. and Rubenstein, B. B. (1940). Adolescence of macaques. *Endocrinology*, **26**, 667–679.

Smithberg, M. and Runner, M. N. (1956). The induction and maintenance of pregnancy in prepuberal mice. *J. exp. Zool.* **133**, 441–457.

Stieve, H. (1919). Die Entwicklung des Eierstockseies der Dohle (*Colaeus monedula*). *Arch. mikr. Anat.* **92**, 137–288.

Swezy, O. and Evans, H. M. (1930). Ovarian changes during pregnancy in the rat. *Science*, **71**, 46.

Talmage, R. V., Buchanan, G. D., Kraintz, F. W., Lazo-Wasem, E. A. and Zarrow, M. X. (1954). The presence of a functional corpus luteum during delayed implantation in the armadillo. *J. Endocrin.* **11**, 44–49.

Tuchmann-Duplessis, H. (1945). Corrélations hypophyso-endocrines chez le triton. Déterminisme hormonal des caractères sexuels secondaires. *Actualités sci. industr.* No. 987, Hermann, Paris. (Quoted by Smith, 1955).

Turner, C. L. (1937). Reproductive cycles and superfetation in Poeciliid fishes. *Biol. Bull., Wood's Hole*, **72**, 145–164.

Turner, C. L. (1938). The reproductive cycle of *Brachyraphis episcopi*, an ovoviviparous Poeciliid fish, in the natural tropical habitat. *Biol. Bull., Wood's Hole*, **75**, 56–65.

Valle, J. R. do and Souza, P. R. de (1942). Observações sobre o sistema endócrino dos ofídios. O corpo amarelo nas serpentes ovovivíparas não venenosas. *Rev. Bras. Biol., Rio de J.* **2**, 81–88.

Vivien, J. H. (1939). Rôle de l'hypophyse dans le déterminisme du cycle génital femelle d'un téléostéen, *Gobius paganellus* L. *C.R. Acad. Sci., Paris*, **208**, 948–949.

Warnick, A. C., Casida, L. E. and Grummer, R. H. (1950). The occurrence of estrus and ovulation in post-partum sows. *J. Anim. Sci.* **9**, 66–72.

Watson, R. H. (1952). Seasonal variation in reproductive activity in ewes. *Aust. vet. J.* **28**, 1–5.

Weekes, H. C. (1934). The corpus luteum in certain oviparous and viviparous reptiles. *Proc. Linn. Soc. N.S.W.* **59**, 380–391.

Weichert, C. K. and Schurgast, A. W. (1942). Variations in size of corpora lutea in the albino rat under normal and experimental conditions. *Anat. Rec.* **83**, 321–334.

Wilder, I. W. (1917). On the breeding habits of *Desmognathus fusca*. *Biol. Bull., Wood's Hole*, **32**, 13–20.

Williams, S. M., Garrigus, U. S., Norton, H. W. and Nalbandov, A. V. (1956). The occurrence of estrus in pregnant ewes. *J. Anim. Sci.* **15**, 978–983.

Wimsatt, W. A. (1944). Growth of the ovarian follicle and ovulation in *Myotis lucifugus lucifugus*. *Amer. J. Anat.* **74**, 129–173.

Wimsatt, W. A. and Trapido, H. (1952). Reproduction and the female reproductive cycle in the tropical American vampire bat, *Desmodus rotundus murinus*. *Amer. J. Anat.* **91**, 415–445.

Witschi, E. (1935). Seasonal sex characters in birds and their hormonal control. *Wilson Bull.* **47**, 177–188.

Woodbury, M. and Woodbury, A. M. (1945). Life history studies of the sage-bush lizard *Sceloporus g. graciosus* with special reference to cycles in reproduction. *Herpetologica*, **2**, 175–196.

Zuckerman, S. and Parkes, A. S. (1932). The menstrual cycle of the primates. Part V. The cycle of the baboon. *Proc. zool. Soc. Lond.* pp. 139–191.

CHAPTER 6

OVARIAN PHYSIOLOGY IN THE NON-PREGNANT FEMALE

P. ECKSTEIN

I. Introduction

Modern notions about the functions of the ovary hinge on the century-old observation that the spayed female is sterile and the much more recent experimental demonstration that bilateral ovariectomy leads to cessation of cyclic activity and ultimate involution of the accessory reproductive organs, both of which can be prevented by grafts and extracts of ovarian tissue or by administration of oestrogenic substances. This, and the convincing evidence identifying the gonad as the actual site of formation of the oestrogenic hormone (see pp. 321 to 323), has led to the customary concept that the ovary, like the testis, performs a dual, i.e. gametogenetic and hormonal, function.

Although occasionally out of step, as for instance during adolescence and lactation, these two functions are essentially associated and complementary; deficiency in either leads to impairment or abolition of reproductive capacity.

Before proceeding to an elaboration of this theme in the following sections, it should be stressed that the ovary forms part of the female reproductive system as a whole. As such, its functions cannot be considered, as it were, in isolation, but must be seen in the context of a chain of organs, extending from the hypothalamus to the external genitalia and linked by an intricate and closely integrated series of endocrine processes. Without the stimuli emanating from the anterior lobe of the pituitary gland maturation of follicles and secretion of ovarian hormones are no more feasible than are the events of the oestrous cycle in the absence of the ovary.

Expression of ovarian activities, moreover, is not absolute but is conditioned by a variety of factors, among the more important of which are age, nutrition and the reproductive pattern of the species concerned. To do them justice the following account would clearly have to be more detailed and comprehensive than is compatible with its scope. It will therefore be mainly, though not entirely, restricted to mammals, and is based on the assumption that the reader is familiar with the basic anatomical and physiological facts of reproduction in the mammalian female. Wherever possible, reference will be made to existing monographs and reviews dealing with specific aspects as well as to other parts in this book. An account of ovarian activity during gestation is provided in Chapter 9.

II. The events of the ovarian cycle

A. Oogenesis and number of follicles

The origin of the germ cells and the process of oogenesis in mammals are fully discussed in Chapter 1 and will not be reconsidered in detail. During embryonic and immediate postnatal development each germ cell becomes surrounded by a single, more or less complete layer of smaller supporting cells. The resulting structure, representing the basic unit of the ovary, is referred to as a primordial follicle and the contained cell as an oocyte. A large proportion of these follicles undergo degeneration, or atresia, and those that survive do not reach the more advanced stages of maturation until the onset of puberty. Actual counts of the total number present in the human ovary vary greatly, but are usually stated to lie between quarter and half a million at birth and to have regressed to about 100,0002—00,000 by the time of puberty (e.g. Simkins, 1932; Block, 1952, 1953; cf. Zuckerman, 1951a, 1960).

It is also thought that the steepest decline occurs before puberty and that the rate of loss of oocytes after birth is under genetic control (for instance in mice, Jones, 1957).

The small number of follicles destined to reach full size and maturity, probably no more than a few hundred in the entire reproductive life of a healthy woman and perhaps 1,000–1,500 in that of a rat, then undergo a series of growth changes which culminate with the release of the ovum, or ovulation, and corpus luteum formation (see p. 315 and Chapter 5).

The origin of the germ cells (and follicles) in the adult ovary and the problem of oogenesis as a whole has not been finally settled, and the evidence relating to this subject is fully examined in Chapter 1, sect. II. Two significant implications that emerge will, however, be briefly referred to.

First, if the classical ('endowment') concept of Waldeyer (1870), and hence the conclusion that postnatal neoformation of oocytes does not occur, is accepted, the lifespan of oocytes must approach that of the female herself, that is to say, 30 or 40 years in the case of a woman. The far-reaching effects that advancing age may have upon the development and ultimate fate of the fertilized ovum are obvious. Second, since all properly conducted counts have invariably revealed a progressive diminution in the total number of oocytes in the ovaries throughout life (Mandl and Zuckerman, 1950, 1951b; Zuckerman, 1951a; Block, 1952), neoformation, even when it does (exceptionally) occur, cannot adequately compensate for the normal losses through atresia and ovulation (cf. Chapter 4; and Krohn, 1957).

B. Follicular maturation and ovulation

The process of follicular maturation has been frequently described (e.g. Brambell, 1956), and its morphological details are too well known to require repetition. It depends, except during the earliest stages (e.g. Smith, 1939; cf. also Chapters 1, 7), on gonadotrophic stimulation from the anterior pituitary and proceeds in waves extending throughout the period of sexual maturity, unless interrupted by pregnancy and lactation or by anoestrus in seasonally breeding species. At each wave a group of follicles enters a rapid phase of growth during which the granulosa cells surrounding the oocyte proliferate and secretion of follicular fluid leads to the formation of an antrum (cf. Chapter 2C). The final maturation process, however, affects only the much smaller number of follicles that are destined to ovulate, and frequently only one (for instance, in women and other primates, the cow and mare). Among the changes exhibited by such large vesicular or Graafian follicles (so called after the Dutch scientist, Regner de Graaf, who described them in his classical account of the mammalian female gonad in 1672; see Corner, 1943a) are: an intense pre-ovulatory growth spurt, accompanied by increasing distension with follicular fluid or liquor, loosening of the granulosa cells constituting the cumulus oöphorus and hypertrophy as well as marked hyperaemia of the theca interna (e.g. Corner, 1946; Hisaw, 1947; Brambell, 1956; Fluhmann, 1956). Eventually, progressive thinning of the follicular wall and its blood vessels lead to the formation of a 'stigma' and to the escape of the ovum within its surrounding 'corona radiata' of cumulus cells and liquor (cf. Chapter 8). It is now established that the ripe Graafian follicle 'oozes' rather than 'bursts' open. In several species it becomes softer and less turgid, and in the hen blanching of the prominent capillaries is a striking feature of the follicular wall at the time of ovulation (Nalbandov, 1958).

C. The ovarian cycle

Such recurrent phases of follicular growth and ovulation, followed by corpus luteum formation, with the associated production of ovarian hormones, constitute the ovarian cycle (itself accompanied by periodic changes in the accessory organs; see below). They occur at regular intervals throughout the period of active reproductive life in all spontaneously ovulating species or, following coitus, in induced ovulators like the rabbit, ferret and cat (see Chapter 5). The length and general pattern of these cycles varies considerably in different mammals (see sect. III, B). Ripening of follicles and ovulation are generally in abeyance during gestation and lactation, but occur normally in the pregnant elephant and mare, as well as immediately after parturition in various species of rodent.

D. The size of the ovum at ovulation

At the time of its release from the Graafian follicle, the mammalian oocyte is remarkably uniform in size. It usually lies within a range of 120–150μ (see Hartman, 1929; Austin and Bishop, 1957), except in many rodents ($ca.$ 60–70μ), marsupials like the Australian native cat ($ca.$ 250μ; Hill, 1910) and in monotremes in which it reaches a diameter of 3–4 mm (Flynn and Hill, 1939).

By contrast, the dimensions of the fully-formed Graafian follicle vary greatly among mammals and are not related to that of the enclosed oocyte (see Chapter 2C).

E. The number of eggs produced in different vertebrates

There are equally marked inter-species variations in the number of follicles which reach maturity and release ova at ovulation. While usually a single follicle ruptures in one ovary during each cycle in women, monkeys, the cow and mare, or once only per year in monoestrous species like deer and seals, between seven and ten may ripen every few weeks in each gonad of the sow or opossum and as many as sixty in *Elephantulus*, the South African elephant shrew; in the latter, however, only a single ovum is able to implant and develop to term, the remainder dying off within the uterus (van der Horst and Gillman, 1942). In lower vertebrates, the numbers of eggs produced are as a rule greater still, e.g. 200–300 per year in the hen, and may be enormous, as for instance in the cod in which more than a million are said to be spawned in a season.

F. Alternation of ovarian function

Although most mammals have paired and equally well developed ovaries, there is a tendency in many for ovulation to occur slightly more frequently from one side (e.g. 60 per cent from the right ovary in cows; Nalbandov, 1958). In monotremes and certain bats one ovary is rudimentary or functionally less active than the other, thereby resembling the condition in birds.

G. The corpus luteum

1. *Formation and persistence*

Following ovulation the ruptured follicle undergoes luteinization and is transformed into a corpus luteum. This is the usual event in mammals, including the monotremes, but probably occurs also in certain viviparous fishes and reptiles. For instance, in viviparous snakes of the genera *Natrix* and *Storeria* removal of the post-ovulatory bodies early during pregnancy leads to death and resorption of foetuses, but not if ovariectomy is performed during the second half of gestation (Clausen, 1940; cf. Nelsen, 1953; Nalbandov, 1958). In other lower vertebrates the ovary after ovulation usually shrinks to a fraction of its previous size or develops corpora of doubtful physiological significance (cf. Chapters 2B and 9).

With the probable exception of birds, luteal bodies occur in every class of vertebrate, both oviparous and viviparous, and their presence is thus no distinctive mammalian feature. Moreover, their development in lower vertebrates does not necessarily depend on stimulation by pituitary gonadotrophins, and prolonged viviparous gestation is possible in the absence of functional corpora (Hisaw, 1959; cf. also Asdell, 1928; *Mem. Soc. Endocrin.* No. 4, 1955; Pickford and Atz, 1957; and Chapters 2B, 7 and 9).

Functionally, the mammalian corpus luteum—so called because of its vivid orange–yellow colour in women and species like the cow—represents a transitory gland of internal secretion, the main purpose of which is the production of progesterone. The active lifespan of this structure in the non-pregnant female varies greatly and depends on several factors (e.g. Robson, 1947; Klein, 1954; Nalbandov, 1958; see also Chapters 5, 7 and 9). Thus in the rat or mouse the corpus luteum of the normal cycle lasts for only 2 or 3 days and is thought to be almost non-functional; should, however, pseudopregnancy supervene as a result of sterile copulation, its lifespan and active hormone production are prolonged to about 2 weeks. Similarly, in non-spontaneously ovulating species like the rabbit and ferret the ovary contains functional corpora lutea only during pseudopregnancy and pregnancy. By contrast, in the bitch the corpora are invariably functional and persist for about 2 months, whether copulation and conception take place or not; this constitutes a condition of obligatory pseudopregnancy. In women and other primates the corpus luteum of the cycle lasts for some 12-15 days, and in ruminants like the cow for about 18 days (Asdell, 1946; see also Chapter 5).

In the event of conception, the corpus luteum remains active for far longer periods than during the sexual cycle. Persistence of the corpora lutea can be induced experimentally by hormonal treatment with either gonadotrophins or oestrogens and in some species, such as the rabbit, guinea pig and rat, by hysterectomy (Loeb, 1923, 1927; Asdell and Hammond, 1933; Loeb and Smith, 1936; Chu et al., 1944; Bradbury et al., 1950). The mode of formation of the corpus luteum in vertebrates has been repeatedly reviewed (e.g. Asdell, 1928; Harrison, 1948; Brambell, 1956), and is described in detail in Chapters 2B and 2C.

The conversion of the empty vesicular follicle into an active corpus luteum represents a most significant feature of the ovarian cycle. Within the space of a few days cells previously responsible for the production of oestrogen become transformed into luteal cells secreting progesterone, a wholly different, if chemically closely related, hormone (see sect. III, and Chapter 12 B). Actual formation of progesterone in the human species has been ascribed by White et al. (1951) to a group of thecal cells, designated by them as 'K-cells' and characterized by the presence of ketonic lipids.

It is probable that the change-over from the secretion of oestrogen to that of progesterone can occur before the release of the ovum. In some mammals thecal luteinization may be present in pre-ovulatory follicles (cf. Harrison, 1948; Turner, 1955; Nalbandov, 1958). In others, such as the insectivores *Elephantulus* (van der Horst and Gillman, 1940, 1942) and *Centetes* (Strauss, 1939), luteal transformation not only precedes ovum release but appears to be the immediate cause of rupture of the follicle. Some of the supporting biochemical evidence is considered below (p. 324). Conversely, there is adequate proof that the fully formed corpus luteum produces oestrogen in addition to progestin (e.g. Zander et al., 1959).

Following its formation, the size and general development of the corpus luteum, as well as production of its hormone, reach a maximum and then decline. When spent, the structure is referred to as a corpus albicans and secretes little or no progesterone. As a rule, corpora albicantia persist histologically for only a few cycles, but in whales they remain recognizable for many years (Mackintosh, 1946; Harrison, 1949; see also Chapter 9).

2. Accessory and aberrant corpora lutea

In some species, in addition to normal corpora lutea, structures referred to as corpora lutea accessoria and aberrantia may arise during the non-pregnant cycle (e.g. the rhesus monkey: Corner et al., 1936; Corner, 1940; cf. Eckstein, 1957). Alternatively, follicles can become luteinized without previous ovulation, and this appears to be a regular feature in some platyrrhine monkeys and the gibbon (Dempsey, 1939, 1940) as well as in certain rodents (e.g. Hisaw, 1925, 1947; Mossman, 1937; Stafford et al., 1942; see also Chapters 2C, 5 and 9).

3. Significance of the corpus luteum in the non-pregnant female

Ovulation and corpus luteum formation constitute at once the culmination and, in the non-pregnant female, the most dispensable aspect of ovarian activities. As mentioned, in various mammals ovulation only occurs following copulation, and even in spontaneously ovulating species it is the most labile and most easily dislocated part of the reproductive cycle. Thus it may be suppressed or irregular during the period (of so-called 'adolescent sterility') intervening between puberty and the establishment of full maturity and, even after its attainment, is not infrequently missing (for instance in women: Fluhmann, 1956; and in rhesus monkeys: Hartman, 1931, 1938; cf. Eckstein and Zuckerman, 1956a). Again, ovulation tends to disappear earlier than any of the other manifestations of cyclic ovarian activity as a female approaches the end of her reproductive life (cf. Eckstein, 1955; also Ingram et al., 1958).

For the same reason, the corpus luteum and its hormone must be considered as less essential, respectively, than the Graafian follicle and oestrogen in the control of cyclic phenomena in the non-pregnant female (see sect. III, B). As recently shown, ovulation may also fail to occur in rodents maintained in the laboratory (van der Lee and Boot, 1955, 1956; Whitten, 1957, 1958, 1959; Dewar, 1959; Lamond, 1959a), although in such cases the length and phasing of the oestrous cycle are invariably affected.

H. The interstitial cells

In addition to the follicular and luteal components and their respective derivatives, the ovaries of many, and probably all, mammals

contain large epithelial, glandular-looking elements known as interstitial cells.

The number and distribution of these cells varies widely in different
species. In some, like the rabbit, ferret, mole, bats and certain New
World monkeys (Dempsey, 1939), they form distinct and conspicuous
masses (Brambell, 1956; see also Chapter 2C); they are much less prominent or apparently absent in the cow, mouse and woman.

During the greater part of foetal life the gonads of the horse and seal
are almost entirely made up of interstitial cells and may exceed the
maternal ovaries in size (Cole *et al.*, 1933; Amoroso, 1945; see also
Chapter 9). In the adult female the cells undergo marked hypertrophy
during pregnancy and lactation when they assume the appearance of
luteal elements (for instance in the rabbit, water shrew (Price, 1953;
cf. Brambell, 1956) and various primates including women). Luteal
transformation of the interstitial elements during pregnancy is so
marked in spider and howler monkeys, as well as in the gibbon, that
the ovaries become solidly luteinized and the identity of the original
corpus luteum of pregnancy is entirely lost (Dempsey, 1939, 1940;
cf. Eckstein, 1957). Such a transformation also occurs in the non-pregnant pocket gopher, *Geomys bursarius*, and in the guinea pig. The
theca interna in both species is markedly hypertrophied and constitutes a 'thecal gland' which shows the structural features of an
endocrine organ (Mossman, 1937; Stafford *et al.*, 1942).

The origin and cytological characters of the interstitial cells in
different mammals are reviewed in Chapter 2C, while their physiological
significance is briefly considered below (p. 322).

I. The hilus cells

The hilus and mesovarium of the human ovary frequently contain
microscopic collections of cells morphologically indistinguishable
from the interstitial elements of the testis (Berger, 1922; Kohn, 1928;
van Campenhout, 1947; Sternberg, 1949; Dhom, 1955; cf. also Chapter
2C). Cells of this type have been found in about 80 per cent of ovaries
examined (Sternberg, 1949), and are especially conspicuous during
pregnancy and at the menopause.

They are also intimately associated with non-myelinated nerves and
have been considered as part of the chromaffin tissue. Their histological
appearance, cytochemical reactions (including the occasional presence of
crystalloids of Reinke) and likely steroidogenic function strongly
suggest, however, that they are homologous with testicular Leydig
cells (Dhom, 1955; Morris and Scully, 1958).

Hyperplasia or tumours of the ovarian hilus cells are not infrequently
found in virilizing syndromes (e.g. Berger, 1942; cf. also Chapter 23).

This, their other features referred to, as well as their proved sensitivity to gonadotrophic stimulation (Sternberg *et al.*, 1949) indicate that they may be an important source of ovarian androgen in the human female (see also p. 327).

III. Endocrine activities of the ovary

Basic knowledge of the ovary as an organ of internal secretion stems from the demonstration of involutionary changes in the uterus and vagina following bilateral ovariectomy and their reversal by administration of active ovarian extracts (e.g. Marshall and Jolly, 1905; cf. Marshall, 1922; Parkes, 1929). A vast amount of information obtained during the last 30 years or so has, however, shown that the biological effects of the ovarian hormones are more diverse and complex than was at first thought. It is now clear that the ovary, by means of its hormonal secretions, controls not only pubertal development and subsequent maintenance of the accessory reproductive tract, secondary sexual characters and psycho-sexual behaviour of the female, but also many other bodily functions not directly concerned with reproduction. Thus ovariectomy, apart from its specific genital effects, influences other endocrine and systemic organs, somatic growth and configuration, as well as a variety of general and metabolic processes. These particular effects, like those in the reproductive sphere, can be partially reversed or prevented by treatment with oestrogens, and are exerted through salt- and water-retaining, protein-anabolic and other properties of the hormones concerned which have little or no connection with sexual function as such.

Some of these generalized actions will be briefly considered below (see sect. III, C), but most of what follows will deal primarily with the ovary's hormonal functions as related to reproductive processes. These, in their most concise definition, are, first, to condition the female to accept the male and, second, to create an environment within the accessory sex tract that is suitable for both gamete transport and for fertilization and subsequent development of the ovum.

A. Production of hormones by the ovary

The ovary is believed to be responsible for the elaboration of oestrogenic and luteal hormones and, at least potentially, also for that of androgen and corticosteroids (cf. Morris and Scully, 1958; see also p. 327 and Chapter 16). It holds, however, no monopoly of production since oestrogens occur in other endrocrine tissues such as the adrenal gland and placenta, as well as in the testis and body fluids of the male; they are, moreover, known to persist, albeit at a low level, in the urine of ovariectomized females (see p. 326). Progesterone has been identified, apart from the corpus luteum, in adrenocortical and placental extracts.

Most of these facts become comprehensible in the light, first, of the potentially bisexual nature of the gonads and their close association with the adrenal cortex during embryological development and, second, of the pronounced similarities in the chemistry of these compounds (see Chapter 12). Whether the ovary of the non-pregnant female also produces the pelvis-relaxing factor, relaxin, as it can during gestation, (see Hisaw, 1925, 1926; Hisaw and Zarrow, 1950; Frieden and Hisaw, 1953; Steinetz *et al.*, 1959) does not appear to be fully established (cf. Chapter 9 and Emmens 1959).

1. *The oestrogenic hormone*

Demonstration of the oestrus-inducing properties of ovarian tissue, although previously suspected, was first achieved by Allen and Doisy (1923) who used the test of vaginal cornification in spayed rodents (Stockard and Papanicolaou, 1917; Allen, 1922) as a specific index of oestrogenic activity. Chemical identification of the active principle in Allen and Doisy's material—obtained from follicular fluid of sows' ovaries—followed, and shortly afterwards the first preparation of oestrogens in crystalline form was accomplished almost simultaneously in various countries (for reviews see Allen, 1939; Corner, 1943b; Burrows, 1949; Marrian, 1950).

In the non-pregnant female the ovary is the principal site of oestrogen production, but during pregnancy the placenta becomes a much more potent source so that at parturition the total excretion of oestrogens may be many times greater than at conception (Dorfman, 1955; Brown, 1956, 1957).

The chemistry of oestrogens is fully described in Chapter 12A and will therefore only be briefly touched upon.

In the human species various oestrogenic substances have been identified. The three most important and 'classical' ones are oestradiol-17β, oestrone and oestriol. Of these, oestradiol is the most potent, and believed to be actually secreted by the ovary. Next in potency is oestrone, the first oestrogenic compound to be isolated in crystalline form, and the third, oestriol, the predominating oestrogen in human pregnancy urine. Recently, 16-*epi*oestriol, 16α-hydroxyoestrone and several additional oestrogens have also been identified in human urine (Marrian and Bauld, 1955; Marrian *et al.*, 1957a, b; Marrian, 1960; cf. also Diczfalusy, 1957). Whether they are of physiological significance and what their natural source of origin is remains to be established. The main oestrogenic constituents in the urine of the mare are equilin and equilenin.

Oestrogens have been demonstrated in the ovaries of several mammalian species. Both oestradiol-17β and oestrone were chemically identified in human Graafian follicles and corpora lutea (Zander *et al.*, 1959) and oestradiol in the follicular fluid of the cow (Velle, 1959). In addition to these two compounds, Short (1960a) has reported the presence of a further oestrogenic 17-ketosteroid, progesterone and several other steroids in the follicular fluid of the mare.

Follicular fluid can be regarded as a plasma filtrate (e.g. Lutwak-Mann, 1954; Caravaglios and Cilotti, 1957; Zachariae and Jensen, 1958), and the concentration of steroids in it provides a clue to the ratios in which these compounds are secreted by the various ovarian elements (cf. Short, 1960a).

It seems to be established that the human ovary secretes both oestradiol and oestrone, but, unlike the placenta, very little if any oestriol. Such oestriol as appears in the urine during the cycle is believed to be derived from the metabolic breakdown of the other two.

Both oestradiol-17β and oestrone are easily and rapidly interconverted in the organism, and it is doubtful whether either compound can be present in the body fluids or tissues without (some of) the other (Zander *et al.*, 1959).

It seems likely that the ovaries of all vertebrates produce oestrogen. This is the conclusion arrived at in a recent survey by Dean and Chester Jones (1959), following their own provisional identification of the three principal oestrogenic compounds in ovarian tissue from lungfish, *Protopterus annectens* Owen (see also Chapter 7).

(a) *Source of oestrogen production in the ovary*

The actual site of production of oestrogen in the ovary has not been determined with certainty and remains controversial. The generally close temporal, though not invariable,* association of oestrous behaviour and oestrous changes in the vagina with the presence of mature follicles in the ovary suggests that the Graafian follicle or some of its cellular constituents must be involved, and in 1938 Corner concluded that the most probable site of production is the theca interna. It is, however, known that the ovary can produce a certain amount of oestrogen before puberty and may do so during foetal life (see sect. IV). This implies that elaboration of ovarian hormones does not depend on structurally organized follicles. That this is also true of the adult

---

* Among the few exceptions are certain types of bat, such as *Vesperugo pipistrellus*, in which oestrus and mating occur in the autumn, but follicular maturation, ovulation and fertilization do not take place until several months later, after the end of hibernation (cf. Eckstein and Zuckerman, 1956a).

ovary was first demonstrated by Parkes over 30 years ago when
he observed that oestrous cycles and behavioural oestrus could continue in mice whose ovaries had been X-irradiated sufficiently to destroy
all Graafian follicles (Parkes, 1926, 1927a, b, 1929; Brambell and
Parkes, 1927). These findings have been confirmed more recently and
with an improved technique, in both mice and rats, by Mandl and
Zuckerman (1956a, b). They found that after X-irradiation of the
ovaries in rats irregular cycles persist for up to about 6 weeks, followed
by continuous vaginal oestrus (cornification) between 1 and 14 weeks,
and ultimately by anoestrus. This indicates clearly that oestrogen may
be formed by ovarian cells other than those constituting the normal
follicle, even though the nature of the cellular elements involved,
persisting after irradiation, has not been established (see also Chapter
22).

While these experiments make it clear that in rodents, at any rate,
the structural integrity of Graafian follicles is no prerequisite for
oestrogen formation, they are in no way inconsistent with the view
that in the intact gonad oestrogen-producing cells are present in the
follicular wall (including the theca interna), and are, in fact, responsible
for the normal output of oestrogenic hormone by the ovary.

In further attempts to localize the site of production of oestrogen,
cytochemical methods have been extensively employed (e.g. Claesson
and Hillarp, 1947; McKay and Robinson, 1947; McKay et al., 1949;
Deane and Barker, 1952), but have not yielded uniform findings.
Since, in addition, the reliability of histochemical techniques in revealing the presence of steroid material is not firmly established, no ultimate
conclusions seem justified at present (see Jailer and Engle, 1954;
Morris and Scully, 1958; cf. also Chapter 3). It may be that hormone
production is an inherent property of all four major cellular elements
of the ovary, the granulosa, theca interna, corpus luteum and interstitial cells, and that factors like their relative distribution within,
and the histological state of, the ovary determine whether they exercise
it and to what extent.

(b) *Function of the interstitial cells*

The controversial problem of the functional significance of the
interstitial cells, no less than their origin, has defied analysis for many
years and is by no means settled. Early workers such as Steinach and
Lipschütz, impressed by the relative abundance of the tissue before
puberty in animals like the rabbit and by its similarity to the Leydig
cells of the testis, considered it as an important endocrine element
of the ovary and referred to it as the puberty gland ('Pubertätsdrüse')
(cf. Parkes, 1929).

More recent studies have emphasized the close histogenetic relationship between the theca interna of atretic follicles and interstitial cells (see Chapter 2 C; Brambell, 1956) and considered both systems as to some extent functionally interchangeable.

There is considerable evidence to support such a view. It may explain the presence of a so-called 'thecal gland' (believed to produce oestrogen) in certain rodents during prooestrus and oestrus (see p. 318) and in women (Dubreuil, 1945; Trapet, 1948). Again, after hypophysectomy both types of cell become transformed into 'deficiency' elements (Selye et al., 1933), out on treatment with chorionic gonadotrophin revert, in similar and specific fashion, to typical glandular cells. Recent histochemical studies by Scandinavian workers summarized by Falck (1959) indicate that the cholesterol content of both the theca interna and interstitial cells is gonadotrophically regulated and appears to be correlated with the secretion of oestrogen. In view of these observations and the growing belief that cholesterol is a precursor of oestrogen (see e.g. Hechter, 1958), Falck concludes that the theca interna and interstitial elements may constitute the 'oestrogen-producing cell system of the ovary'.

Falck's own findings (1959) on the formation of oestrogenic hormone by ovarian micro-transplants fit in with such a concept. He compared the ability of minute grafts of rat ovaries, obtained by micro-dissection and composed of pure cell aggregates, to elaborate oestrogen (as indicated by cornification of a contiguous vaginal graft). Falck found that no single cellular constituent by itself was capable of secreting the hormone and concluded that its production depends on the *joint* action of one of the two principal cell systems of the ovary: (i) the theca interna and interstitial cells, and (ii) the granulosa and corpus luteum cells.

Although Falck's and other recent findings referred to above constitute significant advances in this complex field, various unresolved questions remain. All the evidence so far obtained is indirect and therefore open to other interpretations. Also, as Parkes has pointed out over 30 years ago, the whole problem is complicated by the fact that there is no agreed definition of interstitial tissue and by the uncertain and variable behaviour of atretic follicles and corpora lutea in different mammals.

2. The luteal hormone

The physiological significance of the corpus luteum was not realized until the beginning of this century when Fraenkel (1903, 1910) demonstrated its endocrine nature and the importance of its secretion for the protection of the fertilized ovum. Progesterone was first extracted from luteal tissue in sows' ovaries in 1929 by Corner and Allen and shortly afterwards isolated and chemically identified (see Corner, 1943b; Marrian, 1950; Klein, 1954; cf. also Chapter 12B).

Progesterone is the principal progestational substance in the body; a metabolite, 20α-hydroxydregnenone, has recently been identified in plasma (e.g. Zander et al., 1958), but is biologically much weaker. Chemically, progesterone is a steroid closely related to natural oestrogens and androgens but constitutes, in addition, an important intermediate in the biosynthesis of adrenocortical hormones such as cortisol and corticosterone (Dorfman, 1955). In certain species (women, the chimpanzee, goat and rabbit) it is metabolized to biologically inert pregnanediol and excreted into the urine as pregnanediol glucuronidate. In other animals (such as rodents and probably monkeys) progesterone seems to be eliminated by some other route (bile, faeces) and does not, or only in traces, appear as pregnanediol in the urine.

The main source of the hormone during the cycle is the corpus luteum. It is, however, also produced by the adrenal cortex (Beall and Reichstein, 1938; see Short, 1960b) and, in large quantities, by the placenta; it has equally been isolated from the testis.

Although the luteal cells are generally accepted as the source of ovarian progesterone in the non-pregnant female, there is some evidence that the hormone can also be produced before ovulation and the formation of a corpus luteum. This is implied by the luteal transformation of pre-ovulatory follicles in various mammals (see p. 316, and Bryans, 1951; Amoroso, 1955), as well as by the observation that in certain species normal sexual receptivity and vaginal oestrus appear to depend on the combined action of oestrogen and progesterone (e.g. Dempsey et al., 1936; Boling and Blandau, 1939; see also Forbes, 1953; Green, 1955). Alternatively, however, progesterone may be contributed by the corpus luteum of the preceding cycle, as appears to be the case in the sheep (Robinson, 1955, 1959).

More direct evidence of progesterone secretion prior to ovulation has been obtained by the assay of follicular fluid and blood. Such progestational activity was obtained in follicular fluid from women, rabbits, sows and cows (e.g. Duyvené de Wit, 1938; Hooker and Forbes, 1947; Edgar, 1953; Forbes, 1953) as well as the peripheral blood of women (Forbes, 1950) and monkeys (Bryans, 1951) during the first half of the cycle. More recently and convincingly, progesterone and its metabolites have been chemically identified in follicular fluid (Zander, 1954; Zander et al., 1958; Short, 1960a).

The gonadotrophic principles concerned in the secretion of progesterone by the luteal cells are referred to in Chapter 7.

3. *Secretion of ovarian hormones during the cycle*

At present it is impossible to measure the actual amounts of hormones secreted by the ovaries, and the most satisfactory methods of assessing this aspect of ovarian function are based on chemical estimation in the urine. It must, however, be appreciated that the concentration of steroid metabolites appearing in the urine is an expression of both ovarian and non-ovarian sources of hormones such as the adrenal cortex. Again, it does not necessarily reflect the physiological response of the body to hormone secretion itself, since it and hormone action, metabolism and excretion are all closely interrelated. For that reason techniques for the estimation of blood levels of both oestrogens and progestins are coming increasingly into use.

(a) *Oestrogens*

The recent studies by Brown (1955a, 1957, 1959) and Brown *et al.* (1958), based on assay methods of proven reliability (Brown, 1955b), have confirmed the findings of previous workers that there is a peak in the urinary oestrogen excretion at about the middle of the human menstrual cycle, followed by a rising output of pregnanediol and a second oestrogen peak during the luteal phase. The first rise in the titre of oestrogen begins on day 8 of the normal, ovulatory cycle and culminates in a maximum 4 days later, when some 10–30 μg oestrone, rather less oestradiol-17β and up to 50–70 μg oestriol may be excreted in 24 hours (Brown, 1959). This peak occurs about 14 (11–16) days before the onset of the next menstrual period and is probably associated with ovulation (Brown *et al.*, 1958). It may be before or coincide with, but is never preceded by, an equally characteristic rise in gonadotrophin. The increase in the excretion of pregnanediol generally occurs 2–3 days after the oestrogen peak and provides, perhaps, the most reliable of the several available indirect criteria that ovulation has taken place. The secondary maximum during the luteal phase is thought to be due to oestrogens produced by the growing corpus luteum. By contrast, no such peaks in excretion occur during the anovulatory cycle.

Although the actual quantities of oestrogen eliminated by different women vary considerably, the overall excretion pattern in a given individual is remarkably constant. The total output of oestrogen by the human ovaries, as calculated by a variety of workers and methods, is thought to be approximately 300 μg/day at mid-cycle and somewhat less at the height of the luteal phase (cf. Corner, 1943b; Brown, 1957; Zander *et al.*, 1959).

A fraction of the total urinary oestrogens is probably of adreno-cortical origin. This is indicated by the persistence of small quantities in the urine after ovariectomy, though not after adrenalectomy (e.g. Bulbrook and Greenwood, 1957a, b). The output of such residual urinary oestrogens can be markedly increased by corticotrophin while the adrenals are intact, but the response is abolished when they, too, are removed (Strong et al., 1956; Brown et al., 1959).

Biologically demonstrable amounts of oestrogen may, exceptionally, persist in the urine even after removal of both the ovaries and adrenals or after hypophysectomy (Greenwood and Bulbrook, 1957; Bulbrook et al., 1960). The most likely source of the hormone appears to be accessory cortical tissue after adrenalectomy and residual ovarian or cortical activity persisting after hypophysectomy. This is also borne out by the experimental observation that involution of the uterus occurs more rapidly in spayed than in hypophysectomized rats and is hastened by removal of the ovaries following hypophysectomy (Ingram and Mandl, 1958; cf. also Lamond, 1959b). The inference of the latter observation is that the ovary continues to produce residual amounts of oestrogen in the absence of the pituitary.

The available information on oestrogen levels in the blood has been recently reviewed by Borth (1957; see also Emmens, 1959; Roy and Brown, 1960).

(b) Progestins

The urinary excretion of pregnanediol during the human menstrual cycle has been studied by Venning and Browne (1937), Venning (1955), and, more recently, by Klopper (1957). According to the last author, during menstruation and the follicular part of the cycle elimination is low and of the order of 1–2 mg/24 hours, and appears to be largely due to activity of the adrenal cortex. It increases just before ovulation—as assessed by the rise in basal body temperature—and afterwards reaches a maximum during the luteal phase when some 7 mg/day may be excreted by parous women. The level declines again shortly before the onset of bleeding. It is now clearly established that pregnanediol, like oestrogen, persists in the urine after ovariectomy and that in subjects with healthy adrenals its excretion is increased by corticotrophin (Klopper et al., 1957; Nabarro and Moxham, 1957). Since, moreover, progesterone and its metabolites are present in the adrenal venous blood of man and other mammals (e.g. Balfour et al., 1957, 1959), the secretion of these compounds by the adrenal glands can no longer be doubted (Short, 1960b).

Determination of the concentration of progesterone in the blood plasma is difficult owing to the great rapidity with which the substance is eliminated from the circulation so that its half-life is believed to be little more than 5 minutes (Pearlman, 1957; Short and Eton, 1959).

The existing assay methods, both biological and chemical (see Borth, 1957), are subject to considerable error and have yielded discrepant results (e.g. Emmens, 1959; Edgar *et al.*, 1959; Robinson, 1959). For this reason the very diverse findings reported in recent years on blood titres in non-pregnant monkeys (Hooker and Forbes, 1949; Bryans, 1951) and domestic animals (Edgar, 1953; Neher and Zarrow, 1954; Edgar and Ronaldson, 1958; Short and Moore, 1959) must be accepted with some caution. It seems clear, however, that in general blood levels of progesterone are remarkably low (*ca.* 1 μg/100 ml.) during the luteal phase of the cycle (e.g. in mares, Short, 1959) and not invariably higher during gestation (Short and Moore, 1959). The total amount of progesterone produced by the human corpus luteum during the second half of the cycle is believed to be of the order of 20 mg/day (Corner, 1943b; Zander *et al.*, 1958, 1959).

A progesterone-like substance occurs in the blood of both laying and non-laying hens (Nalbandov, 1958), and has also been identified in the ovaries of snakes (Bragdon *et al.*, 1954) and certain fish (see Dean and Chester Jones, 1959; and Chapter 5 and 7).

4. *Androgens*

It has been known for a long time that androgen can be extracted from the ovaries of the sow and that the atrophy of the comb of the hen induced by spaying can be restored by administration of male hormone, but not by either oestrogen or progesterone (Parkes, 1937, 1950). This, and the very recent identification of androstenedione and *epi*testosterone in the follicular fluid of the mare (Short, 1960a), clearly suggest that the ovaries in at least several mammalian species, and even in the immature female (Burrill and Greene, 1941), may normally produce androgens. That they do so also under abnormal or experimental circumstances, both in women and lower vertebrates, is now firmly established, and the available evidence on this subject is fully considered in Chapter 16 (see also Parkes, 1950; Ponse, 1954).

What remains to be shown is the identity and source of such 'paradoxically' produced androgens. Most workers, studying the androgenic activity of autoplastically transplanted ovaries of rodents, have stressed the marked development of luteinized theca interna and interstitial cells (e.g. Deanesly, 1938; Hernandez, 1943), but no such correlation was found by Hill (1941). There is also uncertainty about the precise nature of the compounds concerned, but it is thought that they are chemically different from, though physiologically identical with, the androgens of the testes (e.g. Hill and Strong, 1938, 1940; see Chapter 16).

Parkes (1950) has concluded that the androgenicity of the ovary, like that of the adrenal cortex, should be regarded as the exaggeration of a latent potentiality rather than as a new, separate endocrine activity. The experimental studies referred to, the probable androgen production of the hilus cells in the human ovary (see p. 318) and the occurrence of masculinizing ovarian tumours such as arrhenoblastomas (see Chapters 11 and 23) all appear to fit in with such a concept.

5. Corticosteroids

Proof that the ovary may secrete adrenal corticoids is slender. It seems to rest mainly on Hill's observation that in mice ovarian homografts can markedly prolong the survival of adrenalectomized males (see Chapters 16 and 21). In addition, it has been demonstrated that following bilateral adrenalectomy in ground squirrels adrenal cortex-like cells appear in the ovarian stroma and the ovary as a whole assumes adrenocortical functions (Groat, 1944). Similar suggestions have also been made in connection with certain adrenal-like tumours in the human ovary (e.g. Sauramo, 1954). Nodules of adrenocortical-like cells (Marchand's rests) are relatively frequent in the vicinity of the mesovarium and ovarian ligaments both in infants and adult women (Falls, 1955; Morris and Scully, 1958).

B. Physiological manifestations

1. The ovary and the control of sexual cycles

Under normal physiological conditions the hormonal activity of the ovary manifests itself by cyclically recurring structural changes in the accessory organs and in correlated phases of heat or 'oestrus' during which the female becomes receptive to the male. Such periodic changes constitute the sexual cycle, which may be either of the oestrous type characteristic of laboratory rodents or of the menstrual variety, as in women and higher primates, but is basically similar in all mammals (Heape, 1900).

In their detailed features the oestrous cycles exhibited by mammals show many variations (e.g. Asdell, 1946; Robson, 1947; Eckstein, 1949; Eckstein and Zuckerman, 1956a). In some they continue uninterruptedly throughout the year, but in others they are restricted to breeding seasons lasting from a few weeks to several months. Animals like the bitch and doe display only a single cycle during each sexual season and are therefore known as monoestrous, while others, such as rodents, experience a rapid succession of cycles and are referred to as polyoestrous. The length of the cycle, too, varies greatly among different mammals (from 4–5 days in rats and mice to a month or more in primates). In all of them, however, removal of the ovaries brings cyclic changes quickly to an end* or prevents their onset in the immature female. The ovary must, therefore, be considered as the essential or main (if not the only) source of both oestrogenic and luteal hormones in the non-pregnant animal, and the accessory reproductive tract as the principal target for their action.

The central event in the mammalian cycle is ovulation, and is usually the time at which copulation and fertilization take place. As previously mentioned, ovulation occurs spontaneously in most mammals, including primates, but depends in a minority, such as the ferret, rabbit, cat, mink and ground-squirrel, on coition or some other sexual stimulus causing an orgasm. Except for the earliest phases of follicular growth (see p. 313, and Chapter 7), all aspects of the ovarian cycle are controlled directly, and the associated endocrine functions of the ovary indirectly, by the follicle-stimulating and luteinizing hormones (FSH and LH) of the anterior pituitary. The ovary, in turn, by means of its own hormonal secretions, regulates the activity of the accessory sex tract and thus ultimately the sexual cycle. Furthermore, it is generally assumed that the gonadotrophic activity of the adenohypophysis is itself related by a feed-back mechanism to the concentration of ovarian hormones in the blood, in this way completing the circuit of mutual interdependence and coordination between the three sets of organs on which normal reproductive function in the female depends (see Chapter 7). There is evidence to suggest that not only the production but also the 'use' or 'consumption' of gonadotrophic hormones by the ovary is involved in this mechanism and that the maintenance of a correct ovarian-hypophysial relationship depends upon a balance between both production and use of gonadotrophin (e.g. Jungck et al., 1947; Bruzzone et al., 1952).

Recent studies summarized by Leathem (1958a, 1959) show that nutritional factors, no less than hormonal ones, affect the expression of ovarian function. Inanition or a low protein diet may cause atrophy of the ovaries and disrupt oestrous cycles (Guilbert and Goss, 1932; Selye and Collip, 1936; Mulinos et al., 1939; Stephens, 1941); the inhibition of both the cycle and reproduction as a whole can be reversed by refeeding or raising the ration of protein (Ball et al., 1947; Schultze, 1955). Again, the type and degree of the ovarian response to injected gonadotrophins is influenced by the amount of protein in the diet (Leathem, 1958a), while specific deficiency of amino acids may cause failure to release these hormones from the anterior pituitary.

* Incomplete vaginal cycles may, however, persist after ovariectomy (e.g. Mandl, 1951); they are probably due to oestrogens produced by the adrenal cortex (see p. 326).

2. *Interrelationships with other endocrine organs*

A full discussion of this subject is beyond the scope of this chapter, but some of the more important and better established facts concerning the ovary's interrelations with the thyroid and adrenal glands will be briefly referred to.

(a) *Thyro-ovarian relations*

The influence of thyroid secretions on gonadal activity and reproductive function in general is well known, but its experimental investigation has usually yielded variable or controversial findings, and the exact relationship between the thyroid and ovary remains far from clear (cf. Lederer, 1946; Maqsood, 1952).

Myxoedema in women is frequently associated with menstrual irregularities and relative infertility, which can be improved by thyroid medication (e.g. Means, 1948). Similarly, experimentally induced hypothyroidism in laboratory animals tends to disturb or inhibit both oestrous and menstrual cycles (e.g. Engle, 1944; Morris *et al.*, 1946; Krohn and White, 1950; cf. Maqsood, 1952)—probably by a direct effect upon the ovary. Thus, in some species such as the mouse, hypothyroidism interferes with normal development and onset of function of the reproductive organs, and may also cause ovarian degeneration in the mature female (Dalton *et al.*, 1945; Morris *et al.*, 1946); in poultry it lowers egg production and egg weight (cf. Maqsood, 1952). There are, however, marked species differences in response, and similar effects have been variously produced by both deficiency and excess of thyroid hormone (e.g. Ershoff, 1945; Maqsood, 1952).

Thyroidectomy or feeding with anti-thyroid drugs, while rarely abolishing reproductive capacity altogether, usually result in lowered fecundity and other adverse effects such as abortion and foetal resorption (e.g. Chu, 1944; Krohn and White, 1950; Leathem, 1959). Conversely, treatment of intact animals with thyroxine may lead to litters of greater than normal size (Peterson *et al.*, 1952).

Although it seems clear that the thyroid gland is closely connected with normal reproductive function, its influence probably involves a complex series of interactions. Thus it is not known whether any of the above-mentioned effects are mediated through the anterior pituitary, by an altered output of, or ovarian sensitivity to, gonadotrophins, or by a more generalized effect on tissue metabolism. Leathem's recent studies (1958b, 1959) on the connection between hypothyroidism and the formation of ovarian cysts in experimental animals represent a deliberate attempt to obtain more specific information about these complex and insufficiently understood interrelationships. His finding that following thiouracil treatment the response of the rat's ovary to gonadotrophin is altered so that luteinizing gonadotrophin becomes predominantly follicle-stimulating and induces cyst formation is an interesting and significant contribution.

(b) *Adrenocortical-ovarian relations*

The existence of close functional relationships between the adrenal cortex and ovary is firmly established and based on many clinical and experimental observations (cf. Parkes, 1945; Hartman and Brownell, 1949; Turner, 1955; Chester Jones, 1955).

The similarity in embryological origin between both glands and in the chemistry of their respective hormonal secretions has already been referred to (p. 320), as has the fact that each organ can to some extent substitute for the other. Thus the adrenals seem normally capable of secreting minimal amounts of both oestrogen and progestin (p. 326), and in certain strains of rodents may maintain the accessory reproductive organs following ovariectomy shortly after birth (Woolley *et al.*, 1939; Fekete *et al.*, 1941; Woolley and Little, 1945). In other mammals, however, and when carried out at later stages, spaying leads to adrenal atrophy, although the effect depends on the functional state of the ovaries at the time of their removal (Gompertz and Mandl, 1958). Conversely, transplanted ovaries may assume adrenocortical functions (see p. 328 and Chapter 16), while pseudopregnancy and injection of progesterone are known to increase the survival of adrenalectomized animals (see Hartman and Brownell, 1949).

The influence of the adrenals on reproductive processes is shown by several observations. After adrenalectomy or during chronic cortical deficiency oestrous and menstrual cycles are disturbed or abolished, but can be restored by corticosteroids and, in rats, even by sodium chloride alone (e.g. Kutz *et al.*, 1934). Again, in laboratory rodents as well as seasonally breeding species such as the mole and ground-squirrel, the size of the adrenals varies during the cycle, generally increasing at oestrus or ovulation (cf. Andersen and Kennedy, 1932; Bourne and Zuckerman, 1941a). In rats this is due to enlargement of the cortex, itself brought about by hypertrophy of the cells in the zona fasciculata (Bourne and Zuckerman, 1941b). It has also been shown that artificial 'threshold-cycles' may continue in spayed rats and monkeys injected with constant low doses of oestrogen (Zuckerman, 1941; Bourne and Zuckerman, 1941b). This suggests that the occurrence of such cycles depends on the presence of the adrenals, even though the exact nature of their influence remains to be elucidated.

3. *The effect of ovariectomy*

After spaying the prepubertal female remains sexually immature, while in the adult one oestrous or menstrual cycles cease,* the secondary sex characters regress and the animal displays either permanent anoestrus or, in the case of a woman, develops a specific menopausal syndrome (see Chapter 10).

In most mammals (and presumably other vertebrates) with paired ovaries, unilateral ovariectomy causes none of these effects. The surviving gonad hypertrophies and is able to compensate, both hormonally and in number of ovulations, for the loss of the other, but in such conditions the single ovary uses up its supply of oocytes more quickly than would be the case in the intact animal (Hunter, 1787; Mandl and Zuckerman, 1951a; Zuckerman, 1951a; Jones, 1957; Jones and Krohn, 1960; see also Chapter 1).

In the great majority of birds, however, only the left ovary is functional, and its removal may lead to the differentiation of either a testis, an ovary or an intermediate structure from the originally rudimentary, right gonad (cf. Nalbandov, 1958; also Chapters 1 and 2B).

(a) *Changes in the accessory organs*†

The uterus, uterine (Fallopian) tubes, vagina and, to a lesser extent, mammary glands shrink rapidly in size after spaying. For instance, in the rabbit the uterus loses half its weight in a few weeks and becomes pale, flabby and thin. In a rat or mouse the vaginal epithelium is reduced to a mere two or three layers of low cuboidal cells, compared with ten to twelve partly cornified layers in the intact female and the vaginal smear contains only a few leucocytes and epithelial, but no more cornified cells. In mature primates, after as a rule a single post-operative bleeding, all menstrual cycles come to an end and with them the cyclical changes—reddening or swelling—in the so-called 'sexual skin' (see below, p. 336). In lower mammals sex drive and mating behaviour are lost, but this is much less pronounced in primates, including women. This complex subject is fully discussed in Chapter 20.

(b) *Additional effects*

Another associated effect is the appearance of increased amounts of FSH in the blood and urine, owing to the removal of the inhibition normally exerted by the ovaries upon the anterior pituitary. As a

---

* Very rarely, oestrus may reappear following bilateral ovariectomy in rodents, and is thought to be due to regeneration of ovarian tissue (e.g. Parkes *et al.*, 1927; Parkes, 1929; see also p. 329).

† These changes and their reversal by suitable treatment with ovarian hormones have been frequently described in the literature (e.g. Allen, 1939; Robson, 1947; Pincus and Thimann, 1950, 1955; Turner, 1955) and only a few, selected aspects will be considered here.

result, the release of FSH rises and that of LH ceases, while the basophil cells in the anterior lobe, which are thought to be responsible for the elaboration of gonadotrophins, tend to increase in number and to become vacuolated 'castration cells' (see Chapter 7). Conversely, a 'chemical hypophysectomy', manifesting itself by inhibition of growth and gonadal regression, can be brought about experimentally by means of continued treatment with high doses of oestrogen (e.g. Burrows, 1949; Nalbandov, 1958; see also Chapter 7).

Several examples of the physiological interrelations between the ovary and other endocrine or systemic organs were referred to above (pp. 330 to 331); another is the hypertrophy of the thymus which occurs almost invariably after spaying. Hypophysectomy induces regression and cessation of cyclical activity in the reproductive tract comparable to, though less pronounced than those caused by removal of the ovaries (see pp. 326 and 332).

Prepubertal ovariectomy in mammals prevents the appearance of many secondary sex characteristics, among them, in women, feminine contours, typical widening of the pelvis and development of breasts and sexual hair (see sect. IV, B); it also tends to delay closure of the epiphyseal cartilages.

A very different type of influence is indicated by the observation that an exceptionally early menopause predisposes to myocardial infarction (e.g. Spitzer *et al.*, 1957). It implies that some factor associated with the menstrual cycle protects women against coronary thrombosis.

C. The biological effects of ovarian hormones

The morphological and histological changes which take place in the accessory sex organs of spayed females treated with oestrogen alone and in combination with progestin have been fully described (cf. Allen, 1939; Burrows, 1949; Turner, 1955; Emmens, 1959) and will only be selectively and summarily considered below.* Some of them, such as the response of the endometrium to oestrogen, are identical with those observed during the corresponding (follicular) phase of the oestrous or menstrual cycle in intact females. Others, however, are not exact replicas of the physiological condition, probably because during the normal cycle secretion and physiological effects of both oestrogen and progesterone overlap, so that neither ever acts in isolation.

1. *Effects of oestrogen*

Generally speaking, oestrogens appear to act as growth hormones capable of specifically stimulating tissues derived from the Müllerian

---

*The response of females with intact gonads to ovarian hormones will not be separately dealt with; for a summary see Pincus (1950).

ducts and urogenital sinus (cf. Chapter 15 and Zuckerman, 1940). In addition, they promote the growth of the nipples and duct system of the mammary glands (e.g. Folley, 1955, 1956; Jacobsohn, 1958; Tindal and McNaught, 1958) and that of other genital and extra-genital tissues (see below); they also induce characteristic responses in behaviour (Chapter 20).

(a) *Vagina*

In the vagina of the spayed or immature female oestrogens cause an intense wave of mitosis and consequent proliferation of the mucosa with cornification and desquamation of the superficial layers. A vaginal smear or 'lavage' taken from a mouse or rat at this stage, the 'oestrus' phase of the cycle, consists entirely of cornified squamous epithelial cells, and this is the basis of the classical Allen-Doisy method for the bioassay of the oestrogenic hormone (cf. Emmens, 1950, 1955). If oestrogen treatment is stopped, the vascular and proliferative changes cease and the vagina becomes invaded by leucocytes which penetrate into the lumen and displace the cornified elements in the vaginal smear.

Vaginal cornification in the spayed rodent is a highly sensitive and specific response to oestrogen and can be evoked by as little as $0·0003$ μg of oestradiol if applied intravaginally (cf. Emmens, 1941, 1950, 1959). It has also been obtained on slices of mouse vagina maintained in tissue culture (Hardy *et al.*, 1953), and so clearly does not depend on an intact blood supply or other hormones. A positive test is, however, not equivalent to psychological oestrus or the readiness to mate (Emmens, 1959). Again, oestrogens promote deposition of glycogen and a characteristic lowering in the pH of the vagina. Recently, two other very sensitive assay methods, based on the ability of oestrogens to increase the number of mitoses and thickness of the vaginal epithelium and to reduce triphenyltetrazolium to formazan, have been described by Martin and Claringbold (1960) and Martin (1960).

(b) *Uterus*

In the uterus oestrogen induces three basic changes: an initial hyperaemia and oedema, followed by increased cell proliferation and hypertrophy of the endometrium. The relative contribution of these different manifestations, and hence the general appearance of the oestrogen-stimulated organ, varies with the species. In rodents the uterus becomes hyperaemic and thin-walled as the result of accumulation of water within the lumen (e.g. Williams, 1948). In other mammals there is no such distension of the uterine lumen, but the endometrium itself becomes oedematous. In primates, there is also much more intense development of the glandular elements. In addition, the uterine muscle hypertrophies under the influence of oestrogen and its motility, as well as reactivity to the action of posterior pituitary extract, increases.

The collection of free fluid in the lumen is preceded by a marked rise in the weight, water and glycogen content of the uterus of the rat (Astwood, 1939; Boettiger, 1946), changes which equal those in the endometrium of rhesus monkeys (van Dyke and Ch'en, 1936). In this and other primates, however, deposition of glycogen seems to depend on progesterone rather than oestrogen.

(c) *Mammary glands*

The effects of oestrogens and other hormones on the mammary glands have been repeatedly described by Folley and his associates (e.g. Folley, 1955, 1956; cf. also Lyons *et al.*, 1955).

(d) *Possible intra-ovarian effects*

Oestrogens, in addition to their main actions on the accessory sex organs and the body in general, may also have some influence on the ovary itself. Their ability to stimulate hyperplasia of the granulosa cells and follicular growth in hypophysectomized rodents was first demonstrated some 20 years ago (Pencharz, 1940; Williams, 1940) and has been repeatedly confirmed since (see Falck, 1959; also Chapter 7).

The effect is also observed after hyster- and adrenalectomy, but is greatly enhanced when oestrogenic and gonadotrophic stimulation are combined (Pencharz, 1940; Simpson *et al.*, 1941; Williams, 1944, 1945). In view of these findings and the close proximity of the granulosa cells to the theca interna, it has been suggested that oestrogen released by the theca cells may normally exert a direct or local effect on the granulosa (e.g. Hisaw, 1947). Similarily, it has been shown that oestrogens can maintain the structural and secretory integrity of the corpora lutea in the hypophysectomized female (for instance the rabbit: Robson, 1937, 1947; Hammond and Robson, 1951). They may thus also be concerned in the normal function of the corpus luteum.

(e) *Hormonal control of menstrual cycles*

The uterus of spayed primates responds to administration of oestrogen with the histological and biochemical changes characteristic of the first, proliferative phase of the cycle, and with secretory activity when progesterone is subsequently added. Cessation of an adequate oestrogenic or progestational stimulus will lead to disintegration of the endometrium and, after an appropriate interval, to macroscopic 'withdrawal' bleeding (Allen, 1927; Zuckerman, 1937; cf. also Corner, 1943b; Zuckerman, 1949, 1951b).

These two firmly established facts provide at once an explanation for the hormonal control of and a way of artificially reproducing the primate menstrual cycle. They also account for instances of menstruation occurring from an 'interval' type of endometrium in anovulatory cycles (see sect. IV).

According to this concept, the basic hormonal mechanism is a wave of oestrogenic stimulation which lasts throughout the first half of the cycle and then declines. If ovulation fails to occur the gradually weakening oestrogenic stimulus becomes incapable of maintaining the endometrium in a turgid, hydrated state and eventually macroscopic breakdown of the proliferative type of mucosa takes place when the stimulus is reduced to a sub-threshold level. Should ovulation occur, a progestational stimulus becomes superimposed upon the continuing oestrogenic one, and prevents withdrawal bleeding until it, too, is reduced to a critical level and ultimate breakdown and bleeding take place—from a progestational endometrium.

This scheme and some elaborations, including the associated one of Markee's hypothesis about the mechanism of menstruation itself (see p. 338), have been fully described and discussed by Zuckerman (1949, 1951b) and Eckstein and Zuckerman (1956b) and reference is made to their accounts. It should be added that although they act far more efficiently in combination with oestrogen, both progesterone and androgens alone can bring about withdrawal bleeding in spayed monkeys. To do so, they must, however, be administered in higher doses and for longer periods than oestrogens (Eckstein, 1950).

(f) *Sexual skin*

Among the actions of oestrogens on other parts of the reproductive tract only the response of the specialized circumgenital tissues constituting the sexual skin of certain primates will be referred to.

This region undergoes an elaborate maturation process during puberty (e.g. Zuckerman *et al.*, 1938; Eckstein, 1948). The response of the fully developed sexual skin at the end of the follicular phase in mature cyclic females is characterized by either hyperaemia without swelling (e.g. in rhesus monkeys) or by most conspicuous turgescence unaccompanied by reddening (as in pig-tailed macaques, baboons or chimpanzees). Following its mid-cycle peak of development the sexual skin regresses and returns to its previous quiescent state which continues until the onset of menstrual bleeding when it begins to swell again.

Corresponding changes in the sexual skin of these animals are brought about, after spaying, by oestrogenic hormone and thus provide a sensitive physiological indicator of its activity, similar to the vaginal cycle. They consist, in the main, of marked hypertrophy of the connective tissue cells and accumulation of a highly viscous fluid containing water and mucopolysaccharides (Aykroyd and Zuckerman, 1938; see Zuckerman, 1955). In certain types of monkey the amount of water that can be retained in this way in the sexual skin may amount to as much as a fifth of the total body weight. The normal alternation of swelling and subsidence in intact females is correlated both with the phases of the ovarian and menstrual cycles and with the daily water balance, the amount of water eliminated being much greater in the second half of the cycle than in the first (Krohn and Zuckerman, 1937). Prolonged administration of oestrogen may cause the oedema to spread from the region of the sexual skin over much of the body surface as far as the head, both in females and males (see Zuckerman *et al.*, 1938).

It appears likely that factors other than hormones may be involved in some of the biological reactions in which oestrogens take part. This is suggested by the reported inhibition of the oestrogen response of the chicken's oviduct (Hertz, 1945) and of the primate sexual skin (see above; Hertz, 1948) by deficiency in folic acid or treatment with folic acid antagonist, and by the occurrence of vaginal cornification as the result of deprivation of vitamin A or mechanical irritation of the vagina (e.g. Wade and Doisy, 1935; cf. Eckstein and Zuckerman, 1956b).

(g) *Metabolic manifestations of oestrogens and effects on extragenital tissues*

The changes induced by oestrogenic stimulation in the sexual skin and in the rodent uterus are examples of the general salt and water-retaining effect oestrogens appear to have on all the tissues of the body. Several reported facts are consistent with this concept. Among them are the clinical observation of generalized oedema and a rise in body weight during the human 'premenstrual syndrome'; the retention of sodium and chloride at mid-cycle in women (Eckstein *et al.*, 1941; cf. Fluhmann, 1956); the ability of oestrogens to cause retention of water, salt and nitrogen in the male dog (Thorn and Harrop, 1937; Thorn and Engel, 1938); and the reported histochemical alterations in the uterus of primates (van Dyke and Ch'en, 1936, 1940) and rats (Talbot *et al.*, 1940) during oestrogenic stimulation. Further proof was obtained by Zuckerman *et al.* (1950) who showed that a single injection of oestradiol-17β causes a diphasic retention of water in practically all tissues of young female rats, including the skin, muscle and brain. The earliest and most marked shift, amounting to an increase in water content of 5–6 per cent, was observed in the uterus, being more

2B

variable in timing and less pronounced in other tissues, as well as after stimulation with progesterone.

Another important general effect of oestrogen is to promote hyperaemia throughout the body, but especially in the reproductive tract and the nasal, buccal and gingival mucosae, exerted through alterations in the capillary bed. Vasodilatation is, as mentioned, one of the first changes induced in the endometrium of the rat by an injection of oestrogen (Williams, 1948). It is equally displayed by the uterus of the intact guinea pig (Markee, 1929) and by the sex skin and endometrium of rhesus monkeys.

This phenomenon is the basis of the concept of the mechanism of primate menstruation associated with the name of Markee (1940, 1950). It and its implications on the mechanism of menstrual bleeding have been repeatedly reviewed (e.g. Zuckerman, 1949, 1951b; Eckstein and Zuckerman, 1956b; Fluhmann, 1956).

Oestrogens, moreover, increase pigmentation, for instance of the areolae, and appear to raise the anti-bacterial activity of the uterus, while progesterone and a state of pseudopregnancy tend to reduce it (e.g. Rowson et al., 1953; Broome et al., 1959; see also Nalbandov, 1958).

In addition to these and their more specific and localized actions, oestrogens exert certain general metabolic effects. Thus, according to Hagerman and Villee (1959), the metabolic rate of specific target organs is raised, leading to an increase in tissue (protein) synthesis. In hens the blood level of calcium and phosphorus is greatly raised at the time of laying and the same effect is obtained by injection of oestrogen. The additional mineral is needed for eggshell formation, and is accompanied by the deposition of medullary bone (Pfeiffer and Gardner, 1938; Gardner and Pfeiffer, 1939); this has been confirmed by the demonstration that oestrogen accelerates incorporation of radiophosphorus into pigeon bones (Govaerts and Dallemagne, 1948). Of mammals, only rodents show a similar response (cf. Irving, 1957). In other mammalian species, including man, oestrogens are generally thought to inhibit bone growth and to intensify ossification, thereby accelerating closure of epiphyses. In this way dwarfism may be produced in experimental animals (e.g. Krohn, 1948). Severe anaemia following intensive treatment with oestrogens has been observed in dogs (Tyslowitz and Dingemanse, 1941).

The effects of ovarian hormones in domestic animals and lower vertebrates are reviewed by Cole and Cupps (1959) and Dodd (1955). Among the most important extragenital actions of oestrogen in birds is the control of plumage in the female (Parkes and Emmens, 1944; Nalbandov, 1958; see also Chapter 17).

2. *Effects of progestin*

Progesterone is primarily a progestational or pregnancy hormone, that is to say, it converts the proliferative into a secretory type of endometrium which is essential for the reception and early care of the fertilized ovum (Corner and Allen, 1928). It has therefore been referred to as the 'hormone of the mother' to distinguish it from oestrogen, the 'hormone of the female' (Corner, 1943b). Although recent experimental work has thrown some doubt on this concept (e.g. Mayer, 1959), it remains probably true that under natural conditions progesterone, in combination with oestrogen, is indispensable for early survival and implantation of the mammalian blastocyst.

In the non-pregnant female the most important effects of progesterone are exerted on the uterus in which it induces a characteristic decidual reaction affecting both the endometrial glands and stromal cells and, after suitable stimulation in rodents and primates, formation of a nodule of deciduomatous stromal cells or 'deciduoma' (Loeb, 1907). The uterus as a whole enlarges under the influence of luteal hormone, and its spontaneous motility, as well as response to oxytocin from the posterior pituitary, is reduced or abolished in several species by treatment with progesterone (e.g. Robson, 1947; Knaus, 1950).

Progestins, both natural and synthetic, also suppress ovulation and follicular development (cf. Robson, 1947; Klein, 1954; Emmens, 1959). In all probability the effect, which is manifest both in the non-pregnant and pregnant female, is an indirect one, and brought about by depressing the output of gonadotrophin of the anterior pituitary. This, too, is thought to be the mode of action of 19-norsteroids and similar progestational compounds which are being increasingly explored as oral contraceptives.

In the vagina of rodents mucification is produced and in the mammary gland development of the alveolar system. For a full description of all these genital and extra-genital effects of progesterone, such as the raising of basal body temperature and electrolyte and water retention, reference is made to the accounts of Asdell (1928), Hisaw (1939), Pearlman (1948), Klein (1954), Turner (1955), and Emmens (1959).

It must be emphasized that the biological actions of progesterone are greatly, and during the normal cycle inevitably, influenced by the presence of oestrogen. As a rule the interaction between both hormones is one of synergism (for instance, on the mammary apparatus or endometrium (e.g. Hisaw, 1950) and during the menstrual cycle, see p. 336), but may be antagonistic (e.g. on the vagina: Courrier, 1950; or on arborization of the cervical mucus: Zondek and Rozin, 1954).

The action of ovarian hormones on behaviour and, in particular, psychic oestrus or 'heat' is highly complex, and is fully reviewed in Chapter 20. In the production of psychic oestrus co-operation between oestrogens and progesterone is probably usual, but, as Emmens (1959) has pointed out, the exact relationship of both hormones varies between different species. Thus induction of sexual receptivity in rodents like the rat and guinea pig requires an oestrogenic stimulus followed by progesterone, but the reverse sequence in the case of the ewe. In the latter endogenous oestrogen production is apparently insufficient to cause complete psychic and physiological oestrus except after previous conditioning with progesterone (Robinson, 1955, 1959).

IV. Ovarian function in relation to age

A. Before the onset of puberty

Before the onset of puberty the ovary is usually a small, inert-looking ('dormant') organ and physiologically sterile, but it is neither insensitive to hormonal stimulation nor altogether devoid of endocrine activities.

1. *Sensitivity to hormonal stimuli*

That the embryonic ovary can be affected by its hormonal environment is indicated by the abnormal condition of the gonads of the female freemartin in heterosexual twin pregnancy of cattle. This is usually attributed to the action of hormones elaborated by the male co-twin and conveyed through the conjoined placental vessels (Lillie, 1916, 1917; see also Chapters 13 and 14B). Again, the foetal ovary in various mammals undergoes marked hypertrophy in the uterus, later followed by involution and regression, in this way resembling the embryologically closely related adrenal cortex and the uterus. Thus the gonads of the foetal horse, seal and African elephant during advanced gestation show marked hypertrophy of the interstitial cells and those of the foal may approach or exceed the maternal ovaries in bulk (Cole *et al.*, 1933; Amoroso *et al.*, 1951; cf. Amoroso, 1955, and Chapter 9). More recently Kellas *et al.* (1958) have described advanced follicular development and the presence of corpus luteum-like structures in the ovaries of the giraffe during late gestation and shortly after birth. They inferred from the condition of the gonads and that of the accessory organs that in this species the foetal ovaries exercise both hormonal and gametogenetic functions. The occasional presence of ripe Graafian follicles and luteinization in the ovaries of the human newborn has also been reported. Similarly, multiovular follicles and multinuclear oocytes have been described in near-term human ovaries and their subsequent regression has been linked with the disappearance of maternal gonadotrophins after birth (Bacsich, 1949, 1951).

The hypertrophy of the interstitial elements in the gonads of the foetal horse has been ascribed to the effects of maternal oestrogens, a conclusion borne out by the disintegration of these elements which occurs shortly before birth and coincides with a reduced output of oestrogen from the mother (Amoroso and Rowlands, 1951); no such correlation has yet been established in the case of the other species in which the foetal gonads display similar changes. The fact that foetal ovaries contain oestrogen has been demonstrated in cattle by Zephiroff (cf. Burrows, 1949).

Following this stage, the ovaries pass through a phase of relative insensitivity to hormones, the length of which varies with the species (e.g. Price and Ortiz, 1944; Ortiz, 1947; Marden, 1951; Picon, 1956), but which invariably ends some time before puberty itself. It seems that the interstitial tissue responds earlier than the follicular elements which develop gradually and, it is thought, autonomously, to the point at which antra appear in the follicles. Progress beyond this stage depends on the ability of the anterior pituitary to release adequate amounts of gonadotrophin and that of the ovary to respond by secreting sufficient oestrogen to induce the first cycle and the other manifestations of puberty.

2. Hormonal activities

The part which secretions of the foetal ovaries play during intra-uterine development is still far from clear, and is considered in detail in Chapter 14A.

It is generally accepted that the development of the indifferent (ambisexual) gonad into either a testis or ovary depends upon its chromosome constitution, but that sex differentiation of the accessory reproductive organs is influenced by gonadal secretions. In mammals the influence of the foetal ovarian secretions appears to be relatively slight and to be confined to effects on the accessory reproductive and external genital organs. The basic sexual type being female, absence of the ovary—as from experimental removal or naturally-occurring agenesis—does not interfere with development along essentially female lines. On the other hand, it has been shown that the uterus and vagina do not develop fully in rats and rabbits except in the presence of oestrogen (Raynaud, 1951; Jost, 1951, 1953, 1955, 1960), and Zuckerman (1955) concludes that "oestrogen, or some analogous ovarian secretion plays a part in the differentiation of the definitive reproductive tract of the female". Whether the hormonal principles involved are

chemically identical with those in the mature organism and whether
they are derived from the foetal gonad or are wholly of maternal or
placental origin remains to be established (cf. also Chapters 14 A and B).
The vicarious menstruation and mammary hypertrophy occasionally
observed in the human newborn, like the 'crise génitale' of lower
mammals (see Courrier, 1945), are probably induced by maternal
oestrogen or gonadotrophin, since they cease after birth (cf. Fluhmann,
1956).

There is little evidence that following their neonatal involution (see
above), the ovaries are hormonally active before the onset of puberty.
In a strain of rats experiencing puberty at an age between 50 and 60
days, some secretion of oestrogen has been demonstrated as early as
the second postnatal week (Price, 1947).

B. The attainment of reproductive maturity
1. *Puberty*

The structural and physiological changes which take place in the
ovaries at puberty are well known, but the factors ultimately responsible for bringing them about still defy description (cf. Robson, 1947;
Harris and Jacobsohn, 1952; Harris, 1955; Krohn, 1957; Wilkins,
1957). There can be no doubt that both the release of the gonadotrophic principles of the anterior pituitary and ovarian reactivity are
involved, but their relative importance and interaction has neither
been determined nor the intervention of additional factors excluded.

The event which both characterizes and proximally determines
puberty is the maturation of follicles in the ovary. As ripe Graafian
follicles appear in the gonads, the concentration of ovarian hormones in
the body fluids begins to approach adult levels and eventually (e.g. in
the human species) to become cyclic. The female experiences her first
oestrous or menstrual cycle (the 'menarche'), and at the same time undergoes the series of external changes associated with sexual maturation.

These have been frequently described, more recently by Tanner (1955)
and Wilkins (1957), and appear to be largely or wholly induced by
oestrogen. Under its influence the characteristic body contours of
the human female take shape, and the external genitalia as well as
mammary glands attain their adult size and conformation. Oestrogens
are also thought to be responsible, though not entirely, for the growth
of axillary hair and the feminine distribution of pubic hair. Within the
reproductive tract the endometrium becomes differentiated into a
basal and a superficial ('functionalis') layer which undergoes proliferative changes, and the cervical glands begin to secrete clear, alkaline
mucus. Glycogen is deposited in the vaginal epithelium and its superficial parts become cornified and desquamate.

It must be understood that the terms 'puberty' and 'adolescence' cannot be equated with the attainment of full reproductive capacity. Usually, a stage of variable length intervenes during which the reproductive processes are being gradually perfected and synchronized. This has been called the period of 'adolescent sterility' (Hartman, 1931, 1932; Montague, 1939, 1946; Fluhmann, 1956) which is characterized by infrequent ovulations, irregular cycles, and, in the event of conception, a relatively high incidence of abortion, difficulties during parturition and lactation, as well as small litters (e.g. Asdell *et al.*, 1941). In women and other primates this phase may last for several years; it appears to be equally present, though of shorter duration, in lower mammals.

2. *Sexual precocity*

The time at which puberty is established varies greatly between different species. It has been observed in a 21-day-old hamster and usually occurs in rodents between 1 and 2 months. In rhesus monkeys it takes place around the end of the 3rd year, and in women of the Northern hemisphere generally between 12 and 13 years (about three-quarters of subjects coming within the range of 10–15 years). It may, however, appear very much earlier in girls in whom no medical or endocrine abnormality is present. This represents the so-called idiopathic or 'constitutional' type of precocity described by Novak (1944). In it all phases of the physiological maturation process (for instance, appearance of secondary sexual characters, excretion of hormones in adult concentrations (e.g. Hain, 1947), menarche and ovulation) are reproduced in their normal sequence but at an exceptionally early age, so that menstrual cycles may be established at between 1 and 2 years and even conception can occur (e.g. Escomel, 1939). It is believed that these subjects may live perfectly normal lives of average length, but nothing appears to be known about the onset of the menopause in them (Fluhmann, 1956). In other instances unduly early establishment of hormonal functions may be unaccompanied by precocious follicular development and ovulation (cf. Wilkins, 1957).

3. *Reproductive maturity*

When the phase of adolescent sterility ends, full sexual maturity and reproductive capacity are established.

The number of ovulations in each cycle and litter size reach and remain at a maximum (e.g. McDowell and Lord, 1925; Perry, 1954; cf. Eckstein, 1955) and intervals between births tend to become constant. Whether the higher reproductive performance is brought about by the release of more gonadotrophin from the anterior pituitary or increased numbers of ovulations, or, again, by improved intrauterine conditions, is largely unknown.

It is now firmly established that even during full maturity cycles may occur which are of the anovular type (e.g. in women and monkeys: Corner, 1923, 1927; Hartman, 1932, 1938; cf. Eckstein and Zuckerman, 1956a). In such cases the ovary contains no or only atretic corpora lutea in addition to follicles, and menstruation takes place from a disintegrating endometrium in the 'interval' phase of development. In mature women anovulatory cycles are particularly frequent during the puerperium (Sharman, 1950). Their incidence in adult women of normal fertility is incompletely known, but is probably of the order of less than 10 per cent (cf. Fluhmann, 1956).

4. *Cessation of reproductive functions*

The length of reproductive life varies greatly in different species of mammals, from 8–9 months in hamsters (Peczenik, 1942) to over 30 years in women and probably not much less in elephants (e.g. Perry, 1953); in lower vertebrates it may comprise only a single breeding season, as in salmon (cf. Nelsen, 1953). So far as the mammalian ovary is concerned, its outstanding feature is the continuous depletion of the number of oocytes, only slightly and temporarily checked by the intervention of pregnancy. It is of interest that marked differences in the rate of atresia of oocytes between species and even between different strains of the same species (e.g. mice), and hence in reproductive potential, have been demonstrated (e.g. Wolfe and Wright, 1943; Fekete, 1953; Jones, 1957). When all oocytes have degenerated or disappeared, and in some species before that stage, reproductive life comes to an end, although this does not necessarily mean the cessation of the ovary's hormonal activities. This and the clinical aspects associated with the human menopause are discussed in Chapter 10.

REFERENCES

Allen, E. (1922). The oestrous cycle in the mouse. *Amer. J. Anat.* **30**, 297–371
Allen, E. (1927). The menstrual cycle in the monkey, *Macacus rhesus*: observations on normal animals, the effect of removal of the ovaries and the effects of injections of ovarian and placental extracts into spayed animals. *Contr. Embryol. Carneg. Instn.* **19**, 1–44.
Allen, E. (1939). "Sex and Internal Secretions." Baillière, Tindall & Cox, London.
Allen, E. and Doisy, E. A. (1923). An ovarian hormone; a preliminary report on its localization, extraction and partial purification, and action in test animals. *J. Amer. med. Ass.* **81**, 819–821.

Allen, W. M. and Corner, G. W. (1929). Physiology of the corpus luteum. III. Normal growth and implantation of embryos after very early ablation of the ovaries under the influence of extracts of the corpus luteum. *Amer. J. Physiol.* **88**, 340–346.

Amoroso, E. C. (1955). Endocrinology of pregnancy. *Brit. med. Bull.* **11**, 117–125.

Amoroso, E. C. and Rowlands, I. W. (1951). Hormonal effects in the pregnant mare and foetal foal. *J. Endocrin.* **7**, 1.

Amoroso, E. C., Harrison, R. J., Matthews, L. H. and Rowlands, I. W. (1951). Reproductive organs of near-term and new-born seals. *Nature, Lond.* **168**, 771–772.

Andersen, D. H. and Kennedy, H. S. (1932). Studies on the physiology of reproduction. IV. Changes in the adrenal gland of the female rat associated with the oestrous cycle. *J. Physiol.* **76**, 247–260.

Asdell, S. A. (1928). The growth and function of the corpus luteum. *Physiol. Rev.* **8**, 313–345.

Asdell, S. A. (1946). "Patterns of Mammalian Reproduction." Comstock, New York.

Asdell, S. A. and Hammond, J. (1933). The effects of prolonging the life of the corpus luteum in the rabbit by hysterectomy. *Amer. J. Physiol.* **103**, 600–605.

Asdell, S. A., Bogart, R. and Sperling, G. (1941). The influence of age and rate of breeding upon the ability of the female rat to reproduce and raise young. *Mem. Cornell agric. Exp. Sta.* No. 238, pp. 3–26.

Astwood, E. B. (1939). Changes in the weight and water content of the uterus of the normal adult rat. *Amer. J. Physiol.* **126**, 162–170.

Austin, C. R. and Bishop, M. W. H. (1957). Fertilization in mammals. *Biol. Rev.* **32**, 296–349.

Aykroyd, O. E. and Zuckerman, S. (1938). Factors in sexual skin oedema. *J. Physiol.* **94**, 13–25.

Bacsich, P. (1949). Multinuclear ova and multiovular follicles in the young human ovary and their probable endocrinological significance. *J. Endocrin.* **6**, i-ii.

Bacsich, P. (1951). Some observations on near-term human foetal ovaries. *J. Endocrin.* **7**, xiv-xvi.

Balfour, W. E., Comline, R. S. and Short, R. V. (1957). Secretion of progesterone by the adrenal gland. *Nature, Lond.* **180**, 1480–1481.

Balfour, W. E., Comline, R. S. and Short, R. V. (1959). Changes in the secretion of 20α-hydroxy-pregn-4-en-3-one by the adrenal gland of young calves. *Nature, Lond.* **183**, 467–468.

Ball, Z. B., Barnes, R. A. and Visscher, M. B. (1947). The effects of dietary caloric restriction on maturity and senescence, with particular reference to fertility and longevity. *Amer. J. Physiol.* **150**, 511–519.

Beall, D. and Reichstein, T. (1938). Isolation of progesterone and allo-pregnanolone from the adrenal. *Nature, Lond.* **142**, 479.

Berger, L. (1922). Sur l'existence de glandes sympathicotropes dans l'ovaire et le testicule humains; leurs rapports avec la glande interstitielle du testicule. *C.R. Acad. Sci., Paris,* **175**, 907–909.

Berger, L. (1942). Tumeur des cellules sympathicotropes de l'ovaire avec virilisation. *Rev. canad. Biol.* **1**, 539–566.

Block, E. (1962). Quantitative morphological investigations of the follicular system in women. *Acta anat.* **14**, 108–123.

Block, E. (1953). A quantitative morphological investigation of the follicular system in newborn female infants. *Acta anat.* **17,** 201–206.

Boettiger, E. G. (1946). Changes in the glycogen and water content of the rat uterus. *J. cell. comp. Physiol.* **27,** 9–14.

Boling, J. L. and Blandau, R. J. (1939). The estrogen-progesterone induction of mating responses in the spayed female rat. *Endocrinology,* **25,** 359–364.

Borth, R. (1957). Steroids in human blood. *Vitam. & Hormon.* **15,** 259–290.

Bourne, G. and Zuckerman, S. (1941a). The influence of the adrenals on cyclical changes in the accessory reproductive organs of female rats. *J. Endocrin.* **2,** 268–282.

Bourne, G. and Zuckerman, S. (1941b). Changes in the adrenals in relation to the normal and artificial threshold oestrous cycle in the rat. *J. Endocrin.* **2,** 283–310.

Bradbury, J. T., Brown, W. E. and Gray, L. A. (1950). Maintenance of the corpus luteum and physiologic actions of progesterone. *Recent Progr. Hormone Res.* **5,** 151–194.

Bragdon, D. E., Lazo-Wasem, E. A., Zarrow, M. X. and Hisaw, F. L. (1954). Progesterone-like activity in the plasma of ovoviviparous snakes. *Proc. Soc. exp. Biol., N.Y.* **86,** 477–480.

Brambell, F. W. R. (1956). Ovarian changes. *In* "Marshall's Physiology of Reproduction" (A. S. Parkes, ed.), vol. I, part 1, 3rd ed., chap. 5. Longmans, Green, London.

Brambell, F. W. R. and Parkes, A. S. (1927). Changes in the ovary of the mouse following exposure to X-rays. 3. Irradiation of the non-parous adult. *Proc. roy. Soc. B.* **101,** 316–328.

Broome, A. W. J., Lamming, G. E. and Woodbine, M. (1959). Studies on the relationship between ovarian hormones and uterine infection. I. The effect of ovarian hormones on the bactericidal activity of blood plasma. *J. Endocrin.* **18,** 209–219.

Brown, J. B. (1955a). Urinary excretion of oestrogens during the menstrual cycle. *Lancet,* **1,** 320–323.

Brown, J. B. (1955b). A chemical method for the determination of oestriol, oestrone and oestradiol in human urine. *Biochem. J.* **60,** 185–193.

Brown, J. B. (1956). Urinary excretion of oestrogens during pregnancy, lactation and the re-establishment of menstruation. *Lancet,* **1,** 704–707.

Brown, J. B. (1957). The relationship between urinary oestrogens and oestrogens produced in the body. *J. Endocrin.* **16,** 202–212.

Brown, J. B. (1959). Estrogen excretion in normal and abnormal menstrual cycles. *In* "Recent Progress in the Endocrinology of Reproduction" (C. W. Lloyd, ed.), pp. 53–65. Academic Press, New York.

Brown, J. B., Klopper, A. and Loraine, J. A. (1958). The urinary excretion of oestrogens, pregnanediol and gonadotrophins during the menstrual cycle. *J. Endocrin.* **17,** 401–410.

Brown, J. B., Falconer, C. W. A. and Strong, J. A. (1959). Urinary oestrogens of adrenal origin in women with breast cancer. *J. Endocrin.* **19,** 52–63.

Bruzzone, S., Lipschutz, A. and Niedmann, L. (1952). The ovarian control of the hypophysial gonadotrophic function. *J. Endocrin.* **8,** 187–194.

Bryans, F. E. (1951). Progesterone of the blood in the menstrual cycle of the monkey. *Endocrinology,* **48,** 733–740.

Bulbrook, R. D. and Greenwood, F. C. (1957a). Persistence of urinary oestrogen excretion after oophorectomy and adrenalectomy. *Brit. med. J.* **1,** 662–666.

Bulbrook, R. D. and Greenwood, F. C. (1957b). The persistence of oestrogen production after endocrine ablation. *Acta endocr., Copenhagen,* **24,** Suppl. 31, 324–325.

Bulbrook, R. D., Greenwood, F. C. and Williams, P. C. (1960). Comparison of biological and chemical estimations of urinary oestrogens. II. Urine from patients with breast cancer maintained on cortisone after oophorectomy-adrenalectomy or hypophysectomy. *J. Endocrin.* **20,** 220–228.

Burrill, M. W. and Greene, R. R. (1941). Androgen production in the female rat. *Endocrinology,* **28,** 871–873.

Burrows, H. (1949). "Biological Actions of Sex Hormones." 2nd ed. Cambridge University Press.

Campenhout, E. van. (1947). Sympathicotropic cells of Berger. *Acta anat.* **4,** 73–78.

Caravaglios, R. and Cilotti, R. (1957). A study of the proteins in the follicular fluid of the cow. *J. Endocrin.* **15,** 273–278.

Chester Jones, I. (1955). Role of the adrenal cortex in reproduction. *Brit. med. Bull.* **11,** 156–160.

Chu, J. P. (1944). Influence of the thyroid on pregnancy and parturition in the rabbit. *J. Endocrin.* **4,** 109–114.

Chu, J. P., Lee, C. C. and You, S. S. (1944). Functional relation between the uterus and the corpus luteum. *J. Endocrin.* **4,** 392–398.

Claesson, L. and Hillarp, N.-Å. (1947). The formation mechanism of oestrogenic hormones. I. The presence of an oestrogen-precursor in the rabbit ovary. *Acta physiol. scand.* **13,** 115–129.

Clausen, H. J. (1940). Studies on the effect of ovariotomy and hypophysectomy on gestation in snakes. *Endocrinology,* **27,** 700–704.

Cole, H. H. and Cupps, P. T. (1959). Eds. "Reproduction in Domestic Animals." Vol. 1. Academic Press, New York.

Cole, H. H., Hart, G. H., Lyons, W. R. and Catchpole, H. R. (1933). The development and hormonal content of foetal horse gonads. *Anat. Rec.* **56,** 275–289.

Corner, G. W. (1923). Oestrus, ovulation and menstruation. *Physiol. Rev.* **3,** 451–481.

Corner, G. W. (1927). The relationship between menstruation and ovulation in the monkey. *J. Amer. med. Ass.* **89,** 1838.

Corner, G. W. (1938). The sites of formation of estrogenic substances in the animal body. *Physiol. Rev.* **18,** 154–172.

Corner, G. W. (1940). Accessory corpora lutea in the ovary of the monkey, *Macaca rhesus. Anal. Fac. Med., Montevideo,* **25,** 553–560.

Corner, G. W. (1943a). Translation of "On the female testes or ovaries", by Regner de Graaf. *In* "Essays in Biology", 121–137. University of California Press.

Corner, G. W. (1943b). "The Hormones in Human Reproduction." Princeton University Press.

Corner, G. W. (1946). The ovary at the time of ovulation. *In* "The Problem of Fertility." (E. T. Engle, ed.), pp. 67–73. Princeton University Press.

Corner, G. W. and Allen, W. M. (1928). Physiology of the corpus luteum. I. The effect of very early ablation of the corpus luteum upon embryos and uterus. *Amer. J. Physiol.* **86,** 74–81.

Corner, G. W. and Allen, W. M. (1929). Physiology of the corpus luteum; production of special uterine reaction (progestational proliferation) by extracts of corpus luteum. *Amer. J. Physiol.* **88,** 326–339.

Corner, G. W., Bartelmez, G. W. and Hartman, C. G. (1936). On normal and aberrant corpora lutea of the rhesus monkey. *Amer. J. Anat.* **59**, 433–443.

Courrier, R. (1945). "Endocrinologie de la Gestation." Chap. 24. Masson, Paris.

Courrier, R. (1950). Interactions between estrogens and progesterone. *Vitam. & Hormon.* **8**, 179–214.

Dalton, A. J., Morris, H. P. and Dubnik, C. S. (1945). Changes in the organs of female C₃H mice receiving thiourea. *J. nat. Cancer Inst.* **5**, 451–454.

Dean, F. D. and Chester Jones, I. (1959). Sex steroids in the lungfish (*Protopterus annectens* Owen). *J. Endocrin.* **18**, 366–371.

Deane, H. W. and Barker, C. (1952). Cytochemistry of the ovary. *In* "Studies on the Ovary and Testis." (E. T. Engle, ed.), pp. 176–195. Thomas, Springfield.

Deanesly, R. (1938). The androgenic activity of ovarian grafts in castrated male rats. *Proc. roy. Soc.* B. **126**, 122–135.

Dempsey, E. W. (1939). The reproductive cycle of New World monkeys. *Amer. J. Anat.* **64**, 381–405.

Dempsey, E. W. (1940). The structure of the reproductive tract in the female gibbon. *Amer. J. Anat.* **67**, 229–254.

Dempsey, E. W., Hertz, R. and Young, W. C. (1936). The experimental induction of oestrus (sexual receptivity) in the normal and ovariectomized guinea-pig. *Amer. J. Physiol.* **116**, 201–209.

Dewar, A. D. (1959). Observations on pseudopregnancy in the mouse. *J. Endocrin.* **18**, 188–190.

Dhom, G. (1955). Morphologische, quantitative und histochemische Studien zur Funktion der Hiluszellen des Ovars. III. Die Hiluszellen bei endokrinen Störungen. *Z. Geburtsh. Gynäk.* **142**, 289–313.

Diczfalusy, E. (1957). Chemical determinations of oestrogens in urine. *Acta endocr., Copenhagen*, **24**, Suppl. 31, 11–26.

Dodd, J. M. (1955). The hormones of sex and reproduction and their effects in fish and lower chordates. *Mem. Soc. Endocrin.* No. 4, 166–187.

Dorfman, R. I. (1955). Steroid hormone metabolism. *In* "The Hormones." (G. Pincus and K. V. Thimann, eds.), pp. 589–664. Academic Press, New York.

Dubreuil, G. (1945). La glande interstitielle, thécale ou oestrogène de l'ovaire feminin. *C.R. Soc. Biol., Paris*, **139**, 850–852.

Duyvené de Wit, J. J. (1938). Ein neuer Test zum qualitativen und quantitativen Nachweis des Corpus luteum-Hormons. *Klin. Wschr.* **17**, 660–663.

Dyke, H. B. van and Ch'en, G. (1936). Observations on the biochemistry of the genital tract of the female macaque particularly during the menstrual cycle. *Amer. J. Anat.* **58**, 473–499.

Dyke, H. B. van and Chen, G. (1940). The distribution of lipoids in the genital tract of the monkey at different stages of the menstrual cycle. *Amer. J. Anat.* **66**, 411–427.

Eckstein, F. M. P., Lubran, M. and McKeown, T. (1941). Fluctuations in the blood electrolytes in relation to the menstrual cycle. *Guy's Hosp. Rep.* **90**, 28–33.

Eckstein, P. (1948). The growth and development of the rhesus monkey. Thesis. University of Cambridge.

Eckstein, P. (1949). Patterns of the mammalian sexual cycle. *Acta anat.* **7**, 389–410.

Eckstein, P. (1950). The induction of progesterone withdrawal bleeding in spayed rhesus monkeys. *J. Endocrin.* **6**, 405–411.

Eckstein, P. (1955). The duration of reproductive life in the female. *In* "Old Age in the Modern World", pp. 190–199. Livingstone, Edinburgh.

Eckstein, P. (1957). Internal reproductive organs. *In* "Primatologia", Bd. III, Tl. 1 (H. Hofer, A. H. Schultz and D. Starck, eds.), pp. 542–629. Karger, Basel.

Eckstein, P. and Zuckerman, S. (1956a). The oestrous cycle in the Mammalia. *In* "Marshall's Physiology of Reproduction" (A. S. Parkes, ed.), vol. 1, part 1, 3rd ed., chap. 4. Longmans Green, London.

Eckstein, P. and Zuckerman, S. (1956b). Changes in the accessory reproductive organs of the non-pregnant female. *In* "Marshall's Physiology of Reproduction" (A. S. Parkes, ed.), vol. 1, part 1, 3rd ed., chap. 6. Longmans Green, London.

Edgar, D. G. (1953). The progesterone content of body fluids and tissues. *J. Endocrin.* **10**, 54–64.

Edgar, D. G. and Ronaldson, J. W. (1958). Blood levels of progesterone in the ewe. *J. Endocrin.* **16**, 378–384.

Edgar, D. G., Flux, D. S. and Ronaldson, J. W. (1959). Comparison of chemical and biological estimations of plasma progestin. *J. Endocrin.* **19**, 44–51.

Emmens, C. W. (1941). Precursors of oestrogens. *J. Endocrin.* **2**, 444–458.

Emmens, C. W. (1950). Estrogens. *In* "Hormone Assay" (C. W. Emmens, ed.), pp. 391–417. Academic Press, New York.

Emmens, C. W. (1955). Biological assay of the gonadal and gonadotrophic hormones. *Brit. med. Bull.* **11**, 135–139.

Emmens, C. W. (1959). Role of gonadal hormones in reproductive processes. *In* "Reproduction in Domestic Animals" (H. H. Cole and P. T. Cupps, eds.), pp. 111–154. Academic Press, New York.

Engle, E. T. (1944). The effect of hypothyroidism on menstruation in adult rhesus monkeys. *Yale J. Biol. Med.* **17**, 59–66.

Ershoff, B. H. (1945). Effects of thyroid feeding on ovarian development in the rat. *Endocrinology*, **37**, 218–220.

Escomel, E. (1939). La plus jeune mère du monde. *Pr. méd.* **47**, 875.

Falck, B. (1959). Site of production of oestrogen in rat ovary as studied in micro-transplants. *Acta physiol. scand.* **47**, Suppl. 163, pp. 1–101.

Falls, J. L. (1955). Accessory adrenal cortex in the broad ligament. Incidence and functional significance. *Cancer*, **8**, 143–150.

Fekete, E. (1953). A morphological study of the ovaries of virgin mice of eight inbred strains showing quantitative differences in their hormone producing components. *Anat. Rec.* **117**, 93–113.

Fekete, E., Woolley, G. W. and Little, C. C. (1941). Histological changes following ovariectomy in mice. I. dba high tumor strain. *J. exp. Med.* **74**,1–8.

Fluhmann, C. F. (1956). "Management of Menstrual Disorders." Saunders, Philadelphia.

Flynn, T. T. and Hill, J. P. (1939). The development of the Monotremata. Part IV. Growth of the ovarian ovum, maturation, fertilisation and early cleavage. *Trans. zool. Soc. Lond.* **24**, 445–622.

Folley, S. J. (1955). Hormones in mammary growth and function. *Brit. med. Bull.* **11**, 145–150.

Folley, S. J. (1956). "The Physiology and Biochemistry of Lactation." Oliver and Boyd, Edinburgh.

Forbes, T. R. (1950). Systemic plasma progesterone levels during the human menstrual cycle. *Amer. J. Obstet. Gynec.* **60**, 180–186.

Forbes, T. R. (1953). Pre-ovulatory progesterone in the peripheral blood of the rabbit. *Endocrinology*, **53**, 79–87.

Fraenkel, L. (1903). Die Function des Corpus luteum. *Arch. Gynäk.* **68**, 438–545.

Fraenkel, L. (1910). Neue Experimente zur Function des Corpus luteum. *Arch. Gynäk.* **91**, 705–761.

Frieden, E. H. and Hisaw, F. L. (1953). The biochemistry of relaxin. *Recent Progr. Hormone Res.* **8**, 333–378.

Gardner, W. U. and Pfeiffer, C. A. (1939). Sex hormones and bone changes in mice. *Anat. Rec.* **73**, Suppl., 21.

Gompertz, D. and Mandl, A. M. (1958). The effect of pre-pubertal gonadectomy on the adrenal glands. *J. Endocrin.* **17**, 114–120.

Govaerts, J. and Dallemagne, M. J. (1948). Influence of folliculin on bone metabolism studied by means of radiophosphorus $^{32}_{15}P$. *Nature, Lond.* **161**, 977.

Green, J. A. (1955). Hormone secretion by the immature mouse ovary after gonadotrophic stimulation. *Endocrinology*, **56**, 621–627.

Greenwood, F. C. and Bulbrook, R. D. (1957). Effect of hypophysectomy on urinary oestrogen in breast cancer. *Brit. med. J.* **1**, 666–668.

Groat, R. A. (1944). Formation and growth of adrenocortical-like tissue in ovaries of the adrenalectomized ground squirrel. *Anat. Rec.* **89**, 33–41.

Guilbert, H. R. and Goss, H. (1932). Some effects of restricted protein intake on the estrous cycle and gestation in the rat. *J. Nutr.* **5**, 251–265.

Hagerman, D. G. and Villee, C. A. (1959). Metabolic studies of the mechanism of action of estrogens. In "Recent Progress in the Endocrinology of Reproduction" (C. W. Lloyd, ed.), pp. 317–333. Academic Press, New York.

Hain, A. M. (1947). The constitutional type of precocious puberty. *J. clin. Endocrin.* **7**, 171–185.

Hammond, J. and Robson, J. M. (1951). Local maintenance of the rabbit corpus luteum with oestrogen. *Endocrinology*, **49**, 384–389.

Hardy, M. H., Biggers, J. D. and Claringbold, P. J. (1953). Vaginal cornification of the mouse produced by oestrogens in vitro. *Nature, Lond.* **172**, 1196–1197.

Harris, G. W. (1955). "Neural Control of the Pituitary Gland." Arnold, London.

Harris, G. W. and Jacobsohn, D. (1952). Functional grafts of the anterior pituitary gland. *Proc. roy. Soc.* B. **139**, 263–276.

Harrison, R. J. (1948). The development and fate of the corpus luteum in the vertebrate series. *Biol. Rev.* **23**, 296–331.

Harrison, R. J. (1949). Observations on the female reproductive organs of the Ca'ing whale, *Globiocephala melaena* Traill. *J. Anat., Lond.* **83**, 238–253.

Hartman, C. G. (1929). How large is the mammalian egg? *Quart. Rev. Biol.* **4**, 373–388.

Hartman, C. G. (1931). On the relative sterility of the adolescent organism. *Science*, **74**, 226.

Hartman, C. G. (1932). Studies in the reproduction of the monkey (*Macacus* (*Pithecus*) *rhesus*), with special reference to menstruation. *Contr. Embryol. Carneg. Instn.* **23**, 1–161.

Hartman, C. G. (1938). Menstruation without ovulation ('pseudo-menstruation'): incidence and treatment with special reference to the rhesus monkey. In "Les Hormones Sexuelles" (L. Brouha, ed.), pp. 103–118. Hermann, Paris.

Hartman, F. A. and Brownell, K. A. (1949). "The Adrenal Gland." Kimpton, London.

Heape, W. (1900). The 'sexual season' of mammals, and the relation of the 'pro-oestrum' to menstruation. *Quart. J. micr. Sci.* **44**, 1–70.

Hechter, O. (1958). *In* "Cholesterol" (R. P. Cook, ed.), pp. 309–347. Academic Press, New York.

Hernandez, T. (1943). Hormonal ambisexuality of ovarian grafts in female rats. *Amer. J. Anat.* **73**, 127–151.

Hertz, R. (1945). The quantitative relationship between stilboestrol response and dietary 'folic acid' in the chick. *Endocrinology,* **37**, 1–6.

Hertz, R. (1948). The role of factors of the B-complex in estrogen metabolism. *Recent Progr. Hormone Res.* **2**, 161–177.

Hill, J. P. (1910). The early development of the Marsupialia with special reference to the native cat (*Dasyurus viverrinus*). *Quart. J. micr. Sci.* **56**, 1–134.

Hill, R. T. (1941). Fate of ovaries which have been grafted in the ear for long periods of time. *Endocrinology,* **28**, 426–430.

Hill, R. T. and Strong, M. T. (1938). Ovaries secrete male hormones. IV. Effect of ovarian androgens on accessory size in the mouse. *Endocrinology,* **22**, 663–666.

Hill, R. T. and Strong, M. T. (1940). Ovaries secrete male hormones. V. A comparison of some synthetic androgens with naturally occurring ovarian androgen in mice. *Endocrinology,* **27**, 79–82.

Hisaw, F. L. (1925). The influence of the ovary on the resorption of the pubic bones of the pocket gopher, *Geomys bursarius* (Shaw). *J. exp. Zool.* **42**, 411–433.

Hisaw, F. L. (1926). Experimental relaxation of the pubic ligament of the guinea pig. *Proc. Soc. exp. Biol., N.Y.* **23**, 661–663.

Hisaw, F. L. (1939). *In* "Sex and Internal Secretions" (E. Allen, ed.). Williams and Wilkins, Baltimore.

Hisaw, F. L. (1947). Development of the Graafian follicle and ovulation. *Physiol. Rev.* **27**, 95–119.

Hisaw, F. L. (1950). Factors influencing endometrial growth in monkeys (*Macaca mulatta*). *In* "Steroid Hormones" (E. S. Gordon, ed.), pp. 259–276. University of Wisconsin Press.

Hisaw, F. L. (1959). Endocrine adaptations of the mammalian estrous cycle and gestation. *In* "Comparative Endocrinology" (A. Gorbman, ed.), pp. 533–552. Wiley, New York.

Hisaw, F. L. and Zarrow, M. X. (1950). The physiology of relaxin. *Vitam. & Hormon.* **8**, 151–178.

Hooker, C. W. and Forbes, T. R. (1947). A bio-assay for minute amounts of progesterone. *Endocrinology,* **41**, 158–169.

Hooker, C. W. and Forbes, T. R. (1949). The transport of progesterone in blood. *Endocrinology,* **44**, 61–66.

Horst, C. J. van der, and Gillman, J. (1940). Mechanism of ovulation and corpus luteum formation in *Elephantulus*. *Nature, Lond.* **145**, 974.

Horst, C. J. van der, and Gillman, J. (1942). The life history of the corpus luteum of menstruation in *Elephantulus*. *S. Afr. J. med. Sci.* **7**, 21–42.

Hunter, J. (1787). An experiment to determine the effect of extirpating one ovarium upon the number of young produced. *Phil. Trans.* **77**, 233–240.

Ingram, D. L. (1958). Fertility and oocyte numbers after X-irradiation of the ovary. *J. Endocrin.* **17**, 81–90.

Ingram, D. L. and Mandl, A. M. (1958). The secretion of oestrogen after hypophysectomy. *J. Endocrin.* 17, 13–16.

Ingram, D. L., Mandl, A. M. and Zuckerman, S. (1958). The influence of age on litter-size. *J. Endocrin.* 17, 280–285.

Irving, J. T. (1957). A comparison of the influence of hormones, vitamins, and other dietary factors upon the formation of bone, dentine and enamel. *Vitam. & Hormon.* 15, 291–323.

Jacobsohn, D. (1958). Mammary gland growth in relation to hormones with metabolic actions. *Proc. roy. Soc. B.* 149, 325–329.

Jailer, J. W. and Engle, E. T. (1954). The Ovary. *In* "Glandular Physiology and Therapy", 5th ed., pp. 140–161. American Medical Association.

Jones, E. C. (1957). The ageing ovary. Thesis. University of Birmingham.

Jones, E. C. and Krohn, P. L. (1960). The effect of unilateral ovariectomy on the reproductive lifespan of mice. *J. Endocrin.* 20, 129–134.

Jost, A. (1951). Sur le contrôle hormonal de la différenciation sexuelle du lapin. *In* "La Différenciation Sexuelle chez les Vertébrés", pp. 395–425. Centre National de la Recherche Scientifique, Paris.

Jost, A. (1953). Problems of fetal endocrinology: the gonadal and hypophyseal hormones. *Recent Progr. Hormone Res.* 8, 379–418.

Jost, A. (1955). Modalities in the action of gonadal and gonad-stimulating hormones in the foetus. *Mem. Soc. Endocrin.* No. 4, 237–248.

Jost, A. (1960). Hormonal influence in the sex development of bird and mammalian embryos. *Mem. Soc. Endocrin.* No. 7, 49–62.

Jungck, E. C., Heller, C. G. and Nelson, W. O. (1947). Regulation of pituitary gonadotrophic secretion: Inhibition by estrogen or inactivation by the ovaries? *Proc. Soc. exp. Biol., N.Y.* 65, 148–152.

Kellas, L. M., Lennep, E. W. van, and Amoroso, E. C. (1958). Ovaries of some foetal and prepubertal giraffes (*Giraffa camelopardalis* (Linnaeus)). *Nature, Lond.* 181, 487–488.

Klein, M. (1954). La biologie du corps jaune. *In* "La Fonction Lutéale", pp. 1–21. Masson, Paris.

Klopper, A. (1957). The excretion of pregnanediol during the normal menstrual cycle. *J. Obstet. Gynaec., Brit. Emp.* 64, 504–511.

Klopper, A., Strong, J. A., and Cook, L. R. (1957). The excretion of pregnanediol and adrenocortical activity. *J. Endocrin.* 15, 180–189.

Knaus, H. (1950). "Die Physiologie der Zeugung des Menschen", 3. Aufl. Wien.

Kohn, A. (1928). Ueber "Leydigsche Zwischenzellen" im Hilus des menschlichen Eierstockes (extraglanduläre Zwischenzellen). *Endokrinologie,* 1, 3–10.

Krohn, P. L. (1948). The prolonged administration of oestrogen or androgen to immature female monkeys. *J. Endocrin.* 5, xci-xcii.

Krohn, P. L. (1957). The problem of the ageing ovary. *Schweiz. med. Wschr.* 87, 417–419.

Krohn, P. L. and White, H. C. (1950). The effect of hypothyroidism on reproduction in the female albino rat. *J. Endocrin.* 6, 375–385.

Krohn, P. L. and Zuckerman, S. (1937). Water metabolism in relation to the menstrual cycle. *J. Physiol.* 88, 369–387.

Kutz, R. L., McKeown, T. and Selye, H. (1934). Effect of salt treatment on certain changes following adrenalectomy. *Proc. Soc. exp. Biol., N.Y.* 32, 331–332.

Lamond, D. R. (1959a). Effect of stimulation from other animals of the same species on oestrous cycles in mice. *J. Endocrin.* **18**, 343–349.

Lamond, D. R. (1959b). Cessation of ovarian function in the immature mouse after hypophysectomy. *J. Endocrin.* **19**, 103–107.

Leathem, J. H. (1958a). Hormones and protein nutrition. *Recent Progr. Hormone Res.* **14**, 141–182.

Leathem, J. H. (1958b). Hormonal influences on the gonadotrophin sensitive hypothyroid rat ovary. *Anat. Rec.* **131**, 487–497.

Leathem, J. H. (1959). Extragonadal factors in reproduction. *In* "Recent Progress in the Endocrinology of Reproduction" (C. W. Lloyd, ed.), pp. 179–203. Academic Press, New York.

Lederer, J. (1946). "Les Relations Thyro-ovariennes." Masson, Paris.

Lee, S. van der, and Boot, L. M. (1955). Spontaneous pseudopregnancy in mice. I. *Acta physiol. pharm. néerl.* **4**, 442–444.

Lee, S. van der, and Boot, L. M. (1956). Spontaneous pseudopregnancy in mice. II. *Acta physiol. pharm. néerl.* **5**, 213–215.

Lillie, F. R. (1916). The theory of the free-martin. *Science*, **43**, 611–612.

Lillie, F. R. (1917). The freemartin: a study of the action of sex hormones in the foetal life of cattle. *J. exp. Zool.* **23**, 371–453.

Loeb, L. (1907). Über die experimentelle Erzeugung von Knoten von Deciduagewebe in dem Uterus des Meerschweinchens nach stattgefundener Copulation. *Zbl. allg. Path. path. Anat.* **18**, 563–565.

Loeb, L. (1923). The effect of extirpation of the uterus on the life and function of the corpus luteum in the guinea-pig. *Proc. Soc. exp. Biol., N.Y.* **20**, 441–443.

Loeb, L. (1927). Effects of hysterectomy on the system of sex organs and on periodicity of the sexual cycle in the guinea-pig. *Amer. J. Physiol.* **83**, 202–224.

Loeb, L. and Smith, M. G. (1936). The effect of hysterectomy on the duration of life and retrogression of the corpus luteum and on secondary sex organs in the rabbit. *Amer. J. Anat.* **58**, 1–25.

Lutwak-Mann, C. (1954). Note on the chemical composition of bovine follicular fluid. *J. agric. Sci.* **44**, 477–480.

Lyons, W. R., Johnson, R. E., Cole, R. D. and Li, C. H. (1955). Mammary growth and lactation in male rats. *In* "The Hypophyseal Growth Hormone, Nature and Actions" (R. W. Smith, O. H. Gaebler and C. N. H. Long, eds.), pp. 461–472. Blakiston, New York.

McDowell, E. C. and Lord, E. M. (1925). The number of corpora lutea in successive mouse pregnancies. *Anat. Rec.* **31**, 131–141.

McKay, D. G. and Robinson, D. (1947). Observations on fluorescence, birefringence and histochemistry of the human ovary during the menstrual cycle. *Endocrinology*, **41**, 378–394.

McKay, D. G., Robinson, D. and Hertig, A. T. (1949). Histochemical observations on granulosa-cell tumors, thecomas, and fibromas of the ovary. *Amer. J. Obstet. Gynec.* **58**, 625–639.

Mackintosh, N. A. (1946). The natural history of whalebone whales. *Biol. Rev.* **21**, 60–74.

Mandl, A. M. (1951). Cyclical changes in the vaginal smear of adult ovariectomized rats. *J. exp. Biol.* **28**, 585–592.

Mandl, A. M. and Zuckerman, S. (1950). The numbers of normal and atretic ova in the mature rat. *J. Endocrin.* **6**, 426–435.

Mandl, A. M. and Zuckerman, S. (1951a). Numbers of normal and atretic oocytes in unilaterally spayed rats. *J. Endocrin.* **7**, 112–119.

Mandl, A. M. and Zuckerman, S. (1951b). The relation of age to numbers of oocytes. *J. Endocrin.* **7**, 190–193.

Mandl, A. M. and Zuckerman, S. (1956a). The reactivity of the X-irradiated ovary. *J. Endocrin.* **13**, 243–261.

Mandl, A. M. and Zuckerman, S. (1956b). Changes in the mouse after X-ray sterilization. *J. Endocrin.* **13**, 262–268.

Maqsood, M. (1952). Thyroid function in relation to reproduction of mammals and birds. *Biol. Rev.* **27**, 281–319.

Marden, W. G. R. (1951). The hormone control of ovulation in the calf. *J. Physiol.* **115**, 22–23P.

Markee, J. E. (1929). Rhythmic variations in the vascularity of the uterus of the guinea-pig during the estrous cycle. *Amer. J. Obstet. Gynec.* **17**, 205–208.

Markee, J. E. (1940). Menstruation in intraocular endometrial transplants in the rhesus monkey. *Contr. Embryol. Carneg. Instn.* **28**, 219–308.

Markee, J. E. (1950). The relation of blood flow to endometrial growth and the inception of menstruation. *In* "Menstruation and its Disorders" (E. T. Engle, ed.), pp. 165–185. Thomas, Springfield.

Marrian, G. F. (1950). The steroids—a historical review. *In* "A Symposium on Steroid Hormones" (E. S. Gordon, ed.), pp. 3–13. University of Wisconsin Press.

Marrian, G. F. (1961). Advances in oestrogen biochemistry, 1949–1959. *Mem. Soc. Endocrin.* No. 10, 1–11.

Marrian, G. F. and Bauld, W. S. (1955). The isolation of 16-*epi*-oestriol from the urine of pregnant women. *Biochem. J.* **59**, 136–141.

Marrian, G. F., Watson, E. J. D. and Panattoni, M. (1957a). The isolation of a ketonic dihydroxy Kober chromogen from the urine of pregnant women. *Biochem. J.* **65**, 12–18.

Marrian, G. F., Loke, K. H., Watson, E. J. D. and Panattoni, M. (1957b). 16α-Hydroxyoestrone in the urine of pregnant women. *Biochem. J.* **66**, 60–65.

Marshall, F. H. A. (1922). "The Physiology of Reproduction." 2nd ed. Longmans Green, London.

Marshall, F. H. A. and Jolly, W. A. (1905). Contributions to the physiology of mammalian reproduction. Part 1. The oestrous cycle in the dog. Part II. The ovary as an organ of internal secretion. *Phil. Trans.* B. **198**, 99–141.

Martin, L. (1960). The use of 2-3-5-triphenyltetrazolium chloride in the biological assay of oestrogens. *J. Endocrin.* **20**, 187–197.

Martin, L. and Claringbold, P. J. (1960). The mitogenic action of oestrogens in the vaginal epithelium of the ovariectomized mouse. *J. Endocrin.* **20**, 173–186.

Mayer, G. (1959). Recent studies on hormonal control of delayed implantation and superimplantation in the rat. *Mem. Soc. Endocrin.* No. 6, 76–83.

Means, J. H. (1948). "The Thyroid and its Disease." 2nd ed. Lippincott, Philadelphia.

Memoirs of the Society for Endocrinology (1955). No. 4. Comparative physiology of reproduction. Cambridge University Press.

Montague, F. H. A. (1939). Adolescent sterility. *Quart. Rev. Biol.* **14**, 192–219.

Montague, F. H. A. (1946). "Adolescent Sterility." Thomas, Springfield.

Morris, H. P., Dubnik, C. S. and Dalton, A. J. (1946). Effect of prolonged ingestion of thiourea on mammary glands and the appearance of mammary tumours in adult C₃H mice. *J. nat. Cancer Inst.* **7**, 159–169.

Morris, J. L. and Scully, R. E. (1958). "Endocrine Pathology of the Ovary." Kimpton, London.

Mossman, H. W. (1937). The thecal gland and its relation to the reproductive cycle. A study of the cyclic changes in the ovary of the pocket gopher, *Geomys bursarius* (Shaw). *Amer. J. Anat.* **61**, 289–319.

Mulinos, M. G., Pomerantz, L., Smelser, J. and Kurzrok, R. (1939). Estrus-inhibiting effects of inanition. *Proc. Soc. exp. Biol., N.Y.* **40**, 79–83.

Nabarro, J. D. N. and Moxham, A. (1957). Effect of corticotrophin on urinary excretion of pregnanediol and pregnanetriol. *Lancet*, **2**, 624–625.

Nalbandov, A. V. (1958). "Reproductive Physiology." Freeman, San Francisco.

Neher, G. M. and Zarrow, M. X. (1954). Concentration of progestin in the serum of the non-pregnant, pregnant and post-partum ewe. *J. Endocrin.* **11**, 323–330.

Nelsen, O. E. (1953). "Comparative Embryology of the Vertebrates." Constable, London.

Novak, E. (1944). The constitutional type of female precocious puberty with a report of nine cases. *Amer. J. Obstet. Gynec.* **47**, 20–47.

Ortiz, E. (1947). Postnatal development of the reproductive system of the golden hamster (*Cricetus auratus*) and its reactivity to hormones. *Physiol. Zoöl.* **20**, 45–66.

Parkes, A. S. (1926). On the occurrence of the oestrous cycle after X-ray sterilization. I. Irradiation of mice at three weeks old. *Proc. roy. Soc.* B. **100**, 172–199.

Parkes, A. S. (1927a). Occurrence of oestrous cycle after X-ray sterilization of adult. *Proc. roy. Soc.* B. **101**, 421–449.

Parkes, A. S. (1927b). Occurrence of oestrous cycle after X-ray sterilization. Irradiation of adult during pregnancy and lactation; and general summary. *Proc. roy. Soc.* B. **102**, 51–62.

Parkes, A. S. (1929). "The Internal Secretions of the Ovary." Longmans Green, London.

Parkes, A. S. (1937). Androgenic activity of ovarian extracts. *Nature, Lond.* **139**, 965.

Parkes, A. S. (1945). The adrenal-gonad relationship. *Physiol. Rev.* **25**, 203–254.

Parkes, A. S. (1950). Androgenic activity of the ovary. *Recent Progr. Hormone Res.* **5**, 101–114.

Parkes, A. S. and Emmens, C. W. (1944). Effect of androgens and estrogens on birds. *Vitam. & Hormon.* **2**, 361–408.

Parkes, A. S., Fielding, U. and Brambell, F. W. R. (1927). Ovarian regeneration in the mouse after complete double ovariotomy. *Proc. roy. Soc.* B. **101**, 328–354.

Pearlman, W. H. (1948). Chemistry and metabolism of progesterone. *In* "The Hormones" (G. Pincus and K. V. Thimann, eds.), vol. 1, pp. 408–465. Academic Press, New York.

Peczenik, O. (1942). Actions of sex hormones on oestrous cycle and reproduction of the golden hamster. *J. Endocrin.* **3**, 157–167.

Pencharz, R. I. (1940). Effect of estrogens and androgens alone and in combination with chorionic gonadotrophin on the ovary of the hypophysectomized rat. *Science*, **91**, 554–555.

Perry, J. S. (1953). The reproduction of the African elephant, *Loxodonta africana. Phil. Trans.* B. **237**, 93.

Perry, J. S. (1954). Fecundity and embryonic mortality in pigs. *J. Embryol. exp. Morph.* **2**, 308–322.

Peterson, R. R., Webster, R. C., Rayner, B. and Young, W. C. (1952). The thyroid and reproductive performance in the adult female guinea pig. *Endocrinology*, **51**, 405–518.

Pfeiffer, C. A. and Gardner, W. U. (1938). Skeletal changes and blood serum calcium levels in pigeons receiving estrogens. *Endocrinology*, **23**, 485–491.

Pickford, G. E. and Atz, J. W. (1957). "The Physiology of the Pituitary Gland of Fishes." New York Zoological Society.

Picon, L. (1956). Sur le rôle de l'âge dans la sensibilité de l'ovaire à l'hormone gonadotrophe chez le rat. *Arch. Anat. micr. Morph. exp.* **45**, 311–341.

Pincus, G. (1950). Physiology of ovarian hormones. *In* "The Hormones" (G. Pincus and K. V. Thimann, eds.), vol. II, pp. 1–31. Academic Press, New York.

Pincus, G., and Thimann, K. V. (1950). Eds. "The Hormones", vol. II. Academic Press, New York.

Pincus, G., and Thimann, K. V. (1955). Eds. "The Hormones", vol. III. Academic Press, New York.

Ponse, K. (1954). Gonadotropines chorioniques et fonction androgène de l'ovaire. *In* "La Fonction Lutéale," pp. 57–61. Masson, Paris.

Price, D. (1947). An analysis of the factors influencing growth and development of the mammalian reproductive tract. *Physiol. Zoöl.* **20**, 214–247.

Price, D. and Ortiz, E. (1944). The relation of age to reactivity in the reproductive system of the rat. *Endocrinology*, **34**, 215–239.

Price, M. (1953). The reproductive cycle of the water shrew, *Neomys sodiens bicolor* Shaw. *Proc. zool. Soc. Lond.* **123**, 599–621.

Raynaud, A. (1951). Recherches expérimentales sur le développement de l'appareil génital et le fonctionnement des glandes endocrines des foetus de souris et de mulots. *In* "La Différenciation Sexuelle chez les Vertébrés", pp. 336–394. Centre National de la Recherche Scientifique, Paris.

Robinson, T. J. (1955). Quantitative studies on the hormonal induction of oestrus in spayed ewes. *J. Endocrin.* **12**, 163–173.

Robinson, T. J. (1959). The estrous cycle of the ewe and doe. *In* "Reproduction in Domestic Animals" (H. H. Cole and P. T. Cupps, eds.), pp. 292–333. Academic Press, New York.

Robson, J. M. (1937). Maintenance by oestrin of the luteal function in hypophysectomized rabbits. *J. Physiol.* **90**, 435–439.

Robson, J. M. (1947). "Recent Advances in Sex and Reproductive Physiology," 3rd ed. Churchill, London.

Rowson, L. E., Lamming, G. E. and Fry, R. M. (1953). The relationship between ovarian hormones and uterine infection. *Vet. Rec.* **65**, 335–340.

Roy, E. J. and Brown, J. B. (1960). A method for the estimation of oestriol, oestrone and oestradiol-17β in the blood of the pregnant woman and of the foetus. *J. Endocrin.* **21**, 9–23.

Sauramo, H. (1954). Development, occurrence and pathology of aberrant adrenocortical tissue in the region of the ovary. *Acta obstet. gynec. scand.* Suppl. 2, 49–58.

Schultze, M. O. (1955). Effects of malnutrition in early life on subsequent growth and reproduction of rats. *J. Nutr.* **56**, 25–33.

Selye, H. and Collip, J. B. (1936). Fundamental factors in the interpretation of stimuli influencing endocrine glands. *Endocrinology*, **20**, 667–672.

6. NORMAL OVARIAN PHYSIOLOGY 357

Selye, H., Collip, J. B. and Thomson, D. L. (1933). On the effect of the anterior pituitary-like hormone on the ovary of the hypophysectomized rat. *Endocrinology*, **17**, 494–500.

Sharman, A. (1950). Re-establishment of ovulation post partum and post abortum. *Proc. Soc. Study Fertil.* **1**, 29–30.

Short, R. V. (1959). Progesterone in blood. IV. Progesterone in the blood of mares. *J. Endocrin.* **19**, 207–210.

Short, R. V. (1960a). Steroids present in the follicular fluid of the mare. *J. Endocrin.* **20**, 147–156.

Short, R. V. (1960b). The secretion of sex hormones by the adrenal gland. *Biochem. Soc. Symp.* **18**, 59–84.

Short, R. V. and Eton, B. (1959). Progesterone in blood. III. Progesterone in the peripheral blood of pregnant women. *J. Endocrin.* **18**, 418–425.

Short, R. V. and Moore, N. W. (1959). Progesterone in blood. V. Progesterone and 20α-hydroxypregn-4-en-3-one in the placentae and blood of ewes. *J. Endocrin.* **19**, 288–293.

Simkins, C. S. (1932). Development of the human ovary from birth to sexual maturity. *Amer. J. Anat.* **51**, 465.

Simpson, M. E., Evans, H. M., Fraenkel-Conrat, H. L. and Li, C. H. (1941). Synergism of estrogens with pituitary gonadotropins in hypophysectomized rats. *Endocrinology*, **28**, 37–41.

Smith, P. E. (1939). The effect on the gonads of the ablation and implantation of the hypophysis and the potency of the hypophysis under various conditions. *In* "Sex and Internal Secretions" (E. Allen, C. H. Danforth and E. A. Doisy, eds.), chap. 16. Baillière, Tindall and Cox, London.

Spitzer, R. S., Lee, K. T. and Thomas, W. A. (1957). Early age of menopause in young women with fatal acute myocardial infarction. *Amer. Heart J.* **53**, 805–808.

Stafford, W. T., Collins, R. F. and Mossman, H. W. (1942). The thecal gland in the guinea-pig ovary. *Anat. Rec.* **83**, 193–207.

Steinetz, B. G., Beach, V. L. and Kroc, R. L. (1959). The physiology of relaxin in laboratory animals. *In* "Recent Progress in the Endocrinology of Reproduction" (C. W. Lloyd, ed.), pp. 389–427. Academic Press, New York.

Stephens, D. J. (1941). Anorexia nervosa; endocrine factors in undernutrition. *J. clin. Endocrin.* **1**, 257–268.

Sternberg, W. H. (1949). The morphology, androgenic function, hyperplasia, and tumors of the human ovarian hilus cells. *Amer. J. Path.* **26**, 493–521.

Sternberg, W. H., Segaloff, A. and Gaskill, C. J. (1949). Influence of chorionic gonadotrophin on the hilus cells of the human ovary. *Fed. Proc.* **8**, 370–371.

Stockard, C. R. and Papanicolaou, G. N. (1917). The existence of a typical oestrous cycle in the guinea-pig—with a study of its histological and physiological changes. *Amer. J. Anat.* **22**, 225–283.

Strauss, F. (1939). Die Bildung des Corpus luteum bei Centetiden. *Biomorphosis*, **1**, 489–544.

Strong, J. A., Brown, J. B., Bruce, J., Douglas, M., Klopper, A. I. and Loraine, J. A. (1956). Sex-hormone excretion after bilateral adrenalectomy and oöphorectomy in patients with mammary carcinoma. *Lancet*, **2**, 955–959.

Talbot, N. B., Lowry, O. H. and Astwood, E. B. (1940). Influence of estrogen on the electrolyte pattern of the immature rat uterus. *J. biol. Chem.* **132**, 1–9.

Tanner, J. M. (1955). "Growth at Adolescence." Blackwell Scientific Publications, Oxford.

Tindal, J. S. and McNaught, M. L. (1958). Hormonal factors in breast development and milk secretion. In "Modern Trends in Endocrinology" (H. Gardiner-Hill, ed.), chap. 16. Butterworth, London.

Thorn, G. W. and Engel, L. L. (1938). Effect of sex hormones on renal excretion of electrolytes. J. exp. Med. 68, 299–312.

Thorn, G. W. and Harrop, G. A. (1937). The 'sodium retaining effect' of the sex hormones. Science, 86, 40–41.

Trapet, P. (1948). "La Glande Thécale de l'Ovaire de la Femme." Vigot Frères, Paris.

Turner, C. D. (1955). "General Endocrinology", 2nd ed. Saunders, Philadelphia.

Tyslowitz, R. and Dingemanse, C. (1941). Effect of large doses of estrogens on the blood picture of dogs. Endocrinology, 29, 817–827.

Velle, W. (1959). Thesis. Norges Veterinaerhøgskole, Oslo, p. 109. (Cited by Short, 1960a).

Venning, E. H. (1955). Clinical value of hormone estimations. Brit. med. Bull. 11, 140–144.

Venning, E. H. and Browne, J. S. L. (1937). Studies on corpus luteum function. I. The urinary excretion of sodium pregnanediol glucuronidate in the human menstrual cycle. Endocrinology, 21, 711–721.

Wade, N. J. and Doisy, E. A. (1935). Cornification of vaginal epithelium of ovariectomized rat produced by smearing. Proc. Soc. exp. Biol., N.Y. 32, 707–709.

Waldeyer, W. (1870). "Eierstock und Ei. Ein Beitrag zur Anatomie und Entwicklungsgeschichte der Sexualorgane." Engelmann, Leipzig.

White, R. F., Hertig, A. T., Rock, J. and Adams, E. C. (1951). Histological and histochemical observations on the corpus luteum of human pregnancy. Contr. Embryol. Carneg. Instn. 34, 57–74.

Whitten, W. K. (1957). Effect of exteroceptive factors on the oestrous cycle of mice. Nature, Lond. 180, 1436.

Whitten, W. K. (1958). Modification of the oestrous cycle of the mouse by external stimuli associated with the male. Changes in the oestrous cycle determined by vaginal smears. J. Endocrin. 17, 307–313.

Whitten, W. K. (1959). Occurrence of anoestrus in mice caged in groups. J. Endocrin. 18, 102–107.

Wilkins, L. (1957). "The Diagnosis and Treatment of Endocrine Disorders in Childhood and Adolescence." 2nd ed. Thomas, Springfield.

Williams, M. F. (1948). The vascular architecture of the rat uterus as influenced by estrogen and progesterone. Amer. J. Anat. 83, 247–307.

Williams, P. C. (1940). Effect of stilboestrol on the ovaries of hypophysectomized rats. Nature, Lond. 145, 388–389.

Williams, P. C. (1944). Ovarian stimulation by oestrogens: effects in immature hypophysectomized rats. Proc. roy. Soc. B. 132, 189–199.

Williams, P. C. (1945). Ovarian stimulation by oestrogens. II. Stimulation in the absence of hypophysis, uterus, and adrenal glands. J. Endocrin. 4, 125–126.

Wolfe, J. M. and Wright, A. W. (1943). A comparative histological study of the anterior hypophysis and the ovaries of two strains of rats, one of which is characterized by a high incidence of mammary fibroadenoma. Cancer Res. 3, 497–508.

Woolley, G. W. and Little, C. C. (1945). The incidence of adrenal cortical carcinoma in gonadectomized female mice of the extreme dilution strain. II. Observations on the accessory sex organs. *Cancer Res.* **5**, 203–210.

Woolley, G. W., Fekete, E. and Little, C. C. (1939). Mammary tumor development in mice ovariectomized at birth. *Proc. nat. Acad. Sci.*, *Wash.* **25**, 277–279.

Zachariae, F. and Jensen, C. E. (1958). Studies on the mechanism of ovulation. *Acta endocr.*, *Copenhagen*, **27**, 343–355.

Zander, J. (1954). Progesterone in human blood and tissues. *Nature, Lond.* **174**, 406–407.

Zander, J., Forbes, T. R., Münstermann, A. M. von, and Neher, R. (1958). Δ^4-3-Ketopregnene-20α-ol and Δ^4-3-ketopregnene-20β-ol, two naturally occurring metabolites of progesterone. Isolation, identification, biologic activity and concentration in human tissues. *J. clin. Endocrin.* **18**, 337–353.

Zander, J., Brendle, E., Münstermann, A. M. von, Diczfalusy, E., Martinsen, B. and Tillinger, K.-G. (1959). Identification and estimation of oestradiol-17β and oestrone in human ovaries. *Acta obstet. gynec. scand.* **38**, 724–736.

Zondek, B. and Rozin, S. (1954). Cervical mucus arborization. *Obstet. Gynec.* **3**, 463–470.

Zuckerman, S. (1937). The menstrual cycle of the primates. XII. The interaction of ovarian hormones in the cycle. *Proc. roy. Soc.* B. **124**, 150–162.

Zuckerman, S. (1940). The histogenesis of tissues sensitive to oestrogens. *Biol. Rev.* **15**, 231–271.

Zuckerman, S. (1941). Periodic uterine bleeding in spayed rhesus monkeys injected daily with a constant threshold dose of oestrone. *J. Endocrin.* **2**, 263–267.

Zuckerman, S. (1949). The menstrual cycle. *Lancet*, **1**, 1031–1035.

Zuckerman, S. (1951a). The number of oocytes in the mature ovary. *Recent Progr. Hormone Res.* **6**, 63–109.

Zuckerman, S. (1951b). The hormonal basis of uterine bleeding. *Acta endocr.*, *Copenhagen*, **7**, 378–388.

Zuckerman, S. (1955). Biology of oestrogens. *Brit. med. Bull.* **11**, 111–116.

Zuckerman, S. (1956). The regenerative capacity of ovarian tissue. *Ciba Foundation Colloquia on Ageing*, **2**, 31–54.

Zuckerman, S. (1960). Origin and development of oocytes in foetal and mature mammals. *Mem. Soc. Endocrin.* No. 7, 63–70.

Zuckerman, S., Wagenen. G. van, and Gardiner, R. H. (1938). The sexual skin of the rhesus monkey. *Proc. zool. Soc. Lond.* A. **108**, 385–401.

Zuckerman, S., Palmer, A. and Hanson, D. A. (1950). The effect of steroid hormones on the water content of tissues. *J. Endocrin.* **6**, 261–276.

CHAPTER 7

OVARIAN–PITUITARY RELATIONSHIPS

I. CHESTER JONES AND J. N. BALL

I. Introduction

The anterior lobe of the pituitary is essential for normal ovarian function in the Eutheria and probably in all vertebrates. A functional interrelationship between the ovary and the pituitary was recognized early in this century (Fichera, 1905; Crowe *et al.*, 1910; Aschner, 1912; Smith, 1916), and readily confirmed once the technique of hypophysectomy was perfected (see Smith, 1939).

The interdependence of the two glands was demonstrated experimentally by the original observation of Carmichael and Marshall in 1908, constantly substantiated thereafter, that unilateral ovariectomy leads to compensatory hypertrophy of the contralateral gland. It is now firmly established that at each ovulation the remaining ovary sheds the full number of eggs characteristic of the species (see Chapter 1, sect. II, I; also Brambell, 1956).

Ovarian changes are for the most part continuous, and normally cyclical in nature. In mammals they can be divided into two phases characterized by follicular maturation and formation of corpora lutea. Following Smith's (1927) observation of a follicular response to pituitary implants, and Evans and Simpson's (1928) finding that alkaline extracts of pituitaries induced luteinization, the existence of two separate gonadotrophic factors, was postulated (Wiesner and Crewe, 1930; Zondek, 1930; Wiesner and Marshall, 1931; Aschheim, 1933). About the same time, two fractions of the anterior lobe of the pituitary were prepared, one with follicle-stimulating and the other with luteinizing properties (Fevold et al., 1931; van Dyke and Wallen-Lawrence, 1933; Evans et al., 1936). The terms 'follicle-stimulating hormone' and 'luteinizing hormone' thus first entered the literature. Astwood and Fevold (1939) and Astwood (1941) later suggested that a third gonadotrophin, luteotrophin, activated the corpus luteum. Since that time, investigations in the field have been numerous, and it is the purpose of the present chapter to bring some of the knowledge together, not only for Eutheria, but for vertebrates as a whole.

Two other gonadotrophins, that derived from pregnant mares' serum (PMS) and human chorionic gonadotrophin (HCG) are considered in Chapter 9 and will be referred to here only when they have been used to simulate the effects of hypophysial gonadotrophins. The standardization of gonadotrophins, which has recently attracted much attention (Emmens, 1950; Albert, 1956; Loraine, 1958; Segaloff and Steelman, 1959), is also outside the scope of the present chapter.

II. Physico-chemical properties of pituitary gonadotrophins

For purposes of the present review, the three gonadotrophic activities of the pituitary will be regarded as due to separate hormones. The validity of this view will be discussed in section III (p. 374).

One of the three gonadotrophins is generally known as follicle-stimulating hormone (FSH), rarely as follicle-ripening hormone (FRH) as in Burrows (1949). The second hormone was originally designated luteinizing hormone (LH: Fevold et al., 1931; Wiesner and Marshall, 1931), though later the term interstitial cell-stimulating hormone (ICSH) was equally employed (Li et al., 1940d, e; 1942a). Coffin and van Dyke (1941) proposed the term thylakentrin for FSH and metakentrin for LH (ICSH), but these are not currently used. The third substance, luteotrophin (LTH), has a well-established status as a gonadotrophin, and is commonly regarded as identical with another pituitary hormone, prolactin or lactogenic hormone (Astwood and Fevold, 1939; Astwood, 1941).

For the most part, methods of extraction have been applied to pituitary glands from those species that can be obtained in large numbers, i.e. from bulls, cows and bullocks (referred to in the literature as ox, beef or bovine), from sheep (ovine) or from pigs (swine, hog or porcine). It seems that man, horse, sheep and pig pituitaries are relatively rich in FSH compared with the few other species so far studied (Fevold, 1943), while the LH (ICSH) content of the glands decreases in the following order: sheep, rabbit, pig, rat, dog, horse, man and cattle (Li and Evans, 1948). These estimates, however, do not take into consideration the biological condition of the animals at autopsy, nor, probably, will further investigations confirm them (see Steelman and Segaloff, 1959).

The most intensive work on the isolation and characterization of the gonadotrophins took place between 1937 and 1949. The purity of protein hormones was then judged on physico-chemical criteria which have now proved inadequate (cf. Shedlovsky, 1943). In a more recent discussion Li (1956) said that individual criteria of purity of proteins are insufficient, and even agreement among a large number of criteria merely increases the probability without guaranteeing purity: "Indeed, a single new criterion may perhaps show that the protein under investigation is in fact a mixture."

The inability to prepare the gonadotrophins as pure chemical substances renders the evaluation of biological data all the more difficult (see p. 385). However, the recent resurgence of interest in the problem holds out hope for its resolution (Leonora et al., 1958; Li and Cummins, 1958; Jutisz and Squire, 1958; Squire and Li, 1958; Steelman and Segaloff, 1959; Ward et al., 1959, among others).

A. Follicle-stimulating hormone (FSH)

There are four main methods for the preparation of a gonadotrophic fraction rich in follicle-stimulating activity:

(i) van Dyke's method (Chow et al., 1942; van Dyke et al., 1950);

(ii) Li's method (Li et al., 1949; Li, 1949a);

(iii) McShan's method (McShan et al., 1954; McShan and Meyer, 1955; Leonora et al., 1956);

(iv) Steelman's method (Steelman et al., 1953, 1956a; Steelman, 1958; Steelman and Segaloff, 1959).

Some physico-chemical properties and amino acid and carbohydrate analyses of various FSH preparations are brought together in Tables I and II. FSH is a glyco-protein, the sugars present including mannose in the preparation of van Dyke, hexose in that of Li and fucose in that of Steelman (Table II). The problem of the protein moiety in FSH is, however, unresolved. The difficulty is that, although pituitary fractions with very high FSH activity can be obtained, there always seems to be some remaining contamination, however slight, to mar the apparent homogeneity of the product. Only one of the several preparations of

TABLE I

Some physico-chemical properties of gonadotrophins

	LTH			FSH				LH		
	Sheep[1,2,3,4,5]	Cattle[5,6]	Pig[7]	Sheep[8]	Sheep[9]	Pig[9] 'digested'	Sheep[10]	Sheep[11]	Sheep[12]	Pig[10]
Molecular weight:										
Osmotic pressure	26,500						40,000			
Analytical data	33,000									
Sedimentation-diffusion	24,100 24,200	32,000		67,000	25,000 to 30,000	29,000		30,000	28,000 ∓ 4,000	100,000
Diffusion-viscosity	22,000									
Diffusion coefficient ($D_{20\omega}$)	8.44×10^{-7}	7.5×10^{-7}		6×10^{-7}		7.43×10^{-7}		7.54×10^{-7}		5.9×10^{-7}
Sedimentation constant ($S_{20\omega}$)	2·19 2·05	2·65		4·7		2·49	3·6	2·47	2·32 ± 0·07	5·4
Partial specific volume (V_{20})	0·721 0·739			0·718						
Isoelectric point, pH	5·73	5·73	4·8	4·5	< 5·0	5·1-5·2	4·6	7·3(4·8)[9]		7·45
Specific rotation	−40·5°									

Compiled from: 1 Li et al. (1941a)   5 Li et al. (1940a)   9 Steelman and Segaloff (1959)
2 Li (1949b)   6 White et al. (1942)   10 Li and Evans (1948)
3 Li (1957)   7 Chow (1943)   11 Squire and Li (1958)
4 Li (1942)   8 Li and Pedersen (1952)   12 Ward et al. (1959)

TABLE II

Composition of pituitary gonadotrophins

Elements (%)		LTH		FSH		LH	
	No. of residues	Sheep[1]	Cattle[2]	Sheep[3,5,7]	Pig[4] 'digested'	Sheep[5,7]	Pig[6]
C		50·72	52·04	44·93			
H		6·63	7·01	6·67			
N		15·86	16·84	15·10		14·20	14·93
S		1·79	2·05	1·50			
Amino acids (%)							
alanine	11	3·25			3·5		
arginine	11	7·13		5·3	3·6		
cystine and cysteine	3	2·54	3·36	4·3	6·5		
aspartic acid	19	9·08		9·3	11·6		
glutamic acid	22	11·79		13·4	9·2		
glycine	12	2·84			2·9		
histidine	7	3·99		3·7	2·8		
leucine and isoleucine	37	17·38		9·2	4·0		
				3·3	2·8		
lysine	10	5·32		11·1	5·7		
methionine	7	3·81		1·0	1·5		
phenylalanine	8	4·89		5·8	3·3		
proline	14	5·64		5·2	4·4		
serine	18	6·51			4·4		
threonine	11	4·62		4·7	5·4		
valine	12	4·94		5·8	3·9		
tyrosine	7	4·74	5·71	3·8	4·5	4·5	
tryptophan	2	1·55	1·3		0·7	1·0	3·8
amine NH3	17						
	211	100·02			80·7		
Carbohydrates (%)							
galactose					1·2		
mannose					1·4	4·5	2·8
fucose					1·1		
hexose				1·23			
hexosamine				1·51	3·7	5·8	2·2
				2·74	7·4	10·3	5·0

Compiled from:
[1] Li (1949a, b, 1957) [5] Gurin (1942)
[2] White *et al.* (1942) [6] Chow *et al.* (1942)
[3] Li and Pedersen (1952) [7] Li and Evans (1948)
[4] Steelman and Segaloff (1959)

Li's FSH derived from sheep pituitaries was homogeneous on analysis in the ultracentrifuge, although all were satisfactory electrophoretically (Li and Pedersen, 1952). Van Dyke *et al.* (1950) estimated their preparations from pig pituitaries to be only 80–85 per cent pure although possessing similar electrophoretic mobility and isoelectric point to the sheep FSH of Li. Despite the newer methods of extraction, including fractional electrical transport (Steelman *et al.*, 1956a), purification of alcoholic-acetate extracts (Koenig and King, 1950; Ward *et al.*, 1959) and chromatography on DEAE cellulose (Steelman *et al.*, 1956b; Ellis, 1958), all of which yield very potent follicle-stimulating preparations, these are not homogeneous proteins (Steelman, 1958; Steelman and Segaloff, 1959). The greatest promise of obtaining pure FSH lies in the use of enzymic digestion, so-called 'digested FSH'. Steelman and co-workers (1955), using a pig FSH (after Steelman *et al.*, 1953), showed that there was no loss in biological activity after digestion at 37°C for 3 hours with pancreatin. Further purification by repeated column chromatography on DEAE cellulose produced a major fraction which was 'essentially' homogeneous chromatographically and by electrophoretic and ultracentrifugal analysis (Steelman *et al.*, 1956b; Steelman and Segaloff, 1959).

The problem whether or not pancreatin actually degrades the 'FSH molecule' is still to be resolved. Steelman *et al.* (1955) concluded that, as the digested preparation was not dialyzable, it did not consist of a small active molecule of FSH attached to a protein of large molecular weight. It may be that, like ACTH (Morris, 1955), its activity is due to a very small amount of a highly active component which is associated with other protein molecules of similar properties, or that it is a highly charged molecule bound to other proteins by electrostatic forces (Steelman *et al.*, 1955).

Various additional observations have been made on the characteristics of FSH preparations, though interpretation is often difficult. Steelman and Segaloff (1959) pointed out that their FSH preparations all had similar mobilities in paper electrophoresis, while Li's FSH moved twice as rapidly. The stability of FSH preparations, except the 'digested' product, is poor after lyophilization (Li and Pedersen, 1952; Steelman and Segaloff, 1959). A distinction can be made between the FSH preparations of Li and of van Dyke by immunological tests (van Dyke *et al.*, 1950). Moreover, the activity of Li's FSH is reduced by treatment with dilute HCl and lost after heating or treatment with ketene (Li and Pedersen, 1952). Disulphide groups are apparently necessary for a preparation to show gonadotrophic activity (Fraenkel-Conrat *et al.*, 1939, 1940a, b). Versene and cysteine reduce the activity of 'digested' pig FSH (Steelman and Segaloff, 1959).

B. Luteinizing hormone (LH; ICSH)

The older methods for the preparation of LH are:

(i) Li's LH, from sheep pituitaries (Li *et al.*, 1940 d, e, 1942a; see Li and Evans 1948; Li, 1949a);

(ii) van Dyke's LH, from pig pituitaries (Shedlovsky *et al.*, 1940; Chow *et al.*, 1942).

These methods were regarded, until recently, as producing pure preparations which could justifiably be called luteinizing hormone. Both Li's and van Dyke's LH seem to be homogeneous preparations when examined by solubility tests, electrophoresis and by ultracentrifugation (Li *et al.*, 1942b; Chow *et al.*, 1942). The two preparations differ in their carbohydrate content, in immunological tests and in their isoelectric points (Chow, 1942; Tables I and II).

Attempts were made to find the effective part of the LH molecule but no full amino acid analysis has yet been undertaken. Disulphide groups (Fraenkel-Conrat *et al.*, 1939, 1940 a, b) and free amino groups (Li *et al.*, 1939d, 1940d) have both been considered essential for the activity of LH, though these assumptions may be invalid (Li and Evans, 1948). Several workers have examined the effect of enzymes on different preparations of LH (McShan and Meyer, 1938, 1939; Abramowitz and Hisaw, 1939; Chen and van Dyke, 1939; Chow *et al.*, 1939, 1942). Pancreatin and trypsin destroy LH activity and attempts to separate a more active moiety by these means were unsuccessful (Chow *et al.*, 1939, 1942).

Other methods for the preparation of LH have been developed recently (Leonora *et al.*, 1958; Squire and Li, 1958; Jutisz and Squire, 1958; Ward *et al.*, 1959). Using sheep pituitaries, Squire and Li found that purification by chromatography and zone electrophoresis with subsequent re-chromatography gave 'LH' with more than one protein component. One fraction, which they called β ICSH, was homogeneous by chromotography, zone electrophoresis, boundary electrophoresis and ultracentrifugation (see Table I). However, Jutisz and Squire (1958), using a similar original fraction as starting material, but processing by zone electrophoresis on packed columns, obtained five components possessing ICSH activity. Ward and his co-workers (1959) fractionated sheep pituitaries by the method of Koenig and King (1950) combined with chromatography on carboxylmethyl cellulose and hydroxyl apatite ion exchange agents, and obtained two fractions with luteinizing hormone properties, LH_1 and LH_2. They concluded that LH_2, into which LH_1 could be partially dissociated, consisted of a single component (Table I). They attempted to determine the N-terminal amino acids and although they demonstrated the presence of serine, threonine with lesser quantities of glycine, lysine and glutamic and/or aspartic acid, they were unable to reach firm conclusions. Their estimate of contamination by biological assay was about 0·3 per cent follicle-stimulating hormone and 2 per cent thyrotrophic hormone.

It is clear that the chemical status of LH (ICSH) is in doubt. The danger exists that chemical processes produce their own artefacts with no biological relevance, and the possibility that the luteinizing property resides in small groups of amino acids, the extraction procedures only serving to distribute them in a random quantitative manner among the various protein fractions obtained, cannot be eliminated.

C. Luteotrophin (LTH)

Luteotrophin is usually presumed to be identical with prolactin (lactogenic hormone, galactin, mammotrophin). As prolactin is relatively stable to chemical reagents, a variety of procedures have been used to prepare it from pituitary tissue. The commonest method, extraction by acid-acetone, gives an extract which is rich in prolactin and free from other hypophysial hormones except adrenocorticotrophin which can readily be removed.

The preparation of a lactogenic substance was originally described by Lyons (1937a, b); later modifications are given by Li et al. (1942b) and Li and Evans (1948). Other methods are given by White et al. (1937, 1942), White (1943) and Riddle and Bates (1939). More recently, Cole and Li (1955) and Li (1957) have produced a simplified procedure.

In a series of papers, Li and his co-workers have made a thorough examination of some of the properties of prolactin (Li et al., 1939a, b, c, 1940a, b, c, 1941b, c; Li, 1942, 1943; Li and Kalman, 1946; Li and Fraenkel-Conrat, 1947; Li, 1949b, 1957; Li and Cummins, 1958). A summary of these findings is given in Tables I and II. The field has been reviewed by Li and Evans (1948), White (1949) and Li (1949a, 1957).

Prolactin obtained from cattle and sheep behaves as a homogeneous protein as judged by electrophoresis, ultracentrifugation, by solubility tests and by its behaviour in both counter-current distribution and chromatography on hydroxyl apatite columns (Shipley et al., 1939; Li et al., 1940a, b, 1941a, b; White et al., 1942; Li, 1957). These preparations are very similar, differing only in some solubility characteristics (Li et al., 1941a, b; Fleischer, 1943), in their tyrosine content (Table II; Li, 1957), and in the partition coefficient obtained in the 2-butanol-0·4 per cent dichloroacetic acid system (Li, 1957).

Various methods have been used in order to gain some idea of the characteristics of the protein which render it biologically active.

No clear conclusions can be drawn from retention of activity after exposure to high temperatures (Riddle and Bates, 1939), its unusual stability after treatment with urea (Li et al., 1941a; Li, 1944), or its inactivation with thiol compounds, cysteine in 200-fold quantity, thioglycolic acid (Fraenkel-Conrat et al., 1942; Fraenkel-Conrat, 1942); or after hydrolysis with pepsin, trypsin and HCl (Bates et al., 1934; McShan and French, 1937; White et al., 1942). It has been suggested that the presence of tyrosine (Li et al., 1941c), free amino acid groups (Li et al., 1939d; Li and Kalman, 1946) and carboxyl groups (Li and Fraenkel-Conrat, 1947) is essential for biological activity, though this is not certain (McShan and French, 1937; Li et al., 1939a; Bottomly and Folley, 1940; White, 1949).

Recent work has considerably clarified the chemical nature of prolactin. It is reasonably certain that prolactin consists of a single polypeptide chain with the sequence Thr · Pro · Val · Thr · Pro at the N-terminus and with a loop formed by a disulphide bridge at the C-terminus (Cole et al., 1957; Li and Cummins, 1958). Li and Cummins suggest the sequence Tyr · Leu · Asp (NH₂) CySH at the C-terminus of the protein molecule after reduction with cysteic acid as the C-terminal residue. It appears that the integrity of the disulphide bridge is essential for the biological activity of prolactin (Li and Cummins, 1958).

III. Ovarian-pituitary relationships

A. Eutheria

1. Introduction

The intricate interrelationships of the ovary and the anterior lobe of the pituitary have been analysed and reviewed on many occasions (Smith, 1939; Hisaw, 1947; Burrows, 1949; Evans and Simpson, 1950; Cowie and Folley, 1955, among others). This section is limited to a consideration of the glands themselves; other factors influencing ovarian function are dealt with elsewhere (Chapters 5, 6, 9, 18 and 19). It is confined to the Eutheria because knowledge about monotremes and marsupials is insufficient to make discussion worthwhile.

2. The ovary

(a) The ovary after hypophysectomy

Removal of the anterior lobe of the pituitary, and consequently withdrawal of gonadotrophins, is followed by degenerative changes in the ovaries (Fig. 1, 1 and 2), the rate of degeneration being influenced to some extent by the deficiency of other hypophysial hormones.

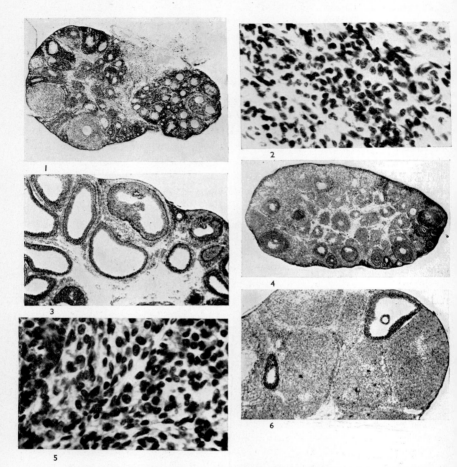

FIG. 1. Effects of purified preparations of pituitary gonadotrophin on the ovary of the rat hypophysectomized at the age of 27 days and killed 7 days later.   Doses of hormone given in g dry weight of pituitary tissue. Photographs and data kindly supplied by Professor W. H. McShan. (1) Uninjected hypophysectomized control (× 35). (2) As (1). Note 'deficiency cells' in interstitium and theca (× 386). (3) Injected with 0·5 g equiv. FSH from days 29 to 33.   Note large stimulated follicles but little stimulation of interstitial tissue.   No corpora lutea (× 26). (4) Injected with 5 g equiv. LH from days 29 to 33. Note increased interstitial tissue between small unstimulated follicles. No corpora lutea (× 26). (5) As (4). Note repair of 'deficiency cells' in interstitium and theca (× 386). (6) Injected with 0·5 g equiv. FSH plus 0·5 g equiv. LH from days 29 to 33.   Note large stimulated follicles and well-formed corpora lutea (× 26). (Reproduced by permission from Leonora et al., 1958.)

In general, the ovaries in all eutherian mammals react in the same way to hypophysial deficiency. If hypophysectomy is performed on mature animals, the ovaries are greatly reduced in size and large follicles regress. The interstitial cells show degenerative changes, characterized by shrunken nuclei, reduced cytoplasm and chromatin 'wheel' formation ('deficiency cells' of Selye *et al.*, 1933; Fig. 1, 2). Hisaw (1947) suggested that degeneration of the granulosa was precipitated by changes in the theca interna which plays an important role not only in vascularization but also in the secretion of oestrogen (which, in turn, may directly influence the growth and differentiation of the follicle; see below). Corpora lutea already in existence at the time of operation follow the same pattern of regression as they do in the normal animal. In the rat, however, these bodies may persist for exceptionally long periods (Bunde and Greep, 1936; Greep, 1938; Smith, 1939).

A quantitative study of the number of oocytes at different stages of development in the hypophysectomized rat (Ingram, 1953) showed that only a few follicles with more than one layer of granulosa cells persisted; many of these were atretic (see Chapter 4, sect. III, D). The mean diameter of twenty such follicles measured was 192μ (range $151–302\mu$), as compared with a mean of 294μ (range $133–605\mu$) for the largest follicles in the normal animal (Mandl and Zuckerman, 1952). The follicle thus appears to be able to grow up to a certain point independently of hypophysial stimulation. Development beyond the stage where the follicle is covered by about four layers of granulosa cells, however, is dependent upon gonadotrophins—a conclusion also supported by the observation that the number of follicles measuring less than 250μ in diameter does not vary in phase with the oestrous cycle (Mandl and Zuckerman, 1952).

It is worth noting that Talbert *et al.* (1951) have shown that Graafian follicles in rats that have been hypophysectomized at the beginning of pro-oestrus rarely contained pyknotic cells until 19 hours after the operation, while degenerative changes in the ova were not detected until 48 hours or later. The latter were often flattened against the wall of the antrum, and occasionally showed maturation (or pseudomaturation) changes. Nevertheless, loss of ability to respond to an ovulatory stimulus occurred some 8–12 hours after hypophysectomy. Physiological changes, therefore, appear to take place before histologically demonstrable variations can be detected. Moreover, these observations clearly indicate that the maturation of the ovum, like the early growth of the primordial oocytes in most vertebrates investigated (see pp. 389 to 406), can occur in the absence of hypophysial gonadotrophins (Hisaw, 1947).

It should be noted, however, that the ovary of the adult rat (Ingram and Mandl, 1958), though not that of the immature mouse (Lamond, 1959), may be capable of producing small amounts of oestrogen in the absence of hypophysial stimulation. It is possible that this observation, together with the recent report by Croes-Buth et al. (1959) that as little as 0·5μg oestradiol benzoate/day is sufficient to stimulate follicular growth in hypophysectomized animals, will demand a re-interpretation of the results reported by Talbert et al. (1951).

(b) *The ovary after injection of FSH preparations*

The processes involved in the more advanced development of follicles, i.e. the secretion of liquor folliculi, the mitotic proliferation of granulosa cells and the moulding of the surrounding stroma into an investing layer of thecal cells, are considered to be dependent on FSH. The assignment of these properties to a separate gonadotrophic component of the pituitary hormones rests principally on the work of Greep et al. (1942). These authors showed that administration of their FSH preparation to immature hypophysectomized female rats led to an increase in ovarian weight, associated with a growth of follicles which passed through a cycle of maturation and atresia without becoming either cystic or luteinized (Fig. 1, 3). FSH neither stimulated the interstitial cells nor caused secretion of oestrogen as judged by uterine weight. In this work, such limitations of the properties of FSH were quite clear. This type of FSH preparation, however, when given in high doses, not only stimulated follicular growth in similar test animals, but also produced repair of 'deficiency cells', thickening and luteinization of the theca, marked mitotic activity of the granulosa cells and some secretion of oestrogen (van Dyke et al., 1950). These latter biological effects are supposedly due to LH. This suggests that although follicular stimulation is a convenient descriptive term, definitive proof that the ripening of the Graafian follicle can occur without the presence of LH is still lacking.

It might be argued, on the other hand, that the boundaries of the action of FSH become blurred only when large doses are administered. Thus follicle-stimulating activity of Li's FSH can be detected in hypophysectomized female rats after injection of minimal amounts (2–3μg; Fraenkel-Conrat et al., 1943; Li et al., 1949), which induced no effects that could be attributed to LH (Fraenkel-Conrat et al., 1943). Whilst ten to twenty times the minimal effective dose was still only follicle-stimulating, larger amounts of FSH induced oestrus, formation of corpora lutea and repair of interstitial tissue (Simpson et al., 1951). Similarly, high doses of the most recent preparation, 'digested' FSH, appear to induce secretion of oestrogen (Steelman and Segaloff, 1959), while moderate doses lead to an increase of 100–150 per cent in ovarian weight without affecting the size of the uterus.

(c) *The ovary after injection of LH preparations*

Moderate doses of LH preparations given to hypophysectomized rats are not followed by either an increase in ovarian weight or secretion of oestrogen. Their salient effects are repair and stimulation of interstitial cells and enlargement of thecal cells without follicular maturation (Fig. 1, *4* and *5*; see Li *et. al.*, 1940d; Greep *et al.*, 1942; Simpson *et al.*, 1942; Fraenkel-Conrat *et al.*, 1943). When given in large doses, most LH preparations (although apparently not van Dyke's; see Greep *et al.*, 1942) can also cause secretion of oestrogen, follicular growth and ovulation (Leonora *et al.*, 1958; Steelman and Segaloff, 1959). The persistence of large corpora lutea in the hypophysectomized rat is curtailed by the administration of gonadotrophic preparations with luteinizing properties (Bunde and Greep, 1936; Greep, 1938).

(d) *The ovary after injection of FSH and LH*

A combination of suitable amounts of FSH and LH given to the hypophysectomized rat can cause a twofold increase in ovarian weight, maturation of numerous follicles, ovulation and formation of corpora lutea (Fig. 1, *6*) associated with stimulation of thecal and interstitial cells and secretion of oestrogen (Greep *et al.*, 1942; Fraenkel-Conrat *et al.*, 1943; Hisaw, 1947; Evans and Simpson, 1950). Even minute quantities of LH can act synergistically with FSH to produce secretion of oestrogen without obvious histological changes in the interstitial cells (Evans and co-workers, *op. cit.*). This 'augmentation effect' was confirmed by the use of human chorionic gonadotrophin which, although chemically dissimilar to LH, possesses many of its biological properties (Simpson *et al.*, 1951; Steelman and Pohley, 1953).

(e) *Experimental factors*

(i) *Site of injection.* The site of injection of different gonadotrophic preparations influences their ultimate effect. It seems that LH given intraperitoneally will decrease the activity of other gonadotrophins (Fraenkel-Conrat *et al.*, 1940b). A similar effect has been claimed for FSH also (van Dyke *et al.*, 1950; see also App. 1, p. 434). Further, FSH activity may be more pronounced when the preparation is given subcutaneously rather than intraperitoneally. Some of these differences are presumably due to differential rates of absorption.

(ii) *'Anti-gonadotrophins'*. Animals may become refractory to repeated injections of a gonadotrophin (Collip, 1932; Collip and Anderson, 1935; Meyer and Gustus, 1935; Zondek and Sulman, 1937; Leathem, 1949; Deutsch *et al.*, 1950). As this effect rarely occurs after administration of homologous pituitary extracts, it is presumably due to the formation of antibodies. Once formed, such 'anti-gonadotrophins' may be effective in other animals, and this forms the basis for their assay. The formation of these substances occurs less readily in rats than in rabbits. In man it constitutes a serious obstacle to certain treatments. Inhibitory substances formed against one gonadotrophic preparation may not necessarily suppress the activity of another, probably because of differences in the nature of the protein. Indeed, should the activity of gonadotrophins reside in a small group of amino acids, the phenomenon of 'antihormones' may be misnamed, the so-called 'anti-gonadotrophins' being effectively antagonists to the heterologous carrier-protein rather than to the active constituents.

(f) The concept of FSH and LH

The separate identities of FSH and LH have not been unequivocally demonstrated. They may comprise one gonadotrophin and distinctions are made on quantitative bases (Aron *et al.*, 1954; Marescaux *et al.*, 1957); or they may be completely distinct but (i) have not yet been chemically purified and/or (ii) possess a common moiety which induces similar biological effects when large amounts of either preparation are given.

It is suggested that the terms FSH and LH should be retained for the following reasons: firstly, they are convenient and descriptive; secondly, given in minimal effective doses, the actions of FSH and LH are distinct and clear; and thirdly, recent progress in protein chemistry suggests that FSH and LH will prove to be relatively simple polypeptides (see App. 2, p. 434).

(g) Luteotrophin

(i) *General.* Evidence for the existence of prolactin in pigeons (Riddle and Braucher, 1931; Riddle *et al.*, 1932) and for lactogenic hormone in mammals (Stricker and Grueter, 1928; see Cowie and Folley, 1955) came well before the suggestion that there was a third gonadotrophin, luteotrophin (Astwood and Fevold, 1939; Astwood, 1941). Luteotrophin is currently considered to be that secretion of the anterior lobe of the pituitary which will sustain the function of the corpus luteum, the formation of which had been induced by LH (p. 373).

(ii) *Rat and mouse.* The criteria used to evaluate the secretion of progesterone, and hence of luteotrophic activity, are: (i) size and histology of corpora lutea and (ii) the histological appearance of the vagina, uterus and mammae. Chemical methods will undoubtedly also be used in the future.

Early observations demonstrated the capacity of hypophysial extracts to prolong the normal oestrous cycle in rats and mice (Long and Evans, 1922; Teel, 1926), prolactin in particular (Dresel, 1935; Lahr and Riddle, 1936) possessing luteotrophic activity. Later it was shown that in hypophysectomized rats, injections of prolactin could produce functional corpora lutea (Astwood, 1941), induce pseudopregnancy with formation of deciduomata after uterine traumatization (Evans et al., 1941), and maintain pregnancy (Cutuly, 1941, 1942; Lyons et al., 1943). In the latter case, however, placental gonadotrophins may reinforce luteal activity (Astwood and Greep, 1938; Mayer and Klein, 1949; Mayer, 1951; Mayer and Canivenc, 1951). Later work has confirmed and extended these observations in the rat, and reference may be made to Lyon (1942), Tobin (1942), Everett (1943, 1944), Fluhmann and Laqueur (1943), Sydnor (1945), Desclin (1948, 1949), Greep and Chester Jones (1950a) and Astwood (1953); see also App. 3, p. 434.

Recent studies have shown that in the rat, homologous grafts of the adenohypophysis to the kidney capsule will maintain the youngest corpora lutea in a functional state for long periods (Everett, 1954, 1956; Nikitovitch-Winer and Everett, 1958). As these corpora lutea were also larger than non-functional ones, it seems that luteotrophin secreted by the graft caused both hyperplasia and secretion. Since other hypophysial target organs were atrophic (presence of 'deficiency cells' and lack of large follicles), Everett's conclusion that only luteotrophin was produced seems reasonable.

This observation indicates that the pituitary, when no longer juxtaposed to the median eminence, is capable only of luteotrophic secretion. Alternatively, the adenohypophysis once given over to excessive and abnormal secretion of one hormone cannot produce others in normal amounts (Selye, 1947; Nowell and Chester Jones, 1957). It might be anticipated, then, that pituitary grafts under different conditions and in other species might secrete predominantly a trophic hormone other than LTH. In effect Schweizer et al. (1937) have demonstrated that such grafts in female guinea pigs produced a state of constant oestrus with persistent cystic follicles, while Courrier (1956) noted well-maintained testes in rats bearing pituitary grafts (see Martinovitch and Pavic, 1960).

(iii) *Other mammals.* A specific luteotrophic activity of the pituitary has not been clearly demonstrated for mammals except the rat and the mouse. While there are slight indications that LTH may participate in the normal menstrual cycle (Holstrom and Jones, 1949; Coppedge and Segaloff, 1951; Fried and Rakoff, 1952), injections of prolactin failed to prolong the life of the corpus luteum in the rabbit (Mayer, 1951) or significantly lengthen the luteal phase of the menstrual cycle in either the monkey (Hisaw, 1944; Bryans, 1948) or woman (Kupperman et al., 1944; Holstrom and Jones, 1949; Bradbury et al., 1950).

On the other hand, injections of prolactin into anoestrous ewes, in which corpora lutea had been artificially induced, caused progestational activity; when given to animals possessing spontaneous corpora lutea in the breeding season, such effects were observed in only half the animals (Moore and Nalbandov, 1953, 1955; Nalbandov et al., 1955).

The failure to demonstrate activation and/or maintenance of the corpus luteum by prolactin in many species may indicate that (i) prolactin is not luteotrophic; (ii) that it is subject to species specificity; or (iii) that the life-span of the corpus luteum is in any case limited (Astwood, 1941; Hisaw, 1944; Bradbury et al., 1950). Presumably the corpus luteum normally regresses because LTH is withdrawn, or the secretion of LH, which in some species maintains its structure, lessens. In the latter case, exogenous prolactin given towards the end of the luteal phase would not be expected to prolong the secretory life of a corpus luteum which is structurally failing. Similarly, prolonged injections of prolactin fail to extend pseudopregnancy beyond its usual limit.

In view of the above observations, it seems possible that luteotrophic activity has not been demonstrated in many animals because the crucial experiments have not been performed. One such experiment, as Greep (unpublished) has suggested, would be the injection of LTH, alone or combined with LH, into hypophysectomized or intact rabbits immediately after ovulation (see also App. 4, p. 434).

3. Changes in the pituitary

(a) Gonadotrophins after ovariectomy

Gonadectomy in all species studied is accompanied by an increased storage of gonadotrophins by the pituitary (see Burrows, 1949). This gain in potency has been clearly demonstrated by experiments on the rat. A dose of one pituitary from an ovariectomized female causes a six-fold increase in ovarian weight in the recipient hypophysectomized immature animal, while the pituitaries from three normal adult females were ineffective (Hellbaum and Greep, 1946; Greep and Chester Jones 1950b). Stored gonadotrophin in the spayed female rat is predominantly LH (Greep and Chester Jones, 1950b). On the other hand significant amounts of FSH were detected in the blood (Cozens and

Nelson, 1958; Gans, 1959a), where some LH may also be present (Gans, 1959b). The FSH content of the pituitary is enhanced in post-menopausal women (see Henderson and Rowlands, 1938; Noble *et al.*, 1939; Bahn *et al.*, 1953a, b), the proportion of FSH to LH changing from 1 : 1 to 3 : 1 (Albert, 1956). Increased amounts of gonadotrophin appear in the urine (post-menopausal gonadotrophin, PMG), but its constitution is in doubt (Albert, 1956; Loraine, 1958; Segaloff and Steelman, 1959).

It is clear that deficiency of ovarian oestrogens and progesterone allows increased elaboration of FSH and LH. The relationship between the storage and secretion of these two gonadotrophins has as yet to be clarified (see p. 379).

(b) *Gonadotrophins after injections of steroids*

(i) *Pituitary of spayed animals.* The gonadotrophic potency of the pituitary of ovariectomized animals can be reduced by the injection of oestrogens (Meyer *et al.*, 1932; Hellbaum and Greep, 1946; Burrows, 1949). The amount of steroid required to show this effect depends on the age of the animal and the length of time after operation (Takewaki and Maekawa, 1952; Maekawa, 1953a). There is some doubt whether this reduction can be achieved with doses of oestrogen within the physiological range. There is evidence that oestrogens (i) have no effect on stored gonadotrophins (Lauson *et al.*, 1938; Jungck *et al.*, 1947); (ii) effect an increase (Burch and Cunningham, 1930; Meyer *et al.*, 1946a); or (iii) change the proportions of FSH and LH in one direction or the other (Wolfe, 1931; Kraul, 1931; Hellbaum and Greep, 1946; Finerty and Meyer, 1950; Greep and Chester Jones, 1950a, b).

These variations in response depend on the dosages of oestrogens given and the duration of the treatment. Large amounts of oestrogens cause a marked increase in adenohypophysial weight (Simpson and Williams, 1946), and when given chronically, pituitary adenomas (see Burrows, 1949). Greep and Chester Jones (1950b) found that rats spayed at the age of 30 days, injected for 45 days with 1 (0·166μg) or 5 units of oestradiol benzoate, showed a considerable reduction in gonadotrophic potency of the pituitary, with LH more strongly suppressed than FSH (see also Finerty and Meyer, 1950). Normal physiological reactions, however, may be more readily revealed by the use of small amounts of oestrogen over short periods. Following Wolfe (1931), Meyer and his co-workers (Meyer *et al.*, 1946a; Finerty and Meyer, 1950) concluded that at low concentrations, oestrogen stimulates the secretion of LH and inhibits that of FSH. This implies that,

2E

in these circumstances, increased secretion accompanies reduction in stored LH, and confirms the opinion of Hellbaum and Greep (1946) regarding the relationship between LH and oestrogen. However, Gans (1959a, b) showed that the amount of FSH and LH in the blood of ovariectomized rats is significantly decreased by daily injections of 2μg oestradiol benzoate for 4 weeks. It is probable, therefore, that both storage and secretion of gonadotrophins in ovariectomized rats can be reduced by what may be considered to be 'physiological' doses of oestrogens.

(ii) *Pituitary of normal animals*. The pituitary of the normal animal stores only small amounts of FSH and LH (Greep and Chester Jones, 1950b), and their secretory rates are difficult to estimate, particularly as they can be barely detected in the blood with the test methods available (Cozens and Nelson, 1958; Gans, 1959a, b).

Such evidence as we possess indicates that in normal females oestrogens can produce luteinizing effects attributable to the release of LH. Hohlweg (1934) originally showed that a single injection of oestrogen produced corpora lutea in female rats on the threshold of sexual maturity. This concept of the relationship between LH and oestrogens has been supported by many workers (Fevold et al., 1937; Hellbaum and Greep, 1946; Bradbury, 1947; Everett, 1948; Finerty and Meyer, 1950; Kempf, 1950), although results with immature rats are not so clear-cut (Bradbury, 1947; Greep and Chester Jones, 1950b; Paesi, 1952). The simplicity of the hypothesis is marred by the possibility that oestrogen and FSH may also be intimately connected (see Hollander and Hollander, 1958). In an attempt to clarify the position, Byrnes and Meyer (1951a) concluded that oestrogens in small quantities suppress FSH, in larger amounts increase the secretion of LH, and that only 'non-physiological' high doses given over prolonged periods reduce the secretion of LH.

It is interesting to note that injections of oestrogens early in post-natal life can produce a long-lasting sterility due to the suppression of gonadotrophins, totally for LH and almost so for FSH (Takasugi, 1952; Barraclough and Leathem, 1954). This finding re-emphasizes the importance of ovarian secretions for pituitary function, but the finer details of the reciprocal balance between the two organs have yet to be elucidated.

4. *Interrelations of ovary and pituitary*

(a) *Changes during life*

(i) *The foetus*. The pituitary of the foetus may contain a small quantity of gonadotrophins (Hellbaum, 1935), or may show signs of being able to produce them (Smith and Dortzbach, 1929). The foetal pituitary influences the development of the embryo (see Jost, 1953, 1954, 1955), but no real case has been made out for the dependence of foetal ovaries on gonadotrophins derived from the foetal pituitary.

(ii) *Immaturity.* The consensus is that the actual gonadotrophic content of the pituitary gradually increases in post-natal life, but not markedly so until the approach of puberty (Smith and Engle, 1927; Wolfe and Cleveland, 1931; Clark, 1935; Bergman and Turner, 1942; de Jongh and Paesi, 1958). It is assumed that increase in gonadotrophic content is accompanied by increase in secretion. This may not be the case in man, however, since urinary gonadotrophins are virtually absent before puberty (Albert, 1956).

The absence of mature follicles and ovulation in the immature animal may be due either to the lack of gonadotrophin secretion or the refractoriness of the ovary to gonadotrophic stimulation which, in the rat for example, is displayed up to about 15 days of age (Hertz and Hisaw, 1934; Hisaw, 1947). At some post-natal period, perhaps when the theca of the follicles has differentiated, the ovary seems to gain 'competence' to react to gonadotrophins (Hisaw, 1947). Maturity does not supervene immediately, however, even when the ovary is competent to respond. There is a gradual development of the ovarian-pituitary interrelationships, the mechanism of which still remains obscure, the ovary having a checking effect on the hypophysial secretion of gonadotrophins. It may be that a gradual increase in oestrogen secretion retards the pace of gonadotrophin elaboration, though no firm evidence for this is available (Zephiroff and Dobrovolskaya-Zavadskaya, 1940; Rennels, 1951). An alternative suggestion is that changes leading from immaturity to the cyclical phenomena of maturity depend on variations in the proportion of FSH and LH in the gonadotrophic complex (Hollandbeck et al., 1956). These authors suggest that in the pig, the pituitary secretes predominantly FSH at the time of birth, thereby accounting for the gonadotrophic potency of the gland at that age. With increasing age, there might well be a decrease in FSH secretion coupled with an increase in the rate of LH secretion, the critical ratio between the two hormones being reached at the age of about 225 days when ovulation first occurs in this species. This latter part of their theory is acceptable, but the supposition that gonadotrophic content must represent gonadotrophic secretion remains suspect. Moreover, the extension of their argument from the pig to the Eutheria in general may not be valid, particularly in view of the fact that this animal and the horse are exceptional in containing within their pituitaries demonstrable gonadotrophins at an early age (Smith, 1939). In this connection it should be noted that follicular development can be induced in the calf as early as

2E*

the 1st week after birth by injections of hypophysial extracts, and, moreover, that the ovaries of calves aged 3 weeks respond as well as those at the age of 20 weeks (Casida *et al.*, .1943; Marden, 1952). If gonadotrophins are circulating in immature animals, then the limiting factor in progress towards maturity must lie within the ovaries themselves.

(iii) *Puberty and maturity.* Early work on the variations in pituitary gonadotrophic potency during the oestrous cycle by Smith and Engle (1929), Wolfe (1930, 1931), Lane and Hisaw (1934) and Schmidt (1937) indicates that oestrus itself is associated with a low content of pituitary gonadotrophin; higher values were found before oestrus, and even lower ones in the luteal phase. The rabbit appears to be exceptional in that its pituitary assayed at a comparatively high figure at oestrus (Hill, 1934). More recently Nalbandov and his co-workers have shown that in both the pig and the sheep, gonadotrophic content of the pituitary is low at oestrus; the potency increases linearly in sheep from the onset of heat until a maximum is reached on the 16th or 17th day of the cycle (Robinson and Nalbandov, 1951; Kammlade *et al.*, 1952).

Season may be an over-riding factor in the control of ovarian activity. The ovary becomes quiescent during hibernation, and becomes less reactive to gonadotrophins (Smith, 1951). In some species the gonadotrophic potency of the pituitary itself is low (e.g. mule deer: Grieser and Browman, 1956; male cottontails: Elder and Finerty, 1943) but not in others (female cottontails: Elder and Finerty, 1943; sheep: Kammlade *et al.*, 1952). The total gonadotrophic potency of sheep pituitary was uniformly higher during the non-breeding than the breeding season. Kammlade *et al.* (1952) concluded from a study of the size and number of follicles in the ovaries of non-breeding ewes that some gonadotrophin was being secreted during anoestrus; they also suggested that anoestrus is characterized by the exclusive elaboration of FSH resulting in follicular maturation without ovulation or secretion of oestrogen. The latter occur during the breeding season and are associated with the elaboration of LH.

The FSH content of the pituitary of the young monkey (*Macaca mulatta*) was found to be highest on day 9 of the menstrual cycle perhaps correlated with the pre-ovulatory spurt of follicular growth the content of LH was highest in the pre-ovulatory and ovulatory period, and increased relatively more during the middle of the cycle than did FSH (Simpson *et al.*, 1956). This observation is consistent with the belief that LH and FSH act synergistically in inducing advanced follicular enlargement (see also Knobil *et al.*, 1959).

The normal pattern of the secretion of gonadotrophins has not been determined for the human being (Loraine, 1958). Extracts of urinary gonadotrophins have luteinizing properties throughout the menstrual cycle (Loraine and Brown, 1956), but there may be a peak at midcycle (McArthur, 1952). It should be borne in mind, however, that the composition of urinary gonadotrophins, hypophysial in origin though they may be (Blackburn *et al.*, 1956), is in doubt (Albert, 1956; Segaloff and Steelman, 1959), and that the biological potency of the extracts is relatively less than that of follicle-stimulating and luteinizing fractions of pituitary preparations.

(iv) *Senescence.* It has already been suggested that during immaturity, the developing ovary passes from a stage of unresponsiveness to gonadotrophins to that of competence. Similarly, it appears that in some species, unresponsiveness returns in old age. It would seem that the life-span of the ovary is an intrinsic property, influenced but not determined by the anterior lobe of the pituitary. The results of ovarian failure with the passage of reproductive years are most clearly seen in post-menopausal women, in whom high titres of gonadotrophins are found in blood and urine (Loraine, 1958).

In contrast, however, senescence is not necessarily associated with ovarian incapacity to respond to gonadotrophins (Ingram, 1959; Burack and Wolfe, 1959). For example, the ovaries of rats do not become devoid of follicles even in very old age (Mandl and Shelton, 1959; Shelton, 1959), and following unilateral ovariectomy some compensatory hypertrophy occurs (Ingram, 1959).

It is also of interest to note that the ovaries of senile virgin rats contain excessively large corpora lutea associated with 'deficiency cells', indicating perhaps that the pituitary is secreting LTH at the expense of LH (Mandl, 1959). Recent results also indicate that oestrous cycles are less regular in senile virgin than breeding rats (Mandl, 1961; see App. 9, p. 434), associated with a higher incidence of spontaneous mammary and pituitary tumours than in breeding animals (Howell and Mandl, 1961; see App. 10, p. 434). The interplay between ovarian and hypophysial hormones in old animals belonging to species lacking a clear-cut menopausal phase needs to be further investigated.

(b) *Ovarian transplantation experiments*

Experiments in which ovaries have been transplanted into the spleen (e.g. Biskind and Biskind, 1944) have yielded particularly interesting results. In preparations of this type, ovarian secretions are routed into the portal circulation and are inactivated in the liver before reaching the general circulation. The pituitary may thus undergo changes normally associated with ovariectomy even though the animal possesses ovaries capable of responding to gonadotrophic stimulation.

The gonadotrophic content of pituitaries of animals bearing intra-splenic grafts is equivalent to that of spayed animals, provided that there are no abdominal adhesions allowing leaks of steroid hormones into the peripheral circulation (cf. Heller and Jungck, 1947; Jungck *et al.*, 1947; Gans, 1950; Greep and Chester Jones, 1950b; Takewaki *et al.*, 1952; Takewaki, 1953). The grafts contain follicles which are being formed continuously and which luteinize, but the corpora lutea fail to involute (Maekawa, 1954; Maekawa and Imai, 1954). These effects indicate that FSH and LH are being secreted in copious quantities (see p. 373). Administration of oestrogens inhibits secretion of LH completely (Takewaki *et al.*, 1954), with slight impairment in FSH output, particularly in young animals (Takewaki, 1952). Progesterone did not show any influence on the secretion of gonadotrophins, even when given in doses exceeding those of oestrogen (cf. Chapter 21).

(c) *Parabiosis*

The technique of parabiosis (see Finerty, 1952) has proved valuable in some respects, but since the junction of capillary anastomoses may not necessarily allow completely free passage of all hormones, some perplexing problems have arisen. Moreover, animals united parabiotically exist under unnatural conditions.

It has nevertheless been clearly demonstrated that the pituitary of the spayed female, which stores gonadotrophins, also secretes them in significant amounts. In ovariectomized-hypophysectomized female parabionts, there are only large ovarian follicles, indicating that the spayed rat secretes principally FSH (Biddulph and Meyer, 1946). Since the hypophysectomized partner remains in constant oestrus, and the production of oestrogen according to some authorities (Meyer and Biddulph, 1941; Meyer *et al.*, 1946b; Greep and Chester Jones, 1950a) requires the synergistic action of FSH and LH, the possibility that LH also is secreted remains.

Parabiotic preparations have been used to show that oestrogens influence the secretion of gonadotrophins and, in particular, that they regulate the hypersecretion which follows ovariectomy (Finerty, 1952). Injection of small amounts of oestrogen to the spayed partner of a spayed female–normal female pair completely inhibited the ovarian hypertrophy which normally occurs in the intact animal, the degree of inhibition being a function of the dose (Meyer and Hertz, 1937; Bunster and Meyer, 1938; Byrnes and Meyer, 1951b).

(d) *Some other factors*

(i) *Oestrogens.* The function of oestrogens has been discussed elsewhere (pp. 377 to 378; also Chapters 5 and 6). In this section, attention is focused on the direct action of oestrogens on the ovary (Pencharz, 1940; Williams, 1940, 1944, 1945; Payne and Hellbaum, 1955). Many ovarian changes following oestrogen administration are mediated through the pituitary, but it has been shown that in hypophysectomized animals, the hormone can cause follicular growth (Simpson *et al.*, 1941; Gaarenstroom, 1942; de Wit, 1953) and maintenance of corpora lutea (Robson, 1937). The capacity of oestrogen to stimulate follicular growth in hypophysectomized animals may be detected following doses as low as 0·5 µg oestradiol benzoate/day (Croes-Buth *et al.*, 1959). The above observations indicate that the action of gonadotrophins upon the ovary may be facilitated by the secretions which they evoke.

(ii) *Thyroid gland.* The ovary of hypothyroid animals shows atrophic changes associated with a marked decrease in the number of follicles and luteinization (Janes, 1944; Williams *et al.*, 1944; Kopf *et al.*, 1948; Szontagh and Lichner, 1951). The ovaries of thyroidectomized and thiouracil-treated animals are hypersensitive to gonadotrophins (Fluhmann, 1934; Johnson and Meites, 1950; Mandl, 1957; Leathem, 1958), and become filled with excessively large cysts (Leathem, 1958). Conversely, the administration of thyroxine decreases ovarian response (Fluhmann, 1934; Tolksdorf and Jensen, 1939; Warner and Meyer, 1949).

Two processes may be involved: firstly, the elaboration of gonadotrophins may be decreased in hypo- and increased in hyperthyroidism (Evans and Simpson, 1930; Van Horn, 1931, 1933; Cohen, 1935; Leathem, 1945; Jones *et al.*, 1946); or secondly, thyroxine may increase the rate of inactivation of gonadotrophins, thus leading to a diminished ovarian response; the withdrawal of thyroxine would allow FSH and LH to act to the full limit of their availability (Mandl, 1957). The possibility also exists that the effect of sex hormones on the hypophysis may be modified by variations in the circulating level of thyroid hormone (Smelser, 1939; Warner and Meyer, 1949; Maekawa, 1953b).

(iii) *Adrenal cortex.* General reviews are to be found in Parkes (1945), Courrier *et al.* (1953), Moore (1953), Zuckerman (1953) and Chester Jones (1957).

Adrenocortical insufficiency is accompanied by a general decline in the condition of the animal, of which gonadal failure with cessation of sexual cycles are but one manifestation. Adrenalectomized animals maintained in good health by means of salt therapy, however, underwent regular oestrous cycles, though the ovaries and the numbers of follicles declined (Mandl, 1954). Mandl concluded that this ovarian change was due to impaired sensitivity to FSH rather than to a decrease in the endogenous production of this hormone. Response to

LH was unchanged in adult, but somewhat impaired in immature adrenalectomized animals. Ovarian reactions to gonadotrophins could be restored to the normal level by injection of cortisone or hydrocortisone (Payne, 1951; Mandl, 1954; Smith, E. K., 1955).

Adrenocortical hormones may act by 'facilitating' (Ingle, 1952) the action of FSH at the cellular level (Mandl, 1954, 1957). They do not, however, appear to be significantly involved with the action of LH on the ovaries (Swingle et al., 1951; Mandl, op. cit.). This differentiation between ovarian response to FSH and LH in the adrenalectomized animal may be due not only to varying ovarian sensitivity, but also to interactions of pituitary hormones. However, it seems unlikely that ACTH acts antagonistically or thyrotrophin synergistically with gonadotrophins (Mandl, 1954, 1957). Nevertheless, disturbance of hypophysial secretions in adrenal and thyroid imbalance may contribute to ovarian dysfunction primarily occasioned by deficiency in cortical steroids and thyroxine.

(iv) *Nutrition.* The gross manifestation of restricted caloric intake is cessation of oestrous cycles (Ershoff, 1952) or amenorrhoea (Zubiran and Gomez-Mont, 1953), associated with a decrease in the level of urinary gonadotrophin (Albert, 1956). The effects of malnutrition, reversible by resumption of an adequate diet, are a decrease in the secretion of gonadotrophins, although their elaboration and storage in the pituitary may either be enhanced or normal (Meites and Reed, 1949; Rinaldini, 1949; Meites, 1953). The problem why, in inanition, gonadotrophins are elaborated but not released, and why the ovaries remain capable of responding to their stimuli, remains unresolved.

It is possible that inanition is not the prime cause of these disturbances, but that the latter are associated with a lack of specific factors such as vitamins (see also Chapter 18, sect. II, A). In pyridoxine (B$_6$)-deficient rats, reproductive disturbances are due both to absence of ovarian hormones and to pituitary change (Nelson et al., 1951, 1953). Wooten et al. (1955) showed that pituitaries derived from B$_6$-deficient rats possessed approximately seven times as much FSH activity as those of normal females; the ICSH (LH) activity was only slightly higher, and the content of lactogenic hormone remained unchanged. It would thus appear that neither the synthesis of gonadotrophic hormones nor their release and utilization were impaired. Moreover, as the deficient animals lost only 10 per cent body weight, it would seem likely that the changes in gonadotrophins were due specifically to the lack of vitamin B$_6$ rather than to inanition.

More recent experiments have shown that the response of B$_6$-deficient rats to FSH was markedly decreased, while that to ICSH was only slightly impaired (Wooten et al., 1958). The most probable explanation is that the deficiency is accompanied by a lessening sensitivity of the ovary; the concomitant increase in the gonadotrophic potency of the pituitary supports this view.

5. *General considerations*

A comprehensive survey of ovarian-pituitary interrelationships must of necessity include the control of ovulation, changes in pregnancy, and the role of the hypothalamus and neural mechanisms. All these facets are considered in separate chapters (Chapters 6, 9 and 19), and in this section we shall only consider to what extent it is possible to regard the gonadotrophins on the one hand, and the ovarian steroids on the other, as comprising a closed circuit with reciprocal interactions to which such terms as 'push-pull' and 'feedback' have been applied.

In the previous sections it became clear that much work has been directed towards the effects of oestrogens on the two gonadotrophic components, FSH and LH. Yet in the normal animal the factors luteinizing, follicle-stimulating and luteotrophic must be set against not only oestrogens but also progestins.

Progesterone has been shown to suppress the oestrous cycle of rats, guinea pigs and sheep and to inhibit ovulation (Selye *et al.*, 1936; Dempsey, 1937; Makepeace *et al.*, 1937; Phillips, 1937; Dutt and Casida, 1948). On the other hand, removal of functional corpora lutea from the ovaries of the cow and the ewe will hasten the onset of oestrus (e.g. Hammond, 1927). These observations gave rise to the hypothesis that progesterone inhibits the release of gonadotrophins, particularly LH, and accounts for the absence of ovulation in both the luteal phase of the sexual cycle and in pseudopregnancy and pregnancy (Dempsey, 1937; Makepeace *et al.*, 1937; Astwood and Fevold, 1939; Bradbury, 1947). However, Everett (1948), following up his earlier work, concluded that, in fact, progesterone consistently facilitates ovulation and only in special circumstances is it inhibitory. It became clear that progesterone might act on gonadotrophic secretion through neurogenic mechanisms (cf. Chapters 5 and 19; also Everett and Sawyer, 1949; Sawyer and Everett, 1959) and this would explain its apparent lack of effect in many experiments (e.g. p. 382), except in large doses (see App. 5, p. 434).

There is a growing body of evidence showing that progesterone secretion occurs before as well as after ovulation (Astwood, 1941; Everett, 1945; Everett and Sawyer, 1949; Forbes, 1953; Green, 1955, among others). The site of pre-ovulatory progesterone secretion may be either the thecal cells of the maturing follicle or the luteal tissue formed in the previous cycle and transitorily reactivated. This occurrence of progesterone might merely represent an intermediate stage in steroid metabolism. Nevertheless, it is likely that progesterone plays an essential part in the events leading up to increased LH secretion and the initiation of ovulation (Chapters 5 and 19). If progesterone arises from recognizable luteal tissue by the action of LH and LTH, then the simplest explanation would be that such secretion of progesterone as may occur in the pre-ovulatory phases of mammalian sexual cycles is the direct result of stimulation by these gonadotrophic factors, and that some thecal cells (to which the secretion of oestrogen by the action of FSH and LH has been assigned) might turn to the production of progesterone immediately before ovulation. This suggestion would imply, however, that luteotrophin is secreted in the pre-ovulatory phase. It may be that progesterone acts (i) directly on the adenohypophysis, forming a reciprocal relationship with luteotrophin, and (ii) indirectly through neural mechanisms mediating alterations in the rate of secretion of LH.

This consideration of the role of progesterone is but one facet of the complications inherent in the problem of the hormonal control of sexual cycles. Permutations and combinations of the five suggested controlling factors, FSH, LH, LTH, oestrogen and progesterone, are numerous. The confusion, exemplified in the literature, arises because at one time or another many of the theoretical possibilities of interaction have been advanced in attempts to explain cyclical phenomena. No decision as to the nature of the ebb and flow of hormones during sexual cycles can be arrived at because of insufficient data and definitive experiments. It is useful, however, to list the possibilities involved in the hormonal control of sexual cycles contained, either overtly or implied, in the work of numerous investigators.

(a) *Gonadotrophins*

1. FSH and LH are one gonadotrophin only, and the manifestations of diverse biological activities are due to varying rates of secretion.

2. There are two gonadotrophins, FSH and LH, and possibly a third, LTH; or, these are factors or components of the adenohypophysial protein complex.

3. FSH is elaborated at a constant rate and the sexual cycle occasioned by variations in the secretion of LH.

4. The rates of secretion of FSH and LH fluctuate. One theory, common to several authors, supposes that the sexual cycle is initiated by the rising titre of FSH which is then complemented by increasing secretion of LH to produce oestrogens and ovulation. The corpus luteum is formed under the influence of LH, the secretion of which is maintained while that of FSH is reduced. Generally it is supposed that some LH always accompanies FSH secretion because there is

slight secretion of oestrogen even at the beginning of the sexual cycle. On the definition of FSH (p. 372), this really means that FSH never acts without concomitant secretion of oestrogen. An alternative hypothesis is that the hypophysial factor responsible for follicular maturation also stimulates ovarian cells to produce oestrogen (see possibility 1, above).

5. The theory that the rates of secretion of FSH and LH fluctuate according to the phase of the sexual cycle can be supplemented by considering the contribution of a third gonadotrophin, LTH. This concept is usually joined to 4, above. Thus, once the corpus luteum is formed under the influence of LH, the secretion of progesterone is brought about by LTH. It is possible that (i) both LH and LTH continue to be secreted in the luteal phase, or (ii) LTH alone maintains the corpus luteum after its formation and stimulates its secretion of progestin. The second possibility implies that neither FSH nor LH is secreted in any quantity during the luteal phase.

(b) *Oestrogens*

6. Oestrogens are produced by one gonadotrophin acting on ovarian cells, the theca interna and the interstitium.

7. Oestrogens are produced by the synergistic action of FSH and LH. Only very small amounts of LH are required to add the ability of eliciting the secretion of oestrogen to the principal function of FSH (control of follicular maturation). The point raised in 4 above, again applies: FSH may normally be secreted with concomitant LH properties; or FSH may be capable of inducing elaboration of oestrogen, as exemplified by animals showing persistent oestrus (spontaneously, as in rabbits or some strains of rats, or experimentally induced by continuous light or hypothalamic lesions). In these cases it is supposed that LH is absent and that ovulation ensues on its reappearance or administration. It is clear on the general theory of FSH and LH interaction that we must either suppose that slight amounts of LH are secreted even in persistent oestrus; or, as in possibility 6 above, that the follicle-stimulating factor has the inherent ability to stimulate the production of oestrogens.

8. The relationship between oestrogens and FSH is such that increasing amounts inhibit the secretion of the latter while stimulating that of LH. The sexual cycle is presumably initiated by secretion of FSH (via neural mechanisms?), the release of small amounts of LH acting synergistically to induce secretion of oestrogen which, in turn, facilitates increased secretion of LH; according to the 'feedback' hypothesis the oestrogens would lessen production of FSH, thus preventing further follicular maturation and leading the way to ovulation.

This means that the phases of the cycle are conditioned by fluctuations in levels of oestrogen, low levels tending to inhibit FSH and encourage LH, while high levels inhibit not only FSH but LH also.

9. Oestrogens are in reciprocal balance with LH ('feedback' principle) but not with FSH. This implies that fluctuations in FSH secretion rest mainly on inherent neural rhythms.

10. Oestrogens cause or facilitate the ovulatory stimulus (LH).

11. Oestrogens facilitate the action of gonadotrophins on the ovary by improving vascularization, or by a direct action at the cellular level.

(c) Progesterone

12. Progesterone is formed in the corpus luteum by (i) the action of LH, (ii) the combined action of LH and LTH, or (iii) by LTH alone.

13. Progesterone is also formed in the pre-ovulatory phase by corpora lutea of the preceding cycle and/or by the theca interna under the influence of LH and/or LTH.

14. Progesterone in the amounts secreted by the corpus luteum can suppress the action of oestrogens on the pituitary, while in the amounts present in the pre-ovulatory phase, it facilitates the release of LH (or of the ovulatory stimulus).

15. The sexual cycle must be initiated by FSH, the secretion of which cannot be triggered off by the products of its target organ, the ovary, the impetus originating in the pituitary itself (via neural mechanisms). Similarly the sexual cycle must end, not because the life of the corpus luteum is inherently limited, but because the pituitary hormones maintaining the corpus luteum cease to be secreted (see App. 6, p. 434).

This review of the various possibilities makes it clear that no clear-cut pattern of the events mediating the hormonal control of eutherian sexual cycles emerges. The crux of the problem lies in the real nature of the gonadotrophins themselves. The evidence for the acceptance of prolactin as luteotrophin, the third gonadotrophin, is still but slender. Although the existence of distinct follicle-stimulating and luteinizing hormones rests on much stronger evidence, their chemical status is in doubt. The terms FSH and LH are often only linguistic conveniences for pituitary changes correlated with the follicular and luteal phases of sexual cycles and in this way they have frequently been used in the above sections. Clearly, the avoidance of such circumlocutions as "those hypophysial factors essential for the maturation of follicles, or for ovulation or for oestrogen and progesterone secretion" by the use of abbreviations does not establish gonadotrophic identity. Indeed, the confusion of the word for the fact is a biological pitfall.

B. Cyclostomata

The cyclostomes, the most primitive living chordates possessing a pituitary gland, have a well-defined breeding season and thus provide suitable material for the elucidation of the fundamental relationship between hypophysis and ovary. It is unfortunate, therefore, that there is no detailed information available about the reproductive physiology of hagfishes and lampreys.

It can be inferred from the few known facts that the maturation and secretions of the cyclostome ovary are dependent on the pituitary. Dodd *et al.* (1960) showed that removal of the pituitary from a young female *Lampetra fluviatilis* resulted in continued ovarian immaturity and lack of development of secondary sexual characters over the period when normal and sham-operated animals became sexually mature. Early work by Calvet (1932) and Damas (1933) designed to demonstrate the stimulation of ovarian development in ammocoetes and adult lampreys with mammalian gonadotrophins has not been confirmed (Damas, 1951; Dodd *et al.*, 1960). Though the existence of cyclostome gonadotrophins has not been shown, mammalian gonadotrophins can produce marked stimulatory effects on the secondary sexual characters of adult lampreys and their precocious appearance in ammocoetes (Calvet, 1932; Damas, 1933; Young and Bellerby, 1935; Knowles, 1939), due perhaps to ovarian hormones, probably oestrogens (Knowles, 1939; Dodd, 1955).

C. Elasmobranchii

Of the two main living groups of this ancient class of cartilaginous fish, only the Euselachii have been studied and nothing is known of the reproductive physiology of the Holocephali. The anatomy of the pituitary is particularly interesting and difficult to compare with that of other vertebrates. It comprises an anterior rostral lobe with a ventral lobe below, and a posterior neurointermediate lobe. Earlier workers (de Beer, 1926; Howes, 1936) considered that the ventral lobe is homologous with the pars tuberalis of the tetrapods. It now seems likely that the rostral and ventral lobes together are homologous with the pars anterior of the tetrapods and the mesoadenohypophysis of teleosts (Pickford and Atz, 1957).

1. *The ovary after hypophysectomy*

Total hypophysectomy of the dogfish is not easy and some workers may have removed only the rostral lobe of the pituitary, though the ventral lobe, which is difficult to reach, is the probable site of gonadotrophic secretions (Dodd *et al.*, 1960). These authors, extending the earlier

2F

observations of Vivien (1939a, 1940, 1941) and Abramowitz and Hisaw (1939; see Dodd, 1955) found that removal of the rostral and/or neuro-intermediate lobes did not affect the reproductive processes and structures of the dogfish. In contrast, ablation of the ventral lobe of *Scyliorhinus caniculus* was followed by cessation of gonadal development and vitellogenesis; all oocytes advanced in vitellogenesis form corpora atretica which, in an extended post-operative period of 14 months, eventually degenerate and disappear. Egg-laying stops by 10 days after ventral-lobectomy when those eggs which had either ovulated or were about to ovulate at the time of operation had been laid. Fish with one or both of the other lobes removed as well as normal and sham-operated fish continued to lay pairs of eggs regularly at intervals of about 3 weeks.

It would seem that oocyte formation up to the formation of yolk is autonomous and once this 'critical stage' (Vivien, 1941) is reached, further development, including vitellogenesis and subsequent ovulation, is dependent on the pituitary.

2. *The effects of pituitary preparations on the ovary*

Vivien (1941) found that at the beginning of vitellogenesis the dog-fish oocyte becomes sensitive to homoplastic pituitary implants or injections. Such treatment did not stimulate the growth of the pre-vitellogenic oocytes of immature fish but did re-establish vitellogenesis, oocyte growth and ovulation in maturing fish in which these processes had been arrested by hypophysectomy (see also Dodd, 1955).

Presumably the ventral lobe of the elasmobranch pituitary secretes gonadotrophins though their nature is not clear. Mammalian gonado-trophic preparations in large doses have produced some ovarian development in dogfish (Vivien, 1941; Dodd, 1955). Witschi (1955), using the rat vaginal cornification and the weaver finch feather tests, considered that shark pituitaries contained both FSH and LH. Elasmobranch pituitaries produce premature vitellogenesis and spawning in teleosts (Vivien, 1941; Ichikawa and Kawakami, 1948) but not ovulation in ripe amphibians (Berk and Shapiro, 1939).

3. *Possible ovarian secretions**

The identification of oestradiol-17β in extracts of dogfish ovaries (Wotiz *et al.*, 1958) makes it probable that oestrogens are normal gonadal secretions. This suggestion is supported by the observation of oestrogenic stimulation of the Müllerian duct system which after hypophysectomy shows regression, as judged by histological changes (Vivien,

---

* The reader is also referred to Chapter 17, sect. III, B.

1941), although its macroscopic appearance shows little alteration (Dodd et al., 1960).

It is possible that progesterone is also present in dogfish ovaries (Hisaw, personal communication). There is no evidence, however, that this steroid is secreted by the post-ovulatory corpora lutea or correlated with the wide-spread viviparity found in this group (see p. 407; also Dodd, 1955; Pickford and Atz, 1957; Amoroso, 1960). The corpus luteum has, however, been described as better developed and more persistent in a viviparous ray than in an oviparous shark (Samuel, 1943, 1946), but the endocrine basis of viviparity has yet to be determined. Ovariectomy or hypophysectomy, for example, have no effect on uterine gestation in *Mustellus canis* and the corpus luteum is formed and maintained independently of the pituitary (Hisaw; see Dodd, 1955; Pickford and Atz, 1957). Skates and rays have different modes of viviparity, yet to be investigated (Amoroso, 1960).

D. Actinopterygii

The extensive literature on reproduction in bony fish is reviewed by Pickford and Atz (1957), Ball (1960) and Marshall (1960).

1. *The ovary after hypophysectomy*

Hypophysectomy of the teleost arrests oocyte development at the first phase—up to the beginning of vitellogenesis (Fig. 2, 7 and 8). More advanced oocytes in the second (vitellogenic) phase cease development and are converted into corpora atretica (Vivien, 1941, 1952; Buser-Lahaye, 1953; Ball, 1960) and ovulation is prevented (Vivien, 1941).

2. *The effects of pituitary preparations on the ovary*

The regressing ovaries of hypophysectomized fish (*Gobius paganellus* and *Xiphophorus helleri*) can be rendered normal, and ovulation restored, by administration of homoplastic pituitaries. Significant observations in the copious literature on the effects of giving fish pituitaries to intact fish of the same or different species are summarized in Table III. They show that hypophysial factors can stimulate vitellogenesis, produce maturation of the immature ovary, hasten the ripening of eggs in the adult and cause ovulation. The spectacular results achieved by Stoll (1957) are illustrated in Fig. 2, 9 and 10.

Changes in the ovaries and in pituitary activity of fish are closely correlated with temperature and the season of the year (Nusenbaum, 1950; Ball and Bacon, 1954). The ovary displays varying responsiveness to gonadotrophin; thus the amount of pituitary material from

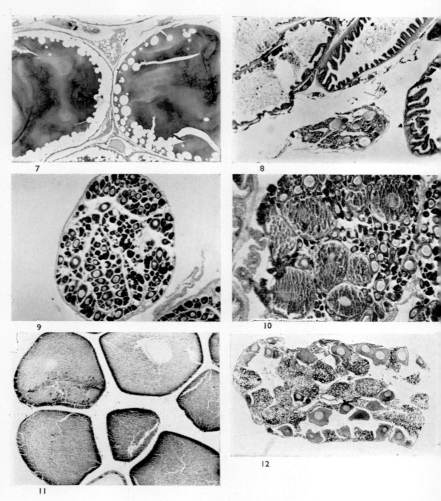

Fig. 2. The ovary in non-mammalian vertebrates. Teleostei: (7) Adult non-pregnant *Mollienesia latipinna*. Fully developed yolk-filled oocytes (× 36). (8) Adult *M. latipinna*, 36 days after total hypophysectomy. Four days after the operation, the fish gave birth to a normal brood. Normally first-phase oocytes would then have grown in a few days to full size as in (7). After hypophysectomy this growth did not occur (× 36). (Reproduced by permission from Ball, 1960). (9) *Bathygobius soporator*. Normal juvenile fish (× 30). (10) *B. soporator*, juvenile fish, 1 week after implantation of three adult pituitaries (× 30). (Reproduced by permission from Stoll, 1957). Amphibia: (11) Normal adult axolotl. Large yolk-filled oocytes (× 30). (12) Adult axolotl, 8 months after hypophysectomy. Note survival of pre-vitellogenic oocytes. The heavily-pigmented bodies are corpora atretica resulting from the resorption of large oocytes (× 30). (Reproduced by permission from Burns and Buyse, 1932).

ripe carp needed to induce ovulation in *Semotilus atromaculatus* was much less just before the spawning period than earlier in the season (Ball and Bacon, 1954). Variations in the amount of gonadotrophin stored in the pituitary at different seasons of the year (Gerbilsky and Kaschenko, 1937; Gerbilsky, 1940; de Menezes, 1945; Kazansky, 1951, 1952; Fontenele, 1955; Stoll, 1957) may reflect different secretory rates. Thus the gradual process of gonadal maturation is probably correlated with an increasing output of gonadotrophin which declines rapidly after spawning to be slowly restored to initiate another reproductive cycle.

Oocyte growth, vitellogenesis and ovulation can be evoked in fish by using pituitary preparations from elasmobranchs, amphibians, reptiles and mammals and with pregnant mares' serum and human chorionic gonadotrophin, though many negative results have been recorded (Pickford and Atz, 1957). In general, the effective dose of non-piscine material is high and this has been explained in terms of phylogenetic specificity (Creaser and Gorbman, 1939; Pickford and Atz 1957; Ball, 1960). Even between fishes, there are indications of relative gonadotrophic specificity correlated with phylogenetic relationship (Kazansky, 1940; Ramaswami and Sundararaj, 1957).

The converse approach of demonstrating the gonadotrophic action of fish pituitaries in other vertebrates has been successful in some hands (Wills *et al.*, 1933; Stroganov and Alpatov, 1951; Eliakova, 1954; Ramaswami and Lakshman, 1959) but not in others (Houssay *et al.*, 1929; Houssay and Giusti, 1930; Rostand, 1934; Del Castillo and Novelli, 1938; Creaser and Gorbman, 1939; Atz and Pickford, 1954; Hansen, 1955; Ball, 1960).

TABLE III

Some results of the administration of homologous pituitary extracts to intact bony fishes

Intact recipients	Donor*	Mode of administration	Effects	Ref.
Bathygobius soporator (juvenile)	*Bathygobius soporator*	i.p. implant	oocyte growth and vitellogenesis	1
Fundulus heteroclitus (immature)	*Fundulus heteroclitus*	i.p. implants	oocyte growth and vitellogenesis	2
obius paganellus	*Gadus* sp.	i.c. implants	oocyte growth	3
. paganellus and *Blennius*	*Gadus luscus* and *Scyliorhinus caniculus*	i.m. injection	vitellogenesis and ovulation only obtained within 1 month of natural spawning time.	4

[*Table continued on p. 394*

TABLE III—continued.

Intact recipients	Donor*	Mode of administration	Effects	R
Semotilus atromaculatus	Cyprinus carpio (ripe or nearly ripe, acetone dried)	i.p. injection	oocyte growth	
Pimelodus clarias	diff. sp. (not named)	i.m. injection	up to 30% increase in ovarian weight	
Astyanax mexicanus	C. carpio	i.p. injections	oocyte growth and vitellogenesis, incr. height of granulosa cells	
Carassius auratus	C. carpio (acetone dried)	i.p. injection	oocyte growth and ovulation	
Salmo gairdneri	C. carpio (fresh and acetone dried)	i.p. injection	oocyte growth and ovulation	
S. gairdneri	Oncorhynchus keta (acetone dried)	i.p. or i.m. injection	premature ripening	
O. keta	Oncorhynchus keta (acetone dried)	i.p. injection	premature ripening	
O. nerka	O. keta (acetone dried)	i.m. injection	oocyte growth	
Cobitis taenia and Esox lucius	C. carpio	i.p. injection	oocyte growth	
C. carpio	C. carpio		premature spawning	
Misgurnus fossilis	Abramis brama, M. fossilis and Lucioperca lucioperca	i.m. injection	premature spawning	
Acipenser guldenstadti and A. stellatus	A. guldenstadti and A. stellatus (acetone dried)	injection, u.	maturation and/or ovulation	
C. carpio	C. carpio (acetone dried)	i.m. injection	premature spawning	
M. fossilis	A. brama (acetone dried)	injection, u.	maturation	
Astyanax bimaculatus and Prochilodus argenteus	Hoplias malabaricus	i.m. injection	spawning	

i.m. = intramuscular   i.c. = intracranial   i.p. = intraperitoneal   u. = route unspecif
* = fresh pituitaries were used unless otherwise stated.

1 Stoll (1957)
2 Matthews (1940)
3 Vivien (1939a, b, c)
4 Vivien (1939a, b, 1941)
5 Ball and Bacon (1954)
6 Cardosa (1934)
7 Rasquin (1951)
8 Hasler and Meyer (1942)
9 Hasler et al. (1939)
10 Nishino (1948)
11 Nishino (1949a, b)
12 Palmer et al. (1954)
13 Tchechovitch (1952)
14 Balandin (1941)
15 Chernyshev (1941)
16 Kazansky (1950a)
17 Kazansky (1950b)
18 Kazansky (1952)
19 Von Ihering (193

It is clear that the pituitary of the bony fish produces gonadotrophins comprising factors which control both follicular maturation and ovulation. There is a little evidence (Kirshenblat, 1949a, b, 1956; Witschi, 1955) that these factors may have the status of FSH and LH as in the Eutheria, but further work on chemical extraction (Robertson and Rinfret, 1957; Ramaswami and Sundararaj, 1958) correlated with biological assay is required.

3. *Possible ovarian secretions*

Analysis of ovarian extracts has indicated the presence of oestrogens and progesterone in lungfish (*Protopterus annectens*, Choanichthyes; Dean and Chester Jones, 1959) as well as the dogfish (Wotiz *et al.*, 1958), and these findings imply their widespread occurrence throughout the vertebrates. Earlier work supports this view (Fellner, 1925; Fleischmann and Kann, 1932; Weisman *et al.*, 1937; Donahue, 1941, 1949; Brull and Cuypers, 1954). It seems likely that these sex steroids are produced by the ovary under the influence of the pituitary. Thus, hypophysectomy of the goby results in atrophy of the oviduct and genital papilla (Vivien, 1939c, 1941), structures which are regarded with good reason as being under ovarian control (Ball, 1960); they are restored to normal by injection of fish pituitaries. Such secondary sexual characters as nuptial colouration, very probably dependent on ovarian oestrogen secretion, can readily be elicited by injection of pregnancy urine extract (HCG) (Kinoshita, 1938) or of fish pituitaries (Palmer *et al.*, 1954). It has been suggested that a pituitary factor effects the conversion of oocytes into corpora atretica which then secrete steroid hormones (Bretschneider and de Wit, 1947), and though clear evidence is lacking (Pickford and Atz 1957), it is possible that corpora atretica are sites of steroid production (Ball, 1960).

The secretions of the ovary and pituitary of fish and their interrelationships are not yet known, though some evidence exists (Egami, 1954a, b) that endogenous oestrogens and gonadotrophins are in reciprocal balance.

4. *Viviparity*

Viviparity seems to have arisen repeatedly and independently in various families of teleosts (see Turner, 1942, 1947; Norman, 1947; Amoroso, 1952, 1960; Matthews, 1955; Hoar, 1955; Bertin, 1958; also Chapter 5).

It would be anticipated that hormones influence the establishment and course of gestation in viviparous fish, but direct evidence is scanty. It is probable that in poeciliids the process of follicular rupture and the expulsion of the embryo into the ovarian cavity, resembling in essence normal ovulation in oviparous fish (Turner, 1942, 1947; Robinson and Rugh, 1943), is under pituitary control. Administration of cattle pituitary extracts to *Xiphophorus helleri* and *Lebistes reticulatus* lessened the interval between successive births (Regnier, 1938; Haempel, 1950). Injection of fish and mammalian pituitaries into gravid *Cnesterodon decemmaculatus* and *Lebistes* brought about premature release of partly-developed embryos (Houssay, 1931; Haempel, 1950; see also App. 7, p. 434).

Oocyte development is under pituitary control in viviparous forms (Vivien, 1952) as it is in oviparous fish. The presence of developing embryos in the poeciliid ovary appears to retard the growth of the next batch of oocytes. Following parturition, these oocytes grow rapidly and are ready for fertilization by 8 days (Turner, 1937). Perhaps the gonadotrophin responsible for oocyte growth is inhibited during pregnancy. Superfoetation, which occurs normally in some species, can be induced experimentally in others by manipulation of light and temperature in ways that suggest stimulation of the pituitary, perhaps involving abnormal release of gonadotrophin during pregnancy (Scrimshaw, 1944; Rosenthal, 1952).

In the family Goodeidae, Mendoza (1939, 1940) found that the ovaries of non-pregnant females underwent cycles of development and regression during the breeding season, the changes resembling those in the pregnant ovary. In both virgin and breeding females, the development of the ovary coincided with integumentary colour changes. This, and other observations, indicate the possible existence of some sort of 'oestrous cycle' in viviparous cyprinodonts, related to the pituitary-ovarian axis with the production of sex steroids (Turner, 1933; Mendoza, 1943; Clark and Aronson, 1951; Rosenthal, 1952).

E. Amphibia

The subject has been reviewed by Tuchmann-Duplessis (1945), Houssay (1949) and Smith, C. L. (1955).

1. *The ovary after hypophysectomy*

Ovarian atrophy consequent on hypophysectomy has been described in detail by Burns (1932) for half-grown axolotls, and his account serves as a basic pattern for all Amphibia. He was able to demonstrate that hypophysectomy was the specific cause of atresia in oocytes above 400μ in diameter, the size at which yolk formation started (Fig. 2, *11* and *12*). Unoperated controls were neither better nourished nor more vigorous than the experimental animals, but did not display atresia. Ovarian atresia following hypophysectomy shows a similar pattern in adult and immature female newts (Woronozowa and Blacher,

1930; Burns and Buyse, 1932; Tuchmann-Duplessis, 1945) and in frogs and toads (Gallien, 1938, 1939a, b, 1940; Rey, 1939).

Regression of the ovaries can be obtained in Amphibia by means other than hypophysectomy, especially by a wide variety of unfavourable environmental circumstances, which presumably cause pituitary dysfunction (Hogben *et al.*, 1931; Shapiro and Shapiro, 1934; Alexander and Bellerby, 1938; Bellerby, 1938; Bellerby and Hogben, 1938; Tuchmann-Duplessis, 1945; Penhos and Cardeza, 1952).

Experiments using techniques of hypophysectomy have, therefore, demonstrated the dependence of the oocyte on the pituitary for its maturation. Pituitary gonadotrophic factors are only necessary for oocyte growth beyond a 'critical stage' (cf. fish, p. 390), that is when they have reached a diameter of about 300 to 500μ. Smaller oocytes seem to be independent of the pituitary, and in the larvae of Amphibia, hypophysectomy does not prevent the growth of gonads up to the stage normally attained at metamorphosis (Burns, 1932; Atwell, 1933; Smith, 1939; Witschi, 1937).

2. *The effects of pituitary preparations on the ovary*

(a) *General*

Ovarian atrophy following hypophysectomy can be prevented by the injection of human chorionic gonadotrophin (Waring *et al.*, 1941), and mammalian pituitary preparations (Mayo, 1937), though less successfully with PMS (Tuchmann-Duplessis, 1945). In intact animals, oocyte growth can be stimulated by mammalian pituitary preparations (Burns and Buyse, 1931, 1933; March, 1937; Gitlin, 1942).

Amphibian pituitaries can produce gonadotrophic effects in fish (Artemov, 1936; Artemov and Smirnov, 1937; Gallien, 1942; Kubota, 1953; Egami, 1954a) and in mammals (Adams and Granger, 1938; Adams and Tukey, 1938; Del Castillo and Novelli, 1938; Zwarenstein, 1939; Witschi, 1955).

In Amphibia, then, there is ample evidence that oocyte growth beyond a certain stage, and vitellogenesis, are dependent upon the pituitary. If the pituitary influence is withdrawn, oocytes beyond this stage undergo a characteristic atresia in which the cells of the follicular epithelium proliferate and hypertrophy, and phagocytose the degenerating ooplasm and yolk.

(b) *Ovulation*

Rugh (1935a) summarized earlier work and reported that ovulation had been induced by homoplastic pituitary implants and injections in two urodeles and ten anurans, and by heteroplastic (amphibian)

2G

material in six urodeles and ten anurans. Subsequent work has been concentrated on *Bufo arenarum, Xenopus laevis* and *Rana pipiens*. Houssay (1947), reviewing the work on *Bufo arenarum*, has pointed out that while homoplastic pituitaries readily produce ovulation in this species, material from other species of *Bufo* and from *Leptodactylus ocellatus* is less effective and *Xenopus laevis* glands are totally ineffective. On the other hand, pituitaries from *B. arenarum* cause ovulation in all the amphibians mentioned including *Xenopus*. Thus the effects of a reciprocal exchange of pituitary material differ according to the direction of the exchange (Houssay, 1950a).

Ovulation can be induced at any time of the year in laboratory stocks of *Xenopus laevis* by homoplastic pituitary grafts (Hogben *et al.*, 1931); this animal is extremely sensitive to mammalian gonadotrophins to which it responds by partial ovulation at any time of the year (Hogben *et al.*, 1931; Sutherland and Zwarenstein, 1939; Landgrebe, 1939; Waring *et al.*, 1941 amongst others). Other anurans generally either do not respond to mammalian extracts at all or only to large doses (Rugh, 1935b, 1948; Creaser and Gorbman, 1939; Gallien, 1940; Houssay, 1952), although urodeles commonly give positive results (Creaser and Gorbman, 1939; Rugh, 1948).

In *Rana temporaria, R. pipiens* and *Bufo vulgaris*, ovulation can be produced by administration of pituitaries from animals of the same species and from mammals, though the latter are relatively less effective (Rugh, 1934, 1937; Ponse, 1936; Gallien, 1937, 1940; March, 1937). The number of eggs liberated is a direct function of the dose of gonadotrophin given (Novelli, 1932a; Rugh, 1934, 1937; Gallien, 1937, 1940). The season of the year is important in relation to the sensitivity of the ovaries to gonadotrophins (Rugh, 1937).

Under suitable circumstances gonadotrophins can produce ovulation in the excised amphibian ovary as a specific effect (Ryan and Grant, 1940; Astrada *et al.*, 1951; cf. Samartino and Rugh, 1945). Chang and Witschi (1957) used *in vitro* preparations to show that cortisone acetate increased the number of eggs shed in response to homoplastic pituitary treatment. They proposed the theory that in natural ovulation increased secretion of oestrogen caused the release of ACTH from the pituitary which in turn evoked secretion of cortisone; the latter then acted synergistically with endogenous gonadotrophins to produce the release of eggs. This hypothesis may be regarded as a little premature in view of the absence of real knowledge about amphibian gonadotrophins and their mechanism of release and action.

There is some evidence for the existence of two gonadotrophic factor in amphibians, equivalent to mammalian FSH and LH, and for the view that some control is exercised through the hypothalamus (Mayo

1937; Wright, 1945, 1946). Wright and Hisaw (1946) found that in *Rana pipiens* a fairly pure FSH preparation from sheep pituitary did not cause ovulation in the hypophysectomized animal but sensitized the ovaries, combinations of FSH and LH in suitable doses inducing ovulation in both normal and hypophysectomized frogs. These experiments are in keeping with one theory applicable to mammals, namely that ovulation requires the secretion of LH acting upon the ovary prepared by FSH.

3. *Possible ovarian secretions*

Direct chemical analysis on the ovaries has not been done. Secondary sexual structures such as the oviduct appear to depend on the ovary for their normal development (see Galli-Mainini, 1950), but the position is complicated by the direct control by the pituitary of the oviduct and its secretions (Smith, C. L., 1955). The possibility exists that pituitary gonadotrophins act upon the ovary to produce progesterone or progestins (Galli-Mainini, 1950, 1951; Smith, C. L., 1955).

The progestational hormone, if it be a real entity, may be produced by (i) cells of the follicular epithelium (granulosa) which undergo transient hypertrophy immediately following ovulation (de Robertis, 1947; C. L. Smith, pers. comm.), though they do not look like typical luteal cells; or (ii) corpora atretica resulting from the involution of young oocytes (the pre-ovulatory corpora lutea of Bretschneider and de Wit, 1947). It seems possible that the secretion of the oviduct may rely in part on a progesterone-like hormone while the actual structure of this organ depends on oestrogens. Thus atrophy of the oviduct consequent upon ovariectomy can be prevented and even reversed by oestrogens (Wolf, 1928; Galli-Mainini, 1950) or ovarian grafts (Adams, 1930a, b), and oestrogens are known to stimulate hypertrophy of the ducts in intact individuals (March, 1937; Galli-Mainini, 1950). At the present time it is impossible to state that sex steroids are secreted by the amphibian ovary though it may well be that future investigations will show their existence.

There is little information concerning the effect of possible ovarian secretions on the amphibian pituitary. There is some cytological evidence of pituitary change after castration (Zahl, 1937; Tuchmann-Duplessis, 1945; Zuber-Vogeli, 1953; Cordier, 1953) indicative of the presence of actively secreting gonadotrophins. On the other hand, Novelli (1932b) found that castration had no effect on the gonadotrophic potency of the pars distalis of male *Bufo arenarum*, and Freire (1938) injected oestrone into the same species and could detect no change in pituitary gonadotrophic potency.

The injection of steroids in amphibians will cause ovulation though this may not be a specific effect. *Xenopus*, which has been frequently examined, will ovulate in response to a wide range of substances. Shapiro (1939) showed that the intact *Xenopus* would ovulate in response to the administration of ten steroids, including progesterone and testosterone. *Rana esculenta* was found to be unresponsive to progesterone, though recently Ramaswami and Lakshman (1958) have caused ovulation in *R. cyanocephalyctis* by both testosterone and progesterone, and DCA will cause ovulation in the newt (Kambara, 1954).

There is a lamentable lack of evidence about ovarian secretions in the Amphibia, and whilst it is often tacitly assumed that both progesterone and oestrogens are produced, and this is likely, definite experimental evidence is required.

F. Reptilia

Specific endocrinological work on reptiles is rare and the only general review available is that of Kehl and Combescot (1955).

1. *The ovary after hypophysectomy*

Bragdon (1952) found in the garter snake *Thamnophis sirtalis* that hypophysectomy before ovulation in mature females resulted in atresia of the large ripe follicles (diameter apparently about 1 cm at maturity) which commenced within 2 weeks of the operation. Smaller oocytes (diameter 0·4–0·8 mm), supposedly destined for ovulation in subsequent years, were normal 9 weeks after hypophysectomy. Cieslak (1945), using another garter snake, *T. radix*, concluded, on the basis of cytological changes in the pituitary, that hypophysial secretory activity initiated the growth of small oocytes in the spring, eventually to lead to the final rapid growth after the hibernation period. Probably, then, vitellogenesis in reptiles, as in fish and amphibians, cannot proceed in the absence of pituitary secretions.

2. *The effects of pituitary preparations on the ovary*

(a) *General*

There is only one report on the effects of homologous extracts of reptilian pituitaries on the reptilian ovary. Evans (1935a) briefly remarked that four female *Anolis carolinensis* which received four or five whole pituitaries from males of the same species during the winter displayed great hypertrophy of the whole genital system, compared with control animals, and one female ovulated prematurely.

Evidence for the pituitary control of ovarian activity, therefore, is for the most part gained by the use of mammalian preparations; evidence which is helpful but essentially unsatisfactory for revealing the characteristics of the class itself. Mellish and Meyer (1937) gave unfractionated sheep anterior pituitary, FSH (after Fevold and Hisaw, 1934), two preparations of LH (after Fevold and Hisaw, 1934; Evans et al., 1936) and PMS to female horned lizards, *Phrynosoma cornutum*. Injections were made during December–February when the gonads are normally in a state of retrogression. Both FSH and LH given to animals at 32°C caused a great increase in ovarian weight, mainly by promoting the deposition of yolk in growing oocytes. One LH preparation had only very weak luteinizing and ovarian weight-augmenting properties in immature female rats, and was correspondingly poorer than the other LH preparation in promoting vitellogenesis in the lizard. The unfractionated sheep pituitary had no gonadotrophic action in lizards kept hibernating at 5°C. PMS injected into animals at 32°C caused ovarian development comparable to that produced with the fractionated gonadotrophins. It is likely, as the authors concluded, that the induced ovarian stimulation depended on both the injected preparations and on endogenous gonadotrophin. This would help to explain why both FSH and LH had identical effects (promotion of yolk deposition), in contrast to the findings of Mayo (1937) who gave similar preparations to hypophysectomized and intact urodeles (pp. 398 to 399).

(b) *Ovulation*

Pituitary extracts can lead not only to ovarian stimulation but may also effect ovulation. Homologous pituitary extracts have induced ovulation in the South American snake *Xenodon merreni* (Houssay, 1931) and in the lizard *A. carolinensis*. Mammalian preparations have been effective in a few cases (Evans, 1935a, b; Cunningham and Smart, 1934).

It is clear that there is not enough evidence to decide on the nature of the pituitary gonadotrophin secretion in reptiles. Nor are the data obtained from the administration of reptilian pituitaries to other classes of vertebrates particularly illuminating. Negative results have been reported by Houssay and Giusti (1929a, b) and Rostand (1934) for reptiles to amphibians, and by Kazansky (1940) for reptile to fish (*Vimba vimba*). Indeed, only Watanabe et al. (1950) have succeeded in this line of investigation, evoking ovulation in loaches with pituitary material from *Elaphe* and *Takydromus*. Whilst undoubtedly the reptiles will fall into a pattern to be discerned throughout the vertebrates, much more work must be done before the tentative statement that the pituitary influences maturation and ovulation in reptiles by the production of a gonadotrophin can be expanded.

3. Possible ovarian secretions*

The presence of oestrogens in reptiles has been indicated by indirect means though no chemical data are available. The evidence rests on the changes that can be produced in the oviduct by the injection of oestrogens and of gonadotrophic preparations. After ovariectomy, the oviduct becomes atrophic in *Lacerta agilis* (Regamey, 1935) and in *Natrix tigrina tigrina* (Takewaki and Hatta, 1941). While oestrogens have not been given to the ovariectomized animal, marked hypertrophy of the oviduct can be obtained by this method in immature tortoises, terrapins and *Uromastix* (Forbes, 1937; Risley, 1941; Kehl and Combescot, 1955; cf. Dantschakoff and Kinderis, 1938). The implication of the pituitary in oviducal change has been suggested by the atrophy of this accessory structure after hypophysectomy in *N.t. tigrina* (Takewaki and Hatta, 1941).

Complementary experiments, though only on intact animals, have been performed and show that treatment with mammalian gonadotrophins induces marked development of the oviducts in immature or sexually quiescent adult reptiles, *Anolis* (Evans, 1935a, b), *Eumeces laticeps* (Turner, 1935), alligators (Forbes, 1937) and *Phrynosoma cornutum* (Mellish and Meyer, 1937). It may be concluded, therefore, that the ovary of reptiles may produce oestrogens under the influence of pituitary gonadotrophin. Some ancillary, though inconclusive, support for this statement lies in the effects of gonadectomy and of oestrogens on the pituitary which have been investigated by cytological methods (Poris, 1941; Hatta, 1941).

The possibility that the ovary might secrete progesterone is bound up with the occurrence of viviparity in reptiles, discussed in Chapters 5 and 9, in which the necessity for the presence of the ovary and the pituitary for the maintenance of pregnancy is examined. In this section the interest is focused on the appearance of post-ovulatory corpora lutea not only in viviparous and oviviparous forms but also in oviparous animals (Boyd, 1940; Cunningham and Smart, 1934; Weekes, 1934; Rahn, 1942; Bragdon, 1951, 1952; Panigel, 1951). The structure of these bodies is, in general, similar. The parenchymal cells arise from the follicular epithelial cells and the stroma from the theca of the ovarian follicles, although in *Thamnophis sirtalis* (Bragdon, 1952) and in the oviparous box turtle (Altland, 1951) thecal cells also become luteinized. The widespread occurrence of a corpus luteum, of a type

---

* See also Chapter 17, sect. V.

reminiscent of that in mammals, but not necessarily associated with gestation, raises the question whether or not the reptilian ovary secretes progesterone under gonadotrophic influence. The most suggestive observation is that of Bragdon *et al.* (1954) who found a progesterone-like substance in the plasma (Hooker-Forbes test), the concentration of which increased throughout pregnancy, in the viviparous snake *Natrix s. sipedon.* The same substance was present in the plasma of male snakes at about the same concentration as in non-pregnant females. This finding renders the assignment of progesterone secretion to the corpus luteum hazardous, however attractive the hypothesis might be on analogy with the Mammalia. Moreover, though the corpus luteum in reptiles may be organized under the influence of the pituitary, the evidence so far available indicates that this structure may form and maintain a secretory appearance in the absence of the hypophysis (Bragdon, 1952); gestation also continues after hypophysectomy (Bragdon, 1951).

G. Aves

Most of the work on birds has been done on the domestic fowl and the grounds for extending the concepts gained therefrom may be unsure. Aspects of gonadal function in birds are also considered in Chapters 5 and 19 and some recent reviews are given by Nalbandov (1953, 1959), Sturkie (1954), Breneman (1955) and Fraps (1955).

1. *The ovary after hypophysectomy*

Mitchell (1929) and Nalbandov and Card (1943) showed that hypophysectomy of the chicken was followed by regression of the ovaries and those structures that they control. Hill and Parkes (1934) found that hypophysectomy of laying hens was followed by cessation of laying and rapid regression of the ovaries which came to resemble those of the non-laying bird at the height of moult. Oocyte growth was arrested at a diameter of 2–3 mm.

The hypophysectomized pigeon can survive up to 43 days post-operatively, with regression of the oviduct and ovaries in which pre-existing follicles degenerate and new follicular growth does not occur (Chu, 1940).

2. *The effects of pituitary preparations on the ovary*

(a) *Immature birds*

In general, the ovary of the immature bird responds poorly to gonadotrophic preparations (Jaap, 1935; Breneman, 1936, 1955; Domm and Dennis, 1937; Uotila, 1939; Benoit, 1950). Nalbandov and Card (1946) used mammalian preparations of fairly pure FSH and LH and found that chicks responded by the age of 180 days with pronounced follicular growth and premature ovulation. Taber (1948) attempted to distinguish between FSH and LH effects but found, as did Kornfeld and Nalbandov (1954), that mammalian preparations did not simulate exactly the action of endogenous gonadotrophins. These findings led Das and Nalbandov (1955) to show that whole chicken pituitaries, but not mammalian gonadotrophins, induced follicular growth and vitellogenesis in normal chickens and restored the atrophied ovary of hypophysectomized animals. Thus, there seems to be a qualitative difference between the gonadotrophins of birds and mammals (Nalbandov et al., 1951; Taber et al., 1958).

(b) *Mature birds*

(i) *Laying.* Egg-laying ceases after hypophysectomy and is restored by avian but not mammalian pituitary extracts (Nalbandov, 1953). However, mammalian preparations, largely FSH in nature, were effective in maintaining the ovary of the hypophysectomized pigeon; over long periods ovarian and oviducal regression set in, perhaps due to the formation of 'anti-gonadotrophins' (Chu, 1940). In intact birds, injection of follicle-stimulating preparations leads to a cessation of laying, though there is growth of many follicles which can be ovulated with LH (Bates et al., 1935; Fraps and Riley, 1942; Nalbandov and Card, 1946). Presumptive LH, FSH, ACTH and growth fractions have been obtained from the pituitaries of male birds and assayed in laying hens. Hence a gonadotrophic complex exists in fowl, though its equivalence to that of mammals has not been clearly demonstrated (Neher and Fraps, 1946; Fraps et al., 1947).

(ii) *Non-laying.* Whilst administration of preparations with follicle-stimulating activity interrupts the reproductive rhythm of laying birds, they may be remedial in non-laying birds. Mammalian pituitary extracts stimulate egg production in birds that have almost stopped laying (Sturkie, 1954) and, in the quiescent bird, they can evoke follicular development (Nalbandov and Card, 1946). Follicular maturation can be brought about in other birds by similar treatment—ring doves (Riddle and Bates, 1933), English sparrows and the African weaver finch (Witschi, 1935). Witschi (1955) injected sexually inactive female sparrows with extracts of human, beef and turkey pituitaries and obtained some stimulation of the ovary which displayed full oocyte growth after administration of PMS.

(c) *Prolactin*

Prolactin has an inhibitory effect on the ovary (Riddle and Bates, 1939; Breneman, 1942). Further growth of advanced oocytes is prevented and there is resorption of large oocytes and cessation of laying.

It is supposed that the mechanism of this inhibitory action is through the pituitary since it is opposed by mammalian FSH given simultaneously (Riddle and Bates, 1939; Kornfeld and Nalbandov, 1954). The definitive experiment of giving prolactin together with avian gonadotrophins to hypophysectomized birds has yet to be done.

3. Interrelations of ovary and pituitary

(a) *Gonadotrophic content of the pituitary*

The gonadotrophic content of the pituitary is lower in the female than in the male bird (Meyer et al., 1939; Riley and Fraps, 1942a, b; Phillips, 1943; Greeley and Meyer, 1953) with prolactin present in both sexes (Sturkie, 1954). In the domestic hen, the gonadotrophic potency of the non-laying bird is significantly greater than that of the laying (Phillips, 1942; Riley and Fraps, 1942b; Saeki et al., 1956). The usual interpretation is that, during active egg production, gonadotrophins are secreted and not stored (Breneman, 1955; cf. Schooley and Riddle, 1938). However, the finding of more gonadotrophic activity in the blood of non-laying birds than of laying birds requires explanation (Bailey and Phillips, 1952).

The gonadotrophic potency of the pituitary of the ovariectomized bird has not been investigated. The amount of stored gonadotrophins in intact chickens, particularly the follicle-stimulating factor, can be enhanced with androgens (Breneman, 1955) though, in other experiments, combined oestrogens and androgens in physiological amounts had little effect (Breneman, 1956). Oestrogens may influence the release of gonadotrophins since, when given in small doses, they inhibited compensatory hypertrophy of the right gonad of poulards after unilateral ovariectomy. Hypophysectomy was followed by a similar effect (Kornfeld and Nalbandov, 1954; cf. Boas and Ludwig, 1950, for males).

(b) *Ovarian secretions*

The ovary of the domestic hen, and probably of all birds, may secrete not only oestrogens and progesterone but also androgens in significant quantities (Breneman, 1955). Comb growth in chickens is dependent on ovarian androgens (Taber, 1951; Breneman, 1955), the production of which is perhaps stimulated by LH (Nalbandov et al., 1946; Taber, 1948). Oestrogens, although not chemically identified, are considered responsible for the growth of oviducts and this effect can be obtained with mammalian preparations, largely FSH in nature (Taber, 1948).

Progesterone has been identified in hens by chromatography (Fraps et al., 1948, 1949; Lytle and Lorenz, 1958), and may be concerned in broodiness (see below) and in ovulation (Chapters 5 and 8). In the normal bird, there is a high progesterone content at the time of laying and the oviduct, conditioned by oestrogens, enlarges considerably and produces a secretion. These events can be produced in the quiescent bird by injection of oestrogen followed by progesterone (Brant and Nalbandov, 1956). It is considered, therefore, that progesterone has a normal physiological role in the control of oviducal function and the position is reminiscent of that in the Amphibia.

(c) *Broodiness*

It is widely accepted that prolactin induces broodiness not only in hens (Riddle *et al.*, 1935) but in birds generally (Sturkie, 1954). Prolactin may act directly or indirectly by suppressing gonadal function and oestrogen secretion (Godfrey and Jaap, 1950; Nalbandov, 1953). However, progesterone may be an immediate cause of incubatory behaviour (Riddle and Lahr, 1944; Brant and Nalbandov, 1952, 1956; Eisner, 1958), possibly by eliciting the secretion of prolactin from the pituitary (see App. 8, p. 434). The position is complicated as progesterone does not induce the secretion of prolactin in the absence of eggs (Meites and Turner, 1947). In pigeons, progesterone may bring about incubatory behaviour which, in turn, may induce 'psychosomatic' factors leading to an increase in prolactin secretion to give crop-milk (Patel, 1936; Lehrman, 1958). This sequence would be lacking in those birds that do not incubate their eggs, though possessing significant amounts of prolactin in the pituitary (Höhn, 1959).

Prolactin secretion coincides with broodiness which is seemingly dependent on progesterone, and with crop-milk production (Byerly and Burrows, 1936; Lahr and Riddle, 1936; Schooley and Riddle, 1938). One possibility is that prolactin is also luteotrophic and causes secretion of progesterone by the ovary. There are cells in the ovary, particularly in atretic follicles, to which progesterone secretion may be assigned (Marshall and Coombes, 1957). An avian luteotrophin–progesterone relationship would be analogous to the position in Eutheria but there are no data to support this hypothesis.

IV. Conclusions

In the Eutheria, gonadotrophins are considered to be three in number. By definition, follicle-stimulating hormone (FSH) causes follicular maturation, luteinizing hormone (LH) induces the formation of corpora lutea, and luteotrophin (LTH), believed to be identical with prolactin, evokes the secretion of progesterone by corpora lutea which have already been formed by the action of LH. The validity of this definition has been challenged. Neither FSH nor LH has been prepared as a chemically pure substance to which discrete biological activities can be assigned. There is, however, fairly strong chemical and biological evidence for the separate existence of LH, and if this be accepted, the existence of a separate FSH is implied. In mammals, moderate amounts of the best available preparations of FSH do not cause secretion of oestrogen unless LH, even in very small quantities, is also given. Minimal effective doses of the available preparations of gonadotrophins give clearly distinct biological effects in accord with their definition and, within these limits, the status of separate hormones for FSH and LH is justified.

Circumstantial evidence suggests that substances having activities similar to mammalian gonadotrophins occur throughout the vertebrates. It is probably generally true that follicular maturation and concomitant ovarian oestrogen secretion are dependent on gonadotrophins. Moreover, the property of inducing ovulation resides in the pituitaries of all vertebrates, and work on the Eutheria, and to a lesser extent on other animals, has equated the ovulatory agent with luteinizing hormone. It is more questionable, however, whether LH acts as a luteinizing factor in lower vertebrates. Corpora lutea of various kinds, both pre- and post-ovulatory, occur widely, but whether these are maintained by pituitary hormones and whether they consistently secrete progestins has not been established. Progesterone does, however, occur in many such animals, perhaps merely as an intermediate in steroid metabolism, though more likely with a hormonal function. Prolactin has also been detected in many vertebrates. For example, the pituitaries of elasmobranchs have been shown to induce lactation (Carlisle, 1953) and pituitaries from teleosts, amphibians, birds and mammals give typical reactions in the pigeon crop test (Foglia, 1941; Cowie and Folley, 1955; Lehrman, 1958). Prolactin, too, brings about such diverse phenomena as oviducal secretion and colour change in Amphibia (Houssay, 1950b; Pickford and Atz, 1957), the red-eft water drive (Grant and Grant, 1958; Grant and Pickford, 1959) and survival of hypophysectomized killifish (Pickford and Phillips, 1959).

Since both prolactin and some form of lutein tissue, and indeed progesterone, may occur in all vertebrates, it is tempting to postulate that prolactin is primarily luteotrophic and that it acts on lutein cells to secrete progesterone. However, on present evidence, it is equally tenable that prolactin is not universally associated with secretion of progesterone in lower vertebrates.

Finally, if the existence of three gonadotrophins becomes successfully established for all vertebrates, they may not prove to be identical in structure with the mammalian hormones. It seems likely that the latter will prove to be polypeptides but, by analogy with oxytocin and vasopressin, it may be expected that the amino acid sequence will vary from group to group and possibly from species to species.

REFERENCES

Abramowitz, A. A. and Hisaw, F. L. (1939). The effects of proteolytic enzymes on purified gonadotropic hormones. *Endocrinology*, **25**, 633–637.

Adams, A. E. (1930a). Studies on sexual conditions in *Triturus viridescens*. The effects of ovarian grafts in castrated males. *J. exp. Zool.* **55**, 63–85.

Adams, A. E. (1930b). The induction of egg-laying in *Triturus viridescens* by heteroplastic pituitary-gland grafts. *Anat. Rec.* **45**, 250–251.

Adams, A. E. and Granger, B. (1938). Stimulation of the reproductive tract of the infantile female mouse by anuran anterior pituitary substance. *Proc. Soc. exp. Biol., N.Y.* **38**, 585–586.

Adams, A. E. and Tukey, G. R. (1938). The effect of administering frog anterior pituitary substance to immature female mice. *Anat. Rec.* **71**, 1–25.

Albert, A. (1956). Human urinary gonadotrophins. *Recent Progr. Hormone Res.* **12**, 227–296.

Alexander, S. S. and Bellerby, C. W. (1938). Experimental studies on the sexual cycle of the South African clawed toad (*Xenopus laevis*). I. *J. exp. Biol.* **15**, 74–81.

Altland, P. D. (1951). Observations on the structure of the reproductive organs of the box turtle. *J. Morph.* **89**, 599–621.

Amoroso, E. C. (1952). *In* "Marshall's Physiology of Reproduction", 3rd ed. (A. S. Parkes, ed.), Vol. II, p. 127. Longmans, Green & Co., London.

Amoroso, E. C. (1960). *In* "Hormones in Fish." Symposia of the Zoological Society of London, No. 1, pp. 153–181.

Aron, M., Aron, C. and Marescaux, J. (1954). Variations quantitives de l'élimination urinaire de gonadostimuline au cours du cycle oestral chez la femme. *Ann. Endocr., Paris*, **15**, 778–782.

Artemov, N. (1936). Über die Wirkung der Hypophyse auf das Genitalsystem der Fische. I. Mitteilung. Versuche an Weibchen von Bitterlingen. *Bull. Biol. Med. exp., URSS.* **2**, 25–26.

Artemov, N. and Smirnov, K. (1937). Stimulation of maturation of sexual products in fish. *Fish Ind., Moscow*, **17**(4), 29–31.

Aschheim, S. (1933). Über die Wirkungsart gonadotroper Stoffe auf den Eierstock. *Arch. Gynaek.* **155**, 44–66.

Aschner, B. (1912). Über die Funktion der Hypophyse. *Pflüg. Arch. ges. Physiol.* **146**, 1–146.

Astrada, J. J., de Allende, I. L. C. and Onas, O. (1951). Ovulación "in vitro" de ovarias del sapo *Bufo arenarum* Hensel. *Rev. Soc. argent. Biol.* **27**, 220–226.

Astwood, E. B. (1941). The regulation of corpus-luteum function by hypophysial luteotrophin. *Endocrinology*, **28**, 309–320.

Astwood, E. B. (1953). Tests for luteotrophins. *Ciba Foundation Colloquia on Endocrinology*, **5**, 74–86.

Astwood, E. B. and Fevold, H. L. (1939). Action of progesterone on the gonadotropic activity of the pituitary. *Amer. J. Physiol.* **127**, 192–198.

Astwood, E. B. and Greep, R. O. (1938). A corpus-luteum stimulating substance in the rat placenta. *Proc. Soc. exp. Biol., N.Y.* **38**, 713–716.

Atwell, W. J. (1933). Development of the gonads following early removal of the hypophysis in *Rana sylvatica*. *Anat. Rec.* **55**, Suppl., 45.

Atz, E. H. and Pickford, G. E. (1954). Failure to elicit the Galli-Mainini reaction in *Rana pipiens* with spawning reflex fractions and other teleostean pituitary preparations and observations on the response to mammalian gonadotrophins. *Zoologica, N.Y.* **39**, 117–122.

Bahn, R. C., Lorenz, N., Bennet, W. A. and Albert, A. (1953a). Gonadotrophins of the pituitary gland during infancy and early childhood. *Endocrinology*, **52**, 605–606.

Bahn, R. C., Lorenz, N., Bennet, W. A. and Albert, A. (1953b). Gonadotropins of the pituitary of postmenopausal women. *Endocrinology*, **53**, 455–457.

Bailey, R. L. and Phillips, R. E. (1952). Gonadotrophic potency of avian serum. *Poult. Sci.* **31**, 68–71.

Balandin, P. (1941). A new way of using the method of hypophysis injection. *Fish Ind., Moscow*, **21**(2), 18.

Ball, J. N. (1960). *In* "Hormones in Fish." Symposia of the Zoological Society of London, No. 1, pp. 105–134.

Ball, R. C. and Bacon, E. H. (1954). Use of pituitary material in the propagation of minnows. *Progr. Fish Cult.* **16**, 108–113.

Barraclough, C. A. and Leathem, J. H. (1954). Infertility induced in mice by a single injection of testosterone propionate. *Proc. Soc. exp. Biol., N.Y.* **85**, 673–677.

Bates, R. W., Riddle, O. and Lahr, E. L. (1934). On the protein nature of prolactin and of follicle stimulating hormone. *Proc. Soc. exp. Biol., N.Y.* **31**, 1223–1224.

Bates, R. W., Lahr, E. L. and Riddle, O. (1935). The gross action of prolactin and follicle stimulating hormone on the mature ovary and sex accessories of fowl. *Amer. J. Physiol.* **111**, 361–368.

Beer, G. de. (1926). "The Comparative Anatomy, Histology and Development of the Pituitary Body." Oliver and Boyd, London.

Bellerby, C. W. (1938). Experimental studies on the sexual cycle of the South African clawed toad (*Xenopus laevis*). II. *J. exp. Biol.* **15**, 82–90.

Bellerby, C. W. and Hogben, L. (1938). Experimental studies on the sexual cycle of the South African clawed toad (*Xenopus laevis*). III. *J. exp. Biol.* **15**, 91–100.

Benoit, J. (1950). *In* "Traité de Zoologie" (P.-P. Grassé, ed.), **15** (Oiseaux), p. 290. Masson et Cie, Paris.

Bergman, A. J. and Turner, C. W. (1942). Gonadotropic hormone in AP of male and female rabbits during growth. *Endocrinology*, **30**, 11–15.

Berk, L. and Shapiro, H. A. (1939). Studies in the reproduction of *Xenopus laevis*. II. Histological changes in the accessory sex organs of female *Xenopus* induced by the administration of endocrine preparations. *S. Afr. J. med. Sci.* **4**, (Suppl.) 13–17.

Bertin, L. (1958). *In* "Traité de Zoologie" (P.-P. Grassé, ed.), **13**(2) (Poissons), p. 1791. Masson et Cie, Paris.

Biddulph, C. and Meyer, R. K. (1946). Gonadotrophic hormone secretion in immature hypophysectomized parabiotic rats. *Proc. Soc. exp. Biol., N.Y.* **63**, 92–95.

Biskind, M. S. and Biskind, G. R. (1944). Development of tumors in the rat ovary after transplantation into the spleen. *Proc. Soc. exp. Biol., N.Y.* **55**, 176–179.

Blackburn, C. M., Albert, A., Svein, J., Uihlein, A., Lipsett, M. B. and Pearson, O. (1956). Behavior of urinary gonadotropin following hypophysectomy in man. *Proc. Mayo Clin.* **31**(25), 649–652.

Boas, N. F. and Ludwig, A. W. (1950). The mechanism of estrogen inhibition of comb growth in the cockerel with histologic observations. *Endocrinology,* **46**, 299–306.

Bottomly, A. C. and Folley, S. J. (1940). Inactivation of prolactin by treatment with phenyl isocyanate. *Nature, Lond.* **145**, 304.

Boyd, M. M. M. (1940). The structure of the ovary and the formation of the corpus luteum in *Hoplodactylus maculatus* Gray. *Quart. J. micr. Sci.* **82**, 337–376.

Bradbury, J. T. (1947). Ovarian influence on the response of anterior pituitary to estrogens. *Endocrinology,* **41**, 501–513.

Bradbury, J. T., Brown, W. E. and Gray, L. A. (1950). Maintenance of the corpus luteum and physiologic action of progesterone. *Recent Progr. Hormone Res.* **5**, 151–194.

Bragdon, D. E. (1951). The non-essentiality of the corpora lutea for the maintenance of gestation in certain live-bearing snakes. *J. exp. Zool.* **118**, 419–435.

Bragdon, D. E. (1952). Corpus luteum formation and follicular atresia in the common garter snake, *Thamnophis sirtalis.* *J. Morph.* **91**, 413–445.

Bragdon, D. E., Lazo-Wasem, E. A., Zarrow, M. X. and Hisaw, F. L. (1954). Progesterone-like activity in the plasma of ovoviviparous snakes. *Proc. Soc. exp. Biol., N.Y.* **86**, 477–480.

Brambell, F. W. R. (1956). *In* "Marshall's Physiology of Reproduction", 3rd ed. (A. S. Parkes, ed.). Vol. I. Pt. 1, p. 397. Longmans, Green & Co. London.

Brant, J. W. A. and Nalbandov, A. V. (1952). Role of sex hormones in the secretory activity of the oviducts in hens. *Poult. Sci.* **31**, 908–909.

Brant, J. W. A. and Nalbandov, A. V. (1956). Role of sex hormones in albumen secretion by the oviduct of chickens. *Poult. Sci.* **35**, 692–700.

Breneman, W. R. (1936). The effect on the chick of some gonadotropic hormones. *Anat. Rec.* **64**, 211–220.

Breneman, W. R. (1942). Action of prolactin and estrone on weights of reproductive organs and viscera of the cockerel. *Endocrinology,* **30**, 609–615.

Breneman, W. R. (1955). Reproduction in female birds. *Mem. Soc. Endocrin.* No. 4, 94–110.

Breneman, W. R. (1956). Steroid hormones and the development of the reproductive system in the pullet. *Endocrinology,* **58**, 262–271.

Bretschneider, L. H. and de Wit, J. J. D. (1947). "Sexual Endocrinology of Non-mammalian Vertebrates." Monogr. Progr. Res. Holland, 11. Elsevier, Amsterdam.

Brull, L. and Cuypers, Y. (1954). Caractéristiques de *Lophius piscatorius.* *Arch. int. Physiol.* **62**, 70–73.

Bryans, F. E. (1948). Progesterone of the blood in the menstrual cycle of the monkey. *Endocrinology,* **48**, 733–740.

Bunde, C. A. and Greep, R. O. (1936). Suppression of persisting corpora lutea in hypophysectomized rats. *Proc. Soc. exp. Biol., N.Y.* **35**, 235–237.

Bunster, E. and Meyer, R. K. (1938). The effect of estrin on the gonad-stimulating complex of the anterior pituitary of parabiotic rats. *Endocrinology,* **23**, 496–500.

Burack, E. and Wolfe, J. M. (1959). The effects of anterior hypophyseal administration on the ovaries of old rats. *Endocrinology,* **64**, 676–684.

Burch, J. C. and Cunningham, R. S. (1930). Effect of placental extracts on ovarian stimulating properties of the anterior hypophysis. *Proc. Soc. exp. Biol., N.Y.* **27**, 331–332.

Burns, R. K. (1932). Follicular atresia in the ovaries of hypophysectomized salamanders in relation to yolk formation. *J. exp. Zool.* **63**, 309–327.

Burns, R. K. and Buyse, A. (1931). The effects of extracts of the mammalian hypophysis upon immature salamanders. *Anat. Rec.* **51**, 155–185.

Burns, R. K. and Buyse, A. (1932). The effects of hypophysectomy on the reproductive system of salamanders. *Anat. Rec.* **51**, 333–359.

Burns, R. K. and Buyse, A. (1933). The induction of precocious maturity in the reproductive tract of recently metamorphosed female salamanders, by an extract of the mammalian hypophysis. *Anat. Rec.* **58**, 37–53.

Burrows, H. (1949). "Biological Actions of Sex Hormones", 2nd ed. Cambridge University Press.

Buser-Lahaye, J. (1953). Etude expérimentale du déterminisme de la régéneration des nageoires chez les poissons téléostéens. *Ann. Inst. oceanogr., Monaco,* **28**, 1–61.

Byerly, T. C. and Burrows, W. T. (1936). Studies of prolactin in the fowl pituitary. II. Effects of genetic constitution with respect to broodiness on prolactin content. *Proc. Soc. exp. Biol., N.Y.* **34**, 844–846.

Byrnes, W. W. and Meyer, R. K. (1951a). Effect of physiological amounts of estrogen on the secretion of follicle stimulating and luteinizing hormone. *Endocrinology,* **49**, 449–460.

Byrnes, W.W. and Meyer, R. K. (1951b). The inhibition of gonadotrophic hormone secretion by physiological doses of estrogen. *Endocrinology,* **48**,133–136.

Calvet, J. (1932). Action du lobe antérieur d'hypophyse chez divers vertébrés (lamproies, oiseaux). *C.R. Soc. Biol., Paris,* **109**, 595–597.

Cardosa, D. M. (1934). Relations entre l'hypophyse et les organes sexuels chez les poissons. *C.R. Soc. Biol., Paris,* **115**, 1347–1349.

Carlisle, D. B. (1953). Quoted by Medawar, P. B. (1953).

Carmichael, E. S. and Marshall, F. H. A. (1908). On the occurrence of the compensatory hypertrophy of the ovary. *J. Physiol.* **36**, 431–434.

Casida, L. E., Meyer, R. K., McShan, W. H. and Wisnicky, W. (1943). Effects of pituitary gonadotropins on the ovaries and the induction of superfecundity in cattle. *Amer. J. vet. Res.* **4**, 76–94.

Castillo, E. B. del and Novelli, A. (1938). Actions gonadotrophiques synergiques ou antagonistes de l'hypophyse des poissons, des batraciens et des oiseaux. *C.R. Soc. Biol., Paris,* **127**, 1043–1044.

Chang, C. Y. and Witschi, E. (1957). Cortisone effect on ovulation in the frog. *Endocrinology,* **61**, 514–519.

Chen, G. and van Dyke, H. B. (1939). Gonadotropic action of anterior pituitary extract after tryptic digestion. *Proc. Soc. exp. Biol., N.Y.* **40**, 172–176.

Chernyshev, O. B. (1941). Experimentelle Reifung der Geschlechtsprodukte beim Schlammbeisser (*Misgurnus fossilis*) im Winter. *C.R. Acad. Sci., URSS.* **35**, 14–157.

Chester Jones, I. (1957). "The Adrenal Cortex." Cambridge University Press.

Chow, B. F. (1942). Gonadotropins of the swine pituitary. III. Immunological specificity of swine metakentrin. *Endocrinology,* **30**, 657–661.

Chow, B. F. (1943). The chemistry of thylakentrin, the follicle-stimulating hormone of the anterior pituitary. *Ann. N.Y. Acad. Sci.* **43**, 309–320.

Chow, B. F., Greep, R. O. and van Dyke, H. B. (1939). The effects of digestion by proteolytic enzymes on the gonadotrophic and thyrotrophic potency of the anterior pituitary extract. *J. Endocrin.* 1, 440–469.

Chow, B. F., van Dyke, H. B., Greep, R. O., Rothen, A. and Shedlovsky, T. (1942). Gonadotropins of the swine pituitary. II. Preparation, and biological and physico-chemical characterization of a protein apparently identical with metakentrin (ICSH). *Endocrinology,* 30, 650–656.

Chu, J. P. (1940). The effects of oestrone and testosterone, and of pituitary extracts on the gonads of hypophysectomized pigeons. *J. Endocrin.* 2, 21–37.

Cieslak, E. S. (1945). Relations between the reproductive cycle and the pituitary gland in the snake *Thamnophis radix. Physiol. Zoöl.* 18, 299–329.

Clark, E. and Aronson, L. R. (1951). Sexual behaviour in the guppy, *Lebistes reticulatus* (Peters). *Zoologica, N.Y.* 36, 49–66.

Clark, H. M. (1935). a. A prepubertal reversal of the sex differences in the gonadotropic hormone content of the pituitary gland of the rat. b. A sex difference in the change in potency of the anterior hypophysis following bilateral castration in new born rats. *Anat. Rec.* 61, 175–192 and 193–202.

Coffin, H. C. and van Dyke, H. B. (1941). Proposed names for the follicle-stimulating and interstitial-cell-stimulating hormones of the anterior lobe of the pituitary body. *Science,* 93, 61.

Cohen, R. (1935). Effect of experimentally produced hyperthyroidism upon the reproductive and associated organs of the male rat. *Amer. J. Anat.* 56, 143–153.

Cole, R. D. and Li, C. H. (1955). Studies on pituitary lactogenic hormone. XIV. A simplified procedure for isolation. *J. biol. Chem.* 213, 197–201.

Cole, R. D., Geschwind, I. I. and Li, C. H. (1957). Studies on pituitary lactogenic hormone. XV. N-terminal residue analysis and N-terminal sequence analysis. *J. biol. Chem.* 224, 399–405.

Collip, J. B. (1932). Placental hormones. *Int. Clin.* 4, 51–70.

Collip, J. B. and Anderson, E. M. (1935). Studies on thyrotropic hormone of anterior pituitary. *J. Amer. med. Ass.* 104, 965–969.

Coppedge, R. L. and Segaloff, A. (1951). Urinary prolactin excretion in man. *J. clin. Endocrin.* 11, 465–476.

Cordier, R. (1953). L'hypophyse de *Xenopus.* Interpretations histophysiologiques. *Ann. Soc. zool. Belg.* 84, 5–16.

Courrier, R. (1956). Remarque sur la greffe d'hypophyse. *Arch. Biol., Paris,* 67, 461–469.

Courrier, R., Baclesse, M. and Marois, M. (1953). Rapports de la cortico-surrénale et de la sexualité. *J. Physiol. Path. gén.* 45, 327–374.

Cowie, A. T. and Folley, S. J. (1955). *In* "The Hormones" (G. Pincus and K. V. Thimann, eds.), Vol. III, p. 309. Academic Press, Inc., New York.

Cozens, D. A. and Nelson, M. M. (1958). Increased follicle stimulating activity in the plasma of ovariectomized rats. *Proc. Soc. exp. Biol., N.Y.* 98, 617–620.

Creaser, C. W. and Gorbman, A. (1939). Species specificity of the gonadotropic factors in vertebrates. *Quart. Rev. Biol.* 14, 311–331.

Croes-Buth, S., Paesi, F. J. A. and de Jongh, S. E. (1959). Stimulation of ovarian follicles in hypophysectomized rats by low dosage of oestradiol benzoate. *Acta endocr., Copenhagen,* 32, 399–410.

Crowe, S. J., Cushing, H. and Homans, J. (1910). Experimental hypophysectomy. *Johns Hopk. Hosp. Bull.* 21, 127–169.

Cunningham, J. T. and Smart, W. A. M. (1934). The structure and origin of corpora lutea in some of the lower vertebrata. *Proc. roy. Soc.* B. 116, 258–281.

Cutuly, E. (1941). Maintenance of pregnancy in the hypophysectomized rat. *Proc. Soc. exp. Biol., N.Y.* **47**, 126–128.

Cutuly, E. (1942). Effects of lactogenic and gonadotropic hormones on hypophysectomized pregnant rats. *Endocrinology,* **31**, 13–22.

Damas, H. (1933). Note sur l'apparition naturelle et provoquée des caractères sexuels chez la lamproie. *Bull. Soc. Sci., Liège,* **2**, 94–98.

Damas, H. (1951). La ponte en aquarium des lamproies fluviatiles et de planer. *Ann. Soc. zool. Belg.* **81**, 151–162.

Dantschakoff, V. and Kinderis, A. (1938). Sur les réactions que provoque la folliculine dans les ébauches des oviductes et des gonades chez le lézard. *C.R. Soc. Biol., Paris,* **127**, 602–605.

Das, B. C. and Nalbandov, A. V. (1955). Responses of ovaries of immature chickens to avian and mammalian gonadotrophins. *Endocrinology,* **57**, 705–710.

Dean, F. D. and Chester Jones, I. (1959). Sex steroids in the lungfish (*Protopterus annectens* Owen). *J. Endocrin.* **18**, 366–371.

Dempsey, E. W. (1937). Follicular growth rate and ovulation after various experimental procedures in the guinea pig. *Amer. J. Physiol.* **120**, 126–132.

Desclin, L. (1948). Actions de la prolactine sur la structure de l'ovaire du rat normal et hypophysectomisé. *C.R. Soc. Biol., Paris,* **142**, 1436–1438.

Desclin, L. (1949). Observations sur la structure des ovaires chez des rats soumis à l'influence de la prolactine. *Ann. Endocr., Paris,* **10**, 1–18.

Deutsch, H. F., McShan, W. H., Ely, C. A. and Meyer, R. K. (1950). Time of appearance and properties of antigonadotrophic and progonadotrophic substances of rabbit serum. *Amer. J. Physiol.* **162**, 393–405.

Dodd, J. M. (1955). The hormones of sex and reproduction and their effects in fish and lower chordates. *Mem. Soc. Endocrin.* No. 4, 166–187.

Dodd, J. M., Evennett, P. J. and Goddard, C. K. (1960). *In* "Hormones in Fish." Symposia of the Zoological Society of London, No. 1, pp. 77–103.

Domm, L. V. and Dennis, E. A. (1937). Effect of pituitary hebin upon the reproductive system of the chick embryo. *Proc. Soc. exp. Biol., N.Y.* **36**, 766–768.

Donahue, J. K. (1941). Occurrence of estrogens in the ovaries of the winter flounder. *Endocrinology,* **28**, 519–520.

Donahue, J. K. (1949). Determination of natural estrogens in marine eggs by biological and fluorimetric procedures. *Amer. J. Physiol.* **159**, 567–568.

Dresel, L. (1935). The effect of prolactin on the estrous cycle of non-parous mice. *Science,* **82**, 173.

Dutt, H. and Casida, L. E. (1948). Alteration of the estrual cycle in sheep by use of progesterone and its effect upon subsequent ovulation and fertility. *Endocrinology,* **43**, 208–217.

Egami, N. (1954a). Inhibitory effect of estrone benzoate on ovarian growth in the loach, *Misgurnus anguillicaudatus. J. Fac. Sci. Tokyo Univ.* **7**, 113–119.

Egami, N. (1954b). Effects of pituitary substance and estrogen on the development of ovaries of adult females of *Oryzias latipes* in sexually inactive seasons. *Annot. zool. jap.* **27**, 13–18.

Eisner, E. (1958). Incubation and clutch size in gulls. *Anim. Behav.* **6**, 124–125.

Elder, W. H. and Finerty, J. C. (1943). Gonadotropic activity of the pituitary gland in relation to the seasonal sexual cycle of the cottontail rabbit (*Sylvilagus floridanus mearnsi*). *Anat. Rec.* **85**, 1–15.

Eliakova, G. V. (1954). Metamorphosis of axolotls under the influence of the thyrotropic factor of the hypophysis of osetr and sevriuga. *C.R. Acad. Sci.*, *URSS.* **97**, 1097–1100.

Ellis, S. (1958). A scheme for the separation of pituitary proteins. *J. biol. Chem.* **233**, 63–68.

Emmens, C. W. (1950). "Hormone Assay." Academic Press Inc., New York.

Ershoff, B. H. (1952). Nutrition and the anterior pituitary with special reference to the general adaptation syndrome. *Vitam. & Horm.* **10**, 79–140.

Evans, H. M. and Simpson, M. E. (1928). Antagonism of growth and sex hormones of anterior hypophysis. *J. Amer. med. Ass.* **91**, 1337–1338.

Evans, H. M. and Simpson, M. E. (1930). a. Some effects of the hypophysis of hyper- and hypothyroidism. b. Different effects secured from intraperitoneal as contrasted with subcutaneous administration of the anterior–hypophysial hormones. *Anat. Rec.* **45**, Suppl. 215.

Evans, H. M. and Simpson, M. E. (1950). *In* "The Hormones" (G. Pincus and K. V. Thimann, eds.), Vol. II, p. 351. Academic Press Inc., New York.

Evans, H. M., Korpi, K., Pencharz, R. I. and Simpson, M. E. (1936). Fractionation of gonadotropic hormones in pregnant mare serum by means of ammonium sulfate. *Univ. Calif. Publ. Anat.* **10**, 237–245.

Evans, H. M., Simpson, M. E., Lyons, W. R. and Turpeinen, K. (1941). Anterior pituitary hormones which favor the production of traumatic uterine placentomata. *Endocrinology*, **28**, 933–945.

Evans, L. T. (1935a). The effects of pituitary implants and extracts on the genital system of the lizard *Anolis carolinensis*. *Science*, **81**, 468.

Evans, L. T. (1935b). The effects of Antuitrin S and sheep pituitary extract on the female lizard *Anolis carolinensis*. *Biol. Bull., Wood's Hole*, **68**, 355–359.

Everett, J. W. (1943). Further studies on the relationship of progesterone to ovulation and luteinization in the persistent estrous rat. *Endocrinology*, **32**, 285–292.

Everett, J. W. (1944). Evidence suggesting a role of the lactogenic hormone in the estrous cycle of the albino rat. *Endocrinology*, **35**, 507–520.

Everett, J. W. (1945). The microscopically demonstrable lipids of the cyclic corpora lutea in the rat. *Amer. J. Anat.* **77**, 293–323.

Everett, J. W. (1948). Progesterone and estrogen in the experimental control of ovulation time and other features in the estrous cycle in the rat. *Endocrinology*, **43**, 389–405.

Everett, J. W. (1954). Luteotrophic function of autografts of the rat hypophysis. *Endocrinology*, **54**, 685–690.

Everett, J. W. (1956). Functional corpora lutea maintained for months by autografts of rat hypophyses. *Endocrinology*, **58**, 786–796.

Everett, J. W. and Sawyer, C. H. (1949). A neural timing factor in the mechanism by which progesterone advances ovulation in the cyclic rat. *Endocrinology*, **45**, 581–595.

Fellner, O. O. (1925). Über das Vorkommen des femininen Sexuallipoids in Vögeleiern und den Eierstöcken der Fische. *Klin. Wschr.* **4**, 1651–1652.

Fevold, H. L. (1943). The luteinizing hormone of the anterior lobe of the pituitary body. *Ann. N.Y. Acad. Sci.* **43**, 321–339.

Fevold, H. L. and Hisaw, F. L. (1934). Interactions of gonad-stimulating hormones in ovarian development. *Amer. J. Physiol.* **109**, 655–665.

Fevold, H. L., Hisaw, F. L. and Leonard, S. L. (1931). The gonad-stimulating and the luteinizing hormones of the anterior lobe of the hypophysis. *Amer. J. Physiol.* **97**, 291–301.

Fevold, H. L., Hisaw, F. L. and Greep, R. O. (1937). Comparative action of gonad-stimulating hormones on the ovaries of rats. *Endocrinology*, **21**, 343–345.

Fichera, G. (1905). Sur l'hypertrophie de la glande pituitaire consécutive à la castration. *Arch. ital. Biol.* **43**, 405–426.

Finerty, J. C. (1952). Parabiosis in physiological studies. *Physiol. Rev.* **32**, 277–302.

Finerty, J. C. and Meyer, R. K. (1950). The effects of graded dosages of estrogen upon pituitary cytology and function. *Endocrinology*, **46**, 494–502.

Fleischer, G. A. (1943). On the alcohol solubility of prolactin. *J. biol. Chem.* **147**, 525–533.

Fleischmann, W. and Kann, S. (1932). Über eine Funktion des weiblichen Sexualhormons bei Fischen (Wachstum der Legeröhre des Bitterlings). *Pflüg. Arch. ges. Physiol.* **230**, 662–667.

Fluhmann, C. F. (1934). The influence of the thyroid on the action of gonad-stimulating hormones. *Amer. J. Physiol.* **108**, 498–508.

Fluhmann, C. F. and Laqueur, G. L. (1943). Action of testosterone and prolactin on the corpora lutea of the rat. *Proc. Soc. exp. Biol., N.Y.* **54**, 223–225.

Foglia, V. G. (1941). Hormonal action of the toad hypophysis on mammals. *Endocrinology*, **29**, 503–513.

Fontenele, O. (1955). Injecting pituitary (hypophyseal) hormones into fish to induce spawning. *Progr. Fish Cult.* **17**, 71–75.

Forbes, T. R. (1937). Studies on the reproductive system of the alligator. I. The effects of prolonged injection of pituitary whole gland extract in the immature alligator. *Anat. Rec.* **70**, 113–137.

Forbes, T. R. (1953). Pre-ovulatory progesterone in the peripheral blood of the rabbit. *Endocrinology*, **53**, 79–87.

Fraenkel-Conrat, H. (1942). The effect of thiols on the reducing groups of lactogenic hormone. *J. biol. Chem.* **142**, 119–127.

Fraenkel-Conrat, H., Simpson, M. E. and Evans, H. M. (1939). The effect of cysteine on gonadotropic hormones. *J. biol. Chem.* **130**, 243–249.

Fraenkel-Conrat, H., Simpson, M. E. and Evans, H. M. (1940a). The effect of thiol compounds on gonadotrophins. *Science*, **91**, 363–365.

Fraenkel-Conrat, H., Simpson, M. E., Li, C. H. and Evans, H. M. (1940b). Antagonism to gonadotrophins exerted by pituitary gonadotrophic extract. *An. Fac. Med., Montevideo*, **25**, 627–636.

Fraenkel-Conrat, H., Simpson, M. E. and Evans, H. M. (1942). The effect of thiol compounds on the activity of lactogenic hormone. *J. biol. Chem.* **142**, 107–117.

Fraenkel-Conrat, H., Li, C. H. and Simpson, M. E. (1943). *In* "Essays in Biology", p. 185. University of California Press, Berkeley.

Fraps, R. M. (1955). The varying effects of sex hormones in birds. *Mem. Soc. Endocrin.* No. 4, 205–218.

Fraps, R. M. and Riley, G. M. (1942). Hormone-induced ovulation in domestic fowl. *Proc. Soc. exp. Biol., N.Y.* **49**, 253–257.

Fraps, R. M., Fevold, H. L. and Neher, B. H. (1947). Ovulatory response of the hen to presumptive luteinizing and other fractions from fowl anterior pituitary tissue. *Anat. Rec.* **99**, 571–572.

Fraps, R. M., Hooker, C. W. and Forbes, T. R. (1948). Progesterone in blood plasma of the ovulating hen. *Science*, **108**, 86–87.

Fraps, R. M., Hooker, C. W. and Forbes, T. R. (1949). Progesterone in blood plasma of cocks and non-ovulating hens. *Science*, **109**, 493.

Freire, M. A. (1938). Action de l'oestrone sur le pouvoir gonadotropique de l'hypophyse du crapaud *Bufo arenarum*. *C.R. Soc. Biol., Paris*, **127**, 560.

Fried, P. H. and Rakoff, A. E. (1952). The effects of chorionic gonadotropin and prolactin on the maintenance of corpus luteum formation. *J. clin. Endocrin.* **12**, 321–337.

Gaarenstroom, J. H. (1942). L'influence des substances oestrogènes sur l'ovaire de rates non-adultes hypophysectomisées. *Proc. Acad. Sci. Amst.* **45**, 953–959.

Galli-Mainini, C. (1950). Secreción de oviducto del sapo por el ovario en ovulación. *Rev. Soc. argent. Biol.* **26**, 166–178.

Galli-Mainini, C. (1951). Sécrétion de l'oviducte du crapaud par l'ovaire en ovulation. *C.R. Soc. Biol., Paris*, **145**, 131–133.

Gallien, L. (1937). Action masculinisante du propionate de testostérone dans la différenciation du sexe chez *Rana temporaria* Linn. *C.R. Acad. Sci., Paris*, **205**, 375–377.

Gallien, L. (1938). Inhibition du cycle sexuel et involution testiculaire consecutives à l'hypophysectomie chez *Rana temporaria* Linn. *C.R. Soc. Biol., Paris*, **129**, 1043–1045.

Gallien, L. (1939a). Hypophysectomie et cycle sexuel chez la grenouille rousse (*Rana temporaria* L.). *C.R. Acad. Sci., Paris*, **208**, 766–767.

Gallien, L. (1939b). Role de l'hypophyse dans le déterminisme du cycle sexuel de la grenouille rousse (*Rana temporaria* L.). *Bull. Soc. zool. Fr.* **64**, 141–142.

Gallien, L. (1940). Recherche sur la physiologie hypophysaire dans ses relations avec les gonades et le cycle sexuel chez la grenouille rousse *Rana temporaria* Linn. *Bull. biol.* **74**, 1–42.

Gallien, L. (1942). Action de l'hypophyse de grenouille sur le développement ovarien du *Phoxinus laevis*. *C.R. Soc. Biol., Paris*, **136**, 109–111.

Gans, E. (1959a). The FSH content of serum of intact and of gonadectomized rats and of rats treated with sex hormones. *Acta endocr., Copenhagen*, **32**, 362–372.

Gans, E. (1959b). The ICSH content of serum of intact and gonadectomized rats and of rats treated with sex hormones. *Acta endocr., Copenhagen*, **32**, 373–383.

Gans, P. (1950). The "consumption" of follicle-stimulating hormone by the ovaries. *Acta physiol. pharm. néerl.* **1**, 279–287.

Gerbilsky, N. L. (1940). Seasonal changes of the gonadotropic potency of the pituitary gland in fishes. *C.R. Acad. Sci., URSS*. **28**, 571–573.

Gerbilsky, N. L. and Kaschenko, L. A. (1937). The effect of the hypophysis upon the gonads of Teleostei. *Bull. Biol. Med. exp., URSS*. **3**, 158–159.

Gitlin, G. (1942). The effect of repeated injections of sheep anterior pituitary extract on the weight of the ovaries of *Xenopus laevis*. *S. Afr. J. med. Sci.* **7**, 16–20.

Godfrey, E. F. and Jaap, R. G. (1950). Estrogenic interruption of broodiness in the domestic fowl. *Poult. Sci.* **29**, 356–361.

Grant, W. C. and Grant, J. A. (1958). Water drive studies on hypophysectomized efts of *Diemyctylus viridescens*. Part I. The role of lactogenic hormone. *Biol. Bull., Wood's Hole*, **114**, 1–9.

7. OVARIAN–PITUITARY RELATIONSHIPS 417

Grant, W. C. and Pickford, G. E. (1959). Presence of the red eft water-drive factor in the pituitaries of teleosts. *Biol. Bull.*, *Wood's Hole*, 116, 429–435.

Greeley, F. and Meyer, R. K. (1953). Seasonal variations in testis-stimulating activity of male pheasant pituitary glands. *Auk*, 70, 350–358.

Green, J. A. (1955). Hormone secretion by the immature mouse ovary after gonadotrophic stimulation. *Endocrinology*, 56, 621–627.

Greep, R. O. (1938). The effect of gonadotropic hormones on the persisting corpora lutea in hypophysectomized rats. *Endocrinology*, 23, 154–163.

Greep, R. O. and Chester Jones, I. (1950a). *In* "A Symposium on Steroid Hormone" (E. S. Gordon, ed.), p. 330. University of Wisconsin Press, Madison, Wisconsin.

Greep, R. O. and Chester Jones, I. (1950b). Steroid control of pituitary function. *Recent Progr. Hormone Res.* 5, 197–254.

Greep, R. O., van Dyke, H. B. and Chow, B. F. (1942). Gonadotropins of the swine pituitary. I. Various biological effects of purified thylakentrin (FSH) and pure metakentrin (LH). *Endocrinology*, 30, 635–649.

Grieser, K. C. and Browman, L. G. (1956). Total gonadotrophic potency of mule deer pituitaries. *Endocrinology*, 58, 206–211.

Gurin, S. (1942). Carbohydrates of the gonadotropic hormones. *Proc. Soc. exp. Biol.*, *N.Y.* 49, 48–52.

Haempel, O. (1950). Untersuchungen über den Einfluss von Hormonen auf den Geschlechtszyklus von *Lebistes reticulatus* (Pet.). *Z. Vitam.-Horm.-u. Fermentforsch.* 3, 261–277.

Hammond, J. (1927). "The Physiology of Reproduction in the Cow." Cambridge University Press.

Hansen, K. L. (1955). A study of *in vitro* ovulation in the spadefoot toad, *Scaphiopus holbrooki*. Ph.D. Thesis Univ. Florida. Diss. Abstr. 15, 2352–2353.

Hasler, A. D. and Meyer, R. K. (1942). Respiratory responses of normal and castrated goldfish to teleost and mammalian hormones. *J. exp. Zool.* 91, 391–404.

Hasler, A. D., Meyer, R. K. and Field, H. M. (1939). Spawning induced prematurely in trout with the aid of pituitary glands of the carp. *Endocrinology*, 25, 978–983.

Hatta, K. (1941). Seasonal variations and changes after gonadectomy in the anterior hypophysis of the lizard *Takydromus tachydromoides*. *Annot. zool. jap.* 20, 131–141.

Hellbaum, A. A. (1935). The gonad-stimulating activity of pituitary glands from horses of different ages and sex types. *Anat. Rec.* 63, 147–157.

Hellbaum, A. A. and Greep, R. O. (1946). Action of estrogen on release of hypophyseal luteinizing hormone. *Proc. Soc. exp. Biol.*, *N.Y.* 63, 53–56.

Heller, C. G. and Jungck, E. C. (1947). Regulation of ovarian growth: Inhibition by estrogen or stimulation by gonadotrophins? *Proc. Soc. exp. Biol.*, *N.Y.* 65, 152–154.

Henderson, W. R. and Rowlands, I. W. (1938). The gonadotropic activity of the anterior pituitary gland in relation to increased cranial pressure. *Brit. med. J.* 1094–1097.

Hertz, R. and Hisaw, F. L. (1934). Effects of the follicle-stimulating and luteinizing pituitary extracts on the ovaries of the infantile and juvenile rabbit. *Amer. J. Physiol.* 108, 1–13.

Hill, R. T. (1934). Variation in the activity of the rabbit hypophysis during the reproductive cycle. *J. Physiol.* **83**, 129–136.

Hill, R. T. and Parkes, A. S. (1934). Hypophysectomy of birds; effect on gonads, accessory organs and head furnishings. *Proc. roy. Soc.* B. **116**, 221–236.

Hisaw, F. L. (1944). The placental gonadotrophin and luteal function in monkeys (*Macaca mulatta*). *Yale J. Biol. Med.* **17**, 119–137.

Hisaw, F. L. (1947). Development of the Graafian follicle and ovulation. *Physiol. Rev.* **27**, 95–119.

Hoar, W. S. (1955). Reproduction in teleost fishes. *Mem. Soc. Endocrin.* No. 4, 5–22.

Höhn, E. O. (1959). Prolactin in the cowbird's pituitary in relation to avian brood parasitism. *Nature, Lond.* **184**, 2030.

Hogben, L., Charles, E. and Slome, D. (1931). Studies on the pituitary. VIII. The relation of the pituitary gland to calcium metabolism and ovarian function in *Xenopus*. *J. exp. Biol.* **8**, 345–354.

Hohlweg, W. (1934). Veränderungen des Hypophysenvorderlappens und des Ovariums nach Behandlung mit grossen Dosen von Follikelhormon. *Klin. Wschr.* **13**, 92–95.

Hollandbeck, R., Baker, B., Norton, H. W. and Nalbandov, A. V. (1956). Gonadotrophic hormone content of swine pituitary glands in relation to age. *J. Anim. Sci.* **15**, 418–427.

Hollander, N. and Hollander, V. P. (1958). The effect of follicle-stimulating hormone on the biosynthesis in vitro of estradiol-17β from acetate-1-C^{14} and testosterone-4-C^{14}. *J. biol. Chem.* **233**, 1097–1099.

Holstrom, E. G. and Jones, W. J. (1949). The experimental production of menorrhagia by administration of gonadotropins. *Amer. J. Obstet. Gynec.* **58**, 308–317.

Houssay, B. A. (1931). Action sexuelle de l'hypophyse sur les poissons et les reptiles. *C.R. Soc. Biol., Paris*, **106**, 377–378.

Houssay, B. A. (1947). La fonción sexual del sapo *Bufo arenarum* Hensel. *An. Acad. nac. Cienc. B. Aires*, **12**, 103–124.

Houssay, B. A. (1949). Hypophyseal functions in the toad *Bufo arenarum* Hensel. *Quart. Rev. Biol.* **24**, 1–27.

Houssay, B. A. (1950a). Acciones recíprocas de las injecciones de sus hipófisis in *Bufo arenarum* y *Rana pipiens*. *Rev. Soc. argent. Biol.* **26**, 43–46.

Houssay, B. A. (1950b). Gobierno hormonal del oviducto (Discusión de los trabajos de los Dres. Galli-Mainini y Penhos.) *Rev. Soc. argent. Biol.* **26**, 185–187.

Houssay, B. A. (1952). Action des hormones hypophysaires de mammifères chez les crapauds et les grenouilles. *C.R. Soc. Biol., Paris*, **146**, 137–139.

Houssay, B. A. and Giusti, L. (1929a). Les fonctions de l'hypophyse et de la région infundibulo-tubérienne chez le crapaud. *C.R. Soc. Biol., Paris*, **101**, 935–938.

Houssay, B. A. and Giusti, L. (1929b). Las fonciones de la hipófisis y la región infundibulatuberiana en el sapo *Bufo marinus* (L) Schneid. *Rev. Soc. argent. Biol.* **5**, 47–65.

Houssay, B. A. and Giusti, L. (1930). Fonction sexuelle, hypophyse et hypothalamus chez le crapaud. *C.R. Soc. Biol., Paris*, **104**, 1030–1031.

Houssay, B. A., Giusti, L. and Lascano-Gonzales, J. M. (1929). Implantacción de la hipófisis y estimulación sexual en el sapo. *Rev. Soc. argent. Biol.* **5** 397–418.

Howes, N. H. (1936). A study of the histology of the pituitary gland of the skate. *Quart. J. micr. Sci.* **78**, 637–651.

Ichikawa, M. and Kawakami, I. (1948). Spawning induced in the carp with the injection of the pituitary hormone. II. Effects on the mature females which are unable to spawn as well as premature ones. *Seibut. Gyos.* **3**, 53–57.

Ingle, D. J. (1952). The role of the adrenal cortex in homeostasis. *J. Endocrin.* **8**, xxiii–xxxvii.

Ingram, D. L. (1953). The effect of hypophysectomy on the number of oocytes in the adult albino rat. *J. Endocrin.* **9**, 307–321.

Ingram, D. L. (1959). The vaginal smear of senile laboratory rats. *J. Endocrin.* **19**, 182–188.

Ingram, D. L. and Mandl, A. M. (1958). The secretion of oestrogen after hypophysectomy. *J. Endocrin.* **17**, 13–16.

Jaap, R. G. (1935). Gonad-stimulating potency of individual pituitaries. *Poult. Sci.* **14**, 237–246.

Janes, R. G. (1944). Occurrence of follicular cysts in thyroidectomized rats treated with stilboestrol. *Anat. Rec.* **90**, 93–98.

Johnson, T. N. and Meites, J. (1950). Effects of hypo- and hyperthyroidism in rats and mice on ovarian response to equine gonadotrophin. *Proc. Soc. exp. Biol., N.Y.* **75**, 155–157.

Jones, G. E. S., Delfs, E. and Foote, E. C. (1946). The effect of thiouracil hypothyroidism on reproduction in the rat. *Endocrinology*, **38**, 337–344.

Jongh, S. E. de, and Paesi, F. J. A. (1958). The ICSH concentration in the hypophysis of immature and adult rats. *Acta endocr., Copenhagen*, **29**, 413–421.

Jost, A. (1953). Problems of foetal endocrinology: the gonadal and hypophyseal hormones. *Recent Progr. Hormone Res.* **8**, 379–418.

Jost, A. (1954). Hormonal factors in the development of the foetus. *Cold Spr. Harb. Symp. quant. Biol.* **19**, 167–180.

Jost, A. (1955). Modalities in the action of gonadal and gonad-stimulating hormones in the foetus. *Mem. Soc. Endocrin.* No. 4, 237–248.

Jungck, E. C., Heller, C. G. and Nelson, W. O. (1947). Regulation of pituitary gonadotrophic secretion: inhibition by estrogen or inactivation by the ovaries? *Proc. Soc. exp. Biol., N.Y.* **65**, 148–152.

Jutisz, M. and Squire, P. G. (1958). Occurrence of several active components in sheep pituitary interstitial cell-stimulating hormone as evidenced by column electrophoresis. *Bull. Soc. Chim. biol., Paris*, **40**, 1875–1883.

Kambara, S. (1954). Ovulation caused by injection of hormonic steroids in the newt. *Annot. zool. jap.* **27**, 180–187.

Kammlade, W. G., Welch, J. A., Nalbandov, A. V. and Norton, H. W. (1952). Pituitary activity of sheep in relation to the breeding season. *J. Anim. Sci.* **11**, 646–655.

Kazansky, B. N. (1940). Zur Frage der systematischen Spezifität des gonadotropen Hormons der Hypophyse bei den Fischen. *C.R. Acad. Sci., URSS.* **27**, 180–184.

Kazansky, B. N. (1950a). Effects of hypophysis on nuclear processes in the oocytes of fish. *C.R. Acad. Sci., URSS.* **75**, 311–314.

Kazansky, B. N. (1950b). Method of obtaining frontal spawning of carp in pond husbandries and its importance under the climatic conditions of the northwestern (European) part of USSR. *Vestnik Leningrad Univ.* **5**, 147–151.

Kazansky, B. N. (1951). Experimental analysis of the growth of oocytes in fish. *C.R. Acad. Sci., URSS.* **80**, 277–280.

Kazansky, B. N. (1952). Experimental analysis of intermittent spawning in fish. *Zool. Zh.* **31**, 883–896.

Kehl, R. and Combescot, C. (1955). Reproduction in Reptilia. *Mem. Soc. Endocrin.* No. 4, 57–73.

Kempf, R. (1950). Contribution à l'étude du mécanisme de libération des hormones gonadotropes hypophysaires chez le rat. *Arch. Biol., Paris*, **61**, 501–594.

Kinoshita, Y. (1938). On the secondary sexual characters with special remarks on the influence of hormone preparations upon the nuptial coloration in *Chloea sarchynnis* Jordan and Snyder. *J. Sci. Hiroshima Univ.* B, **6**, 5–22.

Kirshenblat, Ia. D. (1949a). The action of gonadotrophic hormones of man on female fish. *Priroda*, **38**, 75–76.

Kirshenblat, Ia. D. (1949b). The effects of hormones from the hypophysis of fish on the mammalian female. *C.R. Acad. Sci., URSS.* **66**, 745–748.

Kirshenblat, Ia. D. (1956). The action of purified pituitary hormones on fish ovaries. *C.R. Acad. Sci., URSS.* **111**, 504–505.

Knobil, E., Kostyo, J. L. and Greep, R. O. (1959). Production of ovulation in the hypophysectomized rhesus monkey. *Endocrinology*, **65**, 487–493.

Knowles, F. G. W. (1939). The influence of anterior-pituitary and testicular hormones on the sexual maturation of lampreys. *J. exp. Biol.* **16**, 535–547.

Koenig, V. L. and King, E. (1950). Extraction studies of sheep pituitary gonadotropic and lactogenic hormones in alcoholic acetate buffers. *Arch. Biochem.* **26**, 219–229.

Kopf, R., Loesser, A. and Mayer, G. (1948). Funktionsänderungen des Ovarium durch Thiouracil und Methylthiouracil. *Klin. Wschr.* **26**, 202–206.

Kornfeld, W. and Nalbandov, A. V. (1954). Endocrine influences on the development of the rudimentary gonad of the fowl. *Endocrinology*, **55**, 751–761.

Kraul, L. (1931). Certain new observations on the action of anterior pituitary. *Amer. J. Obstet. Gynec.* **21**, 301–319.

Kubota, Z. (1953). On the maturing process of loach *Misgurnus anguillicaudatus* (Cantor). *J. Shimonoseki Col. Fish.* **3**, 111–116.

Kupperman, H. S., Fried, P. and Hare, L. Q. (1944). The control of menorrhagia by prolactin. *Amer. J. Obstet. Gynec.* **48**, 228–234.

Lahr, E. L. and Riddle, O. (1936). Temporary suppression of estrous cycles in the rat by prolactin. *Proc. Soc. exp. Biol., N.Y.* **34**, 880–883.

Lamond, D. R. (1959). Cessation of ovarian function in the immature mouse after hypophysectomy. *J. Endocrin.* **19**, 103–107.

Landgrebe, F. W. (1939). The maintenance of reproductive activity in *Xenopus laevis* for pregnancy diagnosis. *J. exp. Biol.* **16**, 89–95.

Lane, C. E. and Hisaw, F. L. (1934). The follicular apparatus of the ovary of the immature rat and some of the factors which influence it. *Anat. Rec.* **60**, Suppl., 52.

Lauson, H. D., Heller, C. G. and Sevringhaus, E. L. (1938). Inadequacies of estradiol substitution in ovariectomized albino rats. *Endocrinology*, **23**, 479–484.

Leathem, J. H. (1945). Influence of thiourea on plasma proteins and organ weights in rats. *Endocrinology*, **36**, 98–103.

Leathem, J. H. (1949). The antihormone problem in endocrine therapy. *Recent Progr. Hormone Res.* **4**, 115–152.

Leathem, J. H. (1958). Hormonal influences on the gonadotrophin sensitive hypothyroid rat ovary. *Anat. Rec.* **131**, 487–499.

Lehrman, D. S. (1958). Effect of female sex hormones on incubation behaviour in the ring dove. *J. comp. physiol. Psychol.* **51**, 142–145.

Leonora, J., McShan, W. H. and Meyer, R. K. (1956). Factors affecting extraction and recovery of follicle stimulating hormone from sheep pituitary glands. *Proc. Soc. exp. Biol., N.Y.* **92**, 524–529.

Leonora, J., McShan, W. H. and Meyer, R. K. (1958). Separation of luteinizing hormone fractions from sheep pituitary glands by use of ion exchange resins. *Endocrinology,* **63**, 867–881.

Li, C. H. (1942). Studies on pituitary lactogenic hormone. VIII. Diffusion and viscosity measurements. *J. biol. Chem.* **146**, 633–638.

Li, C. H. (1943). Studies on pituitary lactogenic hormone. IX. The content of sulfur amino acid. *J. biol. Chem.* **148**, 289–291.

Li, C. H. (1944). Studies on pituitary lactogenic hormone. X. The effect of a detergent. *J. biol. Chem.* **155**, 45–48.

Li, C. H. (1949a). Chemistry of gonadotropic hormones. *Vitam. & Horm.* **7**, 223–252.

Li, C. H. (1949b). Studies on pituitary lactogenic hormone. XIII. The amino acid composition of the hormone obtained from whole sheep pituitary glands. *J. biol. Chem.* **178**, 459–464.

Li, C. H. (1956). *In* "Advances in Protein Chemistry" (M. L. Anson, K. Bailey and J. T. Edsall, eds.), Vol. XI, p. 102. Academic Press Inc., New York.

Li, C. H. (1957). *In* "Advances in Protein Chemistry" (C. B. Anfinsen jr., M. L. Anson, K. Bailey and J. T. Edsall, eds.), Vol. XII, p. 295. Academic Press Inc., New York.

Li, C. H. and Cummins, J. T. (1958). Studies on pituitary lactogenic hormone. XVIII. Reduction of disulfide bridges in the ovine hormone and the nature of the C-terminus. *J. biol. Chem.* **233**, 73–76.

Li, C. H. and Evans, H. M. (1948). *In* "The Hormones" (G. Pincus and K. V. Thimann, eds.), Vol. I, p. 631. Academic Press Inc., New York.

Li, C. H. and Fraenkel-Conrat, H. (1947). Studies on pituitary lactogenic hormone. XII. Effect of esterification with methyl alcohol. *J. biol. Chem.* **167**, 495–498.

Li, C. H. and Kalman, A. (1946). Studies on pituitary lactogenic hormone. XI. Reactions with ketene. *J. Amer. chem. Soc.* **68**, 285–287.

Li, C. H. and Pedersen, K. O. (1952). Physico-chemical characterisation of pituitary follicle-stimulating hormone. *J. gen. Physiol.* **35**, 629–637.

Li, C. H., Lyons, W. R. and Evans, H. M. (1939a). Electrophoretic studies of pituitary lactogenic hormone. *Science,* **90**, 622–623.

Li, C. H., Lyons, W. R., Simpson, M. E. and Evans, H. M. (1939b). Essentiality of primary amino groups for specific activity of the lactogenic hormone. *Science,* **90**, 376–377.

Li, C. H., Simpson, M. E. and Evans, H. M. (1939c). Action of ketene on gonadotropic hormones. *J. biol. Chem.* **131**, 259–266.

Li, C. H., Simpson, M. E. and Evans, H. M. (1939d). Action of ketene on the pituitary lactogenic hormone. *Science,* **90**, 140–141.

Li, C. H., Lyons, W. R. and Evans, H. M. (1940a). Studies on pituitary lactogenic hormone. II. A comparison of the electrophoretic behavior of the lactogenic hormone as prepared from beef and sheep pituitaries. *J. Amer. chem. Soc.* **62**, 2925–2927.

Li, C. H., Lyons, W. R. and Evans, H. M. (1940b). Studies on pituitary lactogenic hormone. I. Electrophoretic behavior. *J. gen. Physiol.* **23**, 433–438.

Li, C. H., Lyons, W. R. and Evans, H. M. (1940c). Studies on pituitary lacto-genic hormone. IV. Tyrosine and tryptophane content. *J. biol. Chem.* **136**, 709–711.

Li, C. H., Simpson, M. E. and Evans, H. M. (1940d). Interstitial cell-stimulating hormone. II. Method of preparation and some physico-chemical studies. *Endocrinology*, **27**, 803–808.

Li, C. H., Simpson, M. E. and Evans, H. M. (1940e). Purification of the pituitary interstitial cell-stimulating hormone. *Science*, **92**, 355–356.

Li, C. H., Lyons, W. R. and Evans, H. M. (1941a). Studies on pituitary lacto-genic hormone. VI. Molecular weight of the pure hormone. *J. biol. Chem.* **140**, 43–53.

Li, C. H., Lyons, W. R. and Evans, H. M. (1941b). Studies on pituitary lacto-genic hormone. III. Solubilities of sheep and beef hormones. *J. gen. Physiol.* **24**, 303–309.

Li, C. H., Lyons, W. R. and Evans, H. M. (1941c). Studies on pituitary lacto-genic hormone. V. Reactions with iodine. *J. biol. Chem.* **139**, 43–55.

Li, C. H., Simpson, M. E. and Evans, H. M. (1942a). Physico-chemical charac-teristics of the interstitial cell-stimulating hormone from sheep pituitary glands. *J. Amer. chem. Soc.* **64**, 367–369.

Li, C. H., Simpson, M. E. and Evans, H. M. (1942b). Studies on pituitary lactogenic hormone. VII. A method of isolation. *J. biol. Chem.* **146**, 627–631.

Li, C. H., Simpson, M. E. and Evans, H. M. (1949). Isolation of pituitary follicle-stimulating hormone (FSH). *Science*, **109**, 445–446.

Long, J. A. and Evans, H. M. (1922). Oestrous cycle in the rat and its associated phenomena. *Mem. Univ. Calif.* **6**, 1–148.

Loraine, J. A. (1958). "Clinical Applications of Hormone Assay." E. & S. Livingstone, Edinburgh and London.

Loraine, J. A. and Brown, J. B. (1956). Further observations on the estimation of urinary gonadotropins in non-pregnant human subjects. *J. clin. Endocrin.* **16**, 1180–1195.

Lyon, R. (1942). Lactogenic hormone prolongs the time during which deciduo-mata may be induced in lactating rats. *Proc. Soc. exp. Biol., N.Y.* **51**, 156–157.

Lyons, W. R. (1937a). Preparation and assay of mammotropic hormone. *Proc. Soc. exp. Biol., N.Y.* **35**, 645–648.

Lyons, W. R. (1937b). Preparation and assay of mammotropin. *Cold Spr. Harb. Symp. quant. Biol.* **5**, 198–207.

Lyons, W. R., Simpson, M. E. and Evans, H. M. (1943). Hormonal requirements for pregnancy and mammary development in hypophysectomized rats. *Proc. Soc. exp. Biol., N.Y.* **52**, 134–136.

Lytle, I. M. and Lorenz, F. W. (1958). Progesterone in the blood of the laying hen. *Nature, Lond.* **182**, 1681.

Maekawa, K. (1953a). Effect of androgenic and estrogenic steroids on intra-splenic ovarian transplants in prepuberally gonadectomized rats. *Annot. zool. jap.* **26**, 106–109.

Maekawa, K. (1953b). Alterations of effects of androgenic and estrogenic steroids on intrasplenic ovarian grafts in prepuberally gonadectomized rats in hyper- and hypothyroid conditions. *Annot. zool. jap.* **26**, 110–114.

Maekawa, K. (1954). Effects of estrogen administration on intrasplenic ovarian grafts in rats in which gonadal secretions are experimentally reduced. *J. Fac. Sci. Univ. Tokyo*, **7**, 161–176.

Maekawa, K. and Imai, K. (1954). Effect of physiological doses of estrogen on intrasplenic ovarian grafts in ovariectomized female rats. *Annot. zool. jap.* 27, 27–32.

Makepeace, A. W., Weinstein, G. L. and Friedman, M. H. (1937). The effect of progestin and progesterone on ovulation in the rabbit. *Amer. J. Physiol.* 119, 512–516.

Mandl, A. M. (1954). The sensitivity of adrenalectomized rats to gonadotrophins. *J. Endocrin.* 11, 359–376.

Mandl, A. M. (1957). Factors influencing ovarian sensitivity to gonadotrophins. *J. Endocrin.* 15, 448–457.

Mandl, A. M. (1959). Corpora lutea in senile virgin laboratory rats. *J. Endocrin.* 18, 438–443.

Mandl, A. M., and Shelton, M. (1959). A quantitative study of oocytes in young and old nulliparous laboratory rats. *J. Endocrin.* 18, 444–450.

Mandl, A. M. and Zuckerman, S. (1952). The growth of the oocyte and follicle in the adult rat. *J. Endocrin.* 8, 126–132.

March, F. (1937). Some hormone effects in Amphibia. *Proc. zool. Soc. Lond.* A. 107, 603–655.

Marden, W. G. R. (1952). Hormone control of ovulation in the calf. *Endocrinology*, 50, 456–461.

Marescaux, J., Aron, C. and Aron, M. (1957). Résultats de l'inoculation intra-ovarienne, chez le cobaye normal ou hypophyséoprivé, d'hormones gonado-stimulantes purifées. *C.R. Soc. Biol., Paris*, 151, 988–990.

Marshall, A. J. (1960). *In* "Hormones in Fish." Symposia of the Zoological Society of London, No. 1, pp. 137–157.

Marshall, A. J. and Coombes, C. J. F. (1957). The interaction of environmental, internal and behavioural factors in the rook, *Corvus f. frugilegus* Linnaeus. *Proc. zool. Soc. Lond.* 128, 545–589.

Martinovitch, P. N., and Pavic, D. (1960). Functional pituitary transplants in rats. *Nature, Lond.* 185, 155–156.

Matthews, L. H. (1955). The evolution of viviparity in vertebrates. *Mem. Soc. Endocrin.* No. 4, 129–148.

Matthews, S. A. (1940). The effects of implanting adult hypophyses into sexually immature *Fundulus*. *Biol. Bull., Wood's Hole*, 79, 207–214.

Mayer, G. (1951). La prolactine facteur lutéotrophique. *Arch. Sci. physiol.* 5, 247–275.

Mayer, G. and Canivenc, R. (1951). Action lutéotrophique et lactogène de la prolactine chez la rate. *C.R. Soc. Biol., Paris*, 145, 100–102.

Mayer, G. and Klein, M. (1949). Effets de l'adminstration de prolactine en fin de grossesse chez la rate. *C.R. Soc. Biol., Paris*, 143, 1195–1197.

Mayo, V. (1937). Some effects of mammalian follicle-stimulating and luteinizing hormones in adult female urodeles. *Biol. Bull., Wood's Hole*, 73, 373–374.

McArthur, J. W. (1952). The identification of pituitary interstitial cell stimulating hormone in human urine. *Endocrinology*, 50, 304–310.

McShan, W. H. and French, H. E. (1937). The chemistry of the lactogenic hormone. *J. biol. Chem.* 117, 111–117.

McShan, W. H. and Meyer, R. K. (1938). The effect of trypsin and ptyalin preparations on the gonadotropic activity of pituitary extracts. *J. biol. Chem.* 126, 361–365.

McShan, W. H. and Meyer, R. K. (1939). Carbohydrate properties of pituitary follicle-stimulating and luteinizing preparations. *Proc. Soc. exp. Biol.*, *N.Y.* **40**, 701–703.

McShan, W. H. and Meyer, R. K. (1955). Further purification and biological action of follicle-stimulating hormone from sheep pituitary glands. *Proc. Soc. exp. Biol.*, *N.Y.* **88**, 278–283.

McShan, W. H., Kagawa, C. M. and Meyer, R. K. (1954). A simplified procedure for obtaining follicle-stimulating hormone from sheep pituitary glands. *Proc. Soc. exp. Biol.*, *N.Y.* **85**, 393–398.

Medawar, P. B. (1953). Some immunological and endocrinological problems raised by the evolution of viviparity in the vertebrates. *Symp. Soc. exp. Biol.* **7**, 320–335.

Meites, J. (1953). Relation of nutrition to endocrine reproductive functions. *Iowa St. Coll. J. Sci.* **28**, 19–44.

Meites, J. and Reed, J. O. (1949). Effects of restricted food intake in intact and ovariectomized rats on pituitary lactogen and gonadotrophin. *Proc. Soc. exp. Biol.*, *N.Y.* **70**, 513–516.

Meites, J. and Turner, C. W. (1947). Effect of sex hormones on pituitary lactogen and crop glands of common pigeons. *Proc. Soc. exp. Biol.*, *N.Y.* **64**, 465–468.

Mellish, C. H. and Meyer, R. K. (1937). The effects of various gonadotropic substances and thyroxine on the ovaries of horned lizards (*Phrynosoma cornutum*). *Anat. Rec.* **69**, 179–189.

Mendoza, G. (1939). The reproductive cycle of the viviparous teleost *Neotoca bilineata*, a member of the family Goodeidae. I. The breeding cycle. *Biol. Bull.*, *Wood's Hole*, **76**, 359–370.

Mendoza, G. (1940). The reproductive cycle of the viviparous teleost *Neotoca bilineata*, a member of the family Goodeidae. II. The cyclic changes in the ovarian stroma during gestation. *Biol. Bull.*, *Wood's Hole*, **78**, 349–365.

Mendoza, G. (1943). The reproductive cycle of the viviparous teleost *Neotoca bilineata*, a member of the family Goodeidae. III. The germinal tissue. *Biol. Bull.*, *Wood's Hole*, **84**, 87–97.

Menezes, R. S. de. (1945). Ação de hipófises de peixes doadores em diestro sôbre peixes reprodutores em estro. *Rev. bras. Biol.* **5**, 535–539.

Meyer, R. K. and Biddulph, C. (1941). The influence of estradiol on the secretion of gonadotropic hormone in adult parabiotic rats. *Amer. J. Physiol.* **134**, 141–146.

Meyer, R. K. and Gustus, E. L. (1935). Refractoriness to ovarian stimulation in the rhesus monkey. *Science*, **81**, 208–210.

Meyer, R. K. and Hertz, R. (1937). The effect of oestrone on the secretion of the gonadotropic complex as evidenced in parabiotic rats. *Amer. J. Physiol.* **120**, 232–237.

Meyer, R. K., Leonard, S. L., Hisaw, F. L. and Martin, S. J. (1932). The influence of oestrin on the gonad-stimulating complex of the anterior pituitary of castrated male and female rats. *Endocrinology*, **16**, 655–665.

Meyer, R. K., Mellish, C. H. and Kupperman, S. (1939). The gonadotropic and adrenotropic hormones of the chicken hypophysis. *J. Pharmacol.* **65**, 104–114.

Meyer, R. K., Biddulph, C. and Finerty, J. C. (1946a). Pituitary-gonad interaction in immature female parabiotic rats. *Endocrinology*, **39**, 23–31.

Meyer, R. K., Biddulph, C. and McShan, W. H. (1946b). Luteinization of the ovaries of immature hypophysectomized parabiotic rats with gonadotrophic hormone preparations. *Proc. Soc. exp. Biol.*, *N.Y.* **63**, 95–98.

Mitchell, J. B. (1929). Experimental studies of the bird hypophysis. I. Effect of hypophysectomy in the brown leghorn fowl. *Physiol. Zoöl.* **2**, 411–437.

Moore, C. R. (1953). Adrenal cortical secretions in relation to the reproductive system of rats. *J. clin. Endocrin.* **13**, 330–368.

Moore, W. W. and Nalbandov, A. V. (1953). Neurogenic effects of uterine distension on the estrous cycle of the ewe. *Endocrinology*, **53**, 1–11.

Moore, W. W. and Nalbandov, A. V. (1955). Maintenance of corpora lutea in sheep with lactogenic hormone. *J. Endocrin.* **13**, 18–25.

Morris, C. J. O. R. (1955). Chemistry of the gonadotrophins. *Brit. med. Bull.* **11**, 101–104.

Nalbandov, A. V. (1953). Endocrine control of physiological functions. *Poult. Sci.* **32**, 88–103.

Nalbandov, A. V. (1959). *In* "Comparative Endocrinology" (A. Gorbman, ed.), pp. 161 and 524. J. Wiley & Sons, New York.

Nalbandov, A. V. and Card, L. E. (1943). Effect of hypophysectomy on growing chicks. *J. exp. Zool.* **94**, 387–413.

Nalbandov, A. V. and Card, L. E. (1946). Effect of FSH and LH upon the ovaries of immature chicks and low-producing hens. *Endocrinology*, **38**, 71–78.

Nalbandov, A. V., Meyer, R. K. and McShan, W. H. (1946). Effect of purified gonadotropes on the androgen-secreting ability of testes in hypophysectomized cocks. *Endocrinology*, **39**, 91–104.

Nalbandov, A. V., Meyer, R. K. and McShan, W. H. (1951). The role of a third gonadotrophic hormone in the mechanism of androgen secretion in chicken testes. *Anat. Rec.* **110**, 475–494.

Nalbandov, A. V., Moore, W. W. and Norton, H. W. (1955). Further studies on the neurogenic control of the estrous cycle by uterine distension. *Endocrinology*, **56**, 225–231.

Neher, B. H. and Fraps, R. M. (1946). Fertility and hatchability of the prematurely ovulated hen's egg. *J. exp. Zool.* **101**, 83–89.

Nelson, M. M., Lyons, W. R. and Evans, H. M. (1951). Maintenance of pregnancy in pyridoxine-deficient rats when injected with estrone and progesterone. *Endocrinology*, **48**, 726–732.

Nelson, M. M., Lyons, W. R. and Evans, H. M. (1953). Comparison of ovarian and pituitary hormones for maintenance of pregnancy in pyridoxine-deficient rats. *Endocrinology*, **52**, 585–589.

Nikitovitch-Winer, M. and Everett, J. W. (1958). Comparative study of luteotrophin secretion by hypophyseal autotransplants in the rat. Effects of site and stages of the estrous cycle. *Endocrinology*, **62**, 522–532.

Nishino, K. (1948). On the acceleration of spawning in the rainbow trout, *Salmo irideus* Gibbon with the aid of *Oncorhynchus keta* (Walbaum) pituitaries. *Sci. Rep. Hokkaido Fish Hatch.* **3**, 23–28.

Nishino, K. (1949a). On the acceleration of maturity of the salmon, *Oncorhynchus keta* (Walbaum), with the aid of salmon pituitaries. *Rep. Hokkaido Fishbreeding Stn.* **4**, 1–3.

Nishino, K. (1949b). On the acceleration of maturity of the salmon, *Oncorhynchus keta* (Walbaum), with the aid of salmon pituitaries. *Rep. Hokkaido Fishbreeding Stn.* **4**, 95–97.

Noble, R. L., Rowlands, I. W., Warwick, M. H. and Williams, P. C. (1939). Comparative effects of certain gonadotrophic extracts on the ovaries of normal and hypophysectomized rats. *J. Endocrin.* **1**, 22–35.

Norman, J. R. (1947). "A History of Fishes", 3rd ed. Benn, London.

Novelli, A. (1932a). Acción sexual del lóbulo anterior de la hipófisis en el sapo hembra. *Rec. Soc. argent. Biol.* **8**, 454–458.

Novelli, A. (1932b). Rôle de la castration sur l'action sexuelle de l'hypophyse du crapaud. *C.R. Soc. Biol.*, *Paris*, **111**, 476.

Nowell, N. W. and Chester Jones, I. (1957). Some aspects of the storage and secretion of corticotrophin and gonadotrophins. *Acta endocr.*, *Copenhagen*, **26**, 273–285.

Nusenbaum, L. M. (1950). Obtaining eggs for piscicultural purposes. *Fish Ind.*, *Moscow*, **26**, 34–36.

Paesi, F. J. A. (1952). The effect of small doses of oestrogen on the ovary of the immature rat. *Acta endocr.*, *Copenhagen*, **11**, 251–267.

Palmer, D. D., Burrows, R. E., Robertson, O. H. and Newman, H. W. (1954). Further studies on the reactions of adult blueback salmon to injected salmon and mammalian gonadotrophins. *Progr. Fish Cult.* **16**, 99–107.

Panigel, M. (1951). Étude anatomohistologique des corps atrétiques pendant la gestation chez le lézard *Zootoca vivipara* W. (*Lacerta vivipara* J.). *Bull. Soc. zool. Fr.* **76**, 75–78.

Parkes, A. S. (1945). The adrenal-gonad relationship. *Physiol. Rev.* **25**, 203–254.

Patel, M. D. (1936). The physiology of the formation of "pigeon's milk." *Physiol. Zoöl.* **9**, 129–152.

Payne, R. W. (1951). Relationship of pituitary and adrenal cortex to ovarian hyperemia reaction in the rat. *Proc. Soc. exp. Biol.*, *N.Y.* **77**, 242–244.

Payne, R. W. and Hellbaum, A. A. (1955). The effect of estrogens on the ovary of the hypophysectomized rat. *Endocrinology*, **57**, 193–199.

Pencharz, R. I. (1940). Effect of estrogens and androgens alone and in combination with chorionic gonadotrophin on the ovary of the hypophysectomized rat. *Science*, **91**, 554–555.

Penhos, J. C. and Cardeza, A. F. (1952). Les glandes endocrines du crapaud hypophysoprivé alimenté. *C.R. Soc. Biol.*, *Paris*, **146**, 132–133.

Phillips, R. E. (1942). Comparative gonadotropic potency of unfractionated extracts of poultry pituitaries. *Poult. Sci.* **21**, 161–172.

Phillips, R. E. (1943). Ovarian response of hens and pullets to injections of ambinon. *Poult. Sci.* **22**, 368–373.

Phillips, W. A. (1937). The inhibition of estrous cycles in the albino rat by progesterone. *Amer. J. Physiol.* **119**, 623–626.

Pickford, G. E. and Atz, J. W. (1957). "The Physiology of the Pituitary Gland of Fishes." Zoological Society, New York.

Pickford, G. E. and Phillips, J. G. (1959). Prolactin, a factor in promoting survival of hypophysectomized killifish in fresh water. *Science*, **130**, 454–455.

Ponse, K. (1936). La ponte artificielle chez *Rana temporaria*. *C.R. Soc. Biol. Paris*, **121**, 1397–1400.

Poris, E. G. (1941). Studies on the endocrines of reptiles. II. Variations in the histology of the hypophysis of *Anolis carolinensis*. *Anat. Rec.* **80**, 99–121.

Rahn, H. (1942). The reproductive cycle of the prairie rattler. *Copeia*, **5**, 233–240.

Ramaswami, L. S. and Lakshman, A. B. (1958). Ovulation induced in frog with mammalian hormones. *Nature, Lond.* **181**, 1210.

Ramaswami, L. S. and Lakshman, A. B. (1959). The skipper-frog as a suitable embryological animal and an account of the action of mammalian hormones on spawning the same. *Proc. nat. Inst. Sci.*, *India*, **25**(B), 68–79.

Ramaswami, L. S., and Sundararaj, B. I. (1957). Induced spawning in the Indian catfish *Heteropneustes* with pituitary injections. *Acta anat.* **31**, 551–562.

Ramaswami, L. S. and Sundararaj, B. I. (1958). Action of enzymes on the gonadotrophic activity of pituitary extracts of the Indian catfish *Heteropneustes*. *Acta endocr., Copenhagen,* **27**, 253–256.

Rasquin, P. (1951). Effects of carp pituitary and mammalian ACTH on the endocrine and lymphoid systems of the teleost *Astyanax mexicanus*. *J. exp. Zool.* **117**, 317–357.

Regamey, J. (1935). Les caractères sexuels du lézard (*Lacerta agilis* L.). *Rev. suisse Zool.* **42**, 87–168.

Regnier, M. T. (1938). Contribution à l'étude de la sexualité des cyprinodonts vivipares (*Xiphophorus helleri, Lebistes reticulatus*). *Bull. biol.* **72**, 385–493.

Rennels, E. G. (1951). Influence of hormones on the histochemistry of ovarian interstitial tissue in the immature rat. *Amer. J. Anat.* **88**, 63–107.

Rey, P. (1939). Modifications du cycle annuel de l'ovaire après ablation du lobe principal de l'hypophyse chez *Bufo vulgaris*. *C.R. Soc. Biol., Paris,* **130**, 957–959.

Riddle, O. and Bates, R. W. (1933). Concerning anterior pituitary hormones. *Endocrinology,* **17**, 689–698.

Riddle, O. and Bates, R. W. (1939). In "Sex and Internal Secretions" (E. Allen, ed.), p. 1088. Williams and Wilkins, Baltimore.

Riddle, O. and Braucher, P. F. (1931). Studies on the physiology of reproduction in birds. XXX. Control of the special secretion of the crop gland in pigeons by an anterior pituitary hormone. *Amer. J. Physiol.* **97**, 617–625.

Riddle, O. and Lahr, E. L. (1944). On broodiness of ring doves following implants of certain steroid hormones. *Endocrinology,* **35**, 255–260.

Riddle, O., Bates, R. W. and Dykshorn, S. W. (1932). A new hormone of the anterior pituitary. *Proc. Soc. exp. Biol., N.Y.* **29**, 1211–1212.

Riddle, O., Bates, R. W., and Lahr, E. L. (1935). Prolactin induces broodiness in fowl. *Amer. J. Physiol.* **111**, 352–360.

Riley, G. M. and Fraps, R. M. (1942a). Biological assays of the male chicken pituitary. *Endocrinology,* **30**, 529–536.

Riley, G. M. and Fraps, R. M. (1942b). Relationships of gonad-stimulating activity of female domestic fowl anterior pituitaries to reproductive activity. *Endocrinology,* **30**, 537–541.

Rinaldini, L. M. (1949). Effect of chronic inanition on the gonadotrophic content of the pituitary gland. *J. Endocrin.* **6**, 54–62.

Risley, P. L. (1941). A comparison of effects of gonadotropic and sex hormones on the urogenital system of juvenile terrapins. *J. exp. Zool.* **87**, 477–515.

Robertis, E. D. P. de. (1947). Ovulación del sapo *Bufo arenarum* Hensel. III. Acción de la hipófisis sobre el folicule ovárico. *Rev. Soc. argent. Biol.* **23**, 207–214.

Robertson, O. H. and Rinfret, A. D. (1957). Maturation of the infantile testes in the rainbow trout (*Salmo gairdneri*) produced by salmon pituitary gonadotrophins administered in cholesterol pellets. *Endocrinology,* **60**, 559–562.

Robinson, E. J. and Rugh, R. (1943). The reproductive processes of the fish, *Oryzias latipes. Biol. Bull., Wood's Hole,* **84**, 115–125.

Robinson, G. E. and Nalbandov, A. V. (1951). Changes in the hormone content of swine pituitaries during the estrual cycle. *J. Anim. Sci.* **10**, 469–478.

Robson, J. M. (1937). Maintenance by oestrin of the luteal function in hypophysectomized rabbits. *J. Physiol.* **90**, 435–439.

Rosenthal, H. L. (1952). Observations on reproduction of the poeciliid *Lebistes reticulatus* (Peters). *Biol. Bull., Wood's Hole*, **102**, 30–38.

Rostand, J. (1934). Hypophyse et ovulation chez les batraciens. *C.R. Soc. Biol., Paris*, **117**, 1079–1081.

Rugh, R. (1934). Induced ovulation and artificial fertilisation in the frog. *Biol. Bull., Wood's Hole*, **66**, 22–29.

Rugh, R. (1935a). Ovulation in the frog. I. Pituitary relations in induced ovulations. *J. exp. Zool.* **71**, 149–162.

Rugh, R. (1935b). Ovulation in the frog. II. Follicular rupture to fertilisation. *J. exp. Zool.* **71**, 163–188.

Rugh, R. (1937). A quantitative analysis of the pituitary-ovulation relation in the frog. *Physiol. Zoöl.* **10**, 84–100.

Rugh, R. (1948). "Experimental Embryology." Burgess Publishing Co., Minneapolis.

Ryan, F. J. and Grant, R. (1940). The stimulus for maturation and for ovulation of the frog's egg. *Physiol. Zoöl.* **13**, 383–390.

Saeki, Y., Himeno, K., Tanabe, Y. and Katsuragi, T. (1956). Comparative gonadotrophic potency of anterior pituitaries from cocks, laying hens and non-laying hens in molt. *Endocr. jap.* **3**, 87–91.

Samartino, G. T. and Rugh, R. (1945). Frog ovulation in vitro. *J. exp. Zool.* **98**, 153–159.

Samuel, M. (1943). Studies on the corpus luteum in *Rhinobatis granulatus* Cuv. *Proc. Indian Acad. Sci.* B. **18**, 133–157.

Samuel, M. (1946). The corpus luteum in *Chiloscyllium griseum* Mull. & Henle. *Proc. Indian Acad. Sci.* B. **22**, 113–122.

Sawyer, C. H. and Everett, J. W. (1959). Stimulatory and inhibitory effects of progesterone on the release of pituitary ovulating hormone in the rabbit. *Endocrinology*, **65**, 644–651.

Schmidt, I. G. (1937). The effects of hypophyseal implants from normal mature guinea pigs on the sex organs of immature guinea pigs. *Endocrinology*, **21**, 461–475.

Schooley, J. P. and Riddle, O. (1938). The morphological basis of pituitary function in pigeons. *Amer. J. Anat.* **62**, 313–349.

Schweizer, M., Charipper, H. A. and Haterius, H. O. (1937). Experimental studies of the anterior pituitary. IV. The replacement capacity and the non-cyclic behaviour of homoplastic anterior pituitary grafts. *Endocrinology*, **21**, 30–39.

Scrimshaw, N. S. (1944). Superfetation in poeciliid fishes. *Copeia*, **4**, 180–183.

Segaloff, A., and Steelman, S. L. (1959). The human gonadotropins. *Recent Progr. Hormone Res.* **15**, 127–134.

Selye, H. (1947). "Textbook of Endocrinology." University of Montreal, Montreal.

Selye, H., Collip, J. B. and Thomson, D. L. (1933). On the effect of the anterior pituitary-like hormone on the ovary of the hypophysectomized rat. *Endocrinology*, **17**, 494–500.

Selye, H., Browne, J. S. L. and Collip, J. B. (1936). Effect of large doses of progesterone in the female rat. *Proc. Soc. exp. Biol., N.Y.* **34**, 472–474.

Shapiro, B. G. and Shapiro, H. A. (1934). Histological changes in the ovaries and ovarian blood vessels of *Xenopus laevis* associated with hypophysectomy, captivity and the normal reproductive cycle. *J. exp. Biol.* **11**, 73–81.

Shapiro, H. A. (1939). Ovulation in *Xenopus laevis* induced by certain steroids. *S. Afr. med. J.* **4**, Suppl., 21–31.

Shedlovsky, T. (1943). Criteria of purity of proteins. *Ann. N.Y. Acad. Sci.* **43**, 259–272.

Shedlovsky, T., Rothen, A., Greep, R. O., van Dyke, H. B. and Chow, B. F. (1940). The isolation in pure form of the interstitial cell-stimulating (luteinizing) hormone of the anterior lobe of the pituitary gland. *Science*, **92**, 178–180.

Shelton, M. (1959). A comparison of the population of oocytes in nulliparous and multiparous senile laboratory rats. *J. Endocrin.* **18**, 451–455.

Shipley, R. A., Stern, K. G. and White, A. (1939). Electrophoresis of anterior pituitary proteins. *J. exp. Med.* **69**, 785–800.

Simpson, S. A. and Williams, P. C. (1946). Increased pituitary weight produced by oestrone in intact and castrated rats. *Endocrinology*, **39**, 272–274.

Simpson, M. E., Evans, H. M., Fraenkel-Conrat, H. and Li, C. H. (1941). Synergism of estrogens with pituitary gonadotropins in hypophysectomized rats. *Endocrinology*, **28**, 37–41.

Simpson, M. E., Li, C. H. and Evans, H. M. (1942). Biological properties of pituitary interstitial-cell-stimulating hormone (ICSH). *Endocrinology*, **30**, 969–976.

Simpson, M. E., Li, C. H. and Evans, H. M. (1951). Synergism between pituitary follicle stimulating hormone (FSH) and human chorionic gonadotrophin (HCG). *Endocrinology*, **48**, 370–383.

Simpson, M. E., van Wagenen, G. and Carter, F. (1956). Hormone content of anterior pituitary of monkey (*Macaca mulatta*) with special reference to gonadotrophins. *Proc. Soc. exp. Biol., N.Y.* **91**, 6–11.

Smelser, G. K. (1939). Testicular function and the action of gonadotropic and male hormones in hyperthyroid male rats. *Anat. Rec.* **73**, 273–295.

Smith, C. L. (1955). Reproduction in female Amphibia. *Mem. Soc. Endocrin.* No. 4, 39–55.

Smith, E. K. (1955). Interrelationships of anterior pituitary and adrenal cortex in the rat ovarian hyperemia reaction. *Endocrinology*, **56**, 567–574.

Smith, E. W. (1951). Seasonal response of follicles in the ovaries of the bat *Myotis grisescens* to pregnancy urine gonadotrophin. *Endocrinology*, **49**, 67–72,

Smith, P. E. (1916). Experimental ablation of the hypophysis in the frog. embryo. *Science*, **44**, 280–282.

Smith, P. E. (1927). The disabilities caused by hypophysectomy and their repair. *J. Amer. med. Ass.* **88**, 158–161.

Smith, P. E. (1939). *In* "Sex and Internal Secretions" (E. Allen, ed.), p. 931. Williams and Wilkins, Baltimore.

Smith, P. E. and Dortzbach, C. (1929). The first appearance in the anterior pituitary of the developing pig foetus of detectable amounts of the hormone stimulating ovarian maturity and general body growth. *Anat. Rec.* **43**, 277–297.

Smith, P. E. and Engle, E. T. (1927). Experimental evidence regarding the role of the anterior pituitary in the development and regulation of the genital system. *Amer. J. Anat.* **40**, 159–217.

Smith, P. E. and Engle, E. T. (1929). Evidence of a correlation between the amount of gonad-stimulating hormone present in the pituitary of the guinea pig and the stage of the reproductive cycle. *Anat. Rec.* **42**, 38.

Squire, P. G. and Li, C. H. (1958). Purification and properties of an interstitial cell stimulating hormone from sheep pituitaries. *Science*, **127**, 32.

Steelman, S. L. (1958). Chromatography of follicle-stimulating hormone (FSH) on hydroxyl apatite. *Biochim. biophys. Acta*, **27**, 405–406.

21

Steelman, S. L. and Pohley, F. M. (1953). Assay of the follicle stimulating hormone, based on the augmentation with human chorionic gonadotropin. *Endocrinology*, **53**, 604–616.

Steelman, S. L., Lamont, W. A., Dittman, W. A. and Jawrylewicz, E. J. (1953). Fractionation of the swine follicle-stimulating hormone. *Proc. Soc. exp. Biol.*, *N.Y.* **82**, 645–647.

Steelman, S. L., Lamont, W. A. and Baltes, B. J. (1955). Preparation of highly active follicle stimulating hormone from swine pituitaries. *Endocrinology*, **56**, 216–217.

Steelman, S. L., Lamont, W. A. and Baltes, B. J. (1956a). Preparation of highly active follicle stimulating hormone from swine pituitary glands. *Acta endocr.*, *Copenhagen*, **22**, 186–190.

Steelman, S. L., Kelly, T. L., Segaloff, A. and Weber, G. F. (1956b). Isolation of an apparently homogeneous follicle-stimulating hormone. *Endocrinology*, **59**, 256.

Steelman, S. L. and Segaloff, A. (1959). Recent studies on the purification of the pituitary gonadotropins. *Recent Progr. Hormone Res.* **15**, 115–125.

Stoll, L. M. (1957). Changes in the cytological structure of the adenohypophysis and gonads in juvenile *Bathygobius soporator* after pituitary implantation. *Zoologica*, *N.Y.* **42**, 99–104.

Stricker, P. and Grueter, F. (1928). Action du lobe antérieur de l'hypophyse sur la montée laiteuse. *C.R. Soc. Biol.*, *Paris*, **99**, 1978–1980.

Stroganov, N. S. and Alpatov, V. V. (1951). A new unit for determining the activity of the hypophysis in fish. *Fish Ind.*, *Moscow*, **27**, 56–60.

Sturkie, P. D. (1954). "Avian Physiology." Comstock Pub. Assoc., New York.

Sutherland, M. and Zwarenstein, H. (1939). The diagnosis of pregnancy by means of human pregnancy urine. *S. Afr. J. med. Sci.* **4**, Suppl., 32–34.

Swingle, W. W., Fedor, E. J., Barlow, G. Jr., Collins, E. J. and Perlmutt, J. (1951). Induction of pseudopregnancy in rat following adrenal removal. *Amer. J. Physiol.* **167**, 593–598.

Sydnor, K. L. (1945). Time relationships of deciduomata formation in prolactin-treated rats and normal pseudo-pregnant rats. *Endocrinology*, **36**, 88–91.

Szontagh, F. E. and Lichner, G. (1951). Effect of methyl- and propylthiouracil on ovarian function. *Experientia*, **7**, 384–385.

Taber, E. (1948). The relation between ovarian growth and sexual characters in brown Leghorn chicks treated with gonadotrophins. *J. exp. Zool.* **107**, 65–107.

Taber, E. (1951). Androgen secretion in the fowl. *Endocrinology*, **48**, 6–16.

Taber, E., Claytor, M., Knight, J., Gambrell, O., Flowers, J. and Ayres, C (1958). Ovarian stimulation in the immature fowl by desiccated avian pituitaries. *Endocrinology*, **62**, 84–89.

Takasugi, N. (1952). Einflüsse von Androgen und Estrogen auf die Ovarien der neugeborenen und reifen, weiblichen Ratten. *Annot. zool. jap.* **25**, 120–127.

Takewaki, K. (1952). Effects of androgenic and estrogenic steroids on intra splenic ovarian transplants in male rats. *Annot. zool. jap.* **25**, 113–119.

Takewaki, K. (1953). Stimulation of ovaries of normal parabionts joined with spayed partners bearing intrasplenic ovarian grafts. *Jap. J. Zool.* **11**, 35–38

Takewaki, K. and Hatta, K. (1941). Effect of gonadectomy and hypophysec tomy on the kidney and genital tract of a snake *Natrix tigrina tigrina*. *Anno. zool. jap.* **20**, 4–8.

Takewaki, K. and Maekawa, K. (1952). Effects of hormonic steroids on intra-splenic ovarian transplants in male and female rats. *Annot. zool. jap.* **25**, 403–410.

Takewaki, K., Takasugi, N. and Maekawa, K. (1952). Ovaries of rats with gonadectomized parabionts bearing intrasplenic ovarian grafts. *Proc. imp. Acad. Japan*, **28**, 97–101.

Takewaki, K., Maekawa, K. and Imai, K. (1954). Effects of juxtaposed pellet of androgen or estrogen on intrasplenic ovarian graft. *J. Fac. Sci. Univ. Tokyo*, **7**, 131–151.

Talbert, G. B., Meyer, R. K. and McShan, W. H. (1951). Effect of hypophysec-tomy at the beginning of proestrus on maturing follicles in the ovary of the rat. *Endocrinology*, **49**, 687–693.

Tchechovitch, G. (1952). La ponte artificielle chez quelques poissons d'eau douce provoquée par les hormones hypophysaires. *Arch. Sci. biol., Belgrade*, **4**, 27–35.

Teel, H. M. (1926). The effects of injecting anterior hypophyseal fluid on the course of gestation in the rat. *Amer. J. Physiol.* **79**, 170–183.

Tobin, C. E. (1942). Effects of lactogen on normal and adrenalectomized female rats. *Endocrinology*, **31**, 197–200.

Tolksdorf, S. and Jensen, H. (1939). Mechanism of pituitary gonadotrophic antagonism. *Proc. Soc. exp. Biol., N.Y.* **42**, 466–469.

Tuchmann-Duplessis, H. (1945). "Correlations hypophysoendocrines chez le triton. Déterminisme hormonal des caractères sexuels secondaires." *Actualités sci. indust.* No. 987. Hermann et Cie, Paris.

Turner, C. D. (1935). The effects of Antuitrin-S on the male genital organs of the lizard, (*Eumeces laticeps*) during seasonal atrophy. *Biol. Bull., Wood's Hole*, **69**, 143–158.

Turner, C. L. (1933). Viviparity in the Goodeidae. *J. Morph.* **55**, 207–251.

Turner, C. L. (1937). Reproductive cycles and superfetation in poeciliid fishes. *Biol. Bull., Wood's Hole*, **72**, 145–164.

Turner, C. L. (1942). Diversity of endocrine function in the reproduction of viviparous fishes. *Amer. Nat.* **76**, 179–190.

Turner, C. L. (1947). Viviparity in teleost fishes. *Sci. Mon., N.Y.* **65**, 508–518.

Uotila, U. U. (1939). The masculinising effects of some gonadotropic hormones on pullets compared with spontaneous ovariogenic virilism in hens. *Anat. Rec.* **74**, 165–188.

van Dyke, H. B. and Wallen-Lawrence, Z. (1933). Further observations on the gonad-stimulating principle of the anterior lobe of the pituitary body. *J. Pharmacol.* **47**, 163–181.

van Dyke, H. B., P'an, S. Y. and Shedlovsky, T. (1950). Follicle stimulating hormones of the anterior pituitary of the sheep and the hog. *Endocrinology*, **46**, 563–573.

Van Horn, W. M. (1931). Relation of the thyroid to the hypophysis and ovary *Anat. Rec.* **51**, Suppl., 38.

Van Horn, W. M. (1933). The relation of the thyroid to the hypophysis and ovary. *Endocrinology*, **17**, 152–162.

Vivien, J. H. (1939a). Relations hypophyso-génitales chez quelques téléostéens et sélaciens. *C.R. Soc. Biol., Paris*, **131**, 1222–1224.

Vivien, J. H. (1939b). Rôle de l'hypophyse dans le déterminisme du cycle génital femelle d'un téléostéen *Gobius paganellus* L. *C.R. Acad. Sci., Paris*, **208**, 948–949.

Vivien, J. H. (1939c). Rôle de l'hypophyse dans le déterminisme du cycle sexuel chez les poissons. *Bull. Soc. zool. Fr.* **64**, 141.

Vivien, J. H. (1940). Quelques résultats expérimentaux concernant les relations hypophysio-génitales chez un sélacien. *C.R. Acad. Sci., Paris*, **210**, 230–231.

Vivien, J. H. (1941). Contributions à l'étude de la physiologie hypophysaire dans ses relations avec l'appareil génital, la thyroïde et les corps suprarénaux chez les poissons sélaciens et téléostéens. *Bull. biol.* **75**, 257–309.

Vivien, J. H. (1952). Rôle de l'hypophyse dans le déterminisme de l'involution ovarienne et de l'inversion sexuelle chez les xiphophores. *J. Physiol. Path. gén.* **44**, 349–351.

Von Ihering, R. (1935). Die Wirkung von Hypophyseninjektion auf den Laichakt von Fischen. *Zool. Anz.* **111**, 273–279.

Ward, D. N., McGregor, R. F. and Griffin, A. C. (1959). Chromatography of luteinizing hormone from sheep pituitary glands. *Biochim. biophys. Acta*, **32**, 305–314.

Waring, H., Landgrebe, F. W. and Neill, R. M. (1941). Ovulation and oviposition in Anura. *J. exp. Biol.* **18**, 11–25.

Warner, E. D. and Meyer, R. K. (1949). The effects of thyroxine on the female reproductive system in parabiotic rats. *Endocrinology*, **45**, 33–41.

Watanabe, M., Yamada, A. and Matsushima, M. (1950). On the effects of the hormones of the anterior lobe of the hypophysis upon the loach. II. *Bull. Jap. Soc. sci. Fish.* **15**, 799–802.

Weekes, H. C. (1934). The corpus luteum in certain oviparous and viviparous reptiles. *Proc. Linn. Soc., N.S.W.* **59**, 380–391.

Weisman, A. I., Mishkind, D. I., Kleiner, I. S. and Coates, C. W. (1937). Estrogenic hormones in the ovaries of swordfish. *Endocrinology*, **21**, 413–414.

White, A. (1943). The lactogenic hormone and mammogen. *Ann. N.Y. Acad. Sci.* **43**, 341–381.

White, A. (1949). The chemistry and physiology of adenohypophyseal luteotropins (Prolactin). *Vitam. & Horm.* **7**, 253–292.

White, A., Catchpole, H. R. and Long, C. N. H. (1937). A crystalline protein with high lactogenic activity. *Science*, **86**, 82–83.

White, A., Bonsnes, R. W. and Long, C. N. H. (1942). Prolactin. *J. biol. Chem.* **143**, 447–464.

Wiesner, B. P. and Crew, F. A. E. (1930). The gonadotrope actions of the anterior lobe of the pituitary. *Proc. roy. Soc. Edinb.* **50**, 79–103.

Wiesner, B. P. and Marshall, P. G. (1931). The gonadotropic hormones (ρ-factors). I. The preparation and properties of extracts of anterior lobe, placenta and pregnancy urine. *Quart. J. exp. Physiol.* **21**, 147–179.

Williams, P. C. (1940). Effect of stilboestrol on the ovaries of hypophysectomized rats. *Nature, Lond.* **145**, 388–389.

Williams, P. C. (1944). Ovarian stimulation by oestrogens: effects in immature hypophysectomized rats. *Proc. roy. Soc. B.* **132**, 189–199.

Williams, P. C. (1945). Studies of the biological action of serum gonadotrophin. 1. Decline in ovarian response after hypophysectomy. 2. Ovarian response after hypophysectomy and oestrogen treatment. *J. Endocrin.* **4**, 127–130 and 131–136.

Williams, R. H., Weinglass, A. R., Bissel, G. W. and Peters, J. B. (1944) Anatomical effects of thiouracil. *Endocrinology*, **34**, 317–328.

Wills, I. A., Riley, G. M. and Stubbs, G. M. (1933). Further experiments on the induction of ovulation in toads. *Proc. Soc. exp. Biol., N.Y.* **30**, 784–786.

Wit, J. C. de (1953). The effect of oestradiol monobenzoate on follicles of various sizes in the ovary of the hypophysectomized rat. *Acta endocr., Copenhagen,* **12,** 123–139.

Witschi, E. (1935). Seasonal sex characters in birds and their hormonal control. *Wilson Bull.* **47,** 177–188.

Witschi, E. (1937). Comparative physiology of the vertebrate hypophysis (anterior and intermediate lobes). *Cold Spr. Harb. Symp. quant. Biol.* **5,** 180–190.

Witschi, E. (1955). Vertebrate gonadotrophins. *Mem. Soc. Endocrin.* No. 4, 149–165.

Wolf, O. M. (1928). The effect of the mammalian follicular extract on the oviducts of the frog (*Rana pipiens* Schreber). *Anat. Rec.* **41,** Suppl., 41.

Wolfe, J. M. (1930). A quantitative study of ovulation in the rabbit. *Proc. Soc. exp. Biol., N.Y.* **28,** 318–319.

Wolfe, J. M. (1931). Observations on a cyclic variation in the capacity of the anterior hypophysis to induce ovulation in the rabbit. *Amer. J. Anat.* **48,** 391–419.

Wolfe, J. M. and Cleveland, R. (1931). Comparison of the capacity of anterior-hypophysial tissue of mature and immature female rabbits to induce ovulation. *Anat. Rec.* **51,** 213–218.

Wooten, E., Nelson, M. M., Simpson, M. E. and Evans, H. M. (1955). Effect of pyridoxine deficiency on the gonadotrophic contents of the anterior pituitary in the rat. *Endocrinology,* **56,** 59–66.

Wooten, E., Nelson, M. M., Simpson, M. E. and Evans, H. M. (1958). Response of vitamin B6-deficient rats to hypophyseal follicle-stimulating and interstitial cell-stimulating hormones. *Endocrinology,* **63,** 860–866.

Woronozowa, M. A. and Blacher, L. J. (1930). Die Hypophyse und die Geschlechtsdrüsen der Amphibien. I. Der Einfluss der Hypophysenextirpation auf die Geschlechtsdrüse bei Urodelen. *Arch. EntwMech. Org.* **121,** 327–344.

Wotiz, H. H., Botticelli, C., Hisaw, F. L. Jr. and Ringler, I. (1958). Identification of estradiol-17β from dogfish ova (*Squalus suckleyi*). *J. biol. Chem.* **231,** 589–592.

Wright, P. A. (1945). Factors effecting *in vitro* ovulation in the frog. *J. exp. Zool.* **100,** 565–575.

Wright, P. A. (1946). Sensitisation of the frog ovary following hypophysectomy. *Physiol. Zoöl.* **19,** 359–364.

Wright, P. A. and Hisaw, F. L. (1946). Effect of mammalian pituitary gonadotrophins on ovulation in the frog, *Rana pipiens. Endocrinology,* **39,** 247–255.

Young, J. Z. and Bellerby, C. W. (1935). The response of the lamprey to injection of anterior lobe pituitary extract. *J. exp. Biol.* **12,** 246–253.

Zahl, P. A. (1937). Cytologische Untersuchungen über die Hypophysis cerebri des weiblichen Frosches. *Z. mikr-anat. Forsch.* **42,** 303–361.

Zephiroff, P. and Dobrovolskaya-Zavadskaya, N. (1940). Sur une substance ambisexuelle isolée de l'urine d'une fillette de quatre ans. *C.R. Soc. Biol., Paris,* **133,** 405–407.

Zondek, B. (1930). Über die Hormone des Hypophysenvorderlappens. *Klin. Wschr.* **9,** 245–248, 393–396 and 679–682.

Zondek, B. and Sulman, F. (1937). The antigonadotropic factor. Origin and preparation. *Proc. Soc. exp. Biol., N.Y.* **36,** 708–712.

Zuber-Vogeli, M. (1953). L'histophysiologie de l'hypophyse de *Bufo vulgaris* L. *Arch. Anat., Strasbourg,* **35,** 77–180.

Zubiran, S. and Gomez-Mont, F. (1953). Endocrine disturbances in chronic human malnutrition. *Vitam. & Horm.* **11**, 97–132.

Zuckerman, S. (1953). *In* "The Suprarenal Cortex" (J. M. Yoffey, ed.), p. 69. Butterworth, London.

Zwarenstein, H. (1939). Induction of precocious sexual maturity in immature female mice with amphibian anterior pituitary. *S. Afr. J. med. Sci.* **4**, Suppl., 18-20.

APPENDIX

1 This antagonistic effect is due to an independent pituitary factor that can be separated from the gonadotrophins by purification (Woods, M. C. and Simpson, M. E., 1961, *Endocrinology*, **68**, 647–661).

2 Hellbaum *et al.* have recently induced differential alterations in the contents of LH and FSH of the rat pituitary by 'physiological' means involving gonadectomy and administration of gonadal steroids (Hellbaum, A. A., McArthur, L. G., Campbell, P. J. and Finerty, J. C., 1961, *Endocrinology*, **68**, 144–153).

3 There is evidence that FSH and/or LH may block the response of the corpus luteum to LTH (Rothchild, I., 1960, *Endocrinology*, **67**, 9–41).

4 Growth hormone in combination with LTH and with ICSH has been shown to stimulate the development of the follicle and ovum in hypophysectomized rats. The relation of this finding to events in the normal cycle is not yet clear. When administered alone, growth hormone apparently stimulated ovarian oestrogen production in hypophysectomized rats, an effect enhanced by combination with ICSH or LTH. LTH or ICSH given alone had little or no effect on oestrogen secretion, but the combination of these two hormones was markedly effective (Grattarola, R. and Li, C. H., 1959, *Endocrinology*, **65**, 802–810; Grattarola, R. and Somigli, A., 1960, *Acta endocr., Copenhagen*, **34**, 225–241 and 242–255).

5 Rothchild and co-workers have produced evidence that in the rat progesterone suppresses the release of FSH and LH. while maintaining the secretion of LTH (1960, *Endocrinology*, **67**, 9–41, 42–47, 48–53 and 54–61).

6 An analysis of factors influencing luteal viability is given by Rothchild, I., 1960, *Endocrinology*, **67**, 9–41.

7 Unpublished work by one of us (J.N.B.) has shown that the pituitary plays no essential part in gestation and the birth-process in the poeciliid *Mollienesia latipinna*.

8 cf. Eisner, E., 1960, *Anim. Behav.* **8**, 155–179.

9 Mandl, A. M. (1961). *J. Endocrin.* **22**, 257–268.

10 Howell, J. S. and Mandl, A. M. (1961). *J. Endocrin.* **22**, 241–255.

CHAPTER 8

THE MECHANISM OF OVULATION

S. A. ASDELL

In this chapter the events that occur within the follicle immediately before and during ovulation are considered. In a few species the process of rupture has been observed or photographed and it is possible to supplement the disconnected histological observations with a description of the gross changes as they happen. Although observations of this nature have been made for many years, the immediate cause of follicular rupture is still obscure. Many theories have been suggested and as many objections to them have been raised. The result is that no theory satisfactory to everyone has yet been advanced. The trend of thought in this regard is summarized.

In many species ovulation is not spontaneous but requires a stimulus originating outside the animal to provoke it. The external stimulus evidently triggers off in some way the hypothalamo-hypophysial mechanism, but the degree of the stimulus and, to some extent, its nature seem to vary from species to species. Information of this nature is brought together but no attempt is made in this chapter to suggest the exact point at which the spontaneous and provoked ovulators diverge in their physiology. Evidence that would enable one to do this is lacking.

I. The process of ovulation

A. Insects

Amongst the insects ovulation takes place, as a rule, spontaneously, as soon as the eggs are ripe. They are arranged in a single row in the ovarioles many of which, together, comprise the ovary. When the foremost oocyte, the one in each ovariole nearest the oviduct, enlarges and becomes ripe it is released when the epithelial plug that bars its passage ruptures. The plug, together with the cells lining the follicle, degenerate and the next ovum presses forward and, when it in turn is ripe, emerges through the debris into the oviduct. The number of eggs shed varies. In some insects many are shed in quick succession, in others there is an interval between ovulations.

B. Fishes

The process of ovulation in the Japanese teleostean fish, *Oryzias latipes*, has been described by Robinson and Rugh (1943). The female of this species, like many other teleosts, has a hollow ovary. The follicle gradually increases in size and a mound-like protrusion develops on its surface in the centre of a vascular plexus. When the follicle ruptures at this protrusion the egg rolls out through the small opening like a big amoeba. The egg is freed into the lumen of the ovary and not into the body cavity as it is in some other fishes and in amphibians. The hole through which the ovum escapes from the follicle is oval at the beginning of the process and, as it increases in size, the blood vessels around it stretch but do not break. It is interesting to note that ovulation usually takes place just before dawn and that the time can be shifted by altering the time of darkness.

Smooth muscle fibres are present in the ovarian wall but these have not been observed to cause movement of the ovary or follicles. In cyclostomes, elasmobranchs and in teleosts that are devoid of oviducts the rupture of the follicle releases the egg directly into the body cavity (Hoar, 1957). This is a point worth noting as a few workers have suggested that the oviduct may exert pressure upon the ovary at the time of ovulation, thus causing an increase in intrafollicular pressure sufficient to rupture the wall.

C. Amphibians

As long ago as 1859 Pflüger and also Aeby were observing ovulation in the frog, *Rana temporaria*. In this species there is no follicular fluid and the ovum is closely enclosed by the follicle wall. The ovary is enclosed by the ovarian membrane (cyst wall) which contains many smooth muscle fibres. These are very active and Pflüger (1859) suggested that their contractions, together with those of other smooth muscle fibres in the ovary, caused ovulation. He spoke of 'ovarian peristalsis' in this connection. But, since the entire ovary is in a state of constant movement, even out of the sexual season, one cannot believe that these contractions cause ovulation. Aeby (1859) also suggested that ovulation was due to the contraction of stromal muscle, but he considered that an additional factor was the contraction of smooth muscle cells in the theca externa. The same view was held by Brandt (1877) who noted the smooth outline of the follicle wall at the point of rupture, a fact that has been stressed in many subsequent papers. It suggests that the rupture cannot be due to a tearing action. Smith (1912, 1916), who observed ovulation in the hellbender, *Cryptobranchus allegheniensis*, considered that rupture in this species is due to the action of intra- and extra-follicular pressure combined. He pointed out that the egg is softer at the time of ovulation than it is at other times. It emerges through the small hole in the follicle wall by elongating and constricting at the point of passage so that it is for the time being shaped like an hour glass. Since there is no follicular fluid, it is difficult to understand how an increase in pressure from the ovary causes such a small opening and why the pressure needed to squeeze the egg through does not increase the size of the hole. These observations do not support the view that the rupture is due entirely to mechanical factors such as increased intra-follicular pressure.

Rugh (1935) has made a careful study of ovulation in *Rana pipiens*. He states that, while the ovarian smooth muscle is active in causing movement of the ovaries, the follicles, themselves, are merely passively swayed. The follicle stalk, the portion where the egg with the follicle protrudes from the ovarian stroma, is not covered by the smooth muscle. Internal pressure also seems to be ruled out because no follicle cells are extruded with the ovum. The rupture first occurs as a pinpoint opening in a small area of the follicle wall surrounded by blood vessels. In spite of their presence there is no bleeding. The small opening rapidly enlarges. A follicle may rupture even though the follicle is removed from the ovary and maintained in Holtfreter's solution.

D. Birds

The process of ovulation has been observed in pigeons and in the domestic fowl. The descriptions do not differ in essentials from those already given of ovulation in frogs. But the much larger size of the follicle, due to the large amount of yolk within the egg, enables one to observe many details more clearly. Thus the fact that the break occurs in an avascular portion of the follicle wall is much clearer, though Rugh (1935) has recorded this feature in the frog.

Bartelmez (1912) described the ovulation process in the pigeon. He noted that an avascular region of the follicle wall, the stigma, lies in the long axis of the follicle. When, during the course of its growth, the follicle reaches the surface of the ovary, the blood vessels become arranged around the centre of the oval-shaped follicle; thus the stigma is formed. The cloacal end of the stigma is not supported by the erect infundibulum at the time of ovulation so that it is the one part of the follicle where the pressure from within is not balanced by any pressure from without. This is the region in which the rupture begins. Usually, before the tear has extended along more that 10 mm of the stigma, the ovum has been squeezed out of the follicle, mainly by the rapidly contracting wall of the latter. The escape of the ovum through an opening one half its own diameter indicates that the wall of the egg at this stage is very elastic.

Phillips and Warren (1937) in their extensive direct observations of follicular growth and ovulation in the fowl emphasized the role of the stigma in the process. As in the pigeon this is a relatively avascular region that traverses the free surface of the follicle in the anterior-posterior axis of the ovary. Within the hour preceding ovulation branches of small blood vessels, which spring from the two large ones running parallel with the stigma and which supply this region with blood, become obliterated. Then the central region of the stigma bulges outward. All over the free surface of the follicle the blood vessels become blurred or obliterated, only to become prominent again after ovulation has occurred. The follicle wall, especially in the stigma, contains smooth muscle fibres. The contraction of these, together with the consequent tension on the ovum, is believed to cause this obliteration. If the bird dies while under observation, but before ovulation has occurred, the follicle becomes flaccid and the blood vessels become prominent again. In the live bird the inner layers of the follicle break first and then a bulged area appears at the point that is to rupture. This begins as a tiny opening and it is almost always at one of the ends of the stigma. This opening spreads as a slit-like tear through the centre of the stigma and along its length. If the follicle stalk is clamped at the last moment before rupture the process is not prevented so that it cannot be due to a last-minute deposition of yolk. Phillips and Warren consider that, since there is no liquor folliculi in the hen's follicle, enzymic action upon the wall is ruled out as a cause.

E. Mammals

Among the mammals the process of ovulation has been observed only in the rabbit and the sheep. Walton and Hammond (1928), Kelly (1931), Hill *et al.* (1935) and Markee and Hinsey (1935–36) have all described the process in the rabbit and cinematographic studies have been made so that its course may be followed at leisure. The rabbit is particularly suitable for observations of this nature because ovulation depends on mating and it occurs about $10\frac{1}{2}$ hours after the doe has copulated. The follicle grows rapidly during the last 2 hours before it ruptures. The blood supply at the surface increases except in a small avascular region near the centre of the portion of the follicle wall that protrudes from the ovary. This region is surrounded by a fine network of small vessels and it evidently corresponds with the stigma of birds. As the time of ovulation approaches the avascular area expands and forms a cone. In the last 20 minutes or so some of the blood vessels surrounding it break, so that a small lake of blood forms at the apex of the follicle. Eventually the point of the cone breaks and the ovum, together with its corona radiata, some other granulosa cells and some follicular fluid, ooze out. This fluid is somewhat viscous as it is extruded and it rapidly becomes more viscous. Odeblad (1954) finds that the viscosity is due to the presence of a sulphomuco-polysaccharide. He suggests that it helps prevent the loss of the ovum in the body cavity. Most observers emphasize two points: firstly, that the fluid oozes from the follicle; there is no explosive spurt of fluid such as one would expect if the wall ruptured as a result of pressure from within. Walton and Hammond (1928) compare the process to the oozing of material from a boil and note that there is very little follicular collapse after the rupture. On the other hand, Hill *et al.* (1935) speak of a rapid volcano-like expulsion of a gelatinous exudate. The other feature stressed is that the outline of the rupture point is round or oval so that a tear is not suggested. Markee and Hinsey (1935–36) made reconstructions of ruptured follicles and these confirm this point. The question at issue is whether the follicle breaks as a result of pressure from within or whether the rupture is due to erosive factors.

McKenzie and Terrill (1937) have observed thirty-six cases of ovulation in the sheep. Conspicuous external changes in the follicle were confined to less than 4 hours before the event. The follicle gradually swelled and became conical, and the membranous wall thinner and more transparent. About an hour before the rupture a small round area, usually near the centre or the peak of the follicle, became very clear and transparent. This area first appeared as a point and gradually increased in height and diameter. A few minutes before rupture one or more tiny cones or projections (usually only one), often from 1 to 3 mm high, swelled out from this clear area. The break took place at the apex of the cone and the follicular fluid flowed from the rupture point. A gradual collapse of the follicle ensued. In some instances bleeding within the follicle was observed just before the rupture. The extruded material was at first thin but became viscous in 2 to 3 minutes.

In six of the thirty-six cases viewed rupture occurred with a decided spurt, but only a small part of the fluid was thus extruded. The flow continued for several seconds and even for a minute or more. In these instances of explosive release the observers were undecided whether manipulation of the ovary may have caused the pressure that occasioned the spurt.

II. The cause of ovulation

A. Early events within the follicle

In order to form a reasoned opinion of the cause of ovulation it is necessary to obtain a picture of the events within the follicle just prior to the rupture. Corner (1946) has described these in some detail. His evidence is drawn mainly from the sow, but he has extended his observations to the rat, cat, ferret and monkey with essentially similar results. As the nucleus moves towards the periphery of the ovum the nuclei of the cumulus cells surrounding the ovum become densely chromatic and contracted, i.e. a pyknotic condition develops. The cytoplasm of these cells shrinks and fluid appears between them so that the ovum is suspended from the granulosa by a long network of cells hanging together by strands. Gradually the whole of the granulosa layer takes on this appearance so that the section stains poorly and looks as if it had been badly fixed. This is not a degenerative condition because these cells later take part in the formation of the corpus luteum. The theca interna cells take on a well-marked epithelioid form and crowd each other in a way that makes them appear block-like. The writer is able to extend these conclusions in all their details to the maturing follicle of the cow. In the last minutes before ovulation two or three loops of capillaries enter the cumulus from the theca. This has been observed in the pig but not in the monkey, rabbit or rat. Häggquist (1921) has described it also as occurring in man. There is general agreement that as part of the changes leading to the formation of the final secondary cone within the clear area of the follicle wall, the theca interna layer is thinned out and even pushed aside to some extent.

The number of guesses as to the cause of follicular rupture is boundless. Almost everyone who has described the structure of ovaries or of follicles has added to the number, but experimental work on the subject is very scanty. Microscopic examination of stained tissues cannot do more than provide a series of disconnected 'stills' extracted from the moving picture of development. The intervening pictures and the operating causes may be hidden from us.

B. Possible mechanical factors

Most suggestions, from Rouget (1858) on, have stressed the role of increasing intrafollicular pressure as the cause of rupture. Rouget himself ascribed this to the action of the smooth muscle of the ovarian stroma. Waldeyer (1870) considered that the increased pressure was due to hypertrophy of the theca interna. Heape (1905) believed that vasodilatation and bursting blood vessels added to the pressure within the follicle at the time of ovulation. Thomson (1919) pointed out that increased secretion of liquor folliculi might be the immediate cause of ovulation. He agreed that smooth muscle fibres are present in the theca interna and in the stroma, but was unable to induce ovulation by stimulating them with a tetanic current. He therefore concluded that they could not be instrumental in causing follicular rupture. Smith and Ketteringham (1938) believed that the increase in liquor folliculi was due to the liberation into the maturing follicle of an osmotically active substance, possibly a carbohydrate. This came, they believed, from the Call-Exner bodies. The evidence they advanced for this theory was the observation that injections of insulin prevented ovulation.

The view that increased pressure upon the ovum causes ovulation in species lacking liquor folliculi has been rejected because no one has been able to bring it about by stimulating the smooth muscle either of the ovarian stroma or of the follicle wall. Rugh (1935) was one of those who attempted this in *Rana pipiens*, with negative results. Likewise, Phillips and Warren (1937) failed in the hen. But since ex- cised follicles rupture normally, they concluded that neither nerve impulses nor increased blood pressure could be involved. They sug- gested that prolonged muscular tension is the probable cause because they had found, also, that injecting water into the follicle did not cause it to rupture. This method was tried following the suggestion by Pearl and Curtis (1914) that increased yolk secretion was the cause of rupture. The latter workers had rejected Patterson's (1910) sug- gestion that the erect infundibulum of the oviduct surrounded the follicle and squeezed it sufficiently to cause release of the egg. This they were led to do because they found that ovulation was normal after the oviduct had been excised.

Obviously, increased pressure of liquor folliculi cannot be the cause of ovulation in species that lack this fluid. This rules out the fish, amphibians and birds as well as, amongst mammals, the tenrec (Strauss, 1938) and the elephant shrew (van der Horst and Gillman, 1940). Strauss attributed follicle rupture in the tenrec to increased pressure due to hypertrophy of the granulosa cells, and van der Horst and Gillman suggested that in *Elephantulus* luteinization of this layer is the cause. In this species the follicular fluid is almost completely reabsorbed before ovulation. Guttmacher and Guttmacher (1921) had previously attempted to induce ovulation in the sow by injecting follicles with saline in order to increase the pressure. Although they did not succeed, they subscribed to the pressure hypothesis and suggested that the muscular wreath of the theca externa produced the necessary tension.

C. Objections to the mechanical theory

In recent years the trend of opinion has been away from the pressure theory. One reason for this is the form of the rupture point. In mammals the development of an ovulation cone in a limited portion of the follicle wall suggests a softening at this particular point. The condition of the margin of the opening, smooth, not resembling a tear, and its regular shape, round or oval, do not suggest an abrupt rupture due to internal pressure. In the fowl a tear is not produced until the egg begins to erupt through the opening that has already been formed. In addition, Evans and Cole (1931) record that in the dog the follicle wall becomes folded in a complex manner before ovulation. This does not suggest increased tension since this might be expected to expand the walls. In the bat, *Myotis lucifugus*, Wimsatt (1944) found that there is a decrease in the size of the follicle and a buckling of the wall immediately before ovulation. In the cow the writer has observed a distinct crenation of the follicle wall in specimens near ovulation and, during the 2 hours before this event, ovarian palpation reveals that the follicle becomes softer to the touch (Hansel, 1958). All these observations suggest that although rapid secretion of liquor folliculi and, perhaps, hypertrophy of the follicle cells may cause the wall to weaken, these factors do not account for its final rupture. Wester (1921) suggested a pressure necrosis of the wall as the cause. He regarded this as resulting from a thinning of the tunica albuginea due to the dome-like bulging of the follicle. He considered that rupture might occur anywhere on the surface of the follicle and denied the existence in mammals of any structure resembling the stigma of birds. It may, indeed, be that the necrosis does occur within the avascular region as a result of the earlier increase in pressure during the phase of rapid growth.

D. Possible chemical factors

Several investigators have suggested that chemical factors cause the break to occur. If this is so, it is difficult to account for the apparent circumscribed area in which it can happen. Schochet (1916) demonstrated that the liquor folliculi of the sow is capable of digesting ovarian tissue, and he suggested that digestion may play a part in weakening the follicle wall in the region of the stigma. Rugh (1935) attempted in the frog to rupture follicles by applying pepsin or trypsin. These alone did not cause rupture but pepsin in hydrochloric acid did produce this effect. He was able to repeat these observations in *Rana catesbeiana* and in the urodele, *Triturus pyrrhogaster*, as well as in *Rana pipiens*. The follicle of the frog does not contain liquor folliculi but a proteolytic enzyme was found in frogs' eggs by Hartog (1904).

E. The hormonal theory

A fairly recent critical evaluation of the evidence has been made by Kraus (1947). She made direct observations upon the frog, hen and rabbit, using suitable gonadotrophic hormones to induce ovulation in each instance. The immersion of excised frog ovaries into distilled water was followed by ovulation and the eggs were forced out through an oval opening, just as they are in natural ovulation. But external pressure failed to cause ovulation in the frog. When pressure was applied to the hen's follicle, rupture sometimes followed but the break occurred not along the stigma, but at unpredictable places along the follicle wall, even at right angles to the stigma. Introduction of warm physiological saline into the follicle did not provoke rupture. In the rabbit, pressure applied at the base of the follicle as well as saline injected in this region caused the follicles to rupture but the secondary cone was not formed. These treatments applied to the hen would cause rupture along the stigma only after death of the bird and in follicles that were near ovulation anyway. These facts led Kraus to infer that a morphological change is involved in normal ovulation. The edge of the follicle wall in the rupture area of a normal ovulation is blunt, while the result of a rupture due to pressure should be fine. This is an argument against the pressure theory. In the rabbit pressure seems not to be the cause because in pressure-induced rupture the fluid spurts out, while in natural ovulation it oozes out.

Attempts were made by Kraus (1947) to produce ovulation by adding smooth muscle stimulants to the fluid in which excised ovaries were placed. In some hens these stimulants were injected intravenously with the ovaries retained *in situ*. These attempts invariably failed in both the frog and the hen. Electrical stimulation of the follicle wall in the frog, hen and rabbit likewise failed to cause egg release.

When the frog ovary was immersed in a proteolytic enzyme solution Kraus (1947) found that the follicle wall gave way but the ova were not fully extruded. Pepsin-HCl gave this partial response but trypsin-Na_2CO_3 did not. However, all attempts to find a proteolytic enzyme in frog follicles were without result. The application of proteolytic enzymes to the follicles of hens and rabbits was without effect.

As a result of this extensive work Kraus (1947) concluded that neither the pressure nor the enzyme theory fitted all the facts and that the immediate cause of ovulation is still unknown. She suggested that morphological changes in the follicle wall induced by the action of gonadotrophic or other hormones are responsible for the phenomenon. The problem still remains in this condition of uncertainty.

Lipner and Maxwell (1960) have observed the behaviour, in rabbits, of follicles grafted into the anterior chamber of the eye. Following injection of luteinizing hormone, or stimulation of the cervix uteri, a wave of contraction passes over the surface of the follicle. The authors attribute this effect to the contraction of muscle cells within the theca externa, and believe it to be an important factor in ovulation. It would appear, however, that a series of radial contractions would have to be postulated in order to account for the shape of the rupture site.

III. Provoked and spontaneous ovulation

In many animal species the physiology of the female is such that ovulation occurs naturally when the follicle reaches the proper stage of ripeness. But in some, further development is arrested after a certain point has been reached. Such species require a stimulus from outside to enable the course of maturation to be resumed and to carry the follicle to the stage at which rupture is inevitable. This stimulus is usually provided by the excitement of coitus and is a cogent argument in favour of the neurohumoral theories of pituitary-hypothalamic relationships. The problem has been most thoroughly studied in mammals (see Chapters 5–7 and 19).

A. Insects

The tsetse fly, *Glossina*, is an example of an insect in which ovulation is provoked by the stimulus of copulation. Normally, only one egg is shed from the ovary at a time, but if several have matured and the stimulus for ovulation has been withheld, coitus releases them all (Mellanby, 1937). In some species the development of eggs is either initiated or accelerated by impregnation but the process of ovulation is spontaneous. In yet other species oviposition, or egg-laying, is influenced by copulation. Whether this denotes the dependence of ovulation upon the same stimulus is not made clear in most of the descriptions. The somewhat numerous instances in which oviposition depends upon coitus are listed by Wigglesworth (1950). In the gypsy moth, *Lymnantria*, oviposition is incomplete when the female mates with a castrated male, in spite of the fact that the bursa of the female is filled by the spermatophore from the male. This suggests that some other influence than a nervous one may be at work in this instance (Vlatt, 1920).

B. Birds

The pigeon is the only bird that is known to belong to the category of provoked ovulators. The external stimulus necessary for yolk formation is 'mating' or the pairing of the female with the male bird. Frequently the presence of two females together, or even the presentation of a fictitious mate by means of a mirror, will fulfil the same purpose (Matthews, 1939).

C. Mammals

Among the mammals the following are classed among the provoked ovulators: rabbit, cat, ferret, mink, European weasel, marten, common shrew, lesser shrew, American shrew, European hedgehogs (*Erinaceus europaeus* and *E. romanicus*), the vole, *Microtus guentheri* and *M. californicus* and thirteen-lined ground-squirrel. Doubtless other species will be added to this list as details of the reproduction become known.

The phenomenon has been investigated mostly in the rabbit. In this species ovulation normally depends upon the stimulus afforded by coitus. This causes the release of luteinizing hormone from the anterior pituitary in sufficient quantity within an hour or so (Fee and Parkes, 1929). The release of ova takes place about $10\frac{1}{2}$ hours after coitus. The necessary stimulus is central, i.e., it is psychic, and not local in the reproductive tract, since anaesthetization of the cervix of the doe will not prevent ovulation (Fee and Parkes, 1930). Also, if one doe jumps another which is sexually excited ovulation follows in some instances. This suggests a nervous and not a hormonal factor in the initial portion of the reaction. Mechanical stimulation of the cervix does not provoke ovulation in does kept isolated from other rabbits. Marshall *et al.* (1939) showed that ovulation follows the injection of picrotoxin, a hypothalamic stimulant, so that it is logical to conclude that the psychic stimulus is fed into the hypothalamus where it sets in motion the train of events that lead to the release of luteinizing hormone from the anterior pituitary. The real problem is to find out why some species require this further stimulus or why it has to be so much more intense than in the spontaneous ovulators. The rabbit has contributed valuable information as to the nature of the ovulatory mechanism but no clue seems to have been found that would point to the answer to this question.

In the mink, Hansson (1947) has found that one copulation is not sufficient to trigger off the ovulation mechanism but that several are necessary for it to occur. Enders (1952) found that ovulation would result not only from copulation or fighting with a male, but also from frequent taking of vaginal smears and from stimulating the cervix with a glass rod. He further recorded that fewer follicles develop and enlarge if females are kept in strict isolation, visual as well as physical. This reminds one of the condition that exists in the pigeon, where deposition of yolk depends to some extent upon visual stimulation (Bartelmez, 1912). Enders gave the interval between copulation and ovulation in the mink as approximately 48 hours but Hansson stated it to be somewhat shorter, about 36–37 hours. Hammond and Walton's (1934) time for the ferret was about 30 hours.

In his work Hansson (1947) encountered a number of instances of ovulation following mounting without intromission. When a re-mating was allowed within 4 days of a first fertile one no ovulation followed, but when the interval was prolonged to 5 or 6 days, a new series of ovulations sometimes followed. If it was more than 6 days the female always ovulated. When a second mating resulted in a new ovulation most of the fertilized eggs from the first series degenerated. Hansson regards superfoetation as a possibility in this species.

Greulich (1934) found that in the cat mechanical stimulation of the cervix was sufficient to provoke ovulation. Gros (1936) recorded that one copulation was sufficient as a stimulus and that ovulation followed in about 26–27 hours.

There is some conflict of opinion regarding the hedgehog. Allanson and Deanesly (1934) found that ovulation was spontaneous, but, according to Zajaczek (1939), it is provoked by copulation. More information is needed respecting the method of keeping the animals. Obviously from data on the mink strict isolation is a *sine qua non* in determining the ovulatory pattern.

In the short-tailed shrew, *Blarina brevicauda*, Pearson (1944) has shown that a large number of matings are necessary to provoke ovulation. He was unable to find ruptured follicles if the number was below nineteen and ovulation did not always follow when this number was considerably exceeded. The interval between the first mating and ovulation was very variable; it depended both on the individual female and on the number of matings. The length of this interval varied between 55 and slightly more than 70 hours, with 64 hours as a fair average.

The vole, *Microtus agrestis*, seems to occupy an intermediate position with regard to spontaneity of ovulation. Chitty and Austin (1957) report that a population of these voles kept in London maintained a prolonged state of oestrus, as shown by continuous vaginal cornification and sexual receptiveness. Ovulation was provoked in these voles by coitus. In a group of voles observed at Oxford the cycle was of the short type usually found in mice and rats. These observers suggested that some unknown environmental factor may have caused the difference between the two groups.

In this connection one may recall that Allen (1922) found that some strains of mice exhibited continuous oestrus and required the stimulus afforded by copulation to cause them to ovulate. Togari (1927) also has explained the irregular cycles of some of the mice examined by him in this way. One hesitates to include the 'persistent oestrus' rats described by Everett *et al.* (1949). Some older rats of a certain strain showed this condition which can occasionally be interrupted by copulation.

REFERENCES

Aeby, C. (1859). Ueber glatte Muskelfasern im Ovarium und Mesovarium von Wirbelthieren. *Arch. Anat.* 675–676.

Allanson, M. and Deanesly, R. (1934). The reaction of anoestrous hedgehogs to experimental conditions. *Proc. roy. Soc.* B. **116**, 170–185.

Allen, E. (1922). The oestrous cycle in the mouse. *Amer. J. Anat.* **30**, 297–371.

Bartelmez, G. W. (1912). The bilaterality of the pigeon's egg. I. A study in egg organization from the first growth period of the oocyte to the beginning of cleavage. *J. Morph.* **23**, 269–329.

Brandt, A. (1877). Fragmentarische Bemerkungen über das Ovarium des Frosches. *Z. wiss. Zool.* **28**, 575–586.

Chitty, H. and Austin, C. R. (1957). Environmental modification of oestrus in the vole. *Nature, Lond.* **179**, 592–593.

Corner, G. W. (1946). *In* "The Problem of Fertility" (E. T. Engle, ed.), pp. 67–73. Princeton Univ. Press, Princeton, New Jersey.

Enders, R. K. (1952). Reproduction in the mink (*Mustela vison*). *Proc. Amer. phil. Soc.* **96**, 691–755.

Evans, H. M. and Cole, H. H. (1931). An introduction to the study of the oestrous cycle in the dog. *Mem. Univ. Calif.* **9**, 65–118.

Everett, J. W., Sawyer, C. H. and Markee, J. E. (1949). A neurogenic timing factor in control of the ovulatory discharge of luteinizing hormone in the cyclic rat. *Endocrinology,* **44**, 234–250.

Fee, A. R. and Parkes, A. S. (1929). Studies on ovulation. I. The relation of the anterior pituitary body to ovulation in the rabbit. *J. Physiol.* **67**, 383–388.

Fee, A. R. and Parkes, A. S. (1930). Studies in ovulation. III. Effect of vaginal anaesthesia on ovulation in the rabbit. *J. Physiol.* **70**, 385–388.

Greulich, W. W. (1934). Artificially induced ovulation in the cat. *Anat. Rec.* **58**, 217–224.

2K*

Gros, G. (1936). "Contribution à l'Endocrinologie Sexuelle. Le Cycle Génital de la Chatte." Thesis, Algiers.

Guttmacher, M. S. and Guttmacher, A. F. (1921). Morphological and physiological studies of the musculature of the mature Graafian follicle of the sow. *Johns Hopk. Hosp. Bull.* **32**, 394–399.

Häggquist, G. (1921). Einige Beobachtungen ueber das Verhältnis der Gefässe zum Cumulus oöphorus im menschlichen Ovarium. *Anat. Anz.* **54**, 264–267.

Hammond, J. and Walton, A. (1934). Notes on ovulation and fertilization in the ferret. *Brit. J. exp. Biol.* **11**, 307.

Hansel, W. (1958). Personal communication.

Hansson, A. (1947). "The Physiology of Reproduction in Mink (*Mustela vison* Schreb.) with Special Reference to Delayed Implantation." A. Bonnier, Stockholm.

Hartog, M. (1904). Note on embryonic ferments. *J. Physiol.* **31**, p. xlvii

Heape, W. (1905). Ovulation and degenerating ova in the rabbit. *Proc. roy. Soc.* B. **76**, 260–268.

Hill, R. T., Allen, E. and Kramer, T. C. (1935). Cinemicrographic studies of rabbit ovulation. *Anat. Rec.* **63**, 239–245.

Hoar, W. S. (1957). *In* "The Physiology of Fishes" (M. E. Brown, ed.). Vol. 1. Academic Press, New York.

Horst, C. J. van der, and Gillman, J. (1940). Ovulation and corpus luteum formation in *Elephantulus*. *S. Afr. J. med. Sci.*, **5**, 73–91.

Kelly, G. L. (1931). Direct observation of rupture of Graafian follicle in the mammal. *J. Fla. med. Ass.* **17**, 422–423.

Kraus, S. D. (1947). Observations on the mechanism of ovulation in the frog, hen and rabbit. *Western J. Surg.* **55**, 424–437.

Lipner, H. J. and Maxwell, B. (1960). Hypothesis concerning the role of follicular contractions in ovulation. *Science*, **131**, 1737–1738.

Markee, J. E. and Hinsey, J. C. (1935–36). Observations on ovulation in the rabbit. *Anat. Rec.* **64**, 309–319.

Marshall, F. H. A., Verney, E. B. and Vogt, M. (1939). The occurrence of ovulation in the rabbit as a result of stimulation of the central nervous system by drugs. *J. Physiol.* **97**, 128–132.

Matthews, L. H. (1939). Visual stimulation and ovulation in pigeons. *Proc. roy. Soc.* B. **126**, 557–560.

McKenzie, F. F. and Terrill, C. E. (1937). Estrus, ovulation, and related phenomena in the ewe. *Res. Bull. Mo. agric. Exp. Sta.* No. 264.

Mellanby, H. (1937). Experimental work on reproduction in the tsetse fly, *Glossina palpalis*. *Parasitology*, **29**, 131–141.

Odeblad, E. (1954). Studies on the physiology of the follicular fluid. *Acta endocr., Copenhagen*, **15**, 313–316.

Patterson, J. T. (1910). Studies on the early development of the hen's egg. I. History of the early cleavage and of the accessory cleavage. *J. Morph.* **21**, 101–134.

Pearl, R. and Curtis, M. R. (1914). Studies on the physiology of reproduction in the domestic fowl. VIII. On some physiological effects of ligation, section or removal of the oviduct. *J. exp. Zool.* **17**, 395–424.

Pearson, O. P. (1944). Reproduction in the shrew (*Blarina brevicauda* Say). *Amer. J. Anat.* **75**, 39–93.

Pflüger, E. (1859). Ueber die Bewegungen der Ovarien. *Arch. Anat.* 30–32.

Phillips, R. E. and Warren, D. C. (1937). Observations concerning the mechanics of ovulation in the fowl. *J. exp. Zool.* **76**, 117–136.

Robinson, E. J. and Rugh, R. (1943). The reproductive processes of the fish, *Oryzias latipes. Biol. Bull., Wood's Hole,* **84**, 115–125.

Rouget, C. (1858). I. Recherches sur les organes erectiles de la femme et sur l'appareil musculaire tubo-ovarien dans leurs rapports avec l'ovulation et la menstruation. *J. Physiol., Paris,* **1**, 320–343.

Rugh, R. (1935). Ovulation in the frog. II. Follicular rupture to fertilization. *J. exp. Zool.* **71**, 163–193.

Schochet, S. S. (1916). A suggestion as to the process of ovulation and ovarian cyst formation. *Anat. Rec.* **10**, 447–457.

Smith, B. G. (1912). The embryology of *Cryptobranchus alleghaniensis* including comparisons with some other vertebrates. I. Introduction; the history of the egg before cleavage. *J. Morph.* **23**, 61–157.

Smith, B. G. (1916). The process of ovulation in the Amphibia. *Rep. Michigan Acad. Sci.* **18**, 102–105.

Smith, J. T. and Ketteringham, R. C. (1938). Rupture of the Graafian follicle. *Amer. J. Obstet. Gynec.* **36**, 453–460.

Strauss, F. (1938). Die Befruchtung und der Vorgang der Ovulation bei *Ericulus* aus der Familie der Centetiden. *Biomorphosis,* **1**, 281–312.

Thomson, A. (1919). The ripe human Graafian follicle, together with some suggestions as to its mode of rupture. *J. Anat., Lond.* **54**, 1–40.

Togari, C. (1927). On the ovulation of the mouse. *Nagoya J. med. Sci.* **2**, 17–50.

Vlatt, B. (1920). Beiträge zur Sexualphysiologie des Schwammspinners. *Biol. Zbl.* **40**, 539–558.

Waldeyer, W. (1870). "Eierstock und Ei." W. Engelmann, Leipzig.

Walton, A. and Hammond, J. (1928). Observations on ovulation in the rabbit. *Brit. J. exp. Biol.* **6**, 190–204.

Wester, J. (1921). "Eierstock und Ei. Befruchtung und Unfruchtbarkeit bei den Haustieren." R. Schoetz, Berlin.

Wigglesworth, V. B. (1950). "The Principles of Insect Physiology." 4th ed. E. P. Dutton, New York.

Wimsatt, W. A. (1944). Growth of the ovarian follicle and ovulation in *Myotis lucifugus. Amer. J. Anat.* **74**, 129–173.

Zajaczek, S. (1939). Untersuchungen über das endokrine System des Igels (*Erinaceus*). II. Histologische Veränderungen in den Eierstöcken und dem Uterus, die periodisch oder unter dem Einfluss von endokrinen Reizen auftreten. *Bull. int. Acad. Cracovie (Acad. pol. Sci.), Cl. Sci. Math. et Nat. Sci. Ser. B*(2). 379–403.

CHAPTER 9

OVARIAN ACTIVITY DURING GESTATION, OVUM TRANSPORT AND IMPLANTATION

E. C AMOROSO AND C. A. FINN

I. Introduction

The purpose of this chapter is not to give a detailed account of the physiology of the ovary, but to provide a summary which will help in understanding the information relating to the part played by this organ, and in particular the corpus luteum, in the initiation, maintenance and termination of pregnancy.

Although John Beard (1897) and Louis Augustus Prenant (1898) had earlier suggested that the corpus luteum might exercise an inhibitory influence on ovulation and the regularity of the oestrous cycle, the discontinuance of pregnancy, following removal of the corpora lutea, offered the first experimental evidence that these bodies are necessary for implantation and maintenance of embryos in the uterus (Fraenkel and Cohn, 1901; Fraenkel, 1903, 1910, 1927). The evidence was derived from the results of experiments on pregnant rabbits in which the ovaries were removed or the corpora lutea destroyed; in each case the pregnancy was brought to an end. Control experiments proved that the effects were not merely due to the operation itself.

Fraenkel, who owed the suggestion to Gustav Born (see Corner, 1947), supposed that these luteal bodies possessed the function of elaborating a hormone which in some way stimulated the growth of the uterine mucosa and assisted in the attachment of the fertilized ovum and in the maintenance of its nutrition during the first half of pregnancy. This opinion was further strengthened by Loeb's (1907) discovery that the corpus luteum specifically induces a decidual response in the uterus of the guinea pig so that implantation becomes possible. He found that mechanical irritation of the endometrium in the non-pregnant uterus from the 2nd to the 8th or 9th day after ovulation elicits the formation of tumour-like decidual growths (deciduomata) at the injured sites in much the same way as the embryo produces a decidual reaction during its interstitial implantation. He showed, moreover, that deciduomata form in transplanted portions of the uterus, and here as well as in the normal uterus, the reaction depends upon the integrity of the corpora lutea.

Fraenkel's (1903) experiments on ovariectomy and the destruction of corpora lutea, as well as those of Loeb (1907) on the production of deciduomata, have been confirmed in several species of mammals and by numerous other investigators (Loeb, 1908a, b; Hammond, 1917; Brouha, 1934; Krehbiel, 1937; Amoroso, 1955a), but it was not until Bouin and Ancel (1909a, b, c, 1910) had shown that the corpus luteum exerts a comparable influence on the rabbit's uterus in pseudopregnancy that the general conclusions regarding the functions of that organ were placed on a completely firm foundation. Indeed, the investigations of Ancel and Bouin might well be regarded as providing the basis for the biochemical studies which led to the isolation, identification and synthesis of the most effective naturally-occurring gestagen, progesterone. The work was reported independently, and at about the same time, by four groups of workers: Allen and Wintersteiner (1934), Butenandt and Westphal (1934a, b), Hartmann and Wettstein, (1934a, b) and Slotta et al. (1934a, b). The chain of evidence establishing the secretory function of the corpus luteum is well told by Corner (1947).

In this connection one can hardly avoid mentioning the story, told in full by Willard M. Allen to the senior author, that the conjoined word 'progesterone' (Allen et al., 1935) was first suggested by A. S. Parkes (14 July 1935) as a compromise for 'progestin' (Allen and Corner) and 'luteosterone' (Butenandt). It is of interest also that 5 years prior to the isolation of progesterone in 1934 from corpus luteum extracts, its metabolite, pregnanediol, was obtained by Marrian (1929) from human pregnancy urine and identified by Butenandt (1930); the isolation was incidental to a search for the follicular hormone.

II. Ovarian changes and the formation of the corpus luteum in mammals

A. The formation of the corpus luteum

The mammalian ovary, having formed and discharged the egg which is its contribution to a future generation, continues to function as an organ of internal secretion and in the presence of fertilized and implanting ova undergoes changes which, in general, define its character for the remainder of the gestation period. After the discharge of the ovum from the ovary, the wall of the ruptured follicle undergoes a series of changes which transforms it into a solid, transient structure, known as the corpus luteum, whose secretions play an important part in the control of the female reproductive processes. Its discovery is usually attributed to Volcherus Coiter in 1573, though Harrison (1948) considers that Vesalius had observed it in the ovary of a young girl some 30 years previously.

While the initial development of the corpus luteum in many mammalian species is essentially similar (see, however, Strauss, 1939), its history after it has become established varies according to whether the animal is non-pregnant, pseudopregnant, pregnant or lactating. When fully formed the corpus luteum of pregnancy attains a size as large as, or larger than, the follicle from which it was formed and consists of large pigmented cells, the luteal cells, separated from one another by an anastomosing framework of richly vascularized connective tissue. In general, these luteal bodies are considerably larger than the similar structures of the oestrous cycle, pseudopregnancy or of lactation (Mayer, 1953), although the individual cells are not greatly altered (Brambell, 1956). According to Bretschneider and de Wit (1947), there are two phenomena which characterize the ovary of monotremes, namely the presence of numerous large corpora atretica and well-formed post-ovulation corpora lutea which are probably associated with lactation.

For a detailed account of the structure and development of the mammalian corpus luteum the interested reader should consult the article by Hett (1933) and the reviews by Harrison (1948) and Brambell (1956), both of them containing extensive bibliographies of the literature (see also Chapter 2C).

B. Inhibition of ovulation and cyclic ovarian activity

Corpora lutea are normally formed from all ruptured follicles, but they soon degenerate if fertilization of the ovum and implantation do not occur (cf. sect. V, B). They are then referred to as corpora lutea of the cycle or corpora lutea of ovulation. In many mammals they persist in a recognizable form for about 10 to 20 days (Asdell, 1928, 1946; Eckstein, 1949). But despite their limited life-span, the cyclical length of the corpora lutea of the majority of spontaneously ovulating species is sufficient to permit the developing egg to reach the stage at which implantation is possible and to maintain uterine sensitivity long enough for implantation to occur. If fertilization and implantation occur, corpora lutea which normally regress become transformed into corpora lutea of pregnancy. On the other hand, ovarian follicles which would have been expected to undergo maturation with the onset of another cycle are inhibited and with them ovulation and oestrus itself (Beard, 1897; Loeb, 1911a, b; and others). This inhibition of oestrus and ovulation in pregnancy, which is usually attributed to the secretions of the corpus luteum—oestrogen (Allen et al., 1925; Frank and Gustavson, 1925; Allen and Meyer, 1933) and progesterone— acting to suppress pituitary hormones responsible for follicular growth (McKay and Robinson, 1947), may be complete or, more rarely, the ovaries may continue to undergo rhythmical changes, especially in early pregnancy (e.g. guinea pig: Loeb, 1911a; Bujard, 1952; Rowlands, 1956; rat: Evans and Swezy, 1931; mare: Cole et al., 1931; Amoroso et al., 1948; Amoroso and Rowlands, 1951; Amoroso, 1955a).

Experimental proof of the importance of the corpus luteum in suppressing ovulation was provided by Loeb (1923a), Drummond-Robinson and Asdell (1926) and by Hammond (1927) when they showed that removal of this organ, in the guinea pig, goat and cow respectively, was soon followed by ovulation regardless of whether the products of conception are expelled immediately or retained temporarily. Additional evidence that the premature occurrence of ovulation following removal of the corpus luteum is due to the withdrawal of the active principle progesterone was provided by Parkes and Bellerby (1927) and Selye et al. (1936).

TABLE I

Time of involution of the corpora lutea in the Metatheria and Eutheria

Orders	No appreciable regression before parturition		Considerable regression before end of gestation	
	Families or species	Authors	Families or species	Authors
Marsupialia	Marsupial cat (*Dasyurus viverrinus*)	Sandes (1903)		
	Tammar (*Protemnodon eugenii*)	Sharman (1955c)		
	Quokka (*Setonix brachyurus*)	Sharman (1955a, b)		
	Opossum (*Didelphys virginiana*)	Hartman (1920, 1921)		
Xenarthra	Nine-banded armadillo (*Dasypus novemcinctus*)	Newman and Paterson (1910)		
Insectivora	Hedgehog (*Erinaceus europaeus*)	Deanesly (1934)	Common shrew (*Sorex araneus*)	Brambell (1935)
	Common mole (*Talpa europaea*)	Matthews (1935)	Lesser shrew (*Sorex minutus*)	Brambell and Hall (1937)
	Elephant shrew (*Elephantulus myurus jamesoni*)	van der Horst and Gillman (1940, 1942, 1945)	American shrew (*Blarina brevicauda*)	Pearson (1944)
Chiroptera	Greater horseshoe bat (*Rhinolophus ferrum-equinum*)	Matthews (1937)	*Nycteris luteola* Thomas	Matthews (1941)
	Lump-nosed bat (*Corynorhinus rafinesquei*)	Pearson et al. (1952)	*Triaenops afer* Peters	
Carnivora	Spotted hyaena (*Crocuta crocuta*)	Matthews (1939)	Dog (*Canis familiaris*)	Goormaghtigh (1927)
	Ferret (*Mustela furo*)	Hammond and Marshall (1930)		
	Mink (*Mustela vison*)	Hansson (1947)	Stoat (*Mustela erminea*)	Deanesly (1935)
	Northern fur seal (*Callorhinus ursinus*)	Enders et al. (1946)	Cat (*Felis domesticus*)	Dawson (1946) and Fig. 2, below
	Grey seal (*Halichoerus grypus*)	Amoroso et al. (1951)		

TABLE I—continued

Time of involution of the corpora lutea in the Metatheria *and* Eutheria

Orders	No appreciable regression before parturition		Considerable regression before end of gestation	
	Families or species	Authors	Families or species	Authors
Cetacea	Dolphin (*Delphinus delphis*)	Khartov (1938)		
	Ca'aing whale (*Globiocephala melaena*)	Harrison (1949)		
	Blue whale (*Sibbaldus musculus*)	} Laws (1958)		
	Fin whale (*Balaenoptera physalus*)			
Lagomorpha	Domestic rabbit (*Oryctolagus cuniculus*)	Hammond (1925)		
	Wild rabbit	Allen *et al.* (1947)		
	Rocky mountain pika (*Ochotona princeps*)	Duke (1952)		
Rodentia	Kangaroo rat (*Dipodomys ordu columbianus*)	Duke (1940)		
	Spermophile (*Citellus tridecemlineatus*)	Drips (1919)		
	Woodchuck (*Marmota monax*)	Rasmussen (1918)		
	Pocket gopher (*Geomys bursarius*)	Mossman (1937)	Grey squirrel (*Sciurus carolinensis*)	Deanesly and Parkes (1933)
	Golden hamster (*Mesocricetus auratus*)	Deanesly (1938)		
	Bank vole (*Clethrionomys glareolus britannicus*)	Brambell and Rowlands (1936)		
	Field vole (*Microtus agrestis*)	Brambell and Hall (1939)		
	Mouse (*Mus musculus*)	Deanesly (1930)		
	Rat (*Rattus norvegicus*)	Long and Evans (1922)		
	Canadian porcupine (*Erethizon dorsatus*)	Mossman and Judas (1949)		
	Guinea pig (*Cavia porcellus*)	Rowlands (1956)		

TABLE I—continued

Time of involution of the corpora lutea in the Metatheria and Eutheria

| Orders | No appreciable regression before parturition | | Considerable regression before end of gestation | |
	Families or species	Authors	Families or species	Authors
Proboscidea			African elephant (*Loxodonta africana*)	Perry (1953)
Artiodactyla	Hippopotamus (*Hippopotamus amphibius*)	Amoroso et al. (1958)	Peccary (*Peccari angulatus*)	Wislocki (1931)
	Domestic pig (*Sus scrofa*)	Corner (1921)		
	Giraffe (*Giraffa camelopardalis*)	Kellas et al. (1958)		
	Domestic cow (*Bos taurus*)	Hammond (1927)	Domestic sheep (*Ovis aries*)	Grant (1934)
			Rhinoceros (*Rhinoceros* (*Diceros*) *bicornis*)	Amoroso (unpublished data)
Perissodactyla			Horse (*Equus caballus*)	Cole et al. (1931)
				Amoroso (1955a, 1959)
Primates			Chacma baboon (*Papio porcarius* Brunnick)	Zuckerman and Parkes (1932)
			Man (*Homo sapiens*)	Watrin (1924, 1926)
				Fraenkel (1952)

458   E. C. AMOROSO AND C. A. FINN

That there is a temporal relationship in the rabbit between mating, release of gonadotrophin, secretion of progesterone and ovulation was first demonstrated by Fee and Parkes (1929) and Deanesly *et al.* (1930), and is emphasized by Forbes (1953). But, notwithstanding the fact that it is the opinion of many investigators that progesterone prevents ovulation, there are others who consider that the hormone facilitates this act. Resolution of the apparent contradiction may well lie in the

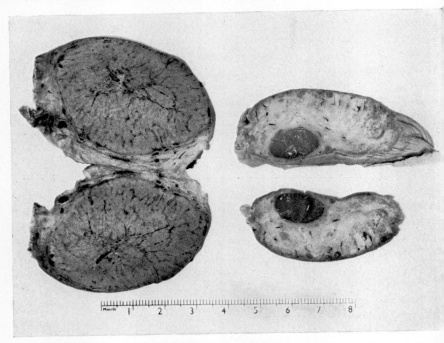

Fig. 1. Photomicrograph of the cut surfaces of the ovaries of an adult giraffe (*Giraffa camelopardalis*) towards the end of pregnancy. No follicles are visible in the ovary containing the corpus luteum which shows few signs of regression. A single large follicle is present in the opposite ovary.

recent suggestion of Everett (1950) and of Sawyer (1952) that progesterone at first makes possible and subsequently blocks the release of gonadotrophins, which in turn precipitates ovulation.

C. The life-span of the corpus luteum

From Table I it will be observed that in many species, including the rat, mouse, guinea pig, porcupine, bank vole, hedgehog, armadillo, dolphin, grey seal, giraffe (Fig. 1), sow, cow and marsupial cat, the corpora lutea of pregnancy do not regress appreciably before parturition

On the other hand, in a number of other species, including the shrews, the rabbit, the grey squirrel, stoat, cat, dog, peccary, baboon and man, retrogression begins considerably before the end of gestation, and the corpora lutea already exhibit marked shrinkage before the end of gestation which, if significance is to be attached to it, indicates degeneration. There are, however, species differences in the relative importance of these apparently degenerating corpora lutea and the long-lasting ones, as shown by the comparative study of the rabbit, cat, rat and guinea pig. In the rabbit, for example, regressive changes can be detected in the corpora lutea towards the end of pregnancy, yet only occasionally can the ovaries be dispensed with and then not unless the foetuses are exteriorized (Courrier, 1941a) or eliminated altogether, leaving the placentae in situ (Klein, 1933). By contrast, in the rat in which the ovaries are likewise necessary throughout pregnancy, no similar regressive changes are noted. In the cat, on the other hand, whereas luteal regression is well under way by the 6th week of pregnancy (Fig. 2), removal of both ovaries at 49 days or later was followed by normal parturition at term (64 days), although spaying at 46 days or earlier regularly interrupted pregnancy (Gros, 1936). Finally, in the guinea pig there is no evidence of degeneration in the corpora lutea till the end of pregnancy, although this may not be interrupted by removal of the ovaries a considerable time before parturition (see, however, Deanesly, 1960).

The evidence here summarized, meagre though it is, shows that 'persistence' of the corpus luteum and lack of 'degeneration' have a different significance. It even cautions us against the peremptory assumption that the endocrine activity of the gland can be adjudged from its histological appearance alone.

In a few other species also, the corpus luteum of pregnancy does not persist. Thus, in the two African bats, Nycteris luteola and Triaenops afer, Matthews (1941) found no trace of a corpus luteum in the ovary during pregnancy after an early stage. Similarly, in the black rhinoceros and in the mare, the luteal bodies disappear from the ovary considerably before the end of gestation (Fig. 3), suggesting that the extra-ovarian tissues supply enough progesterone for the maintenance of pregnancy in these species (see Amoroso, 1955a, 1960a). Another species in which endometrial structures may have an endocrine function is the Chinese hamster, but here the evidence is purely morphological and requires confirmation (Parkes, 1931).

In the monotremes regression of the corpora lutea begins shortly before the eggs are laid (Hill and Gatenby, 1926). As yet, however, their function remains unsolved, although a possible relationship with lactation has been suggested (Bretschneider and de Wit, 1947).

460   E. C. AMOROSO AND C. A. FINN

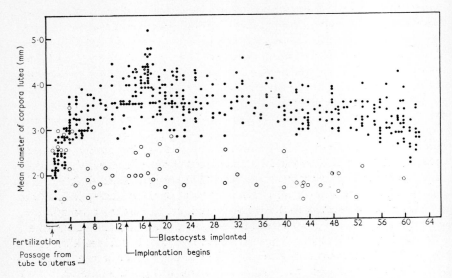

FIG. 2. Graphical representation of the mean diameters of the corpora lutea present in the ovaries of 200 pregnant cats. The successive stages of pregnancy are arranged in order on the abscissa, beginning with fertilization at the origin and ending with approximately full-term on the right. It can be seen that there is an initial period of very rapid growth during the tubal transit of the eggs. A second but less rapid period of growth begins when the blastocysts have entered the uterus and continues until implantation is complete about the 17th day after ovulation. Thereafter, there is a steady decrease in size which continues until parturition. There is some evidence of the occurrence of accessory corpora lutea (open circles), and there is reason to believe that they are formed partly from ruptured follicles and partly from atresia of unruptured follicles.

D. Accessory luteal structures

1. *Accessory corpora lutea of pregnancy*

In some species, for example the horse (Cole *et al.*, 1931; Kimura and Lyons, 1937; Amoroso *et al.*, 1948; Amoroso, 1955a, 1959) and the African elephant (Perry, 1953), the corpus luteum of pregnancy persists only for the length of time for which the normal cyclical corpus luteum persists. A type of gonadotrophic activity then follows, which is attributed to the placenta (Cole and Goss, 1943; Rowlands, 1947; Amoroso, 1952, 1955a; Clegg *et al.*, 1954), and new corpora lutea are formed, partly by direct luteinization and partly by the rupture of follicles (Amoroso *et al.*, 1948; Perry, 1953), though some of them appear to be formed by the luteinization of the theca interna cells with degeneration of the ovum and granulosa (Cole *et al.*, 1931). In the mare, these accessory structures, which are a rich source of progesterone, have a longer life-span than the ones they replace and may be a factor of safety ensuring implantation (Amoroso and Rowlands, 1951; Amoroso, 1959). They degenerate completely by 150 days and from then until the end of gestation the ovaries contain neither corpora lutea nor large follicles. Consequently, the ovaries cannot be regarded as providing a continuing source of progesterone in this species. In the African elephant, on the other hand, Perry (1953) records several

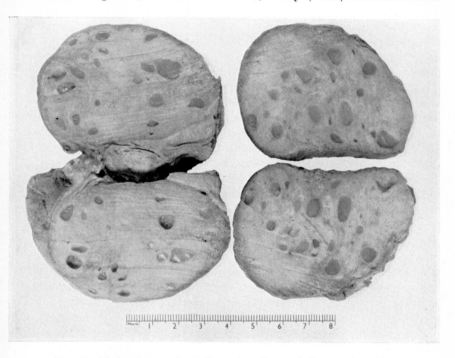

FIG. 3. Photomicrograph of the cut surfaces of the ovaries of an adult black rhinoceros (*Rhinoceros bicornis* L.) towards the end of pregnancy. Only small follicles are present and the ovaries are composed mainly of dense connective tissue in which no trace of luteal tissue is visible.

generations of accessory corpora lutea during pregnancy, some of which persist until term.

The natural occurrence of luteal tissue other than that of the typical corpus luteum has also been described in the ovaries of the armadillo (Newman and Paterson, 1910), monotremes (Bretschneider and de Wit, 1947), the human female (Meyer, 1911, 1913; Fraenkel *et al.*, 1941; Hisaw, 1947; Fraenkel, 1952) and the rhesus monkey (Corner *et al.*, 1936; Corner, 1940). In some species, these accessory luteal structures are formed at the same time as those resulting from an ovulation. In others, including the peccary (Wislocki, 1931), baboon (Zuckerman and Parkes, 1932), bank vole (Brambell and Rowlands, 1936), viscacha (Pearson, 1949), Canadian porcupine (Mossman and Judas, 1949), Norway rat (Hall, 1952), nilgai (Amoroso, 1955a) and sow (du Mesnil du Buisson and Dauzier, 1959) and the cat, they may arise during pregnancy (Fig. 2), but no adequate explanation for the occurrence of these structures is available (see above).

In the Canadian porcupine, *Erethizon dorsatum*, these accessory corpora are formed in large numbers at oestrus and in early pregnancy as a result of luteinization of atretic follicles. They develop in both ovaries, but persist only on the side carrying the normal corpus luteum, an observation which led Mossman and Judas (1949) to suggest that the latter is concerned in their maintenance.

In contrast to the porcupine, a feature of the ovarian cycle in the viscacha, the peccary and the nilgai (*Boselaphus*) is the appearance, about half-way during pregnancy, of large numbers of accessory corpora lutea, probably as a result of luteinization of unruptured follicles. In the peccary and the nilgai they develop in both ovaries, but are found only on the right side in the viscacha, where, in addition to the primary and apparently functional corpus luteum, a dozen of such secondary corpora may be present at the time of parturition. In the ovaries of a pregnant nilgai, bearing twin foetuses, as many as thirty-four have been recorded (Fig. 4).

In the fin whale accessory corpora lutea of ovulation appear to occur as frequently as accessory corpora of pregnancy. The smaller accessory corpora form from unruptured follicles, but the luteal cells are derived from the membrana granulosa (Laws, 1958).

A feature of the ovary of the gibbon is the intensive luteinization of all follicular elements during the luteal phase of the cycle, pregnancy and lactation (Dempsey, 1940). This constitutes a distinctive feature in which the gibbon resembles the New World monkeys (Dempsey, 1939) and differs from man and the Old World monkeys, in whom luteinization of the theca interna takes place only during pregnancy.

2. Luteal structures in the foetal ovary

Widespread luteinization of the follicular elements is also seen in the ovaries of the human full-term foetus (Fraenkel and Papanicolaou, 1938; Fraenkel and Berruti, 1942; Govan and Mukherjee, 1950; Smith, 1951; Potter, 1953) and in those of the foetal giraffe during late gestation (Kellas *et al.*, 1958). Whether these changes reflect a genuine development of ovarian sensitivity to the gonad-stimulating substances which appear in the urine of pregnant women (Zondek, 1928) and the pregnant giraffe (Wilkinson and de Fremery, 1940), or may be referred to some other cause, is not yet clear. Nevertheless, it would appear that the foetal ovary of the giraffe (Fig. 5), as judged by the histological appearances of follicular development and luteinization, may be capable of both secretory and gametogenic activities long before it is normally called upon to exercise these functions.

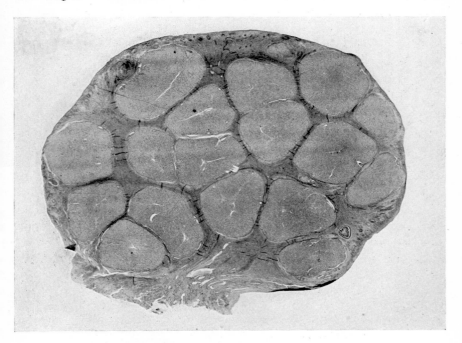

FIG. 4. Photomicrograph of a section of the ovary of a pregnant nilgai (*Boselaphus tragocamelus* Pallas) towards the end of gestation, showing seventeen accessory corpora lutea. × 4. (From Amoroso, 1955a.)

3. *The interstitium of the foetal ovary*

In some other species, e.g. horse (Fig. 6), seal and elephant, the foetal gonads are strikingly enlarged, the large size being due to an enormous development of the interstitial cells (Cole *et al.*, 1933; Amoroso and Rowlands, 1951; Amoroso *et al.*, 1951; Perry, 1953; Amoroso, 1955d, 1956, 1959). The available evidence points to the existence of an association between the concentration of urinary oestrogens in the pregnant mare and the quantitative development and regression of the foetal gonads (Amoroso and Rowlands, 1951). But although similar

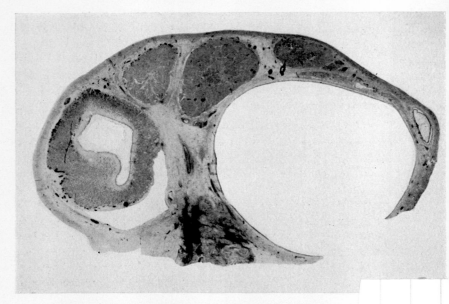

FIG. 5. Photomicrograph of a section of the ovary of a foet
(*Giraffa camelopardalis*) showing large follicles and two ge₁
of corpora lutea. Note luteinization of unruptured follicle on
left of ovary. × 7·5. (From Amoroso, 1955a.)

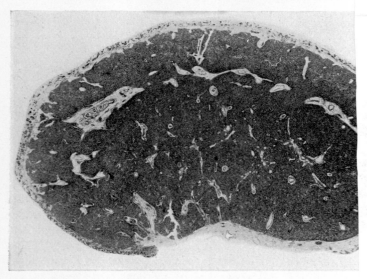

FIG. 6. Photomicrograph of a section of the ovary of a fo₍
at about 120 days. The ovary consists mainly of hypert___
interstitial tissue. × 9.

qualitative and quantitative changes have been observed in the gonads of the foetal elephant (Perry, 1953) and of the grey and elephant seals (Amoroso et al., 1951; Harrison et al., 1952; Bonner, 1955), no correlations between urinary oestrogens and gonadal development have, as yet, been reported.

III. Initiation and maintenance of luteal function

Existing information amply justifies the view that corpora lutea secrete progesterone and that progesterone causes uterine proliferation and maintains pregnancy to term in a variety of mammals deprived of their corpora lutea. Indeed, it can prolong pregnancy beyond its normal term (Wislocki and Snyder, 1933; Snyder, 1934, 1938; Koff and Davis, 1937; Allen and Heckel, 1939), and this luteal secretion might well be regarded as the hormone of pregnancy (Courrier, 1945). Without a source of progesterone no pregnancy can be maintained. Yet the mechanism which causes persistence of the corpus luteum following fertilization in mammals which ovulate spontaneously, and the factors which maintain luteal function, and hence progesterone secretion, remain controversial.

A. The regulation of corpus luteum function by gonadotrophic hormones

1. The role of the pituitary gland

Since the original discovery that luteal activity may follow the injection of pituitary extracts in normal rats (Long and Evans, 1922; Teel, 1926; Brouha, 1938), ample evidence has been accumulated to show that the pituitary is, in some way, implicated in the induction of ovarian function adequate for the maintenance of normal gestation (see Everett, 1956). Evidence for the essential role of the pituitary in luteal function in the rat was given by Pencharz and Long (1931, 1933) and Selye et al. (1933a) who demonstrated that pregnancy was promptly terminated by hypophysectomy performed prior to the 10th or 11th day. Hypophysectomy later in pregnancy does not disturb gestation. For instance, operation at 11–20 days results in prolongation of gestation with the birth of living or dead foetuses several days past term; operation on the 21st day is followed by normal birth at term or a day or two later.

Similarly, in mice (Selye et al., 1933b, 1935a; Newton and Beck, 1939; Newton and Richardson, 1940; Gardner and Allen, 1942), guinea pigs (Pencharz and Lyons, 1934; Nelson, 1935), monkeys (Agate, 1952; P. E. Smith, 1954, 1955) and the human female (Della-Beffa, 1951; Little

2M

et al., 1958) hypophysectomy during the latter part of pregnancy is not followed by premature emptying of the uterus, but living foetuses are retained until birth occurs at term or later. On the other hand, in cats (Allen and Wiles, 1932; McPhail, 1935b), in ferrets (McPhail, 1935a) and goats (Cowie and Tindal, 1960) abortion occurs in some instances in the second half of pregnancy, whilst in another group of mammals, which includes the dog (Aschner, 1912; Houssay, 1935; Votquenne, 1936) and the rabbit (Firor, 1933; White, 1933; Westman and Jacobsohn, 1936; Robson, 1937b, 1940), abortion occurs no matter when the operation is performed.

The mechanism responsible for the interruption of pregnancy following hypophysectomy on the one hand, and the prolongation of it on the other, is revealed by examination of the ovaries. In the rabbit, degeneration of the corpora lutea promptly follows hypophysectomy (Deanesly *et al.*, 1930; Smith and White, 1931). In the rat no similar regressive changes are observed; on the contrary, persistence of the corpora lutea has been observed 15 months or longer in hypophysectomized rats (Smith, 1930). That the corpora lutea do not continue to develop in the guinea pig is reported by Pencharz and Lyons (1934), but as was demonstrated by Loeb and Hesselberg (1917), Loeb (1923a), Herrick (1928), and Young (1938), and more recently by Deanesly (1960), ovariectomy in this species does not invariably terminate pregnancy (see below).

In hypophysectomized rats, pregnancy can be maintained after nidation has occurred or can even be established, using relatively crude lactogenic hormone (Cutuly, 1941a, b, 1942). Similarly, Lyons *et al.* (1943) maintained pregnancy with a preparation of lactogenic hormone which was not entirely pure, but were unable to do so with pure lactogenic hormone. Lyons (1943) also demonstrated that gestation will continue in oöphorectomized-hypophysectomized rats receiving oestrone (1 μg) and progesterone (2·0 mg).

From the foregoing it is thus apparent that the continuation of pregnancy after hypophysectomy during the second half of gestation, in rats and mice at least, must be dependent on the functional activity of the corpora lutea—and this by stimulation from sources other than the pituitary. The balance of evidence available at present suggests that the placenta represents the new source. But since the ovaries can be removed from women, monkeys and horses (see below) without terminating pregnancy, any function of the placenta as an ovarian stimulant is not essential in these species. In the mouse, rat and hamster, on the other hand, and probably in all species in which removal of the ovaries terminates pregnancy, the main feature of the relationship is the luteotrophic activity of the placenta.

2. The placenta as the source of a luteotrophic hormone

It is well established that in post-pubertal female animals which ovulate spontaneously (e.g. many rodents), the life-span of the corpus luteum of the cycle is inferior to that in the pregnant individual. Heape (1905) showed long ago that the rabbit ovulates only after coition and the same is true of the cat, the ferret and other mustelids (Amoroso, 1955c; Amoroso and Marshall, 1960). If, however, pregnancy is prevented in these animals, through coition being rendered sterile, then ovulation takes place and corpora lutea are formed unaccompanied by gestation, that is to say the animals become pseudopregnant. In such circumstances, the corpus luteum of the rabbit survives for about 16 days, whereas during pregnancy it persists for almost the entire period.

That the uterus itself, the normal decidua or the metrial glands are not concerned in luteal stimulation, is suggested by the fact that if animals (e.g. rats, mice, hamsters, guinea pigs, rabbits and cats) are made unilaterally pregnant, the removal of the gravid horn causes rapid involution of the corpora lutea, the reappearance of oestrus and an immediate return of the endometrium to the non-pregnant condition (Klein, 1934, 1935, 1937, 1938a, 1939b; Desclin, 1953, 1954). It is apparent, therefore, that by transforming the cyclic corpus luteum into the corpus luteum of pregnancy, the gravid uterus exerts a sustaining influence on the corpus luteum during pregnancy which it is prevented from exerting during the previous phases of the cycle.

Astwood and Greep (1938) prepared luteotrophic extracts from rat placenta, and their original findings have been confirmed by Astwood (1941), Sussman (1947), Averill et al. (1950) and Ray et al. (1955). Lyons and his collaborators, in addition to confirming the presence of a placental gonadotrophin concerned with the maintenance of pregnancy in the hypophysectomized rat, were able, in ovariectomized-hypophysectomized animals, to elicit mammotrophic, lactogenic and crop-stimulating activities with injections of extracts of 12-day rat placentae. They also reported that when compared with pituitary mammotrophin (prolactin) the rat placenta is potent in regard to its luteotrophic, mammotrophic and lactogenic properties, but weak in its crop-stimulating activity.

Heterotransplants of the human placenta into the anterior chamber of the eye of the mouse (Voss, 1927) or the rabbit (Kido, 1937; Gurchot et al., 1947; Stewart, 1951) have likewise yielded information regarding the secretion of placental gonadotrophins. So, too, have the results of Mayer and Canivenc (1950a), which indicate that rat placental autografts are capable of eliciting luteotrophic, mammotrophic and lactogenic effects. This evidence is, however, inconclusive, since other explanations are possible and only a repetition of the experiments with suitable precautions in hypophysectomized animals could finally settle this point.

B. The effect of uterine distension and of deciduomata on the corpus luteum

Since deciduomata, as Loeb (1907) first demonstrated, prolong the life of the corpus luteum in the guinea pig, and since a quantitative relationship has been shown to exist between the amount of decidual tissue present and the length of prolongation of pseudopregnancy in the rat (Olsen *et al.*, 1951; Velardo *et al.*, 1953), it might be supposed that the products of conception by distending the uterus would prolong the life-span of the corpus luteum (Bourg and Spehl, 1948; Peckham and Greene, 1948). However, when the foetuses are exteriorized (rabbit: Klein and Mayer, 1942a, b; Courrier, 1941a, 1945; cat: Amoroso, 1956), or when the majority of the foetuses are eliminated altogether, thereby reducing the distension of the uterus (e.g. rabbit: Klein, 1934; mouse: Newton, 1935; rat: Selye *et al.*, 1935a; Haterius 1935, 1936; Klein, 1938b; McKeown and Zuckerman, 1938; Huggett and Pritchard, 1945a, b; cat: Courrier and Gros, 1935, 1936; Gros 1936; guinea pig and hamster: Klein, 1938b), neither of these procedures alters the secretory functions of the corpora lutea. Nor was supra-vaginal ligation of the uterine cornua, shortly before the expected date of delivery (thereby prolonging the distension of the uterus effective in maintaining the corpora lutea beyond normal term (Klein and Mayer, 1942a, b). Any influence of uterine distension may thus be ruled out.

But notwithstanding these considerations, and in contra-distinction to the results obtained earlier by Astwood and Greep (1938) and Kamell and Atkinson (1948) in rats and mice respectively, it must be noted that Ershoff and Deuel (1943), Peckham and Greene (1948) and Dawson and Velardo (1952) found that deciduomata suppressed ovulation and vaginal cornification and extended the functional life of the corpus luteum in rats. Similarly, Selye (1934) was able to maintain corpora lutea of pregnancy and prolong "gestation in rats by substituting paraffin for the products of conception". The paraffin was said to stimulate the anterior pituitary gland causing persistence and function of the luteal tissue. The link between the stimulus arising in the uterus and the adenohypophysis was assumed to be neural (see also Keller, 1924; Moore and Nalbandov, 1953; Nalbandov *et al.*, 1955

These observations suggest an interrelationship between the uterus and the pituitary gland, and inasmuch as deciduoma formation i invariably produced by mechanical or electrical stimulation, it is possible that a reflex mechanism, not unlike that associated with the post-coital discharge of ovulating hormones, might be involved (Deanesly et al., 1930; Marshall and Verney, 1936).

There is considerable evidence of neural mediation in the production of luteotrophic substances by the adenohypophysis (cow: Hansel and Trimberger, 1951; rat: Everett, 1952; rabbit: Markee et al., 1952). However, since hypophysectomized mice (Newton and Beck, 1939; Deanesly and Newton, 1940; Newton and Richardson, 1940), rats (Pencharz and Long, 1931; Gardner and Allen, 1942), monkeys (van Wagenen and Newton, 1940, 1943; Smith, 1946, 1954, 1955; Agate, 1952) and women (Della-Beffa, 1951; Little et al., 1958) remain pregnant when the operation is performed during the second half of pregnancy, it is unlikely that the pituitary plays any considerable role as a reflex central pathway for maintaining corpora lutea in these species in the later stages of gestation. Hence it may be inferred that the placenta is, by exclusion, chiefly responsible for furthering luteal function.

C. The influence of the foetus in the maintenance of the corpus luteum

The foetus is so obviously a parasite that the manifestations of pregnancy at any time might be suspected as being the direct result of the demands of the foetus at that time. However, while such factors are contributory they are not essential. Thus the removal of the foetuses, leaving the placentae, from a series of monkeys (van Wagenen and Newton, 1940, 1943) and mice (Selye et al., 1935a; Newton and Beck, 1939; Deanesly and Newton, 1940) did not alter the course of pregnancy as judged by the maintenance of the corpora lutea, the continued growth of the retained placentae, the maintenance of body weight, the development of the interpubic ligament and the occurrence of parturition at the normal time. In short, mice and monkeys remain physiologically pregnant despite the absence of the foetuses.

The same unimportance of the growing foetus in maintaining the changes characteristic of the last week of pregnancy is also found in the rat and has been alluded to above. Yet it would be a mistake to imagine that the foetus is altogether a passenger. Even in the mouse, in which placental pregnancy so closely resembles the normal, the act of parturition may be sluggish (Newton, 1935), mammary development may sometimes be impaired, and lactation occasionally fail (Selye et al., 1933b; Newton, 1935), while pubic separation does not occur (Newton and Lits, 1938). In rats, only an occasional interference with parturition was reported, although pregnancy was usually prolonged (Selye et al., 1933a).

470   E. C. AMOROSO AND C. A. FINN

D. Influence of the uterus on the corpus luteum

It is generally believed that the corpus luteum is the only part of the reproductive tract which is influenced by the uterus, though a contrary opinion has been expressed by Mishell and Motyloff (1941) and Tenney et al. (1955). These investigators have reported that degeneration of the follicular apparatus and hypertrophy of the interstitial cells are the more usual consequences of removing the uterus in the rabbit.

The effects of hysterectomy

Loeb's (1923b, 1927) early demonstration that total hysterectomy following oestrus in adult guinea pigs prevents luteal regression and permits persistence of the corpora lutea for as long as 3 months was confirmed by Brouha (1933) and more recently by Rowlands and Short (1959). The latters' results are summarized in Tables II and III. That the corpora lutea in the unmated guinea pig are functional when prolonged by hysterectomy is shown by the fact that they retain their size and ovulation-inhibiting function for a period equal to that of normal pregnancy and contain more progesterone than at any stage of pregnancy (Rowlands and Short, 1959).

TABLE II

Effect of hysterectomy on ovarian and oestrous cycles

No. of hysterec-tomized guinea pig (HGP)	Time of hysterectomy after ovulation (days)	Postoperative period of observation* (days)	Corpora lutea	
			No.	Mean diameter (mm)
1	5	21	4	1·83
3	5	42	5	1·94
2	5	64	3	1·56
5	9	64	6	1·66
4	15	21	4	1·81
Controls: 4 intact females on 64th day of pregnancy			18	1·81

* Inhibition of oestrous cycle complete in all hysterectomized animals
(From Rowlands and Short, 1959.)

In the pregnant guinea pig, as in most mammals, removal of the products of conception is followed by regression of the corpora lutea, whereas removal of the uterus as well as of its contents lengthens their life-span for 2 months or longer (Desclin, 1932; Klein, 1928, 1939c). Similarly, if the uterus of the gilt is removed during pregnancy (7th to 30th day), there is a tendency for the corpora lutea to persist for a length of time exceeding the average gestation period of 120 days (du Mesnil du Buisson and Dauzier, 1959; Spies *et al.*, 1960). Removal of the uterus on the 7th day of the oestrous cycle also prolongs the life-span of the luteal bodies, and for about the period of normal gestation (du Mesnil du Buisson and Dauzier, 1959; Spies *et al.*, 1960). In heifers and ewes, hysterectomy likewise tends to lengthen the luteal survival time (Wiltbank and Casida, 1956).

TABLE III

Weight and progesterone content of the corpora lutea (C.L.) in non-pregnant (NP), pregnant (P) and hysterectomized (H) guinea pigs

Condition of animal	No. of guinea pigs	Corpora lutea			Progesterone	
		Age (days)	No.	Aver. weight (mg)	Concn. in tissue (μg/g)	Content/c.l. of aver. weight (μg)
NP	11	6	48	3·1	16·2	0·050
	21	11–13	90	3·1	7·7	0·024
P	10	6	53	2·7	14·9	0·040
	12	11–13	49	3·3	15·5	0·051
	10	21–23	46	4·9	25·2	0·123
	7	41–43	32	4·8	26·6	0·128
	24	62–64	92	4·9	23·5	0·115
H	7	62–64	40	4·8	37·6	0·180

(From Rowlands and Short, 1959.)

In certain other species, which include the opossum (Hartman, 1925a), ferret (Deanesly and Parkes, 1933) and monkey (Burford and Diddle, 1936), no effect of hysterectomy on the corpus luteum has been observed, and Long and Evans (1922), Loeb (1927), Murphy (1934), Hechter *et al.* (1940) and Bradbury *et al.* (1950) have shown that the oestrous cycles of rats continue unaltered following removal of the uterus. In contrast, however, Bradbury (1937a), Hechter *et al.* (1940) and Bradbury *et al.* (1950) have reported that hysterectomy of the pregnant or pseudopregnant rat does cause persistence of corpora lutea, the pseudopregnant period in operated animals being prolonged by about 6 days.

In the human female the evidence as to the relation between the ovaries and the uterus is less clear. Degeneration of the ovaries in women following hysterectomy has been attributed, by some gynae-cologists, to the destruction of a large part of the ovarian blood supply, but the majority appear to hold the view that no such changes occur if the ovarian blood supply is safeguarded (cf. Desclin, 1953).

In the rabbit, a non-cyclic animal, there seems to be a distinct difference in the effect of hysterectomy on the life-span of the corpus luteum depending upon when the uterus is removed. Hysterectomy a considerable interval of time before mating (Asdell and Hammond, 1933) or during pseudopregnancy (Siegmund, 1934; Loeb and Smith, 1936; Gillard, 1937; Chu et al., 1946) tends to lengthen the luteal survival time by 6–10 days beyond the 15–16-day pseudopregnant period of normal rabbits. Loeb and Smith also emphasized that the rapid involution of the corpus luteum in the normal animal appeared to be an active inflammatory dissolution, whereas in the hysterectomized rabbit the involution was very slow. On the other hand, removal of the uterus during the first half of pregnancy shortens the life-span of the corpora lutea of pregnancy to approximately that of pseudopregnancy (Micale, 1940; Greep, 1941), whereas hysterectomy during the second half of pregnancy causes an immediate decline in the size of the corpora lutea (Greep, 1941).

The mechanism by which hysterectomy prolongs the life of the corpus luteum is unknown. A common feature in the majority of these experiments on different species of animals appears to be the removal of the uterus in the presence of functional corpora lutea. But this may not be the only factor since hysterectomy in the opossum, monkey or human female has not been followed by persistence of corpora lutea.

Pincus (1937) has shown that the non-involuted uterus of the intact rabbit converts injected oestrone to oestriol, but that the hysterectomized animal did not produce this effect. In view, therefore, of the known stimulating effect of injected oestrogen on the growth and survival of the corpora lutea of the rabbit and rat (see below), Bradbury (1937b) and Heckel (1942) suggested that the effects of hysterectomy might be ascribed to the constant stimulation of the corpora by oestrone which has accumulated, due to interference with its normal metabolism by the removal of the uterus. Moreover, Hechter et al. (1940), Chu et al. (1946) and Bradbury et al. (1950) have made the interesting observation that transplantation of endometrial tissue from oestrous animals, or the injection of endometrial suspensions into hysterectomized rats and rabbits respectively, resulted in regression of the corpora, suggesting that oestrogen may be converted to inactive forms in the presence of a functional uterus. It must be noted, however, that Spies et al. (1960) could not confirm this in gilts and were unable to demonstrate the role of the uterus in maintenance and regression of the corpus luteum (see, however, Bradbury et al., 1950).

Figure 7, taken from Bradbury *et al.* (1950), summarizes the effect of hysterectomy on the duration of pseudopregnancy in the guinea pig, rabbit, rat and ferret. The significant feature brought out in the chart is that in these species the duration of the pseudopregnancy in hysterectomized animals closely approximates that of gestation, and as Bradbury and his associates put it: "The similarities of the duration of function of the corpus luteum in hysterectomized or pregnant rats, rabbits and guinea-pigs would make it possible to postulate that (the)

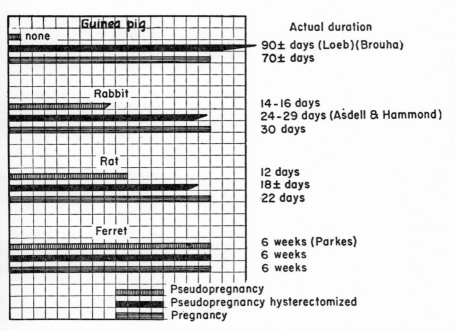

FIG. 7. Graphic representation of the relative duration of pseudo-pregnancy in normal and hysterectomized animals in relation to that of gestation. Gestation has been plotted as a common unit of time for each species. (Reproduced by permission from Bradbury *et al.*, 1950.)

corpus luteum has an inherent span which approximates the duration of gestation. Since these are polyestric species, they may have developed a means of bringing about a more rapid involution of the corpora lutea of non-fertile cycles. In our experiments and in those of Hechter *et al.* (1940), the injection of endometrial suspensions hastened the involution of the corpora lutea. It thus seems possible that the endometrium has an antagonistic or a luteolytic effect on the corpus luteum in certain species (Marx, 1935). This would seem the only logical explanation as to how hysterectomy would have such similar effects as a normal pregnancy." Newton (1935), using mice, has discussed the possibility that the decidua might produce the active agent.

E. Steroid control of luteal function

It is well known that oestrogens can maintain the activity of the corpus luteum in the rabbit (Robson, 1936, 1937a, 1938; Westman and Jacobsohn, 1937; Höhn and Robson, 1949) and rat (Lyons et al., 1943) in the absence of the pituitary. That such luteal tissue exerts its normal secretory activity is shown by the fact that in non-pregnant animals it produces its typical effects on the endometrium, i.e. progestational proliferation, and in pregnant animals it maintains normal gestation (Westman and Jacobsohn, 1937; Robson, 1937b, 1939). Oestrogen treatment, likewise, has been shown to have a beneficial effect on the corpus luteum of unmated rats (Hohlweg, 1934; Desclin, 1935; Selye et al., 1935b; Wolfe, 1935; Merckel and Nelson, 1940) and gilts (Kidder et al., 1955) causing follicular luteinization when injected during the cycle (see, however, Chu and You, 1945). On the other hand, Kidder (1954), Greenstein et al. (1958) and Loy et al. (1960) were unable to demonstrate this in the cow, though Hammond and Day (1947) had earlier reported that corpora lutea persisted for prolonged periods in heifers implanted with stilboestrol.

The stimulating effect of injected oestrogen on the growth and survival of the corpus luteum of pseudopregnant and hysterectomized rabbits has also been reported by Heckel and Allen (1936) and Hammond Jr. (1956), and by Greep (1941) and Chu et al. (1946), respectively. That oestrogen-maintained corpora lutea are functional when their life-span is prolonged in pseudopregnant rabbits is shown by uterine insensitivity to pituitrin (Heckel and Allen, 1936) and uterine histology (Westman and Jacobsohn, 1937), and also by the maintenance of the mammary glands beyond the normal duration of pseudopregnancy (Hammond Jr., 1956). That they are functional after hypophysectomy is shown by maintenance of the uterine gland (Robson, 1937a).

There is other evidence that oestrogen can exert an action on the ovary (Aron and Aron, 1946, 1952) and on luteal function (Hammond Jr., 1952); the results of Lindner et al. (1951), Desclin (1952) and Maekawa (1954, 1956) show that despite continued oestrogen administration, normal female rats fail to show constant oestrus, dioestrous periods of varying length taking place eventually. The work of Heckel and Allen (1939) on the prolongation of pregnancy in the rabbit with continuous oestrogen treatment is of importance, primarily, in showing the effect of oestrogen on the corpora lutea of pregnancy, for the conceptus was dislodged, though not expelled, as soon as the injections were started.

The luteal stimulating influence of exogenous oestrogens has been attributed by some workers (Lindner *et al.*, 1951; Desclin, 1952) to an increase in the output of gonadotrophic hormones (LTH) from the anterior pituitary stimulated by oestrogen and the consequent rise in the secretion of progesterone from the activated corpora lutea. On the other hand, Robson (1947) has suggested that, in the rabbit at least, gonadotrophic hormones have no direct action on luteal function but promote luteal activity by stimulating oestrogen production in the ovary, the effect of oestrogen on maintenance of the corpora lutea of hypophysectomized animals being an indirect one (Höhn and Robson, 1949). The results of Bullough (1942) and those of Hammond Jr. (1952, 1956) in the mouse and rabbit respectively suggest, however, that the effect is a direct one, involving the local action on the ovarian cells by the oestrogen present in the follicular fluids. In this connection it should also be mentioned that Pencharz (1940) and Williams (1940, 1944, 1945) have shown that large doses of oestrogen have a direct action upon the ovary and can bring about ovarian hypertrophy in the hypophysectomized rat. Likewise, Bradbury (1947) and Greep and Chester Jones (1950) have reported that a small dose of oestrogen given to immature female rats (intact or hypophysectomized) will elicit a slight ovarian enlargement.

In contrast to oestrogen, the effects of exogenous progesterone on the corpus luteum are quite variable. No gross or microscopic effects were apparent in the pregnant rat (Sammelwitz *et al.*, 1956; Aldred *et al.*, 1959) or rabbit (Ulberg, 1952). Likewise, Selye (1939) reported no effect of progesterone on corpora lutea of late pregnancy in mice, but Burdick (1942) found that treatment begun 1 or 2 days after mating caused luteal regression. It is postulated that the extent to which the corpora lutea are damaged may depend upon the time of injection in gilts (Sammelwitz and Nalbandov, 1958), ewes (Zimbelman *et al.*, 1959) and heifers (Loy *et al.*, 1960). Moreover, Spies *et al.* (1958) found that progesterone treatment from the 10th to the 25th day after mating caused regression of corpora lutea in hysterectomized as well as in pregnant gilts, indicating that progesterone acts independently of the uterus.

The foregoing considerations naturally raise the question of the existence of two separate controlling mechanisms for the maintenance of the corpus luteum: the one involving the direct action of gonadotrophic hormones on the corpus luteum, the other an oestrogenic substance. But while the stimulating effect of injected oestrogen upon the growth and survival of the corpus luteum of rabbits and rats is undeniable, there is little convincing evidence that naturally secreted oestrogen plays an actual role in the maintenance of pregnancy in these species. Indeed, the fact that both the rabbit and rat experience a post-partum oestrus is strong evidence that the terminal failure of the corpora lutea occurs in the presence of increasing amounts of oestrogen. Moreover, it is well established that the placentae of several rodents play an important role in maintaining luteal activity (see above, p. 467), but there is no evidence to show that this effect is mediated by oestrogen; in fact, the latter substance has not yet been found in extracts of rodent placenta, though it is abundantly present in the placenta of the sow, cow, mare, monkey and human female (for references, see Corner, 1938; Newton, 1938; Mayer and Klein, 1955). This evidence is clearly not conclusive, but it is possible, though actual proof is lacking, that species differences exist in the relative importance of the role of ovarian and gonadotrophic hormones in the control of luteal function.

IV. Endocrine functions of the corpus luteum in the maintenance of pregnancy

A. Secretory activity of the oviduct

The mammalian oviduct is known to undergo profound histological changes with variations in the phases of the reproductive cycle (Corner, 1932; McKenzie and Terrill, 1937). Cell height and secretory activity are maximal during oestrus, intermediate during pregnancy and minimal after ovariectomy (Novak and Everett, 1928; Lucas, 1930). Likewise, demonstrations by cytochemical methods indicate cyclical fluctuations in such components as alkaline phosphatase, mucopolysaccharides, lipid and glycogen in the tubal epithelium of a number of mammals, including the hamster, rat, cat, dog, ewe and man (Hadek, 1955).

Similarly, biochemical studies on the tubal fluids of the rabbit indicate that the fluid contains certain metabolic substrates, notably lactate and phospholipid, which can serve the energy requirements of the spermatozoa and eggs (Bishop, 1956c), and that these, as well as the oxygen tension and pH concentration, vary in response to the oestrogen and progesterone domination of the animal (Bishop, 1956a, b). It must be pointed out, however, that although the secretory function of the oviduct is conditioned by the ovarian hormones, little has been learnt of the precise manner in which this is brought about or how the secretions may modify, positively or negatively, the natural processes of gamete survival, fertilization, ovum transport and blastocyst development.

B. Transport of eggs through the oviduct

The tendency of the ovum to pass more rapidly through the upper portion of the oviduct and more slowly through the lower portion has been observed in several species of mammals (rat: Huber, 1915; Alden, 1942d; pig: Andersen, 1927; sheep: Clark, 1934; mouse: Lewis and Wright, 1935; goat: Amoroso et al., 1939, 1942; horse: Hamilton and Day, 1945; cow: Hamilton and Laing, 1946).

Also of interest is the fact that Sobotta (1895) had long ago emphasized that the rather constant 3–4-day tubal sojourn of the ovum in the majority of species is independent of the length and calibre of the tube, the length of gestation and the ultimate size or degree of development attained. The opossum (Hartman, 1939), the cat (Gros, 1936; Amoroso, 1952) and the bitch (Bonnet, 1907; Griffiths and Amoroso, 1939) are apparently exceptions, the eggs reaching the uterus 1, 5 and 7 days, respectively, after ovulation.

It is now generally agreed that in the oviduct there is a mechanism whereby the developing ovum is delivered to the uterus at a particular time, but the exact nature of the dependence of the ovum upon regulatory conditions remains obscure (Hartman, 1939). It seems probable, however, that both ciliary action and muscular contraction are concerned in the changes in position which the ovum undergoes and that the state of the tubo-uterine junction, responding to nervous or humoral action, is the controlling factor governing the passage of the gametes from oviduct to uterus and vice versa.

Direct observation of the movements of rat ova (within the periovarial space and in the oviduct) suggests that entrance of the egg into the oviduct is effected primarily by the action of cilia (Alden, 1942a, c; Blandau, 1958), the motility of which has been shown to be stimulated by oestrogens (bitch: Courrier and Gerlinger, 1922; monkey: Robertson et al., 1930). However, while ciliary action is the primary force in effecting entrance of the egg into and through the ampulla, action of the tubal musculature is the controlling factor governing further advancement (Alden, 1942c). The result of this muscular action is such as to produce a hesitant advance of the tubal contents, the so-called 'Pendulum Bewegung' observed by Mikulicz-Radecki and Nahmmacher (1925) and Mikulicz-Radecki (1930).

That the tubal musculature may be subject to hormonal action is indicated by sundry types of evidence. Thus the tube-locking of mouse ova with oestrogen injections of proper dosage (Burdick and Pincus, 1935; Pincus and Kirsch, 1936; Whitney and Burdick, 1936) and the acceleration of passage in cases of superovulation in the rabbit (Wislocki and Snyder, 1933; Burdick and Whitney, 1937; Whitney and Burdick, 1938) suggest that ovarian hormones control egg transport; small amounts of oestrogenic substances inhibit egg passage, while progesterone accelerates it (see, however, Alden, 1942b).

Additional support for the view that the loss of transportational function is due to lack of hormones normally secreted by the corpus luteum is provided by the observations of Long and Evans (1922) and those of Burdick et al. (1940). The former investigators have noted that tubal eggs of unmated rats (animals without functional corpora lutea) never reach the uterus, while Burdick et al. (1940) have shown that testosterone propionate—known to repress normal corpora lutea (Selye, 1939), the corpora lutea of early pregnancy (Courrier and Gros, 1938; Burdick and Emerson, 1939) and of induced ovulation (Gray and Lawson, 1939)—causes the retention of blastocysts in the oviducts of mice injected with this hormone. On the other hand, acceleration of the rate of transit of ova through the tubes occurs in pregnant or pseudopregnant rabbits in which a second ovulation has been experimentally induced; ova of the second or induced ovulation reach the uterus in less than $2\frac{1}{2}$ days following injection of extract of pregnancy urine (Wislocki and Snyder, 1933).

Further evidence that the corpora lutea have a decisive role in the nutrition and transport of ova during the period preceding implantation is provided by experiments involving their extirpation. Thus the passage of ova through the tubes, which normally requires 3 days in the rabbit and mouse, may be delayed by removing the ovaries (rabbit: Corner, 1928; Ancel and Vintemberger, 1929; mouse: Whitney and Burdick, 1939), or the corpora lutea alone (Corner, 1928). Corner, who studied the rate of transport of the rabbit ovum after partial or total ovariectomy, found that following ablation of both ovaries, 14–18 hours after mating, the ova developed to the early blastocyst stage, were transported to the uterus $4\frac{1}{2}$–$7\frac{1}{2}$ days later but died soon after entering the uterine cavity. No progestational proliferation occurred, of course, and it was concluded that ". . . the uterine proliferation is necessary not only for implantation, but for the nutrition and protection of the free blastocysts during 3 or 4 days between arrival in the uterus and implantation" (Corner, 1928, p. 81). Removal of corpora lutea alone produced similar results, although the ova were usually found in the tubes, if at all. The discrepancy between these findings was suggested as being most likely caused by adhesions following operative trauma.

In the rat it would seem that although ovarian hormones may, and apparently do, affect the activity of the tubal musculature, ovariectomy following ovulation neither prevents development nor delivery into the uterus, at essentially the proper time, of normally cleaved ova (Alden,

1942b). Moreover, since blastocysts occur, in the rabbit and in the rat, both in the uterus and in the oviduct (Corner, 1928; Alden, 1942b, d) following bilateral removal of the ovaries, it appears that the dependence of the developing embryo upon ovarian secretions may not become real until immediately preceding implantation, when the absence of progestational proliferation, and perhaps full blastocyst expansion, precludes implantation and further development (Corner, 1928; Alden, 1942b).

This would seem to imply that in the absence of progestational hormones, the uterus is incapable of secreting essential substances for the maintenance of the unimplanted blastocysts. It is, of course, possible that the eggs of different species may vary considerably in regard to their dependence on the uterine secretions. Thus, while some investigators (e.g. Courrier and Baclesse, 1955, but not Glenister, 1960) have reported that the rabbit egg is extremely sensitive to changes in its environment, others (e.g. Fawcett et al., 1947; Runner, 1947; Nicolas, 1947; Fawcett, 1950; Whitten, 1958) have shown that mouse and rat eggs survive beneath the kidney capsule and in the anterior chamber of the eye of males as well as females, where they undergo development leading to blastocyst formation.

C. Factors influencing implantation

Implantation involves the attachment of the blastocyst to the uterine mucous membrane. It is a crucial stage in the development of the young individual which depends heavily upon the pituitary and ovaries. The pituitary maintains the activity of the corpus luteum, and the hormones of the ovary—oestrogen and progesterone—are essential for the continued growth of the blastocysts and for the full differentiation of the endometrium. Removal of either the pituitary or the ovaries before this condition has been established prevents implantation and placentation. It must be pointed out, however, that Loeb and Hesselberg (1917), Loeb (1923a), and Deanesly (1960) have shown that provided the uterus has received a minimum of progestational hormone, the whole process of ovo-implantation can occur in the guinea pig in the absence of ovaries or of exogenous hormones, and the embryos will continue to develop normally for several days. The only other records of implantation following ovariectomy are those of Buchanan et al. (1956) who reported that implantation would occur in the armadillo 1 month after ovariectomy if the latter were carried out during the 4-month period when the eggs are normally delayed in the uterus.

The most important function of the endometrium is to furnish nutrients for the products of conception, not only during the stage of implantation, but also throughout pregnancy. The preparation of the endometrium so that adequate amounts of nutritive substances as well as vitamins are made available depends upon the action of oestrogen and progesterone (Lutwak-Mann, 1959), the former steroid effecting primary and secondary endometrial growth principally by stimulating proliferation and growth of blood vessels, while the latter catalyses the actual metabolism of the nutrient materials, particularly carbohydrates, in the endometrial glands. It is desirable, therefore, in any study of ovo-implantation to be fully aware of the role of the extra-embryonic membranes and of the endometrium in providing for the direct mediation of the effects of the maternal metabolism on the growth and differentiation of the embryo. Therefore, an understanding of the physiological factors operating at the time when the embryo is engaging the uterus and when the various extra-embryonic structures come into existence becomes critical in any attempt to elucidate the factors responsible for implantation and embryo development. For a detailed and up-to-date account of the physiology of ovo-implantation, the interested reader should consult the recent review by Mayer (1960) which contains a complete list of bibliographic references.

D. Delayed implantation

The time required for implantation varies tremendously in different groups of mammals. A pre-implantation period of 5–6 days is necessary for the rat, while monkeys take 9 days and cats require 12–17 days for the same series of phenomena (Amoroso, 1952). In still others, there is normally a long period of 'delayed implantation' during which the embryos lie dormant in the uterus as unimplanted blastocysts and await the development of favourable uterine conditions for implantation. This phenomenon of 'delayed implantation' was first observed in the deer by William Harvey (1651) more than 300 years ago and has since been recorded as a normal occurrence in a wide variety of mammals including the mink, marten, badger, weasel, ermine, seal, bear, peccary and armadillo (Courrier and Baclesse, 1955; Canivenc, 1960).

From this list the condition appears to be quite widespread among members of the Mustelidae, and an interesting series of observations based on experiments on the pine marten and mink suggests that artificial illumination at the end of the hours of daylight can hasten implantation, and so shorten the total duration of pregnancy (Enders and Pearson, 1943; Pearson and Enders, 1944; Hansson, 1947; Enders, 1952, 1956; see also Eckstein et al., 1959; Canivenc, 1960; Amoroso and Marshall, 1960). There seems little reason to doubt that the light effect is through the pituitary on the corpus luteum and that the uterus requires conditioning in some special way, not yet understood, before implantation may proceed (Mayer, 1959a). If we assume this much, the question still remains as to the hormone or hormones responsible.

Hammond Jr. (1951) has shown that, in the mink at any rate, implantation is not simply a matter of the supply of progesterone. Accompanying implantation in this species, he postulates the presence of an extra-ovarian factor acting upon the uterus, and clearly enough, its production or activity seems to be regulated by light. In the opinion of Yeates (1954) the existence of some such special uterotrophic hormone is suggested by, and probably accounts for, the fact that whereas implantation is satisfactory in ewes whose sexual season has been reversed by light treatment (Yeates, 1949), it is disappointing in those in which ovulation and oestrus have been induced by gonado-trophin injection during the anoestrum (Robinson, 1951).

In rats, mice and guinea pigs (but not in rabbits), lactating mothers may become pregnant while still nursing young litters. Under these circumstances delayed implantation is a usual event and such preg-nancies are abnormally prolonged. In these animals, in contra-distinction to what happens in many other species, the blastocysts are able to await favourable uterine conditions for implantation. In mice, however, Lataste (1887, 1891) observed that gestation is not prolonged unless more than two young are suckled, whereas in rats implantation is not delayed unless the female is suckling six or more young, nor does there appear to be any definite relation between the number of young in excess of six and the total delay in implantation (Brambell, 1937).

A similar prolongation of gestation during lactation has also been described in other families of rodents and some insectivores. For example, Brambell (1935, 1937) and Brambell and Rowlands (1936) showed that delayed implantation, as a result of the female suckling her young subsequent to mating, probably occurs in the common and lesser shrew (*Sorex araneus* et *minutus*, L.), and in the bank vole (*Clethrionomys glareolus britannicus*, Miller); while a corresponding delay in implantation was found by Lataste (1887, 1891) for the gerbils, *Dipodillus simoni* Lataste and *Meriones longifrons* Lataste, and by Svihla (1932) for the deer mouse, *Peromyscus truei* and *P. maniculatus*, where a single gestation in a lactating mouse lasted 40 days instead of a mean of 26 days in non-lactating females.

That this delay in implantation in rats and mice cannot be due to the functional failure of the corpora lutea, as Weichert (1942) supposed, is suggested by several lines of reasoning and experiment. In the first place, it can be shown that such corpora lutea are still capable of inhibiting the vaginal keratinization which can be induced by oestrogens (Courrier and Baclesse, 1955) and of sensitizing the endometrium so that deciduomata result from mechanical stimulation (Krehbiel, 1941a). In the second place, the hypophysial hormone prolactin, which is essential for the initiation and maintenance of lactation, is known to prolong the secretory life of the corpus luteum in rats (Astwood and Greep, 1938, 1939; Averill et al., 1950; Ray et al., 1955). On the other hand, it is highly probable that normal implantation in the rat is dependent upon the delicately balanced activities of several hormones, chief among which are the oestrogenic hormones of the ovary and the gonadotrophic hormones of the pituitary (Courrier and Baclesse, 1955; Mayer, 1960; Meunier and Mayer, 1960). Thus, it has been shown by Krehbiel (1941a) that in nursing rats, made unilaterally pregnant by ligation of one uterine tube, deciduomata could be produced in the sterile horn at a time when unimplanted blastocysts were present in the fertile horn. Moreover, the injection of small doses of oestrogens into such animals permits the blastocysts to implant at the normal time (Krehbiel, 1941b; Weichert, 1942), suggesting that something more than progestational proliferation is required to produce the physiological conditions favourable for implantation. Canivenc and Laffargue (1956), Cochrane and Meyer (1957) and Whitten (1958) all believe that the prolongation of gestation in lactating mice is due to an inhibition of the blastocyst by progesterone not balanced by oestrogen.

The role of the local environment of the rat uterus in this arrest of development was demonstrated convincingly by Mayer and Canivenc (1951) and by Canivenc et al. (1953). They introduced progesterone locally into one uterine horn on the 3rd day of pregnancy in lactating females and obtained early implanted embryos in the injected horn and delayed implantation in the uninjected horn of the same rat. Equally striking are the observations of Mayer (1956, 1959a, b) who has shown that ovariectomy of non-lactating rats on the 4th day of pregnancy may cause delayed implantation, provided a constant and large dose of progesterone is administered after ovariectomy, but that the administration of minute doses of oestradiol together with progesterone will permit the eggs to implant and growth to proceed. Likewise, in rats suckling only two young and whose skin has been burned on the 4th day of pregnancy, administration of 5 or 10 mg progesterone at any time during the phase of arrest brings about resumption of growth and implantation (Canivenc and Mayer, 1955).

These considerations suffice to show that delayed implantation of the blastocysts in lactating rats can be prevented by oestrogens or by progesterone. Oestrogens act at small dose levels and are believed to produce their effects either by acting synergistically with endogenous progesterone or by reinforcing the activity of the corpora lutea. But although the exact manner by which oestrogen activates the corpora lutea is largely unknown, there is evidence that in the rat it may do so through its effect on the pituitary by causing the release of prolactin (see Meites and Turner, 1948a, b).

E. The role of the corpus luteum after implantation

The effect of loss of luteal tissue or loss of all ovarian tissue on the course of gestation has been studied in a number of vertebrate species (see Table IV and references in Courrier, 1945; Mayer, 1953; Amoroso, 1955a), and the importance of the corpus luteum secretion during implantation has been stressed in these and other reviews on the endocrinology of early pregnancy (Kehl, 1950; Courrier and Baclesse 1955; Mayer, 1959a, b; Eckstein et al., 1959; Amoroso, 1960a).

In all viviparous mammals the ovaries are necessary for the initiation of pregnancy, and with the possible exception of the guinea pig (Loeb and Hesselberg, 1917; Loeb, 1923a; Deanesly, 1960) and armadillo (Talmage et al., 1954; Buchanan et al., 1956; Enders and Buchanan, 1959), for the implantation of the fertilized ovum. On the other hand, although removal of the ovaries or the corpora lutea during the later stages of pregnancy does not disturb the course of gestation in some species, notably the human female, monkey, mare, guinea pig, sheep and cat, in others, including the hamster, rabbit, rat, mouse and goat, abortion or resorption invariably occurs following such operations, irrespective of the times at which they are performed (see Table IV).

In the latter group, evacuation of the uterus is not, however, always immediate. For example, in the rabbit oöphorectomy on the 16th and 21st days of pregnancy caused abortion 4 days later (McIlroy, 1912), and in the guinea pigs in which removal of the ovaries interrupted pregnancy, abortion did not take place till several days after the operation (Herrick, 1928; Nelson, 1934; Artunkal and Colonge, 1949). Similarly, Hain (1934) has demonstrated that pregnancy in the rat is not speedily terminated by removal of the ovaries on the 16th day, and that considerable foetal and placental development takes place thereafter, but for full development of the foetus, the ovaries are necessary throughout pregnancy. Of this, further evidence is afforded by the experimental findings of Zeiner (1943) that foetal survival following two-stage ovariectomy of the pregnant rat might continue for periods of up to 5 days, and that embryos are killed by pressure of the uterus following removal of the ovaries. Contrary to expectation, however, oöphorectomy at normal term (Hain, 1934) did not precipitate parturition, but appears definitely to have delayed it, so that gestation was prolonged and the act of parturition itself was protracted.

The mechanism responsible for the interruption of pregnancy after bilateral removal of the ovary on the one hand, and the maintenance of it on the other, is not surely known. However, the common inference is that since in the majority of mammals so far investigated the corpus luteum is necessary throughout gestation, those few species, such as the guinea pig, mare (cf. Table V), monkey and human female, which can dispense with it, must have some alternative source of oestrogen as well as progesterone. It is generally assumed that the extra-ovarian source is the placenta and the demonstration that the placenta contains the two hormones and that the life-span of this organ coincides with the excretion of their derivatives (Susuki, 1947; Venning, 1957) supports this.

Newton (1938), Mayer and Klein (1955) and Amoroso (1960a) list a number of authors who have isolated steroid hormones and related substances from the placenta, but whether these are secreted in the placenta or whether they represent a placental concentration of substances elaborated elsewhere and stored in the placenta, are moot points. Perfusion of the human placenta has shown that steroids

TABLE IV

Effects of ovariectomy or ablation of corpora lutea on the course of gestation in mammals

1. Animals in which implantation follows ovariectomy in the absence of exogenous steroids

Species	Authorities	Operation	Effect on gestation
Guinea pig	Loeb and Hesselberg (1917); Deanesly (1960)	Corpora lutea cauterized or ovaries removed	Ovariectomy at $3\frac{1}{2}$–5 days post coitum did not prevent implantation which normally occurs $6\frac{1}{2}$–$7\frac{1}{2}$ days p.c.
Armadillo	Buchanan *et al.* (1956)	Bilateral ovariectomy or removal of ovary containing corpus luteum	Implantation could occur 24–30 days after ovariectomy provided the latter was carried out about the middle of the 4-month period of delayed implantation. Administration of progesterone to animals from which the ovary containing the corpus luteum has been removed is compatible with maintenance of the blastocyst. When progesterone is administered to animals after bilateral ovariectomy fewer blastocysts are recovered

2. Animals in which experimental evidence indicates that pregnancy may continue following ovariectomy after a certain stage has been reached

Species	Authorities	Operation	Effect on gestation
Guinea pig	Daels (1908); Loeb (1923a); Herrick (1928); Benazzi (1933); Nelson (1934); Artunkal and Colonge (1949)	Ovariectomy	At 14–27 days p.c. terminated pregnancy and might do so up to about 40 days. After this time, occasionally, pregnancy continues normally
Cat	Gros (1936)	Ovariectomy	Up to 46 days after coitus results in abortion. At 49 days or later young are carried to term
Sheep	Casida and Warwick (1945); Dutt and Casida (1948); Neher and Zarrow (1954); Denamur and Martinet (1955); Foote et al. (1957)	Ovariectomy	Abortion or resorption follows removal before 55th day of pregnancy; thereafter the chances that pregnancy will go to term appear to increase the later the operation is performed. Daily treatment with 1 mg progesterone plus 0·25 µg oestrone (ratio 4000 : 1) will cause embryos to implant and maintain pregnancy
Horse	Hart and Cole (1934); (See also Table V)	Ovariectomy	The ovaries may be removed between 170 and 270 days after breeding without interruption of the pregnancy (term 350 days). After the operation oestrogen excretion falls, but soon rises again to normal level and is maintained within the normal range for the remainder of pregnancy
Monkey	Hartman (1941); Hartman and Corner (1947)	Ovariectomy	May be performed as early as 25th day of pregnancy (term 165 days) without causing abortion. The bright red colour of the sexual skin is maintained throughout gestation and lactation, thus giving further proof that oestrogens are secreted by extragonadal sources or accessory ovarian tissue (cf. Hartman and Corner, 1947)
Women	Blair-Bell (1920); Ask-Upmark (1926); Asdell (1928); Venning (1957)	Ovariectomy	Period of gestation averages 267 days and ovaries have been removed as early as the 40th day without terminating pregnancy

3. Animals in which experimental evidence indicates that pregnancy cannot be maintained in the absence of the ovaries

Species	Authorities	Operation	Effects on pregnancy
Opossum	Hartman (1925b)	Ovariectomy	Death of embryos at all times
Spermophile	Drips (1919); Johnson and Challans (1932)	Ovariectomy	Terminated at all times but could be maintained with corpus luteum extracts
Hamster	Klein (1938a); Orsini and Meyer (1959)	Ovariectomy	Early (2–3 days p.c.) prevents implantation; late (11–13 days) results in abortion. Eggs made to implant with progesterone alone, 4 mg daily
Mouse	Harris (1927); Parkes (1928); Robson (1936)	Ovariectomy or one ovary sterilized with X-rays, fertile ovary removed	At any time during pregnancy causes abortion or resorption of the embryos. Daily injections of 1–1·5 mg progesterone required to repair the effects of oöphorectomy
Rabbit	Fraenkel and Cohn (1901); Fraenkel(1903, 1910); McIlroy (1912); Hammond (1925); Corner (1928); Pincus and Werthessen (1938); Courrier and Kehl (1938); Allen and Heckel (1939)	Ovariectomy or ablation of corpora lutea	Terminated at all times. In ovariectomized does complete maintenance of pregnancy is possible with a dosage of 1 mg/day progesterone during first 10–12 days and 2–4 mg/day thereafter
Armadillo	Hamlett (1935)	Ovariectomy	After implantation always followed by abortion or resorption of embryos
Goat	Drummond-Robinson and Asdell (1926); Meites et al. (1951)	Ovariectomy or dissection of corpora lutea	At any time during pregnancy causes abortion or resorption of embryos. With all corpora lutea removed 15–25 mg of progesterone daily are required to maintain pregnancy
Sow	du Mesnil du Buisson and Dauzier (1957); Day et al. (1959); Spies et al. (1960)	Ovariectomy	As early as 4 days p.c. or as late as 89–106 days, resulted in abortion within 3 days; effects not due to trauma. Treatment with 1·2 mg progesterone plus 0·3 μg oestrone caused embryos to implant but many embryos failed to survive

4. Animals in which the evidence is inconclusive

Species	Authorities	Operation	Effects on pregnancy
Rat	Johnson and Challans (1930); Hain (1934); Selye et al. (1935a); Haterius (1936); McKeown and Zuckerman (1938); Kirsch (1938); Haterius and Kempner (1939); Zeiner (1943); Frazer and Alexander (1954)	Ovariectomy or cauterization of corpora lutea	Most reports state that early removal leads to abortion. After 16th day, pregnancy is not speedily terminated, especially if ovaries are removed in two stages. Pregnancy maintained in absence of ovaries, provided all foetuses but one are removed and all placentae are allowed to remain. Pregnancy will continue in ovariectomized-hypophysectomized rats given 1 μg oestrone plus 2 mg progesterone
Dog	Marshall and Jolly (1905)	Ovariectomy	At 3, 10, 14, 21 and 28 days caused abortion in all cases. No animals ovariectomized after the 1st month. (Full term: 63 days)
Cow	Raeside and Turner (1950); McDonald et al. (1952, 1953); Venable and McDonald (1958)	Ovariectomy or squeezing out corpora lutea	Squeezing out corpora lutea in 10 cows between days 92 and 236 caused prompt abortion, but pregnancy was maintained in 3 cows that were 207, 224 and 230 days pregnant at the time of the operation. Pregnancy was also maintained in cows with corpora removed on day 60 but receiving daily intramuscular injections of 100 mg crystalline progesterone. In such animals discontinuance of treatment on day 162 did not produce abortion, suggesting that endogenous progesterone may be produced elsewhere than in the ovaries (cf. Balfour et al., 1957)

related to progesterone are synthesized there, although neither oestrogen nor progesterone has thus far been identified (Hagopian et al., 1956; see, however, Romanoff, 1959).

But even in those mammalian species in which ovariectomy normally terminates pregnancy, the reduction of the foetuses to a minimum, leaving the supernumerary placentae in situ (rat: Haterius, 1936), or the retention of one or more placentae, the foetuses having been removed (mouse: Newton, 1935; Newton and Lits, 1938; rats: Klein,

1935, 1938b; Kirsch, 1938; hamster: Klein, 1938a), will still result in delivery of the retained foetuses or placentae at term. Likewise, Klein (1933) showed that after removal of the foetuses on the 15th day of pregnancy from the rabbit, the endometrium and myometrium were still typical of pregnancy on the 20th day, provided the placentae were left *in situ*. All of these effects are compatible with secretion of progesterone by the placenta, and the only alternative source which has been suggested is the adrenal (Balfour *et al.*, 1957).

Selye *et al.* (1935a) and Courrier and Gros (1936) believe, on the basis of the endometrial picture after oöphorectomy, that the placenta of the rat and cat, respectively, secretes progesterone, but insufficient to make the uterus accommodate itself to the growing foetuses. They present good evidence that the cause of foetal death is lack of resilience of the uterus and this has been stressed by Haterius (1936), Kirsch (1938) and by Haterius and Kempner (1939). Similarly, Courrier (1941b, 1945) has demonstrated that the ovaries of the rabbit are necessary to maintain the life of the foetus and placenta *in utero*, but are not necessary for the extra-uterine growth of the foetuses, an effect which he believes is compatible with the placental production of progesterone.

In summary, although the evidence from all these lines of investigation falls short of actual proof, taken together it indicates strongly that the corpus luteum is essential for the maintenance of pregnancy so long as the foetus-placenta ratio is not adequate to provide for the maintenance of pregnancy through the agency of the placenta alone. In some species this situation is attained in the natural course of gestation since the corpus luteum is not essential after a fixed period in the first part of pregnancy. In other species, this optimal ratio is not attained in the normal course of pregnancy, so making it necessary for the corpora lutea to remain functional throughout most of gestation.

V. The role of the corpus luteum in the growth of the mammary gland

A. The influence of ovarian hormones on mammary growth

The participation of the corpus luteum in mammary growth had long been suspected. Observations recorded by many workers for various species indicate that in all mammals definite changes occur in the mammary gland with the development of corpora lutea. During pregnancy the corpora lutea of all mammals reach the height of their activity and it has been uniformly observed that the mammary glands show progressive duct and lobule development. Bouin and Ancel

(1909c) and Ancel and Bouin (1911) were the first, however, to demonstrate that the corpora lutea were responsible for mammary development in the rabbit during pregnancy and pseudopregnancy. They showed that removal of the corpora lutea by excision or cauterization prevented mammary development and these observations have been confirmed many times since by various workers.

Although it is generally accepted that the ovarian hormones are primarily responsible for the growth of the mammary glands, there is still some doubt as to the exact roles played by the oestrogenic and luteal hormones. A great deal of this uncertainty is due to definite differences in the reaction of the mammary glands in different species to these hormones. Nevertheless, it has been possible to correlate the changes in the mammary glands with the various types of oestrous cycles, and to show that certain changes in the glands depend upon the factors active in the different phases of the reproductive life of the animal.

It is now fairly generally recognized that the duct system present at birth will grow without hormonal stimulus at the same rate as the rest of the body (isometric growth), whereas at about the time of puberty it becomes significantly faster (allometric growth). It is also well recognized that ovarian hormones are responsible for the growth of the mammary gland at the onset of puberty, but the nature of the mechanism involved and the reason why allometric growth begins just when it does are not known with certainty (see, however, Folley, 1956).

While the pioneer work of Turner (1939) and his co-workers led to the belief that oestrogens are mainly responsible for duct growth and that oestrogen and progesterone together are necessary for normal lobule-alveolar development, later work has demonstrated that in some species (goat, cow, sheep, though not the bitch) considerable, but usually abnormal, growth can be produced with oestrogen alone (Folley, 1950, 1952, 1956; Cowie, 1957; Benson et al., 1959; Meites, 1959; Linzell, 1959). Mixner and Turner (1943) and Cowie et al. (1952) reported that, in the goat, oestrogen alone caused the development of udders often characterized by abnormally large, and even cystic alveoli, whereas combinations of oestrogen and progesterone produced growth more clearly comparable to that seen in normal udders during gestation (Sykes and Wrenn, 1951; Benson et al., 1955).

Although the guinea pig was earlier regarded to be one of those relatively few species whose mammary glands respond to oestrogen with complete growth of both the lobule-alveolar and duct components (Turner, 1939; Folley and Malpress, 1948), Benson et al. (1957) have amassed evidence indicating that progesterone acts synergistically with oestrogen in this animal. Benson et al. (1957), utilizing both objective and subjective methods of assessment, reported that over a wide range of oestrogen dosage greater mammary development was elicited in the spayed guinea pig by oestrone plus progesterone than by oestrone alone. Maximal lobule-alveolar development was observed with a daily dose of 10–50 μg oestrone plus 1000 μg progesterone. These investigators also noted that complete mammary development does not occur with oestrogen alone, as previously reported (Turner and Gomez, 1934; Nelson, 1937), although considerable growth of lobules with normal structure was obtained (Folley, 1952; Cowie, 1957). They conclude that the absolute doses of the two hormones supplied are more important than their ratios. The oestrogen : progesterone ratio had no significance *per se*, since administration of the same ratios, but different doses, of oestrogen and progesterone resulted in differences in mammary responses which varied both quantitatively and qualitatively.

In the rabbit, rat and goat optimal ratios of oestrogen: progesterone are believed to be of the order of 1: 10 – 1: 40, 1: 90 – 1: 150 and 1: 140, respectively (Benson *et al.*, 1957). The requirements for optimal udder growth in cattle has not been adequately determined, though a rough computation for the cow gives a value of 1: 50 – 1: 90 (Catchpole, 1959).

Small doses of progesterone injected simultaneously with oestrogens have been shown by Mixner and Turner (1940) and by Lyons and McGinty (1941) to produce optimal lobule-alveolar growth of the mammary gland in the mouse and rabbit, respectively. In the rat, on the other hand, relatively large doses of progesterone are required to elicit a comparable reaction (Curtis, 1949), though combinations of oestradiol and progesterone which do not produce lobulation of the mammary parenchyma of the ovariectomized rat will do so when ovarian extracts containing relaxin are added to the treatment (Hamolsky and Sparrow, 1945; T. C. Smith, 1954). In this respect, however, the mammary glands of mature rats are less responsive to the action of relaxin than those of immature rats (T. C. Smith, 1954).

Relaxin* also has been shown to influence mammary growth in other species of laboratory animals. Thus, Trentin (1951) has reported that relaxin may increase slightly the percentage of mice showing lobule-alveolar responses to simultaneously administered oestrogen and progesterone. Similarly, Garrett and Talmage (1952) have shown that it potentiates the action of oestrogen on the alveolar system of the guinea pig, but there is insufficient evidence at present to indicate that it may also affect duct growth (see, however, Steinetz *et al.*, 1959).

* The role of relaxin in relation to pubic relaxation is discussed below (see section VII).

B. Pseudopregnancy and mammary growth

Sterile copulation in many animals is followed by a prolonged luteal phase during which the mammary glands show the same type of proliferation as in the first half of pregnancy. In the rabbit (Ancel and Bouin, 1911; Hammond and Marshall, 1914), rat (Long and Evans, 1922) and cat (Gros, 1935, 1936; Foster and Hisaw, 1935; Dawson and Kosters, 1944), this period of pseudopregnancy has a duration which is roughly equivalent to one-half the length of pregnancy, and verd extensive growth of the mammary alveolar system has been observey during this period. In the ferret (Hammond and Marshall, 1930), pseudopregnancy is equivalent to pregnancy in duration and the mammary changes run parallel courses in both conditions. However, as ovulation normally occurs only after coitus in the rabbit (Heape, 1905; Hammond and Marshall, 1914), in the ferret (Hammond and Marshall, 1930) and in the cat (Greulich, 1934; Gros, 1935, 1936; Amoroso, 1952), there is no luteal phase of the cycle in the absence of copulation.

In the bitch and the two marsupials, the Australian native cat (*Dasyurus viverrinus*) and the American opossum (*Didelphys virginiana*), on the other hand, ovulation is spontaneous and in the absence of conception the corpus luteum, unlike that of most forms, is maintained for a period of time equivalent to that of pregnancy. It has been shown by Marshall and Halnan (1917), Evans and Cole (1931) and Turner and Gomez (1934) for the bitch, by O'Donoghue (1911) for the native cat, and by Hartman (1925b) for the opossum, that during the prolonged metoestrum the mammary glands proliferate in a fashion that is entirely equivalent to the development during pregnancy. Indeed, in the case of the bitch, at least, lactation to a degree which allows for the suckling of a litter may occur at the close of pseudopregnancy.

C. Ovarian hormones and mammary growth during pregnancy

Despite the recent evidence of Ray *et al.* (1955) and of Benson *et al.* (1959), indicating a complex of endocrine substances in the glandular control of mammary growth, it remains a basic postulate that growth results from hormonal stimuli set in train by one or both of the ovarian hormones. Numerous experiments on several species of animals show, however, that the presence of the ovary is not essential for full differentiation of the mammary gland. In pregnant rats (Selye *et al.*, 1935a) and mice (Newton and Lits, 1938) from which the foetuses had been removed and in which the placentae were retained, *in spite of oöphorectomy*, the mammary glands developed normally and, in the mice, were indistinguishable on the 18th day from those of normal pregnancy at the same time; in the rats the glands remained in a well developed but non-secretory condition. In the horse there is no corpus luteum during the latter part of pregnancy. Extirpation of the ovaries from a series of mares between 167 and 280 days did not affect the normal course of pregnancy (Table V); parturition occurred at about 350 days, as usual, oestrus failed to reappear post partum, thus confirming the completeness of ovariectomy, mammary development was complete and the mares suckled the foals until weaning.

Selye *et al.* (1935a), on the basis of the histological appearances of the mammary gland and the uterus of the oöphorectomized rat with retained placentae, postulate secretion of progestins by the placenta. It is clear, however, from what has been stated previously, that this development could not have been due solely to progesterone secreted by the placentae, unless only a very small quantity is required to stimulate mammary growth. It would be natural to suppose that the pituitary played some part in the process, but as shown below, full mammary development can be obtained during pregnancy after hypophysectomy. It is clear, therefore, that in circumstances in which the pregnant state is normally terminated through lack of progesterone (and possibly of oestrogen) the presence of living placental tissue is sufficient to determine mammary growth (Newton, 1949; Mayer and Canivenc, 1950b).

Because of the pre-eminent role of the anterior pituitary in the successful control of luteal function, experiments in which hypophysectomy is performed during pregnancy might be expected to yield information concerning the influence of the corpus luteum on mammary development. This situation is, however, complicated by the fact, previously alluded to, that the state of pregnancy is very largely controlled by factors in which the placenta holds a key position. These functions of the placenta entail the responsibility not only of regulating the activities of the reproductive organs through the influence of gonadotrophic and gonadal secretions, but also of maintaining structures not directly concerned with the initiation, maintenance and termination of pregnancy. Accordingly, it may be presumed that species in which pregnancy is not interrupted by hypophysectomy would yield information concerning the trophic effect of the placenta upon the progress of mammary growth during normal pregnancy.

The effect of removal of the pituitary upon the development of the mammary growth during pregnancy has been described for several species; by Allan and Wiles (1932) and McPhail (1935b) for the cat; by Selye *et al.* (1933a), Pencharz and Long (1933), Reece *et al.* (1936), Leonard (1945) and Ray *et al.* (1955) for the rat; by Pencharz and Lyons (1934) and Nelson (1935) for the guinea pig; by Selye *et al.*

TABLE V

Effects of ovariectomy on mares

No. of animals	Date of service	Date of laparotomy	Days pregnant at operation	Ovaries	General results				Remarks
					Abortion (days after operation)	Date of foaling	Days after operation	Duration of pregnancy (days)	
2	8.v.56	8.ii.57	276	Removed		22.iv.57 (Filly)	73	349	Mammary development complete and lactation continued for more than 1 year; oestrus failed to appear post partum
3	27.vii.56	1.xi.56	96	Removed	2	—	—	—	Oestrus failed to appear post partum
4	19.vi.56	16.x.56	119	Removed	3	—	—	—	
5	8.v.56	9.ii.57	277	Exposed, not removed	1	—	—	—	
6	15.vi.56	26.x.56	133	Removed	11	—	—	—	
7	30.v.56	15.xi.56	169	Exposed, not removed		19.v.57 (Colt)	185	354	Mammary development complete and lactation continued for more than 1 year; oestrus did not reappear
8	29.v.56	12.xi.56	167	Removed		11.v.57 (Colt)	180	347	
10	29.vi.59	9.ii.60	228	Removed		14.vi.60 (Colt)	126	354	Mammary development complete; dams still suckling foals after 6 months; oestrus failed to reappear
11	15.v.59	1.ii.60	262	Removed		2.v.60 (Filly)	92	348	

(1933b), Newton and Beck (1939), Newton and Richardson (1940) and Gardner and Allen (1942) for the mouse; and by Agate (1952) for the rhesus monkey. The collective research of these investigators leads to the general conclusion that hypophysectomy during pregnancy results in involution of the mammary gland only when the placenta is removed at the same time. However, lack of the anterior pituitary promptly makes itself felt after parturition, when lactation fails to occur, or at the most makes a transient appearance (see Allan and Wiles, 1932; McPhail, 1935b; Nelson, 1936; Newton and Richardson, 1940; Agate, 1952). It is thus clear that the placenta, in rats and mice at least, plays a special part in mammary development which is largely independent of both ovaries and pituitary.

The question as to why lactation is not normally initiated during pregnancy still remains unanswered. The concept which has probably gained widest acceptance is that the ovarian hormones, particularly oestrogens, inhibit the secretion of prolactin by the pituitary (Nelson, 1936). This view is held despite the fact that no direct evidence has yet demonstrated that the ovarian hormones can reduce prolactin either in the pituitary or circulation. On the contrary, such studies have consistently shown that ovarian hormones, particularly oestrogens, increase the prolactin content of the pituitary (Meites and Turner, 1948a, b). But notwithstanding these considerations Meites and Sgouris (1953) conclude that oestrone and progesterone together can effectively inhibit the milk-secreting action of prolactin on the mammary gland of the rabbit, whereas progesterone alone is ineffective and oestrone alone is only slightly effective in this respect (see, however, Ray et al., 1955).

VI. Ovarian activity in adrenalectomized pregnant animals

Numerous observations by many workers have demonstrated that during late pregnancy in the rat (Andersen and Sperry, 1937) and in the human female (Venning, 1946; Tobian, 1949; Jailer and Knowlton, 1950; Jones et al., 1953; Davis and Plotz, 1956; Plotz and Davis, 1956) secretory activity of the adrenal cortex of the mother appears to be high. Pregnancy is also known to prolong the survival time of adrenalectomized animals* and to relieve temporarily the symptoms of Addison's disease in the human female (Thorn, 1951; Davis and Plotz, 1956). Davis and Plotz (1954) and Jost et al. (1955) have shown

* For example, mice: Pfeiffer and Hooker (1940); rats: Firor and Grollman (1933), Ingle and Fisher (1938), Davis and Plotz (1954), Jost et al. (1955); dogs: Rogoff and Stewart (1927), Billmann and Engel (1939); cats: Corey (1928), Rogoff and Stewart (1929), Collings (1941); ferrets: Gaunt and Hays (1938). (See, however, Gradinesco et al., 1935.)

moreover, that the weight of the foetal adrenals is increased by adrenalectomy of the mother, thus confirming the previous observations of Firor and Grollman (1933), Ingle and Fisher (1938), Walaas and Walaas (1944) and those of Houssay (1945).

It has been suggested by Firor and Grollman (1933), by Billmann and Engel (1939) and by Jost et al. (1955) that the enlarged adrenals of the foetus can secrete sufficient amounts of cortical hormones to maintain the life of the adrenalectomized female during pregnancy. However, while this suggestion may not be completely disregarded, the alternative hypothesis, that the beneficial effect on the symptoms of adrenal cortical insufficiency imposed on the mother by bilateral adrenalectomy is due to the secretions of the corpus luteum and interstitial cells of the ovary, must certainly be given serious consideration.

Thus, pseudopregnancy (Collings, 1941; Gaunt and Hays, 1938) as well as administration of progesterone (Emery and Schwabe, 1936; Schwabe and Emery, 1939; Bourne, 1939; Emery and Greco, 1940) have been shown to maintain adrenalectomized animals in good health, while intensive stimulation and luteinization of the ovaries by different gonadotrophins increased the survival period in some species (Emery and Schwabe, 1936; D'Amour and D'Amour, 1939). Moreover, since it is known from the earlier work of Astwood and Greep (1938, 1939), and more recently confirmed by Averill et al. (1950) and Ray et al. (1955), that the rat placenta at an early stage of development contains a substance which stimulates the corpus luteum to secrete progesterone, it may be presumed that the sustaining effect of pregnancy in adrenalectomized rats is accomplished chiefly through the luteotrophic action of the placenta on the corpus luteum (Emery and Schwabe, 1936).

VII. Pelvic adaptations and pubic separation in mammals

Various writers and especially Hisaw and Zarrow (1950), in emphasizing the striking differences in pelvic architecture that exist among mammals, have pointed to their correlation with conditions of habitat in which the various species live. Hisaw and Zarrow further indicated that in many instances the pelvic outlet might be so narrow that delivery would be impossible were it not for special adaptations to meet the situation.

The most extreme reduction of the pelvic girdle among mammals is found in the Cetacea and Sirenia, both of which are pelagic. In these orders the pelvis is extremely rudimentary, being composed of a pair of elongated, slender bones placed on either side of, and rather below, the vertebral column. Similarly, in some fossorial Insectivora where

the pelvis is greatly reduced in adults (Wood, 1859) marked differences
in pelvic structure have also been demonstrated at different developmental ages; in the adult the pelvic cavity and outlets are so
straight that the pelvic viscera pass below and external to the cavity
instead of through it, making it unnecessary for parturition to take
place through a constricted birth canal (Hisaw and Zilley, 1927;
Amoroso, 1955a).

These arrangements are clearly adaptive and involve no apparent
endocrine mechanisms. However, skeletal adjustments, involving both
the symphysis pubis and the sacro-iliac union, which are definitely
conditioned by hormones, have been described in the pocket gopher
(Hisaw, 1925), guinea pig (Hisaw, 1926, 1929; Ruth, 1937; Talmage,
1947) and mouse (Gardner, 1936; Hall and Newton, 1946a, b; Hall,
1947, 1948, 1956).

In the pocket gopher, the pubic symphysis becomes heavily ossified
in prepubertal animals of both sexes, and in the female is much too
small for the birth of young. As the females become sexually mature,
and therefore before corpora lutea are present in the ovaries, the
symphysis is gradually absorbed leaving the pelvis open ventrally and
thus facilitating the birth of the young (Hisaw, 1925; Hisaw and
Zarrow, 1950).

Pelvic relaxation similar to that in the pregnant gopher has been
described in the guinea pig (Ruth, 1937; Talmage, 1947) and in the
mouse, but in addition, birth is further facilitated by an appreciable
relaxation of the pelvic ligaments. Indeed, in the parturient guinea
pig this relaxation may be so complete that the two halves of the
pelvis can be moved independently of one another.

Guinea pigs are large and considerably advanced in development at
birth and consequently extensive enlargement of the birth canal is
necessary in order to permit parturition. On the other hand, such
reasoning may lead to erroneous conclusions when applied to other
species, since mice, which normally form a long interpubic ligament
during the later stages of pregnancy and in which the pubic bones have
been sutured to prevent any separation, have been observed to give
birth to viable young without any apparent difficulty (Crelin, 1954).
It must, of course, be pointed out that while this experiment on mice
shows that mechanical prevention of symphysial separation did not
preclude uneventful parturition, it does not rule out a definite role of
relaxin in the delivery mechanism in this species (see below).

During pregnancy in the mouse, the pubic bones become resorbed
at their anterior end, and the gap is bridged by a ligament which at
parturition may be 5 or 6 mm long (Gardner, 1936). The separation
becomes apparent on the 13th day of the first pregnancy, and the gap

widens an average of 1 mm per day until parturition. After this the symphysis closes rapidly but never completely and with each succeeding pregnancy is increased slightly (Hall and Newton, 1946a, b). As with the guinea pig, spaying of the prepubertal female mouse results in the retention of the male type of symphysial cartilage (Gardner, 1936).

A. Hormonal factors in the relaxation of the symphysis pubis

1. *General considerations*

It is now more or less taken for granted that, in addition to the gonadal hormones, there is present in the ovaries (especially the corpora lutea) and the placenta of many mammals a relatively large amount of the polypeptide hormone relaxin, but its functions, especially during early gestation, remain uncertain. Until recently relaxin was considered to be concerned primarily with relaxation of the pelvic ligaments during late pregnancy. However, several recent studies in the literature suggest that it may have additional roles during pregnancy and at parturition. Thus it has been established that the hormone is capable of inhibiting spontaneous uterine motility *in vivo* and *in vitro* (Felton *et al.*, 1953; Miller *et al.*, 1957; Bloom *et al.*, 1958; Kroc *et al.*, 1958), and of inducing spontaneous delivery of living young in prepubertal and adult pregnant mice spayed and maintained on progesterone (Smithberg and Runner, 1956; Hall, 1956, 1957). In addition, Hall (1957) has reported that relaxin treatment reduced the daily progesterone requirement for the maintenance of pregnancy in the spayed mouse. But in view of a similar reduction in the progesterone-maintenance dose afforded by small concomitant doses of oestrogen in spayed rats (Kroc *et al.*, 1958) and the further fact that in Hall's experiments a constant dose of oestrogen was also administered, this activity of relaxin must remain equivocal.

2. *Source of relaxin*

The ovary, uterus and placenta have all been suggested as possible sites for the formation of relaxin. In the sow (Hisaw and Zarrow, 1948), the mouse (Newton and Beck, 1939; Hall and Newton, 1947) and the blue whale (Steinetz *et al.*, 1959) the ovaries would appear to be the principal source, whereas the placenta may play a more significant role in the guinea pig (Herrick, 1928; Zarrow, 1948). In the rabbit, under suitable conditions, the ovaries, uterus, placenta and vagina may all secrete relaxin (Zarrow and Rosenberg, 1953). It is also worth remarking that relaxin activity was found in the testes of birds and in homogenates of ovaries of the pregnant shark, but none was found in assays of 'ripe' ovaries of a bony fish, *Mugil cephalus* (Steinetz *et al.*, 1959).

3. *Pubic separation in the guinea pig*

It has been agreed by most investigators that relaxation of the symphysis of the guinea pig and mouse during pregnancy is under hormonal control. There are, however, certain important differences between the guinea pig and the mouse. In the guinea pig, the natural pubic gap of pregnancy appears even though the ovaries have been removed (Herrick, 1928; Courrier and Kehl, 1938), and hypophysectomy on the 40th day of pregnancy (Pencharz and Lyons, 1934) did not interfere with normal pubic relaxation. In guinea pigs neither of these operations interrupts pregnancy. It is evident, therefore, that in the absence of both the ovary and pituitary, the presence of normal placentae can ensure a sufficiency of relaxative hormones for the natural separation of the pubic bones in pregnancy in this species. That the placenta is not the only source in the guinea pig is suggested by the fact that pubic separation occurs when the animal is non-pregnant, i.e. at oestrus.

Another feature of the guinea pig is that progesterone itself will produce a relaxation of the symphysis pubis (presumably by causing the liberation of relaxin) in the presence of the uterus, but not otherwise (Courrier, 1941a, b). The reason for suspecting that the uterus is involved in relaxin production stems from the observations of Hisaw *et al.* (1944). These investigators showed that the relaxation produced by progesterone was delayed 3–4 days, as compared with that produced by relaxin, and that it did not occur in hysterectomized guinea pigs, whereas hysterectomy made no difference to the response to relaxin which ordinarily occurred within 6 hours following the injection of relaxin.

4. *Pubic separation in the mouse*

Newton and his collaborators were chiefly responsible for the view that the production of relaxin in the mouse is apparently different from that observed in guinea pigs and rabbits. It will be recalled that the mouse is one of those species in which oöphorectomy normally terminates pregnancy, but retained placentae (the foetuses having been removed) may occasionally survive to full term and can be encouraged to do so by incising the uterine wall to relieve the tension. When the ovaries are present, pubic separation is normal, but in their absence it does not occur (Newton and Lits, 1938). Pregnancy may also be maintained in spayed mice and again no pubic separation occurs (Hall and Newton, 1946b). Relaxin, as judged by the state of the symphysis pubis, is absent under these conditions (Newton and Lits, 1938), and it may be assumed that absence of the ovaries is the cause of the non-occurrence of the gap. Hall (1949) suggested that the inhibitory effect of progesterone in mice is caused by an antagonism between progesterone and oestrogen, but it does not seem to operate during normal pregnancy. Such antagonisms are discussed in detail by Courrier (1950).

From what is known of the hypophysial control of gonadotrophic activity, it would be natural to suppose that the pituitary gland played some part in pubic relaxation in the mouse. It has been shown, however, that hypophysectomy during pregnancy does not influence pubic separation provided the placentae are not lost; hence a placental-ovarian relationship may be assumed (Newton and Beck, 1939). Hall and Newton (1947) suggest that in the mouse the placenta acts by stimulating the production of relaxin in the ovary, probably by means of the luteotrophic hormone (Astwood and Greep, 1938, 1939; Deanesly and Newton, 1940). Smithberg and Runner (1956, 1957), on the other hand, though they have confirmed the findings of Newton and Beck (1939) that a trophic effect from the placenta influences the interpubic ligament, assert that oestrogen, produced by the mouse placenta, can account for the 'trophic influence'.

Gardner, long ago (1936), observed that oestrogen alone would, in time, cause separation of the symphysis pubis and formation of the interpubic ligament in spayed female mice. The separation is, however, too rapid and extensive during pregnancy to be explained by the effects of oestrogen alone. On the other hand, optimal effects of relaxin on the symphysis of the mouse are elicited after priming with oestrogen and the rate of separation more nearly approximates that seen in pregnancy (Hall and Newton, 1946a, 1947). Finally, in the guinea pig and rabbit, but not in the mouse, pre-treatment with oestrogen and progesterone have been reported to induce the endogenous formation of relaxin in the uterus, emphasizing once again the dependence of this hormone on the ovarian steroids for its formation and action (Marois, 1948, 1949; Hisaw and Zarrow, 1950).

B. Gonadal hormones and relaxin in the induction of parturition

The extent to which gonadal hormones participate in the mechanism of labour is far from settled, and this despite the sustained and exact investigations of Csapo and his associates on the contractile mechanics and physiological chemistry of the uterus of the pregnant and non-pregnant rabbit. Detailed studies of the isometric tension developed by uterine muscle dominated by oestrogen and by progesterone in uterine strips or in intact animals have been reported by Corner and

Csapo (1953), Csapo (1956), and Schofield (1954, 1957). The pattern of contractility was found to vary according to whether the dominating hormone was oestrogen or progesterone; the progesterone-dominated myometrium develops less tension when stimulated (negative staircase effect) than the oestrogen-dominated myometrium (positive staircase).

Using this test on pregnant rabbits, it was found that at the time of mating oestrogen fully dominated the uterus, but within 20 hours post coitum progesterone becomes the dominant hormone, as indicated by a negative staircase effect, and remains so until about 24 hours before parturition. Thereafter, the uterus becomes progressively more dominated by oestrogen (positive staircase) until maximal contractile power is developed at labour (Csapo, 1956; Schofield, 1957). There are also indications that the post-parturient uterus displays spontaneous rhythmic contractions (Ferguson, 1941) essentially similar to those of oestrous or oestrogenized animals (Harris, 1947; Cross, 1959).

The occurrence of this myometrial activity in the rabbit corresponds in time with the removal of the 'progesterone block' which occurs about 24–48 hours before the onset of parturition and which Csapo (1956) and Schofield (1957) believe may be associated with terminal secretory failure of locally acting placental progesterone. Furthermore, with the withdrawal of progesterone restraint, the myometrium, which for most of pregnancy is unresponsive to intravenously injected oxytocin, now reacts to the posterior lobe hormone and myometrial sensitivity increases from then on to parturition, that is to say, the threshold dose of oxytocin for activation of the myometrium progressively falls (Schofield, 1957).

It thus appears that there are good grounds for the belief that in the rabbit, at least, the dominating influence of progesterone throughout most of pregnancy renders the myometrium quiescent and irresponsive to such stimuli as oxytocin, thus shielding the developing foetus. On the other hand, when, with the onset of terminal degenerative changes, placental production of progesterone fails, the block to myometrial contractility is removed and co-ordinated rhythmic contractions of the whole uterus become possible. In view, however, of the favourable effect of relaxin on parturition (to be discussed below) and because the rabbit is a species in which the relaxin content of the blood is especially high in late pregnancy (Marder and Money, 1944; Hisaw and Zarrow, 1950), any interpretation of the mechanism of parturition which fails to consider relaxin as a complicating factor must be accepted with considerable reservation.

Turning to the state of affairs at the end of pregnancy in the mouse, it seems likely that yet another factor may be involved in parturition.

In this animal the occurrence of parturition at *the normal time* has been reported to depend upon the simultaneous presence of the ovaries and placentae (Newton, 1935; Newton and Lits, 1938), and the same appears to be true of the rat (Haterius, 1936; Kirsch, 1938). Similarly, from what we have learnt previously, it is clear that retained placentae determine the normal reabsorption of the symphysis pubis in mice, if the ovaries are present, but not if they are removed, suggesting that relaxin might play a role in delivery.

Other suggestive, though not conclusive, evidence that relaxin may participate in the mechanism of labour is its favourable effect in inducing spontaneous delivery in pre-pubertal and adult spayed, as well as genetically sterile-obese mice, maintained on oestrogen and progesterone (Hall, 1956, 1957; Smithberg and Runner, 1956, 1957). On the other hand, when progesterone and oestrogen were the only treatments, parturition generally failed even after progesterone was discontinued.

VIII. The corpus luteum in lower vertebrates and its role in the maintenance of gestation

Although the corpus luteum has generally been regarded as a mammalian organ, structures of similar origin and appearance have been found in representatives of other vertebrate classes and certain protochordates. It is, nevertheless, a matter of opinion whether the term *corpus luteum* can be applied properly to the discharged follicles in all these forms on grounds of analogy with those of mammals, the endocrine functions of which alone are beyond dispute.

Among lower vertebrates, 'post-ovulation' corpora lutea (Bretschneider and de Wit, 1947), formed by proliferation of cells of the emptied follicle, are not restricted to vivipara, but are present also in ovipara and ovovivipara. Their functional significance is, however, not clear, though by some (Bretschneider and de Wit, 1947; Hoar, 1955) they are regarded as being less significant as endocrine organs than the 'pre-ovulation' corporal utea or corpora atretica produced by glandular transformation of immature follicles.

In ascidians the corpus luteum is of the pre-ovulatory type, and Carlisle (1955) provides evidence that in *Ciona* it has a secretory function. In ovoviviparous ascidians the corpora lutea persist throughout retention of embryos in the brood pouch (Amoroso, 1955b).

1. *Elasmobranchs*

Oviparity, ovoviviparity and viviparity are all encountered in elasmobranchs and corpora lutea and corpora atretica have been described in all species examined (Giacomini, 1896; Wallace, 1903; Champy and Gley, 1923; ten Cate Hoedemaker, 1933; Samuel, 1943; Hisaw and Albert, 1947; Matthews, 1955; Hisaw and Hisaw, 1959; Amoroso, 1960b; Dodd *et al.*, 1960). Opinion is, however, divided as to the part these corpora lutea may play as glands of internal secretion.

Te Winkel (1950), on the basis of his own and other morphological studies, concluded that ovarian hormones present at the time of ovulation, or slightly preceding it, in Selachii may stimulate the secretion of the egg case by the oviducal glands. Similarly, Matthews (1955), on indirect evidence and by analogy with mammals, has suggested that luteal hormones may stimulate the hypertrophy of the uterine mucosa so that the folds wrapping the eggs in separate compartments are formed in *Mustelus* and others, as well as the more elaborate uterine changes seen in such forms as *Scoliodon* (Amoroso, 1952).

At the present time, there is no evidence that the corpora lutea secrete progesterone, or that they help to maintain pregnancy in viviparous species. The most significant experiments are those of Hisaw and his collaborators (Hisaw and Abramowitz, 1938, 1939; Hisaw, 1959). They found that hypophysectomy of the viviparous dogfish, *Mustelus canis*, soon after the eggs had entered the uterus, neither prevented the development of the young for at least the first few months of gestation, nor the development of corpora atretica from regressing follicles. This is clear evidence that the corpora lutea do not function as endocrine glands of gestation, nor are they, as suggested by Bretschneider and de Wit (1947), a result of pituitary luteinizing action.

2. *Teleosts*

In teleosts the situation is again that corpora lutea are formed as the result of two different processes, ovulation and follicular atresia, and their presence in both oviparous and viviparous species (e.g. *Sebastes*: Williamson, 1910; *Anableps*: Turner, 1938) indicates that they are not functionally related to viviparity. The diverse histories of the ovarian follicles in bony fishes are shown diagrammatically in Fig. 8.

It has been suggested that the so-called pre-ovulation corpora lutea, which are universally present in fish ovaries, form the main mass of endocrine tissue of the teleost ovary (Bretschneider and de Wit, 1947; Hoar, 1955; Ball, 1960). As yet, however, the chemical nature and site of production of the hormone or hormones remain unknown (Pickford and Atz, 1957), and there is no answer to the question whether these luteal bodies have an endocrine function in controlling gestation. Indeed, there is a strong case for its being unanswerable, for ablation of the corpora lutea is unlikely to be successfully performed on a pregnant teleost and would in any case certainly terminate pregnancy.

3. *Amphibians*

There is no doubt that structures previously called corpora atretica, but now described by Bretschneider and de Wit (1947) as pre-ovulatory

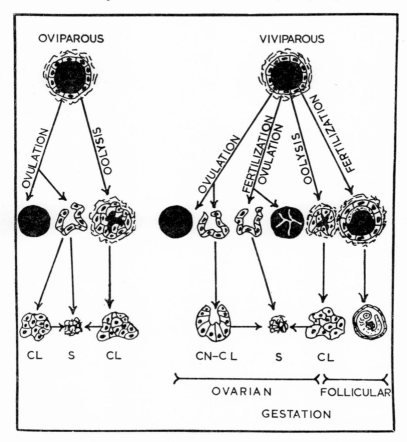

FIG. 8.   History of the ovarian follicle in different teleosts.
CL, corpus luteum; *CN–CL*, calyx nutricius which may be somewhat luteinized; *S*, scar. (Reproduced by permission from Hoar, 1955.)

corpora lutea, regularly occur in the amphibian ovary. But, contrary to the opinion of the Dutch workers, the morphological formation of the corpus atreticum is independent of pituitary stimulation (C. L. Smith, 1955). Whether, on the other hand, the formation of steroid hormones in these structures is under pituitary control remains to be

demonstrated. Such control is implied by the evidence of gonadotrophic control of secondary sexual characters in amphibians and in
other lower vertebrates with similar ovarian histology (Tuchmann-
Duplessis, 1945; Houssay, 1949). Tuchmann-Duplessis (1945) considered that some secondary sexual characters of *Triton* were directly
dependent on the anterior pituitary for their maintenance. For instance, the nuptial array during the breeding season disappeared
slowly after castration but very rapidly after hypophysectomy. The
oviducts, on the other hand, were more dependent on gonadal hormones,
as they regressed more rapidly after ovariectomy than after hypophysectomy.

Post-ovulatory changes in the follicles have also been described by
Burns (1932) in *Amblystoma tigrinum* and by Rugh (1935) in *Rana
pipiens*, both of which are oviparous; Burns states that there is no
evidence for any functional importance for this structure. However,
Galli-Mainini (1950) obtained evidence for an ovarian hormone in
Bufo arenarum that brought about the secretion of jelly by the oviducal
glands, and although it was not chemically identified, other experiments by Houssay (1947, 1949) indicated the presence of a progesterone-like agent. It was observed that this substance appeared in the
ovary before ovulation, but its site of production is by no means
certain (C. L. Smith, 1955).

The ruptured follicle of the viviparous anuran, *Nectophrynoides
occidentalis*, has been described by Lamotte and Rey (1954), and the
senior author has studied it in the ovoviviparous marsupial frog,
Gastrotheca marsupiata. During gestation (9 months in *N. occidentalis;*
3–4 months in *G. marsupiata*), the corpora persist and become rapidly
transformed into corpora atretica after the young are born. Lamotte
and Rey, on direct evidence, credit the corpora lutea with the inhibition
of ovulation in *N. occidentalis* and emphasize the fact that physiological correlations are striking. They conclude that the corpora lutea control
gestation in this species.

4. Reptiles

Among reptiles the discharged follicles have long been known to
give rise to distinct corpora lutea (Mingazzini, 1893; Lucien, 1903a, b),
and post-ovulation corpora lutea of essentially mammalian structure
(Bretschneider and de Wit, 1947) have now been described in several
species of oviparous and viviparous lizards (Hett, 1924; ten Cate
Hoedemaker, 1933; Cunningham and Smart, 1934; Weekes, 1934;
Boyd, 1940; Miller, 1948; Brambell, 1956; Panigel, 1956) and snakes
(Fraenkel and Martins, 1938; Rahn, 1939; Clausen, 1940; Samuel,
1944; Kasturirangen, 1951; Bragdon, 1952). Corpora lutea have also

been described in the snapping turtle (Rahn, 1938) and the box turtle (Altland, 1951).

The timing of the successive events that occur in the ruptured follicle has been studied most extensively in lizards, and there appears to be a definite correlation between the longevity of the corpus luteum and the egg-laying or -retaining habit of the species. In oviparous species retrogression is rapid and is completed shortly after oviposition (Cunningham and Smart, 1934). In vivipara, on the other hand, the corpora lutea remain well-developed for most, if not the whole of gestation and have regressed completely within 2 weeks post partum (Bragdon, 1952; Cunningham and Smart, 1934; Weekes, 1934).

The specific function of the reptilian corpus luteum is by no means clear, although its presence in both viviparous and oviparous species seems to indicate that it is not primarily related to viviparity (cf. elasmobranchs). Cunningham and Smart (1934), chiefly on indirect evidence, credit the corpora lutea of viviparous lizards with the inhibition of ovulation and dismiss the possibility of their bringing about progestational changes in the uterus. An important chance observation by Boyd (1942) in relation to viviparity (later confirmed by Miller, 1948) shows, however, that the progestational changes of the uterine mucosa are not wholly the consequence of direct stimulation by the foetus. For instance, in certain viviparous lizards, e.g. *Hoplodactylus maculatus* and *Xanthusia vigilis*, if only one oviduct is occupied by developing embryos, the other will remain in a state characteristic of pregnancy throughout the entire period of gestation, indicating the presence of gonadal hormones.

Conflicting evidence has, likewise, been presented as to the necessity of the corpora lutea for the maintenance of gestation in viviparous snakes. On the one hand, the studies of Rahn (1939), Clausen (1940) and of Fraenkel et al. (1940) suggest that pregnancy in the early stages depends on the continued presence of the ovaries, whereas ovariectomy in late pregnancy is not invariably followed by abortion; in these experiments the hypophysis was necessary at all stages of gestation (Table VI). Significantly, exogenous progesterone failed to repair the effects of ovariectomy in early pregnancy, although progestins have been demonstrated in extracts of ovaries containing corpora lutea (Porto, 1942; Valle and Valle, 1943) and in the plasma of pregnant viviparous snakes (Bragdon et al., 1954).

On the other hand, the more recent experiments of Bragdon (1951) on the viviparous garter snake, *Thamnophis*, and the water snake, *Natrix*, and those of Panigel (1956) on the ovoviviparous lizard, *Zootoca*, indicate that ovariectomy and hypophysectomy during gestation will not usually lead to abortion, but will interfere with the process of

TABLE VI

A. Effects of ovariectomy on gestation in snakes (after Clauser, 1940)

Stage of gestation	Water snakes			Garter snakes		Brown snakes
	Natrix cyclopion	*Natrix sipedon confluens*	*Natrix rhombifera*	*Natrix sipedon sipedon*	*Thamnophis sirtalis*	*Storeria dekayi*
Early	Resorption	Resorption	—	Resorption	—	—
Middle	Resorption	Resorption	—	Abortion (all young dead)	—	—
Late	Normal delivery of live young	Normal delivery of live young	Normal delivery of live young	—	Normal delivery of live young	Resorption or abortion

B. Effects of hypophysectomy on gestation in snakes

Stage of gestation	Water snakes		Garter snakes	Brown snakes
	Natrix cyclopion	*Natrix sipedon confluens*	*Thamnophis butleri*	*Storeria dekayi*
Early	—	Resorption	Resorption	Resorption
Middle	—	Abortion (all young dead)	—	—
Late	Abortion	—	—	Abortion (all young dead)

parturition, manifested by retention of the young *in utero* past full term. This interference with parturition was more complete subsequent to hypophysectomy than after ovariectomy, but the mechanism by which it is brought about remains unknown.

5. *Birds*

The derivation of interstitial endocrine cells in the adult ovary from atretic follicles is found also in birds (Marshall and Coombs, 1957). These cells are considered by some to stem ultimately from thecal cells (Firket, 1914; Marshall and Coombs, 1957), whereas, in fishes (Ball, 1960), amphibians (Burns, 1932) and reptiles (Bragdon, 1952) the predominant cell type of the corpus atreticum comes from the granulosa, though probably some thecal cells are incorporated. In some birds, however, the granulosa cells appear to dominate in atresia. It has been shown that the blood of laying hens (Fraps *et al.*, 1948) as well as of cockerels and non-laying hens (Fraps *et al.*, 1949) contains progesterone or a progestin-like substance, although its source remains unknown.

The ruptured avian follicle has long been known to give rise to a solid transient structure, and the relatively few accounts dealing directly with it (cf. Fell, 1924; Brambell, 1956) are limited largely to histological changes incidental to its regression and to discussions of its presumed homology or lack of homology with the mammalian corpus luteum. Opinion is, however, divided as to the part this so-called luteal body plays as a gland of internal secretion. Rothchild and Fraps (1944) suggest that the ruptured ovarian follicle of the domestic hen plays some role in oviposition. As support for this view, they cite experiments showing that if the oldest maturing follicle alone is removed, there is slight delay, but if the ruptured follicle alone, or both the ruptured follicle and the oldest remaining follicle are removed, the delay is greatly extended. Removal of other parts of the ovary at comparable times practically never delayed the time of lay.

The mechanism whereby the discharged avian follicle influences the oviducal history of the egg it once contained has not been established, although an endocrine mechanism may be presumed. Several reports have appeared in the literature which indicate that gonadotrophic hormones of hypophysial origin and from pregnancy urine will reduce the interval between successive ovipositions (Renoult, 1931). On the other hand, the possible function of the ruptured follicle which is postulated by Rothchild and Fraps (1944) is difficult to explain in the light of experiments by Conner and Fraps (1954), as yet unconfirmed, showing that removal of a small part of the ruptured follicle hastens oviposition, whereas removal of a large part delayed oviposition. It would appear, therefore, to be premature to consider the matter as definitely settled, and until more precise information becomes available on the nature of the stimuli required for oviposition and ovulation, as well as on the nature of oviposition itself, the physiological status of the discharged follicle in birds must remain in doubt.

REFERENCES

Agate, F. J. Jr. (1952). The growth and secretory activity of the mammary glands of the pregnant rhesus monkey (*Macaca mulatta*) following hypophysectomy. *Amer. J. Anat.* **90**, 257–276.

Alden, R. H. (1942a). The periovarial sac in the albino rat. *Anat. Rec.* **83**, 421–433.

Alden, R. H. (1942b). Aspects of the egg–ovary–oviduct relationship in the albino rat. I. Egg passage and development following ovariectomy. *J. exp. Zool.* **90**, 159–179.

Alden, R. H. (1942c). The oviduct and egg transport in the albino rat. *Anat. Rec.* **84**, 137–161.

Alden, R. H. (1942d). Aspects of egg–ovary–oviduct relationship in the albino rat. II. Egg development within the oviduct. *J. exp. Zool.* **90**, 171–179.

Aldred, J. P., Sammelwitz, P. H. and Nalbandov, A. V. (1959). Comparative study of mechanisms of maintenance of corpora lutea. *Anat. Rec.* (Suppl.) **133**, 242–243.

Allan, H. and Wiles, P. (1932). The rôle of the pituitary gland in pregnancy and parturition. I. Hypophysectomy. *J. Physiol.* **75**, 23–28.

Allen, E., Pratt, J. P. and Doisy, E. A. (1925). The ovarian follicular hormone. Its distribution in human genital tissues. *J. Amer. med. Ass.* **85**, 399–405.

Allen, P., Brambell, F. W. R. and Mills, I. H. (1947). Studies on sterility and prenatal mortality in wild rabbits. I. The reliability of estimates of prenatal mortality based on counts of corpora lutea, implantation sites and embryos. *J. exp. Biol.* **23**, 312–331.

Allen, W. M. and Heckel, G. P. (1939). Maintenance of pregnancy by progesterone in rabbits castrated on the 11th day. *Amer. J. Physiol.* **125**, 31–35.

Allen, W. M. and Meyer, R. K. (1933). The quantitative separation of progestin rom oestrin in extracts of the corpus luteum. *Amer. J. Physiol.* **106**, 55–63.

Allen, W. M. and Wintersteiner, O. (1934). Crystalline progestin. *Science*, **80**, 190–191.

Allen, W. M., Butenandt, A., Corner, G. W. and Slotta, K. H. (1935). Nomenclature of corpus luteum hormone. *Science*, **82**, 153.

Altland, P. D. (1951). Observations on the structure of the reproductive organs of the box turtle. *J. Morph.* **89**, 599–616.

Amoroso, E. C. (1952). Placentation. In "Marshall's Physiology of Reproduction" (A. S. Parkes, ed.), vol. II, pp. 127–311. Longmans Green, London.

Amoroso, E. C. (1955a). Endocrinology of pregnancy. *Brit. med. Bull.* **11**, 117–125.

Amoroso, E. C. (1955b). The comparative anatomy and histology of the placental barrier. In "Gestation" (L. B. Flexner, ed.), vol. I, pp. 119–224. Josiah Macy Jr. Foundation, New York.

Amoroso, E. C. (1955c). Hormone control of the oestrous cycle. *Vet. Rec.* **67**, 1072–1086.

Amoroso, E. C. (1955d). De la signification du placenta dans l'évolution de la gestation chez les animaux vivipares. *Ann. Endocr., Paris,* **16**, 435–447.

Amoroso, E. C. (1956). The endocrine environment of the foetus. *Proc. III. int. Congr. Anim. Reprod., Cambridge,* **1**, 25–32.

Amoroso, E. C. (1959). The biology of the placenta. *In* "Gestation" (C. A. Villee, ed.), vol. V, pp. 13–76. Josiah Macy Jr. Foundation, New York.

Amoroso, E. C. (1960a). Comparative aspects of the hormonal functions. *In* "The Placenta and Fetal Membranes" (C. A. Villee, ed.), pp. 3–28. Williams and Wilkins, Baltimore.

Amoroso, E. C. (1960b). Viviparity in fishes. *In* "Hormones in Fishes" (I. Chester Jones, ed.). *Symp. zool. Soc. Lond.,* No. 1. pp. 153–181.

Amoroso, E. C. and Marshall, F. H. A. (1960). External factors in sexual periodicity. *In* "Marshall's Physiology of Reproduction" (A. S. Parkes, ed.), vol. 1, part 2, pp. 707–831. Longmans Green, London.

Amoroso, E. C. and Rowlands, I. W. (1951). Hormonal effects in the pregnant mare and foetal foal. *J. Endocrin.* **7**, l–liii.

Amoroso, E. C., Griffiths, W. B. and Hamilton, W. J. (1939). Living tubal ova of the goat. *Vet. Rec.* **51**, 1009–1010.

Amoroso, E. C., Griffiths, W. F. B. and Hamilton, W. J. (1942). The early development of the goat (*Capra hircus*). *J. Anat., Lond.* **76**, 377–406.

Amoroso, E. C., Hancock, J. L. and Rowlands, I. W. (1948). Ovarian activity in the pregnant mare. *Nature, Lond.* **161**, 355–356.

Amoroso, E. C., Harrison, R. J., Matthews, L. H. and Rowlands, I. W. (1951). Reproductive organs of near-term and new-born seals. *Nature, Lond.* **168**, 771–772.

Amoroso, E. C., Hancock, N. A. and Kellas, L. M. (1958). The foetal membranes and placenta of the hippopotamus (*Hippopotamus amphibius* Linnaeus). *Proc. zool. Soc. Lond.* **130**, 437–447.

Ancel, P. and Bouin, P. (1911). Recherches sur les fonctions du corps jaune gestatif. II. Sur le déterminisme du développement de la glande mammaire au cours de la gestation. *J. Physiol. Path. gén.* **13**, 31–41.

Ancel, P. and Bouin, P. (1924). Sur le déterminisme des phénomènes utérins préparatoires à la nidation de l'oeuf et du développement gravidique de la glande mammaire. *C.R. Assoc. Anat.* **19**, 1–12.

Ancel, P. and Vintemberger, P. (1929). De l'action du corps jaune sur l'évolution des oeufs chez la lapine. *C.R. Soc. Biol., Paris,* **100**, 852–857.

Andersen, D. H. and Sperry, W. M. (1937). A study of cholesterol in the adrenal gland in different phases of reproduction in the female rat. *J. Physiol.* **90**, 296–302.

Anderson, D. (1927). The rate of passage of the mammalian ovum through the various portions of the Fallopian tube. *Amer. J. Physiol.* **82**, 557–569.

Aron, M. and Aron, C. (1946). Action sur l'ovaire du cobaye prémature, du benzoate d'oestradiol, respectivement en injection sous-cutanée et en introduction directe dans l'ovaire. *C.R. Soc. Biol., Paris,* **140**, 1014–1015.

Aron, M. and Aron, C. (1952). "Elements d'Endocrinologie Physiologique." Paris.

Artunkal, T. and Colonge, R. A. (1949). Action de l'ovariectomie sur la gestation du cobaye. *C.R. Soc. Biol., Paris,* **143**, 1590–1592.

Aschner, I. (1912). Über die Funktion der Hypophyse. *Pflüg. Arch. ges. Physiol.* **146**, 1–146.

Asdell, S. A. (1928). The growth and function of the corpus luteum. *Physiol. Rev.* **8**, 313–345.

Asdell, S. A. (1946). "Patterns of Mammalian Reproduction." Comstock, New York.

Asdell, S. A. and Hammond, J. (1933). The effects of prolonging the life of the corpus luteum in the rabbit by hysterectomy. *Amer. J. Physiol.* **103**, 600–605.

Ask-Upmark, M. E. (1926). Le corps jaune est-il nécessaire pour l'accomplissement physiologique de la gravidité humaine? *Acta obstet. gynec. scand.* **5**, 211–229.

Astwood, E. B. (1941). The regulation of corpus luteum function by hypophysial luteotrophin. *Endocrinology*, **28**, 309–320.

Astwood, E. B. and Greep, R. O. (1938). A corpus luteum stimulating substance in the rat placenta. *Proc. Soc. exp. Biol., N.Y.* **38**, 713–716.

Astwood, E. B. and Greep, R. O. (1939). Nomenclature of gonad-stimulating hormones of placental origin. *Science*, **89**, 81.

Averill, S. C., Ray, E. W. and Lyons, W. R. (1950). Maintenance of pregnancy in hypophysectomised rats with placental implants. *Proc. Soc. exp. Biol., N.Y.* **75**, 3–9.

Balfour, W. E., Comline, R. S. and Short, R. V. (1957). Secretion of progesterone by the adrenal gland. *Nature, Lond.* **180**, 1480–1481.

Ball, J. N. (1960). Reproduction in female bony fishes. In "Hormones in Fish" (I. Chester Jones, ed.). *Symp. zool. Soc., Lond.* No. 1, pp. 105–135.

Beard, J. (1897). "The Span of Gestation and the Cause of Birth." Jena.

Benazzi, M. (1933). Sulla funzione ovarica in gravidanza. *Arch. Sci. Biol.* **18**, 409–419.

Benson, G. K., Cowie, A. T., Cox, C. P., Flux, D. S. and Folley, S. J. (1955). Studies on the hormonal induction of mammary growth and lactation in the goat. II. Functional and morphological studies of hormonally developed udders with special reference to the effect of 'triggering' doses of oestrogen. *J. Endocrin.* **13**, 46–58.

Benson, G. K., Cowie, A. T., Cox, C. P. and Goldzveig, S. M. (1957). Effects of oestrone and progesterone on mammary development in the guinea-pig. *J. Endocrin.* **15**, 126–144.

Benson, G. K., Cowie, A. T., Folley, S. J. and Tindal, J. S. (1959). Recent developments in endocrine studies of mammary growth and lactation. In "Recent Progress in the Endocrinology of Reproduction" (C. W. Lloyd, ed.), pp. 457–496. Academic Press, New York.

Billmann, F. and Engel, R. (1939). Vikariierender Einsatz fetaler Nebennieren in der Schwangerschaft beim nebennierenlosen Hund. *Klin. Wschr.* **18**, 599–600.

Bishop, D. W. (1956a). Oxygen concentration in the rabbit genital tract. *Proc. III. int. Congr. Anim. Reprod., Cambridge*, Part 1, pp. 53–55.

Bishop, D. W. (1956b). The tubal secretions of the rabbit oviduct. *Anat. Rec.* **125**, 631.

Bishop, D. W. (1956c). Active secretion in the rabbit oviduct. *Amer. J. Physiol.* **187**, 347–352.

Blair-Bell, W. (1920). "The Sex Complex." London.

Blandau, R. J. (1958). A teaching film on ovulation and egg transport in the rat. *Anat. Rec.* **130**, 468.

Bloom, G., Paul, K.-G. and Wiquist, N. (1958). A uterine-relaxing factor in the pregnant rat. *Acta endocr., Copenhagen*, **28**, 112–118.

Bonner, W. N. (1955). Reproductive organs of foetal and juvenile elephant seals. *Nature, Lond.* **176**, 982–983.

Bonnet, R. (1907). "Lehrbuch der Entwicklungsgeschichte." Berlin.

Bouin, P. and Ancel, P. (1909a). Sur la fonction du corps jaune: action du corps jaune vrai sur l'utérus. *C.R. Soc. Biol., Paris*, **66**, 505–507.

Bouin, P. and Ancel, P. (1909b). Sur les homologies et la signification des glandes à sécrétion interne de l'ovaire. *C.R. Soc. Biol., Paris*, **67**, 466.

Bouin, P. and Ancel, P. (1909c). Le développement de la glande mammaire pendant la gestation est déterminé par le corps jaune. *C.R. Soc. Biol., Paris*, **67**, 466–467.

Bouin, P. and Ancel, P. (1910). Recherches sur les fonctions du corps jaune gestatif. 1. Sur le déterminisme de la préparation de l'utérus à la fixation de l'oeuf. *J. Physiol. Path. gén.* **12**, 1–16.

Bourg, R. and Spehl, E. (1948). Étude histophysiologique des conséquences de la ligature des cornes utérines chez la rate adulte. Pseudo-gestation, hyperplasie glandulo-kystique utérine (H.G.K.) et métaplasie degénérative kystique (M.D.K.). *Bull. Acad. roy. de Med. Biol.* **13**, 118–169.

Bourne, G. (1939). The effect of progesterone on the survival of adrenalectomized rats. *J. Physiol.* **95**, 12–13P.

Boyd, M. M. M. (1940). The structure of the ovary and the formation of the corpus luteum in *Hoplodactylus maculatus*, Gray. *Quart. J. micr. Sci.* **82**, 337–376.

Boyd, M. M. M. (1942). The oviduct, foetal membranes and placentation in *Hoplodactylus maculatus*. *Proc. zool. Soc. Lond.* A. **112** 65–104.

Bradbury, J. T. (1937a). Prolongation of the life of the corpora lutea by hysterectomy in the rat. *Anat. Rec.* (Suppl.) **70**, 51.

Bradbury, J. T. (1937b). Discussion in Pincus (1937).

Bradbury, J. T. (1947). Ovarian influence on the response of the anterior pituitary to estrogens. *Endocrinology*, **41**, 501–513.

Bradbury, J. T., Brown, W. E. and Gray, L. A. (1950). Maintenance of corpus luteum and physiologic action of progesterone. *Recent Progr. Hormone Res.* **5**, 151–194.

Bragdon, D. E. (1951). The non-essentiality of the corpora lutea for the maintenance of gestation in certain live-bearing snakes. *J. exp. Zool.* **118**, 419–435.

Bragdon, D. E. (1952). Corpus luteum formation and follicular atresia in the common garter snake, *Thamnophis sirtalis*. *J. Morph.* **91**, 413–437.

Bragdon, D. E., Lazo-Wasem, E. A., Zarrow, M. X. and Hisaw, F. L. (1954). Progesterone-like activity in the plasma of ovoviviparous snakes. *Proc. Soc. exp. Biol., N.Y.* **86**, 477–480.

Brambell, F. W. R. (1935). Reproduction in the common shrew (*Sorex araneus* Linnaeus). *Phil. Trans.* B. **255**, 1–49.

Brambell, F. W. R. (1937). The influence of lactation on the implantation of the mammalian embryo. *Amer. J. Obstet. Gynec.* **33**, 942–953.

Brambell, F. W. R. (1956). Ovarian changes. *In* "Marshall's Physiology of Reproduction" (A. S. Parkes, ed.), 3rd ed., vol. I, part 1, pp. 397–542. Longmans Green, London.

Brambell, F. W. R. and Hall, K. (1937). Reproduction in the lesser shrew (*Sorex minutus* L.). *Proc. zool. Soc. Lond.* pp. 957–969.

Brambell, F. W. R. and Hall, K. (1939). Reproduction of the field vole, *Microtus agrestis hirtus* Bellamy. *Proc. zool. Soc. Lond.* A. **109**, 133–138.

Brambell, F. W. R. and Rowlands, I. W. (1936). Reproduction in the bank vole (*Evotomys glareolus* Schreber). *Phil. Trans.* B. **226**, 71–97.

512   E. C. AMOROSO AND C. A. FINN

Bretschneider, L. H. and Wit, J. J. D. de (1947). "Sexual Endocrinology of Non-mammalian Vertebrates." (*Monographs on the Progress of Research in Holland during the War*, No. 11). Elsevier, Amsterdam.

Brouha, L. (1933). Les bases expérimentales du problème de la ménopause provoquée. *Gynéc. Obstet.* 28, 243–265.

Brouha, L. (1934). A propos des phénomènes utérins préparatoires à la nidation de l'oeuf. *Brux. méd.* 14, 810–812.

Brouha, L. (1938). *In* "Les Hormones Sexuelles", p. 382. Colloque international Singer-Polignac. Hermann, Paris.

Buchanan, G. D., Enders, A. C. and Talmage, R. V. (1956). Implantation in armadillos ovariectomized during the period of delayed implantation. *J. Endocrin.* 14, 121–128.

Bujard, E. (1952). Le cycle oestral n'est pas effacé dans l'ovaire de cobaye gravide. *Arch. Anat. Histol. Embryol.* 34, 89–94.

Bullough, W. S. (1942). The effects of oestrone on the ovary of the mouse. *J. Endocrin.* 3, 235–243.

Burdick, H. O. (1942). Effect of progesterone on the ovaries and embryos of mice in early pregnancy. *Endocrinology*, 30, 619–622.

Burdick, H. O and Emerson, B. (1939). Repression and resorption of the corpora lutea of early pregnancy following injections of testosterone propionate. *Endocrinology*, 25, 913–918.

Burdick, H. O. and Pincus, G. (1935). The effect of oestrin injection upon the developing ova of mice. *Amer. J. Physiol.* 111, 201–208.

Burdick, H. O. and Whitney, R. (1937). Acceleration of the rate of passage of fertilized ova through the Fallopian tubes of mice by massive injections of oestrogenic substance. *Endocrinology*, 21, 637–643.

Burdick, H. O., Emerson, B. B. and Whitney, R. (1940). Effects of testosterone propionate on pregnancy and on passage of ova through the oviducts of mice. *Endocrinology*, 26, 1081–1086.

Burford, T. H. and Diddle, H. W. (1936). Effect of total hysterectomy upon the ovary of the *Macacus rhesus*. *Surg. Gynec. Obstet.* 62, 701–707.

Burns, R. K. (1932). Follicular atresia in the ovaries of hypophysectomized salamanders in relation to yolk formation. *J. exp. Zool.* 63, 309–322.

Butenandt, A. (1930). Über das Pregnandiol, einen neuen Sterinabkommling aus Schwangeren-harn. *Ber. chem. Ges. Frankfurt*, 63, 659–663.

Butenandt, A. and Westphal, U. (1934a). Zur Isolierung und Charakterisierung des Corpus-luteum-Hormons. *Ber. chem. Ges. Frankfurt*, 67, 1440–1442.

Butenandt, A. and Westphal, U. (1934b). Über die Darstellung des Corpus-luteum-Hormons. *Ber. chem. Ges. Frankfurt*, 67, 2085–2087.

Canivenc, R. (1960). L'ovo-implantation differée des animaux sauvages. *In* "Les Fonctions de Nidation utérine et leurs Troubles", pp. 33–86. Masson, Paris.

Canivenc, R. and Laffargue, M. (1956). Survie prolongée d'oeufs fécondés non implantés dans l'utérus de rattes castrées et injectées de progesterone. *C.R. Acad. Sci., Paris*, 242, 2857–2860.

Canivenc, R. and Mayer, G. (1955). Contribution à l'étude expérimentale de la superfétation chez la rate, recherches basées sur la nidation rétardée. *Ann. Endocr., Paris*, 16, 1–33.

Canivenc, R., Drouville, C. and Mayer, G. (1953). Développement simultané d'embryons d'âge différent chez la rate: réalization expérimentale. *C.R. Acad. Sci., Paris*, 237, 1036.

Carlisle, D. B. (1955). Discussion on "The hormones of sex and reproduction and their effects in fish and lower chordates". *Mem. Soc. Endocrin.* No. 4, 185.

Casida, L. E. and Warwick, E. J. (1945). The necessity of the corpus luteum for maintenance of pregnancy in the ewe. *J. Anim. Sci.* **4**, 34–36.

Catchpole, H. R. (1959). Endocrine mechanisms during pregnancy. *In* "Reproduction in Domestic Animals" (H. H. Cole and P. T. Cupps, eds.), vol. 1, pp. 469–507. Academic Press, New York.

Champy, C. and Gley, P. (1923). Observations cytologiques sur les ovocytes des poissons et de quelques autres vertébrés. *Arch. Anat. micr. morph. exp.* **19**, 241–308.

Chu, J. P. and You, S. S. (1945). The rôle of the thyroid gland and oestrogen on the regulation of gonadotrophic activity of the anterior pituitary. *J. Endocrin.* **4**, 115–124.

Chu, J. P., Lee, C. C. and You, S. S. (1946). Functional relation between the uterus and the corpus luteum. *J. Endocrin.* **4**, 392–398.

Clark, R. T. (1934). Studies on the physiology of reproduction in the sheep. *Anat. Rec.* **60**, 135–160.

Clegg, M. T., Boda, T. M. and Cole, H. H. (1954). The endometrial cups and allantochorionic pouches in the mare with emphasis on the source of equine gonadotrophin. *Endocrinology*, **54**, 448–463.

Clausen, H. J. (1940). Studies on the effects of ovariectomy and hypophysectomy on gestation in snakes. *Endocrinology*, **27**, 700–704.

Cochrane, R. L. and Meyer, R. L. (1957). Delayed nidation in the rat induced by progesterone. *Proc. Soc. exp. Biol., N.Y.* **96**, 155–159.

Cole, H. H. and Goss, H. (1943). The source of equine gonadotrophin. *In* "Essays in Biology." University of California Press.

Cole, H. H., Howell, C. E. and Hart, G. H. (1931). The changes occurring in the ovary of the mare during pregnancy. *Anat. Rec.* **49**, 199–209.

Cole, H. H., Hart, G. H., Lyons, W. R. and Catchpole, H. R. (1933). The development and hormonal content of foetal horse gonads. *Anat. Rec.* **56**, 275–289.

Collings, W. D. (1941). The effect of experimentally induced pseudopregnancy upon the survival of adrenalectomized cats. *Endocrinology*, **28**, 75–82.

Conner, M. H. and Fraps, R. M. (1954). Premature oviposition following subtotal excision of the hen's ruptured follicle. *Poultry Sci.* **33**, 1051.

Corey, E. L. (1928). A study of the survival period in the pregnant and lactating cat following bilateral adrenal extirpation. *Physiol. Zoöl.* **1**, 147–152.

Corner, G. W. (1921). Cyclic changes in the ovaries and uterus of the sow and their relation to the mechanism of implantation. *Contr. Embryol. Carneg. Instn.* **13**, 117–146.

Corner, G. W. (1928). Physiology of the corpus luteum. 1. The effect of very early ablation of the corpus luteum upon embryos and uterus. *Amer. J. Physiol.* **86**, 74–81.

Corner, G. W. (1932). Cytology of the ovum, ovary and fallopian tube. *In* "Special Cytology" (E. V. Cowdry, ed.), vol. 3, p. 1598, Hoeber, New York.

Corner, G. W. (1938). The sites of formation of estrogenic substances in the animal body. *Physiol. Rev.* **18**, 154–172.

Corner, G. W. (1940). Accessory corpora lutea in the ovary of the monkey, *Macaca rhesus. Anal. Fac. Med. Montevideo*, **25**, 553–560.

Corner, G. W. (1947). "The Hormones in Human Reproduction." Princeton University Press.

Corner, G. W. and Csapo, A. (1953). Action of the ovarian hormones on uterine muscle. *Brit. med. J.* **1**, 687–691.

Corner, G. W., Bartelmez, G. W. and Hartman, C. G. (1936). On the normal and aberrant corpora lutea of the rhesus monkey. *Amer. J. Anat.* **59**, 433–443.

Courrier, R. (1941a). Evolution de la grossesse extra-utérine chez la lapine castrée. *C.R. Soc. Biol., Paris*, **135**, 820–822.

Courrier, R. (1941b). Sur le mécanisme d'ouverture de la symphyse pubienne en fin de grossesse chez le cobaye. *Bull. Acad. Med., Paris*, **125**, 230–234.

Courrier, R. (1950). Interactions between oestrogens and progesterone. *Vitam. & Hormon.* **8**, 179–214.

Courrier, R. (1945). "Endocrinologie de la Gestation", chap. VII, pp. 70–93. Masson, Paris.

Courrier, R. and Baclesse, M. (1955). L'équilibre hormonal au cours de la gestation. *In* "L'Équilibre Hormonal de la Gestation; les Androgènes dans l'Organisme Féminin; la Cortisone dans l'Équilibre Hormonal." *Rapports de la IIIe re-union des endocrinologistes de langue française.* Paris.

Courrier, R. and Gerlinger. (1922). Le cycle glandulaire de l'épithélium de l'oviducte chez la chienne. *C.R. Soc. Biol., Paris*, **87**, 1363–1365.

Courrier, R. and Gros, G. (1935). Contribution à l'endocrinologie de la grossesse chez la chatte. *C.R. Soc. Biol., Paris*, **120**, 5–7.

Courrier, R. and Gros, G. (1936). Dissociation foeto-placentaire realisée par la castration chez la chatte. Action endocrinienne du placenta. *C.R. Soc. Biol., Paris*, **121**, 1517–1520.

Courrier, R. and Gros, G. (1938). Influence du propionate de testosterone sur l'utérus. *C.R. Soc. Biol., Paris*, **127**, 921–923.

Courrier, R. and Kehl, R. (1938). Sur le besoin hormonal quantitatif chez la lapine gestante castrée. *C.R. Soc. Biol., Paris*, **128**, 188–191.

Cowie, A. T. (1957). Mammary development and lactation. *In* "Progress in the Physiology of Farm Animals" (J. Hammond, ed.), pp. 907–961. Butterworth, London.

Cowie, A. T. and Tindal, J. S. (1960). Effects of hypophysectomy of the pregnant and lactating goat. Advanced Abstracts. *1st int. Congr. Endocrin., Copenhagen*, pp. 679–680.

Cowie, A. T., Folley, S. J., Malpress, F. H. and Richardson, K. C. (1952). Studies on the hormonal induction of mammary growth and lactation in the goat. *J. Endocrin.* **8**, 64–88.

Crelin, E. S. (1954). Prevention of innominate bone separation during pregnancy in the mouse. *Proc. Soc. exp. Biol., N.Y.* **86**, 22–24.

Cross, B. A. (1959). Neurohypophyseal control of parturition. *In* "Recent Progress in the Endocrinology of Reproduction" (C. W. Lloyd, ed.), pp. 441–453. Academic Press, New York.

Csapo, A. (1956). Progesterone 'block'. *Amer. J. Anat.* **98**, 273–291.

Cunningham, J. T. and Smart, W. A. M. (1934). The structure and origin of corpora lutea in some of the lower vertebrates. *Proc. roy. Soc.* B. **116**, 258–281.

Curtis, C. (1949). Factors influencing lobulo-alveolar development and mammary secretion in the rat. *Endocrinology*, **45**, 284–295.

Cutuly, E. (1941a). Maintenance of pregnancy in hypophysectomized rats. *Proc. Soc. exp. Biol., N.Y.* **47**, 126–128.

Cutuly, E. (1941b). Implantation following mating in hypophysectomised rats injected with lactogenic hormone. *Proc. Soc. exp. Biol., N.Y.* **48**, 315–318.

Cutuly, E. (1942). Effects of lactogenic and gonadotrophic hormones on hypophysectomized pregnant rats. *Endocrinology*, **31**, 13–22.

Daels, F. (1908). On the relations between the ovaries and the uterus. *Surg. Gynec. Obstet.* **6**, 153–159.

D'Amour, M. C. and D'Amour, F. E. (1939). Effect of luteinization on the survival of adrenalectomized rats. *Proc. Soc. exp. Biol., N.Y.* **40**, 417–418.

Davis, M. E. and Plotz, E. J. (1954). Effects of cortisone acetate on intact and adrenalectomized rats during pregnancy. *Endocrinology*, **54**, 384–395.

Davis, M. E. and Plotz, E. J. (1956). The excretion of neutral steroids in the urine of normal non-pregnant women. *Acta endocr., Copenhagen*, **21**, 245–248.

Dawson, A. B. (1946). The post-partum history of the corpus luteum of the cat. *Anat. Rec.* **95**, 29–51.

Dawson, A. B. and Kosters, B. A. (1944). Pre-implantation changes in the uterine mucosa of the cat. *Amer. J. Anat.* **75**, 1–32.

Dawson, A. B. and Velardo, J. T. (1952). A histochemical study of the lipids in the corpora lutea of the rat during normal and prolonged pseudopregnancy. *Anat. Rec.* **113**, 592–593. (Abstr. no. 14.)

Day, B. N., Anderson, L. L., Emmerson, M. A., Hazel, L. N. and Lemampy, R. M. (1959). Effect of estrogen and progesterone on early embryonic mortality in ovariectomized gilts. *J. Anim. Sci.* **18**, 607–613.

Deanesly, R. (1930). The development and vascularization of the corpus luteum in the mouse and rabbit. *Proc. roy. Soc.* B. **107**, 60–76.

Deanesly, R. (1934). The reproductive processes of certain mammals. Part VI. The reproductive cycle of the female hedgehog. *Phil. Trans.* B. **223**, 239–276.

Deanesly, R. (1935). The reproductive processes of certain mammals. Part IX. Growth and reproduction in the stoat (*Mustela erminea*). *Phil. Trans.* B. **225**, 459–492.

Deanesly, R. (1938). The reproductive cycle of the golden hamster. *Proc. zool. Soc. Lond.* A. **108**, 31–37.

Deanesly, R. (1960). Implantation and early pregnancy in ovariectomized guinea pigs. *J. Reprod. Fertil.* **1**, 242–248.

Deanesly, R. and Newton, W. H. (1940). The influence of the placenta on the corpus luteum of pregnancy in the mouse. *J. Endocrin.* **2**, 317–321.

Deanesly, R. and Parkes, A. S. (1933). The oestrous cycle in the grey squirrel (*Sciurus carolinensis*). *Phil. Trans.* B. **222**, 47–48.

Deanesly, R., Fee, A. R. and Parkes, A. S. (1930). Studies on ovulation. II. The effect of hypophysectomy on the formation of the corpus luteum. *J. Physiol.* **70**, 38–44.

Della-Beffa, A. (1951). Gravidanza, parto ed allattamento ad ipofisi distrutta de neoplasia endocranica. *Folia Endocrin.* **4**, 119–132.

Dempsey, E. W. (1939). The reproductive cycle of New World monkeys. *Amer. J. Anat.* **64**, 381–401.

Dempsey, E. W. (1940). The structure of the reproductive tract in the female gibbon. *Amer. J. Anat.* **67**, 229–249.

Denamur, R. and Martinet, J. (1955). Effets de l'ovariectomie chez la brebis pendant la gestation. *C.R. Soc. Biol., Paris*, **149**, 2105–2107.

Desclin, L. (1932). A propos des interactions entre l'utérus et le corps jaune au cours de la grossesse chez le cobaye. *C.R. Soc. Biol., Paris*, **109**, 972–973.

516   E. C. AMOROSO AND C. A. FINN

Desclin, L. (1935). Action de fortes doses d'hormone folliculaire sur la structure de l'ovaire et du lobe antérieur de l'hypophyse chez le rat blanc. *C.R. Soc. Biol., Paris*, **120**, 526–528.

Desclin, L. (1952). Recherches sur le déterminisme des phénomènes de sécrétion dans la glande mammaire du rat. *Ann. Endocr., Paris*, **13**, 120–136.

Desclin, L. (1953). Les facteurs qui déterminent la longueur de vie des corps jaunes et conditionnent leur activité fonctionelle. *In* "Endocrinologie Sexuelle. Questions d'Actualités." *Rapports de la II⁰ réunion d'endocrinologistes de langue française*, pp. 1–30. Paris.

Desclin, L. (1954). L'hypophyse et l'activité physiologique du corps jaune. *In* "La Fonction Lutéale", pp. 23–48. Masson, Paris.

Devis, R. and Devis-van den Eeckhoudt, M. (1949). The urinary corticosteroid excretion in pre-eclampsia and eclampsia. *J. clin. Endocrin.* **9**, 1436–1437.

Dodd, J. M., Evennett, P. J. and Goddard, C. K. (1960). Reproductive endocrinology in cyclostomes and elasmobranchs. *In* "Hormones in Fishes" (I. Chester Jones, ed.). *Symp. zool. Soc. Lond.* No. 1, pp. 77–103.

Drips, D. (1919). Studies on the ovary of the spermophile (*Spermophilus citellus tridecemlineatus*) with special reference to the corpus luteum. *Amer. J. Anat.* **25**, 117–184.

Drummond-Robinson, G. and Asdell, S. A. (1926). The relation between the corpus luteum and the mammary gland. *J. Physiol.* **61**, 608–614.

Duke, K. L. (1940). A preliminary histological study of the ovary of the kangaroo rat, *Dipodomys ordu columbianus*, Merriam. *Gr. Basin Nat.* **1**, 63–72.

Duke, K. L. (1952). Ovarian histology of *Ochotona princeps*, the Rocky Mountain pika. *Anat. Rec.* **112**, 737–751.

Dutt, R. G. and Casida, L. E. (1948). Alteration of the estrual cycle in the sheep by use of progesterone and its effect upon subsequent ovulation and fertility. *Endocrinology*, **43**, 208–217.

Eckstein, P. (1949). Patterns of the mammalian sexual cycle. *Acta anat.* **7**, 389–410.

Eckstein, P., Shelesnyak, M. C. and Amoroso, E. C. (1959). A survey of the physiology of ovum implantation in mammals. *Mem. Soc. Endocrin.* No. 6, 3–12.

Emery, F. E. and Greco, P. A. (1940). The comparative activity of desoxycorticosterone acetate and progesterone in adrenalectomized rats. *Endocrinology*, **27**, 473–476.

Emery, F. E. and Schwabe, E. L. (1936). The rôle of the corpora lutea in prolonging the life of adrenalectomized rats. *Endocrinology*, **20**, 550–555.

Enders, A. C. and Buchanan, G. D. (1959). Some effects of ovariectomy and injection of ovarian hormones in the armadillo. *J. Endocr.* **19**, 251–258.

Enders, R. K. (1952). Reproduction in the mink. *Proc. Amer. phil. Soc.* **96**, 691–755.

Enders, R. K. (1956). Delayed implantation in mammals. *In* "Gestation" (C. Villee, ed.), vol. II, pp. 113–130. Josiah Macy Jr. Foundation, New York.

Enders, R. K. and Pearson, O. P. (1943). Shortening gestation by inducing early implantation with increased light in the marten. *Amer. Fur Breeder*, **15**, 18.

Enders, R. K., Pearson, O. P. and Pearson, A. K. (1946). Certain aspects of reproduction in the fur seal. *Anat. Rec.* **94**, 213–227.

Ershoff, B. H. and Deuel, H. J. (1943). Prolongation of pseudo-pregnancy by induction of deciduomata in rats. *Proc. Soc. exp. Biol., N.Y.* **54**, 167–168.

Evans, H. M. and Cole, H. H. (1931). An introduction to the study of the oestrous cycle in the dog. *Mem. Univ. Calif.* **9**, 65–103.

Evans, H. M. and Simpson, M. E. (1950). Physiology of the gonadotrophins. *In* "The Hormones" (G. Pincus and K. V. Thimann, eds.), vol. II, pp. 351–398. Academic Press, New York.

Evans, H. M. and Swezy, O. (1931). Ovogenesis and the normal follicular cycle in adult mammalia. *Mem. Univ. Calif.* **9**, 119–188.

Everett, J. W. (1950). Pituitary-ovarian relationships. *In* "Progress in Clinical Endocrinology" (S. Soskin, ed.), pp. 319–326, Grune and Stratton, New York.

Everett, J. W. (1952). Presumptive hypothalamic control of spontaneous ovulation. *Ciba Foundation Colloquia on Endocrinology*, **5**, 167–178.

Everett, J. W. (1956). Functional corpora lutea maintained for months by autografts of rat hypophysis. *Endocrinology*, **58**, 786–796.

Fawcett, D. W. (1950). The development of mouse ova under the capsule of the kidney. *Anat. Rec.* **108**, 71–91.

Fawcett, D. W., Wislocki, G. B. and Waldo, C. M. (1947). The development of mouse ova in the anterior chamber of the eye and in the abdominal cavity. *Amer. J. Anat.* **81**, 413–432.

Fee, A. R. and Parkes, A. S. (1929). Studies on ovulation: I. The relation of the anterior pituitary to ovulation in the rabbit. *J. Physiol.* **67**, 383–388.

Fell, H. B. (1924). Histological studies on the gonads of the fowl. 2. The histogenesis of the so-called 'luteal' cells in the ovary. *J. exp. Biol.* **1**, 97–103.

Felton, L. C., Frieden, E. H. and Bryant, H. H. (1953). The effects of ovarian extracts upon activity of the guinea-pig uterus *in situ*. *J. Pharmacol.* **107**, 160–164.

Ferguson, J. K. W. (1941). A study of the motility of the intact uterus at term. *Surg. Gynec. Obstet.* **73**, 359–366.

Firket, J. (1914). Recherches sur l'organogénèse des glandes chez les oiseaux. *Arch. Biol., Paris*, **29**, 201–351.

Firor, W. M. (1933). Hypophysectomy in pregnant rabbits. *Amer. J. Physiol.* **104**, 204–215.

Firor, W. M. and Grollman, A. (1933). Studies on the adrenals. I. Adrenalectomy in mammals with particular reference to the white rat (*Mus norvegicus*). *Amer. J. Physiol.* **103**, 686–698.

Folley, S. J. (1950). Lactational physiology. *In* "Modern Trends in Obstetrics and Gynaecology" (K. Bowes, ed.), pp. 441–453. Butterworth, London.

Folley, S. J. (1952). Lactation. *In* "Marshall's Physiology of Reproduction" (A. S. Parkes, ed.), 2nd ed., vol. II, pp. 525–647. Longmans Green, London.

Folley, S. J. (1956). "The Physiology and Biochemistry of Lactation." Oliver and Boyd, Edinburgh.

Folley, S. J. and Malpress, F. H. (1948). Hormonal control of mammary growth. *In* "The Hormones" (G. Pincus and K. V. Thimann, eds.), vol. I, pp. 695–743. Academic Press, New York.

Foote, W. D., Gooch, L. D., Pole, A. L. and Casida, L. E. (1957). The maintenance of early pregnancy in the ovariectomized ewe by injections of ovarian hormones. *J. Anim. Sci.* **16**, 986–989.

Forbes, T. R. (1953). Pre-ovulatory progesterone in the peripheral blood of the rabbit. *Endocrinology*, **53**, 79–87.

Foster, M. A. and Hisaw, F. L. (1935). Experimental ovulation and the resulting pseudopregnancy in anoestrous cats. *Anat. Rec.* **62**, 75–93.

Fraenkel, L. (1903). Die Function des Corpus luteum. *Arch. Gynaek.* **68**, 438–535.

Fraenkel, L. (1910). Neue Experimente zur Function des Corpus luteum. *Arch. Gynaek.* **91**, 705–761.

Fraenkel, L. (1927). Structure and function of endocrine glands, particularly ovary. *Amer. J. Obstet. Gynec.* **13**, 606–610.

Fraenkel, L. (1952). Zur Histo-Physiologie des Corpus luteum. *Arch. Gynaek.* **181**, 217–221.

Fraenkel, L. and Berruti, P. G. (1942). Thecal proliferations in the ovary of the infant; comparison with hyperthecosis in the adult. *Arch. Soc. Biol. Montevideo*, **10**, 267–273.

Fraenkel, L., Buño, W. and Grosso, O. F. (1941). Sobre las formaciónes para-luteinicas del ovario humano. II. *Congresso Panamer. de Endocrinol., Actas y Trabajos*, **1**, 268.

Fraenkel, L. and Cohn, F. (1901). Experimentelle Untersuchung über den Einfluss des Corpus luteum und die Insertion des Eies. *Anat. Anz.* **20**, 294–300.

Fraenkel, L. and Martins, T. (1938). Sur les corps jaunes des serpents vivipares. *C.R. Soc. Biol., Paris*, **127**, 466–468.

Fraenkel, L., Martins, T. and Mello, R. F. (1940). Studies on the pregnancy of viviparous snakes. *Endocrinology*, **27**, 836–837.

Fraenkel, L. and Papanicolaou, G. N. (1938). Growth desquamation and involution of the vaginal epithelium of foetuses and children with a consideration of the related hormonal factors. *Amer. J. Anat.* **62**, 427–441.

Frank, R. T. and Gustavson, R. G. (1925). The female sex hormone and the gestational gland. *J. Amer. med. Ass.* **84**, 1715–1719.

Fraps, R. M., Hooker, C. W. and Forbes, T. R. (1948). Progesterone in blood plasma of the ovulating hen. *Science*, **108**, 86–87.

Fraps, R. M., Hooker, C. W. and Forbes, T. R. (1949). Progesterone in blood plasma of cocks and non-ovulating hens. *Science*, **109**, 493.

Frazer, J. F. D. and Alexander, D. P. (1954). The effect of spaying in the pregnant rat. *J. Physiol.* **124**, 36–37P.

Galli-Mainini, C. (1950). Secreción de oviducto del sapo por el ovario en ovulación. *Mem. Soc. argent. Biol.* **26**, 166–178.

Gardner, W. U. (1936). Sexual dimorphism of the pelvis of the mouse, the effect of estrogenic hormones upon the pelvis and upon the development of scrotal hernias. *Amer. J. Anat.* **59**, 459–483.

Gardner, W. U. and Allen, E. (1942). Effects of hypophysectomy at mid-pregnancy in the mouse. *Anat. Rec.* **83**, 75–94.

Garrett, F. A. and Talmage, R. V. (1952). The influence of relaxin on mammary gland development in guinea-pigs and rabbits. *J. Endocrin.* **8**, 336–340.

Gaunt, R. and Hays, H. W. (1938). Rôle of progesterone and other hormones in survival of pseudopregnant adrenalectomized ferrets. *Amer. J. Physiol.* **124**, 767–773.

Giacomini, E. (1896). Contributo all'istologia dell' ovario dei selaci con speciale riguardo sopra alcune particolarità di struttura riscontrate nell' ovario di *Myliobatis bovina*, Geoff. St. Hil. *Ric. Lab. Anat. Norm. Univ. Roma*, **5**, 221.

Gillard, J. L. (1937). The effect of hysterectomy on mammary gland development in the rabbit. *Amer. J. Physiol.* **120**, 300–304.

Gillman, J. and Stein, H. B. (1941). The human corpus luteum of pregnancy. *Surg. Gynec. Obstet.* **72**, 129–149.

Glenister, T. W. (1960). Experimental nidation in organ culture. Oral communication. "Colloque de la Societé Nationale pour l'étude de la sterilité et de la fecondité."

Goormaghtigh, N. (1927). Le corps jaune de la chienne gravide. Contribution à l'étude du métabolisme des lipoides. *Arch. Biol., Paris*, **37**, 46–120.

Govan, A. D. T. and Mukherjee, C. L. (1950). Maternal toxaemia and foetal ovarian activity. *J. Obstet. Gynaec., Brit. Emp.* **57**, 525–529.

Gradinesco, A., Sarta, N. and Lucan-Janesco, F. (1935). Influence de la gestation sur la durée de survie chez les animaux surrénalectomisés. *C.R. Soc. Biol., Paris*, **120**, 356–358.

Grant, R. (1934). Studies on the physiology of reproduction in the ewe. Part III. Gross changes in the ovaries. *Trans. roy. Soc. Edinb.* **58**, 36–47.

Gray, L. A. and Lawson, H. (1939). Effects of testosterone propionate on ovulation and luteinization in the rabbit. *Proc. Soc. exp. Biol., N.Y.* **41**, 108–110.

Greenstein, J. S., Murray, R. W. and Foley, R. C. (1958). Effects of exogenous hormones on the reproductive processes of the cycling dairy heifer. *J. Dairy Sci.* **41**, 1834.

Greep, R. O. (1941). Effects of hysterectomy and of estrogen treatment on volume changes in the corpora lutea of pregnant rabbits. *Anat. Rec.* **80**, 465–476.

Greep, R. O. and Chester Jones, I. (1950). Steroid control of pituitary function. *Recent Progr. Hormone Res.* **5**, 197–261.

Greulich, W. W. (1934). Artificially induced ovulation in the cat (*Felix domesticus*). *Anat. Rec.* **58**, 217–224.

Griffiths, W. F. B. and Amoroso, E. C. (1939). Prooestrus, oestrus and mating in the greyhound bitch. *Vet. Rec.* **51**, 1279–1284.

Gros, G. (1935). Evolution de la muqueuse utérine chez la chatte. *C.R. Soc. Biol., Paris*, **131**, 172–174.

Gros, G. (1936). Contribution à l'endocrinologie sexuelle. Le cycle génital de la chatte. Thèse, Université d'Alger. No. 21.

Gurchot, C., Krebs, E. T. Jr., and Krebs, E. T. (1947). Growth of human trophoblast in the eye of the rabbit. Its relationship to the origin of cancer. *Surg. Gynec. Obstet.* **84**, 301–312.

Hadek, R. (1955). The secretory processes in the sheep's oviduct. *Anat. Rec.* **121**, 187–201.

Hagopian, M., Pincus, G., Carlo, J. and Romanoff, E. B. (1956). Isolation of an unknown substance 6-ketoprogesterone from perfusates of human placentae. *Endocrinology*, **58**, 387–388.

Hain, A. M. (1934). The physiology of pregnancy in the rat. Further data bearing on the prolongation of pregnancy, with a study of the effects of oophorectomy during pregnancy. *Quart. J. exp. Physiol.* **24**, 101–112.

Hall, K. (1947). The effects of pregnancy and relaxin on the histology of the pubic symphysis in mice. *J. Endocrin.* **5**, 174–185.

Hall, K. (1948). Further notes on the action of oestrone and relaxin on the pelvis of the spayed mouse, including a single dose test of the potency of relaxin. *J. Endocrin.* **5**, 314–321.

Hall, K. (1949). The rôle of progesterone in the mechanism of pelvic relaxation in the mouse. *Quart. J. exp. Physiol.* **35**, 65–75.

Hall, K. (1956). An evaluation of the rôles of oestrogen, progesterone and relaxin in producing relaxation of the symphysis pubis of the ovariectomized mouse, using the technique of metachromatic staining with toluidine blue. *J. Endocrin.* **13**, 384–393.

520   E. C. AMOROSO AND C. A. FINN

Hall, K. (1957). The effect of relaxin extracts, progesterone and oestradiol on maintenance of pregnancy, parturition and rearing of young after ovariectomy in mice. *J. Endocrin.* **15**, 108–117.

Hall, K. and Newton, W. H. (1946a). The action of 'relaxin' in the mouse. *Lancet*, **1**, 54–55.

Hall, K. and Newton, W. H. (1946b). The normal course of separation of the pubes in pregnant mice. *J. Physiol.* **104**, 346–352.

Hall, K. and Newton, W. H. (1947). The effect of oestrone and relaxin on the X-ray appearance of the pelvis of the mouse. *J. Physiol.* **106**, 18–27.

Hall, O. (1952). Accessory corpora lutea in the wild Norway rat. *Texas Rep. Biol. Med.* **10**, 32–38.

Hamilton, W. J. and Day, F. T. (1945). Cleavage stages of the ova of the horse, with notes on ovulation. *J. Anat., Lond.* **79**, 127–130.

Hamilton, W. J. and Laing, J. A. (1946). Development of the egg of the cow up to the stage of blastocyst formation. *J. Anat., Lond.* **80**, 194–204.

Hamlett, G. W. D. (1935). Delayed implantation and discontinuous development in the mammals. *Quart. Rev. Biol.* **10**, 432–447.

Hammond, J. (1917). On the causes responsible for the developmental progress of the mammary glands in the rabbit during the latter part of pregnancy. *Proc. roy. Soc.* B. **89**, 534–546.

Hammond, J. (1925). "Reproduction in the Rabbit." Oliver and Boyd, Edinburgh.

Hammond, J. (1927). "The Physiology of Reproduction in the Cow." Cambridge University Press.

Hammond, J. and Day, F. T. (1947). Oestrogen treatment of cattle. Induced lactation and other effects. *J. Endocrin.* **4**, 53–82.

Hammond, J. and Marshall, F. H. A. (1914). The functional correlation between the ovaries, uterus and mammary glands in the rabbit, with observations on the oestrous cycle. *Proc. roy. Soc.* B. **87**, 422–440.

Hammond, J. and Marshall, F. H. A. (1930). Oestrus and pseudopregnancy in the ferret. *Proc. roy. Soc.* B. **105**, 607–630.

Hammond, J. Jr. (1951). Failure of progesterone treatment to affect delayed implantation in mink. *J. Endocrin.* **7**, 330–334.

Hammond, J. Jr. (1952). Maintenance of grafted luteal tissue. *Nature, Lond.* **169**, 330–331.

Hammond, J. Jr. (1956). The rabbit corpus luteum: Oestrogen prolongation and the accompanying changes in the genitalia. *Acta endocr., Copenhagen*, **21**, 307–320.

Hamolsky, M. and Sparrow, R. C. (1945). Influence of relaxin on mammary development in sexually immature female rats. *Proc. Soc. exp. Biol., N.Y.* **60**, 8–9.

Hansel, W. and Trimberger, C. W. (1951). Atropine blockade of ovulation in the cow and its possible significance. *J. Anim. Sci.* **10**, 719–724.

Hansson, A. (1947). "The Physiology of Reproduction in Mink (*Mustela vison, Schreb.*): with Special Reference to Delayed Implantation." Stockholm.

Harris, G. W. (1947). The innervation and actions of the neurohypophysis: an investigation using the method of remote-control stimulation. *Phil. Trans.* B. **232**, 385–441.

Harris, R. G. (1927). Effect of bilateral ovariectomy upon duration of pregnancy in mice. *Anat. Rec.* **37**, 83–93.

Harrison, R. J. (1948). The development and fate of the corpus luteum in the vertebrate series. *Biol. Rev.* **23**, 296–351.

Harrison, R. J. (1949). Observations on the female reproductive organs of the Ca'aing whale, *Globiocephala melaena* Traill. *J. Anat. Lond.* **83**, 238–253.

Harrison, R. J., Matthews, L. H. and Roberts, J. M. (1952). Reproduction in some Pinnipedia. *Trans. zool. Soc. Lond.* **27**, 437–540.

Hart, G. H. and Cole, H. H. (1934). The source of oestrin in the pregnant mare. *Amer. J. Physiol.* **109**, 320–323.

Hartman, C. G. (1920). "Studies on the Development of the Opossum (*Didelphys virginiana* L.)." Philadelphia.

Hartman, C. G. (1921). Breeding habits, development and birth of the opossum. *Rep. Smithson. Instn.* **1**, 347–363.

Hartman, C. G. (1925a). Hysterectomy and the oestrous cycle in the opossum. *Amer. J. Anat.* **35**, 25–29.

Hartman, C. G. (1925b). Interruption of pregnancy by ovariectomy in the placental opossum. Study in physiology of implantation. *Amer. J. Physiol.* **71**, 436–454.

Hartman, C. G. (1939). Ovulation, fertilization and the transport and viability of eggs and spermatozoa. *In* "Sex and Internal Secretions" (E. Allen, ed.), 2nd ed., pp. 647–733. Williams and Wilkins, Baltimore.

Hartman, C. G. (1941). Non-effect of ovariectomy on the 25th day of pregnancy in the rhesus monkey. *Proc. Soc. exp. Biol., N.Y.* **48**, 221–223.

Hartman, C. G. and Corner, G. W. (1947). Removal of the corpus luteum and of the ovaries of the rhesus monkey during pregnancy, observations and cautions. *Anat. Rec.* **98**, 539–546.

Hartmann, M. and Wettstein, A. (1934a). Ein krystallisiertes Hormon aus Corpus-luteum. *Helv. chim. acta*, **17**, 878–882.

Hartmann, M. and Wettstein, A. (1934b). Zur Kenntnis des Corpus-luteum Hormon. *Helv. chim. acta*, **17**, 1365–1372.

Harvey, W. (1651). "The Works of William Harvey." Translated by Willis, R. (1847). Sydenham Society, London.

Haterius, H. O. (1935). Oophorectomy and maintenance of pregnancy in the rat. *Proc. Soc. exp. Biol., N.Y.* **33**, 101–102.

Haterius, H. O. (1936). Reduction of litter size and maintenance of pregnancy in the oophorectomized rat: evidence concerning the endocrine rôle of the placenta. *Amer. J. Physiol.* **114**, 399–406.

Haterius, H. O. and Kempner, M. I. (1939). Uterine distention and maintenance of pregnancy following oophorectomy in the rat. *Proc. Soc. exp. Biol., N.Y.* **42**, 322–325.

Heape, W. (1905). Ovulation and degeneration of ova in the rabbit. *Proc. roy. Soc. B.* **76**, 260–268.

Hechter, O., Fraenkel, M., Lev, M. and Soskin, S. (1940). Influence of the uterus on the corpus luteum. *Endocrinology*, **26**, 680–683.

Heckel, G. P. (1942). The oestrogen sparing effect of hysterectomy. *Surg. Gynec. Obstet.* **75**, 379–390.

Heckel, G. P. and Allen, W. M. (1936). Prolongation of the corpus luteum in the pseudopregnant rabbit. *Science*, **84**, 161–162.

Heckel, G. P. and Allen, W. M. (1939). Maintenance of the corpus luteum and inhibition of parturition in the rabbit by injection of oestrogenic hormone. *Endocrinology*, **24**, 137–148.

Herrick, E. H. (1928). Duration of pregnancy in guinea-pigs after removal and also after transplantation of ovaries. *Anat. Rec.* 39, 193–200.

Hett, J. (1924). Das Corpus luteum der Zauneidechse (*Lacerta agilis*). *Arch. mikr.-anat. Forsch.* 1, 41.

Hett, J. (1933). Vergleichende Anatomie der Corpora lutea. *In* "Handbuch der vergleichenden Anatomie der Wirbeltiere" (W. Bolk, E. Göppert, E. Kallius and W. Lubosch, eds.). Bd. VI, pp. 253–266. Urban and Schwarzenberg, Berlin and Vienna.

Hill, J. P. and Gatenby, J. B. (1926). The corpus luteum of the Monotremata. *Proc. Zool. Soc. Lond.* 47, 715–763.

Hisaw, F. L. (1925). The influence of the ovary on the resorption of the pubic bones of the pocket gopher, *Geomys bursarius* (Shaw). *J. exp. Zool.* 42, 411–433.

Hisaw, F. L. (1926). Experimental relaxation of the pelvic ligament of the guinea pig. *Proc. Soc. exp. Biol., N.Y.* 23, 661–663.

Hisaw, F. L. (1929). The corpus luteum hormones. 1. Experimental relaxation of the pelvic ligaments of the guinea pig. *Physiol. Zoöl.* 2, 59–79.

Hisaw, F. L. (1947). Development of the Graafian follicle and ovulation. *Physiol. Rev.* 27, 95–119.

Hisaw, F. L. (1959). Endocrine adaptations of the mammalian estrous cycle and gestation. *In* "Comparative Endocrinology" (A. Gorbman, ed.), pp. 533–552. Academic Press, New York.

Hisaw, F. L. and Abramowitz, A. A. (1938). The physiology of reproduction in the dog fish, *Mustelus canis. Rep. Wood's Hole oceanogr. Instn.* (1937), 21–22.

Hisaw, F. L. and Abramowitz, A. A. (1939). Physiology of reproduction in the dog fish, *Mustelus canis* and *Squalus acanthius. Rep. Wood's Hole oceanogr. Instn.* (1938), 22.

Hisaw, F. L. and Albert, A. (1947). Observations on the reproduction of the spiny dog fish, *Squalus acanthias. Biol. Bull., Wood's Hole*, 92, 187.

Hisaw, F. L. and Zarrow, M. X. (1948). Relaxin in the ovary of the domestic sow. *Proc. Soc. exp. Biol., N.Y.* 69, 395–398.

Hisaw, F. L. and Zarrow, M. X. (1950). The physiology of relaxin. *Vitam. & Hormon.* 8, 151–178.

Hisaw, F. L. and Zilley, M. L. (1927). A study of the pelvic girdle of 20 mm embryos of the mole, *Scalopus aquaticus machrinus* (Ras.) *J. Mammal.* 8, 115–118.

Hisaw, F. L., Zarrow, M. X., Money, W. L., Talmage, R. V. N. and Abramowitz, A. A. (1944). Importance of the female reproductive tract in the formation of relaxin. *Endocrinology*, 34, 122–134.

Hisaw, F. L. Jr. and Hisaw, F. L. (1959). Corpora lutea of elasmobranch fishes. *Anat. Rec.* 135, 269–273.

Hoar, W. S. (1955). Reproduction in bony fishes. *Mem. Soc. Endocrin.* No. 4, 5–24.

Höhn, E. O. and Robson, J. M. (1949). Mode of action of oestrogens on the corpus luteum. *Endocrinology*, 44, 536–541.

Hohlweg, W. (1934). Veränderungen des Hypophysenvorderlappens und des Ovariums nach Behandlung mit grossen Dosen von Follikelhormon. *Klin. Wschr.* 13, 92–95.

Houssay, B. A. (1935). Action de l'hypophysectomie sur la grossesse et la secretion lactée chez la chienne. *C.R. Soc. Biol., Paris*, 120, 496–497.

Houssay, B. A. (1945). Acción de la insuficiencia suprarenal durante la prenez sobre la madre y el hijo. *Rev. Soc. argent. Biol.* **21**, 316–331.

Houssay, B. A. (1947). Ovulación y postura del sapo *Bufo arenarum* Hensel. V. Transporte de los ovulos por el oviducto y el utero. *Rev. Soc. argent. Biol.* **23**, 275–287.

Houssay, B. A. (1949). Hypophyseal functions in the toad *Bufo arenarum* Hensel. *Quart. Rev. Biol.* **24**, 1–27.

Huber, G. C. (1915). The development of the albino rat. *J. Morph.* **26**, 247–358.

Huggett, A. St. G. and Pritchard, J. J. (1945a). Experimental foetal death: The surviving placenta. *Proc. R. Soc. Med.* **38**, 261–266.

Huggett, A. St. G. and Pritchard, J. J. (1945b). Placental growth after foetal death in the rat. *J. Physiol.* **104**, 4P.

Ingle, D. J. and Fisher, G. T. (1938). Effects of adrenalectomy during gestation on the size of the adrenal glands of newborn rats. *Proc. Soc. exp. Biol., N.Y.* **39**, 149–153.

Jailer, J. W. and Knowlton, A. I. (1950). Simulated adrenocortical activity during pregnancy in an Addisonian patient. *J. clin. Invest.* **29**, 1430–1436.

Johnson, G. E. and Challans, J. S. (1930). Ovariectomy and corpus luteum extract experiments in pregnant rats. *Anat. Rec.* **47**, 300–301 (Abstr.).

Johnson, G. E. and Challans, J. S. (1932). Ovariectomy and corpus luteum extract studies on rats and ground squirrels. *Endocrinology*, **16**, 278–284.

Jones, J. M., Lloyd, C. W. and Wyatt, T. C. (1953). A study of the inter-relationship of maternal and fetal adrenal glands of rats. *Endocrinology*, **53**, 182–191.

Jost, A., Jacquot, R. and Cohen, A. (1955). Sur les interrélations entre les hormones corticosurrénaliennes maternelles et la surrénale du foetus de rat. *C.R. Soc. Biol., Paris*, **149**, 1319–1322.

Kamell, S. A. and Atkinson, W. B. (1948). Absence of prolongation of pseudo-pregnancy by induction of deciduomata in the mouse. *Proc. Soc. exp. Biol., N.Y.* **67**, 415–416.

Kasturirangen, L. R. (1951). Placentation in the sea-snakes, *Enhydrina schistosa. Proc. Indian Acad. Sci.* **127**, 142.

Kehl, R. (1950). La nidation normale et pathologique. *Bull. Ass. Gynéc. Lang. Franç.* **2**, 68–70.

Kellas, L. M., Lennep, E. W. van and Amoroso, E. C. (1958). Ovaries of some foetal and prepubertal giraffes (*Giraffa camelopardalis*, Linnaeus). *Nature, Lond.* **181**, 487–488.

Keller, K. (1924). Vergleichende Physiologie der weiblichen Sexualorgane bei den Säugetieren. *In* "Biologie und Pathologie des Weibes" (J. Halban and L. Seitz, eds.), Bd. I, pp. 761–802. Urban and Schwarzenberg, Vienna.

Khartov, V. P. (1938). New information on the durability of retention of the corpus luteum in the dolphin. *Bull. Biol. Med. Exp. U.S.S.R.* **5**, 27–28.

Kidder, H. E. (1954). Studies on fertilization failure and embryonic death: effects of the male and pre-ovulatory environment of ova. Thesis, University of Wisconsin.

Kidder, H. E., Casida, L. E. and Grummer, R. H. (1955). Some effects of estrogen injections on the estrual cycle of gilts. *J. Anim. Sci.* **14**, 470–474.

Kido, I. (1937). Die menschliche Placenta als Produktionsstätte des sogenann-ten Hypophysenvorderlappenhormons. *Zbl. Gynäk.* **61**, 1551–1555.

Kimura, J. and Lyons, W. R. (1937). Progestin in the pregnant mare. *Proc. Soc. exp. Biol., N.Y.* **37**, 423–427.

Kirsch, R. E. (1938). A study in the control of length of gestation in the rat with notes on maintenance and termination of gestation. *Amer. J. Physiol.* **122**, 86–93.

Klein, M. (1928). Relation between the uterus and the ovaries in the pregnant hamster. *Proc. roy. Soc.* B. **125**, 348–364.

Klein, M. (1933). Sur l'ablation des embryons chez la lapine gravide et sur les facteurs qui déterminent le maintien du corps jaune pendant la deuxième partie de la grossesse. *C.R. Soc. Biol., Paris*, **113**, 441–443.

Klein, M. (1934). Le corps jaune de grossesse. Recherches histologiques et physiologiques. *Arch. Anat. Hist. Embryol.* **18**, 1–143.

Klein, M. (1935). Recherches sur le rôle du placenta dans l'arrêt des manifestations du cycle ovarien au cours de la grossesse. *Arch. Anat. micr. Morph. exp.* **31**, 397–416.

Klein, M. (1937). The mucification of the vaginal epithelium in rodents. *Proc. roy. Soc.* B. **124**, 23–29.

Klein, M. (1938a). Relation between the uterus and the ovaries in the pregnant hamster. *Proc. roy. Soc.* B. **125**, 348–364.

Klein, M. (1938b). Sur les facteurs qui maintiennent l'activité fonctionelle du corps jaune gravidique. *In* "Les Hormones Sexuelles", p. 86. Colloque international Singer-Polignac. Hermann, Paris.

Klein, M. (1939a). Prolongation artificielle de la durée du corps jaune de grossesse chez la lapine. *C.R. Soc. Biol., Paris*, **130**, 929–931.

Klein, M. (1939b). Comportement de la corne utérine et de la glande mammaire lors de la prolongation artificielle de la durée du corpe jaune gravidique chez la lapine. *C.R. Soc. Biol., Paris*, **130**, 931–933.

Klein, M. (1939c). Action du placenta sur le corps jaune gravidique et sur le cycle vaginal chez le cobaye. *C.R. Soc. Biol., Paris*, **130**, 1392–1395.

Klein, M. and Mayer, G. (1942a). Sur la parturition partielle chez la rate. *Arch. Phys. Biol., France*, **16**, 125–127.

Klein, M. and Mayer, G. (1942b). Sur la parturition partielle chez la rate. *Arch. Phys. Biol., France*, **16**, 127–128.

Koff, A. K. and Davis, M. E. (1937). Mechanism of prolongation of pregnancy in the rabbit. *Amer. J. Obstet. Gynec.* **34**, 26–37.

Krehbiel, R. H. (1937). Cytological studies of the decidual reaction in the rat during early pregnancy and the production of deciduomata. *Physiol. Zoöl.* **10**, 212–234.

Krehbiel, R. H. (1941a). The effects of lactation on the implantation of ova of a concurrent pregnancy in the rat. *Anat. Rec.* **81**, 43–64.

Krehbiel, R. H. (1941b). The effects of theelin on delayed implantation in the pregnant lactating rat. *Anat. Rec.* **81**, 381–392.

Kroc, R. L., Steinetz, B. G. and Beach, V. L. (1958). The effects of estrogens, progestagens and relaxin in pregnant and non-pregnant laboratory rodents. *Ann. N.Y. Acad. Sci.* **75**, 942–980.

Lamotte, M. and Rey, P. (1954). Existence de corpora lutea chez un batracien anoure vivipare, *Nectophrynoides occidentalis* Angel; leur évolution morphologique. *C.R. Acad. Sci., Paris*, **238**, 393–395.

Lataste, F. (1887). Recherches de zoöetique sur les mammifères de l'ordre des rongeurs. *Act. Soc. Linn., Bordeaux*, **40**, 293–466.

Lataste, F. (1891). Des variations de durée de la gestation chez les mammifères et des circonstances qui déterminent ces variations. Théorie de la gestation retardée. *C.R. Soc. Biol., Paris*, **43**, 21–31.

Laws, R. M. (1958). Recent investigations on fin whale ovaries. *The Norwegian Whaling Gazette*, No. 5, pp. 225–254.

Leonard, S. L. (1945). The relation of the placenta to the growth of the mammary gland of the rat during the last half of pregnancy. *Anat. Rec.* **91**, 65–71.

Lewis, W. H. and Wright, E. S. (1935). On the early development of the mouse egg. *Contr. Embryol. Carneg. Instn.* **25**, 113–144.

Lindner, A., Satke, I. and Voelkel, O. (1951). Die inverse Wirkung von Hexöstrol-implantationen auf den Geschlechtszyklus weiblicher Ratten. *Arch. int. Pharmacodyn.* **86**, 421–433.

Linzell, J. L. (1959). Physiology of the mammary glands. *Physiol. Rev.* **39**, 534–576.

Little, B., Smith, O. W., Kessiman, A. G., Selenkow, H. A., Hoff, W. van't, Eglin, J. M. and Moore, F. D. (1958). Hypophysectomy during pregnancy in a patient with cancer of the breast: case report with hormone studies. *J. clin. Endocrin.* **18**, 425–443.

Lloyd, C. W., Hughes, E. C., Lobotsky, J., Renzo, J. and Avery, G. M. (1952). Some hormone studies in normal and toxaemic pregnancy. *J. clin. Invest.* **31**, 1056–1063.

Loeb, L. (1907). Über die experimentelle Erzeugung von Knoten von Deciduagewebe in dem Uterus des Meerschweinchens nach stattgefundener Copulation. *Zbl. allg. Path. path. Anat.* **18**, 563–565.

Loeb, L. (1908a). The experimental production of the maternal part of the placenta in the rabbit. *Proc. Soc. exp. Biol., N.Y.* **5**, 102–104.

Loeb, L. (1908b). The production of deciduomata and the relation between the ovaries and the formation of the decidua. *J. Amer. med. Ass.* **50**, 1897.

Loeb, L. (1911a). The cyclic changes in the ovary of the guinea pig. *J. Morph.* **22**, 37–70.

Loeb, L. (1911b). Über die Bedeutung des Corpus luteum für die Periodizität des sexuellen Zyklus beim weiblichen Säugetier-organismus. *Dtsch. med. Wschr.* **37**, 17–21.

Loeb, L. (1923a). Mechanism of the sexual cycle with special reference to the corpus luteum. *Amer. J. Anat.* **32**, 305–343.

Loeb, L. (1923b). The effect of extirpation of the uterus on the life and function of the corpus luteum in the guinea pig. *Proc. Soc. exp. Biol., N.Y.* **20**, 441–443.

Loeb, L. (1927). The effects of hysterectomy on the system of sex organs and on the periodicity of the sexual cycle in the guinea pig. *Amer. J. Physiol.* **83**, 202–224.

Loeb, L. and Hesselberg, C. (1917). The cyclic changes in the mammary gland under normal and pathological conditions. 1. The changes in the non-pregnant guinea-pig. *J. exp. Med.* **25**, 285–321.

Loeb, L. and Smith, M. G. (1936). The effect of hysterectomy on the duration of life and retrogression of the corpora lutea and on secondary sex organs in the rabbit. *Amer. J. Anat.* **58**, 1–25.

Long, J. A. and Evans, H. M. (1922). The oestrous cycle in the rat and its associated phenomena. *Mem. Univ. Calif.* **6**, 1–111.

Loy, R. G., Zimbelman, R. G. and Casida, L. E. (1960). Effects of injected ovarian hormones on the corpus luteum of the estrual cycle in cattle. *J. Anim. Sci.* **19**, 175–182.

Lucas, A. M. (1930). The structure and activity of the ciliated epithelium lining the vertebrate Fallopian tube. *Anat. Rec.* **45**, 230 (Abstr.).

Lucien, M. (1903a). Note préliminaire sur les premières phases de la formation des corps jaunes chez certains reptiles. *C.R. Soc. Biol., Paris*, **55**, 1116–1117.

Lucien, M. (1903b). Corpi lutei veri et falsi dei rettili. *Rec. Lab. Anat. Norm. Univ. Roma*, **3**, 105.

Lutwak-Mann, C. (1959). Biochemical approach to the study of ovum implantation in the rabbit. *Mem. Soc. Endocrin.* No. 6, 35–46.

Lutwak-Mann, C. (1960). Aspects biochimiques de l'implantation de l'oeuf. *In* "Les Fonctions de Nidation Utérine et leurs Troubles", pp. 125–138. Masson, Paris.

Lyons, W. R. (1943). Pregnancy maintenance in hypophysectomised-oophorectomised rats injected with estrone and progesterone. *Proc. Soc. exp. Biol., N.Y.* **54**, 65–68.

Lyons, W. R. and McGinty, D. A. (1941). Effect of estrone and progesterone on male rabbit mammary glands with varying doses of progesterone. *Proc. Soc. exp. Biol., N.Y.* **48**, 83–86.

Lyons, W. R., Simpson, M. E. and Evans, H. M. (1943). Hormonal requirements for pregnancy and mammary development in hypophysectomized rats. *Proc. Soc. exp. Biol., N.Y.* **52**, 134–136.

McDonald, L. E., Nichols, R. E. and McNutt, S. H. (1952). Studies on corpus luteum ablation and progesterone replacement therapy during pregnancy in the cow. *Amer. J. vet. Res.* **13**, 446–451.

McDonald, L. E., Nichols, R. E. and McNutt, S. H. (1953). On the essentiality of the bovine corpus luteum of pregnancy. *Amer. J. vet. Res.* **14**, 539–541.

McIlroy, A. L. (1912). Some experimental work upon the physiological function of the ovary. *J. Obstet. Gynaec., Brit. Emp.* **22**, 19–26.

McKay, D. G. and Robinson, D. (1947). Observations on the fluorescence, birefringence and histochemistry of the human ovary during the menstrual cycle. *Endocrinology*, **41**, 378–394.

McKenzie, F. F. and Terrill, C. E. (1937). Estrus, ovulation and related phenomena in the ewe. *Res. Bull. Mo. agric. Exp. Sta.* No. 264.

McKeown, T. and Zuckerman, S. (1938). The suppression of oestrus in the rat during pregnancy and lactation. *Proc. roy. Soc. B.* **124**, 464–475.

McPhail, M. K. (1935a). Studies on the hypophysectomized ferret. 9. The effect of hypophysectomy on pregnancy and lactation. *Proc. roy. Soc. B.* **117** 34–44.

McPhail, M. K. (1935b). Hypophysectomy of the cat. *Proc. roy. Soc. B.* **117**, 45–63.

Maekawa, K. (1954). Effects of estrogen administration on intrasplenic ovarian grafts in rats in which gonadal secretions are experimentally reduced. *J. Fac. Sci., Univ. Tokyo*, **7**, 161–176.

Maekawa, K. (1956). Activation of corpora lutea by oestrogen. *J. Fac. Sci., Univ. Tokyo*, Sec. IV, **7**, 573.

Marder, S. N. and Money, W. L. (1944). Concentration of relaxin in the blood serum of pregnant and postpartum rabbits. *Endocrinology*, **34**, 115–121.

Markee, J. E., Everett, J. W. and Sawyer, C. H. (1952). The relationship of the nervous system to the release of gonadotrophin and the regulation of the sex cycle. *Recent Progr. Hormone Res.* **7**, 139–163.

Marois, M. (1948). Action locale de la progestérone sur la corne utérine et relâchement de la symphyse pubienne du cobaye. *C.R. Soc. Biol. Paris*, **142**, 1407–1408.

Marois, M. (1949). Déciduome traumatique, symphyse pubienne et rapport oestradiol-progestérone chez le cobaye. *C.R. Soc. Biol., Paris*, **143**, 370–372.

Marrian, G. F. (1929). The chemistry of oestrin. I. Preparation from urine and the separation from an unidentified solid alcohol. *Biochem. J.* **23**, 1090–1098.

Marshall, A. J. and Coombs, C. J. F. (1957). The interaction of environmental, internal and behavioural factors in the rook, *Corvus f. frugilegus* Linnaeus. *Proc. zool. Soc. Lond.* **128**, 545–588.

Marshall, F. H. A. and Halnan, E. T. (1917). On the post-oestrous changes occurring in the generative organs and mammary glands of the non-pregnant dog. *Proc. roy. Soc.* B. **89**, 546–559.

Marshall, F. H. A. and Jolly, W. A. (1905a). The oestrous cycle in the dog. The ovary as an organ of internal secretion. *Proc. roy. Soc.* B. **76**, 395–398.

Marshall, F. H. A. and Jolly, W. A. (1905b). The oestrous cycle in the dog. II. The ovary as an organ of internal secretion. *Phil. Trans.* B. **198**, 123–141.

Marshall, F. H. A. and Verney, E. B. (1936). The occurrence of ovulation in the rabbit as a result of central nervous stimulation. *J. Physiol.* **86**, 327–336.

Marx, R. (1935). Influence of hysterectomy on endocrine balance. *Amer. J. Surg.* **28**, 117–121.

Matthews, L. H. (1935). The oestrous cycle and intersexuality in the female mole (*Talpa europaea* Linn.). *Proc. zool. Soc. Lond.* pp. 347–383.

Matthews, L. H. (1937). The female sexual cycle in the British horseshoe bats. *Trans. zool. Soc. Lond.* **23**, 224–255.

Matthews, L. H. (1939). Reproduction in the spotted hyaena *Crocuta crocuta* (Erxleben). *Phil. Trans.* **230**, 1–78.

Matthews, L. H. (1941). The genitalia and reproduction of some African bats. *Proc. zool. Soc. Lond.* B. **111**, 289–346.

Matthews, L. H. (1955). The evolution of viviparity in vertebrates. *Mem. Soc. Endocrin.* No. 4, 129–148.

Mayer, G. (1952). Histophysiologie des corps pro-gestatifs et gestatifs. *Arch. Anat. Histol. Embryol.* **34**, 305–319.

Mayer, G. (1953). Histophysiologie de l'état gravidique. *C.R. Ass. Anat., Paris*, **40**, 28–78.

Mayer, G. (1956). Interférence entre lactation et gestation. *Ann. Endocr., Paris*, **17**, 557–571.

Mayer, G. (1959a). L'ovo-implantation et la vie latente de l'oeuf. *Bull. Soc. Belge Gynéc. Obstet.* **29**, 1.

Mayer, G. (1959b). Recent studies on hormonal control of delayed implantation and superimplantation in the rat. *Mem. Soc. Endocrin.* No. 6, 76–83.

Mayer, G. (1960). Morphologie et physiologie comparées de l'ovo-implantation. Resultats et problèmes. *In* "Les Fonctions de Nidation Utérine et leurs Troubles", pp. 1–32. Masson, Paris.

Mayer, G. and Canivenc, R. (1950a). Autogreffes de placenta chez la rate. *C.R. Soc. Biol., Paris*, **144**, 410–412.

Mayer, G. and Canivenc, R. (1950b). Placenta et lactogénèse. *In* "Mécanisme Physiologique de la Sécrétion Lactée." Colloque International du C.N.R.S. p. 125. Strasbourg.

Mayer, G. and Canivenc, R. (1951). Placenta et équilibre hormonal gravidique chez la rate. Activité du placenta en l'absence d'ovaires. Réaction de la glande mammaire et du vagin. *C.R. Soc. Biol., Paris*, **145**, 1688–1692.

Mayer, G. and Klein, M. (1955). Les hormones du placenta. *In* "L'Équilibre Hormonal de la Gestation; les Androgènes dans l'Organisme Féminin; la Cortisone dans l'Équilibre Hormonal". *Rapports de la IIIe réunion des endocrinologistes de langue française.* Paris.

528   E. C. AMOROSO AND C. A. FINN

Meites, J. (1959). Mammary growth and lactation. *In* "Reproduction in Domestic Animals" (H. H. Cole and P. T. Cupps, eds.), vol. I, pp. 539–593. Academic Press, New York.

Meites, J. and Sgouris, J. T. (1953). Can the ovarian hormones inhibit the mammary response to prolaction? *Endocrinology*, **53**, 17–23.

Meites, J. and Turner, C. W. (1948a). Studies concerning the induction and maintenance of lactation. II. The influence of various factors on the lactogen content of the pituitary. *Res. Bull. Mo. agric. Exp. Sta.* No. 415.

Meites, J. and Turner, C. W. (1948b). Studies concerning the induction of lactation. I. The experimental maintenance and experimental inhibition and augmentation of lactation. *Res. Bull. Mo. agric. Exp. Sta.* No. 416.

Meites, J., Webster, H. D., Young, F. W., Thorpe, F. J. and Hatch, R. N. (1951). Effect of corpora lutea ablation and replacement therapy with progesterone on gestation in goats. *J. Anim. Sci.* **10**, 411–416.

Merckel, C. and Nelson, W. O. (1940). The relation of the estrogenic hormone in the formation and maintenance of corpora lutea in mature and immature rats. *Anat. Rec.* **76**, 391–401.

du Mesnil du Buisson, F. and Dauzier, L. (1957). Influence de l'ovariectomie chez la truie pendant la gestation. *C.R. Soc. Biol., Paris*, **161**, 311–313.

du Mesnil du Buisson, F. and Dauzier, L. (1959). Contrôle mutuel de l'utérus et de l'ovaire chez la truie. *Annales Zootechnie*, (Suppl.), pp. 147–159.

Meunier, J. M. and Mayer, G. (1960). Facteurs neuropituitaires de la nidation retardée. Oral communication. *Colloque de la Société nationale pour l'étude de la Sterilité et de la Fecondité.* Brussels.

Meyer, R. (1911). Ueber Corpus luteum-Bildung beim Menschen. *Arch. Gynaek.* **93**, 354–405.

Meyer, R. (1913). Ueber die Beziehung der Eizelle und des befruchteten Eies zum Follikelapparat, sowie des Corpus luteum zur Menstruation. *Arch. Gynaek.* **100**, 1–19.

Micale, G. (1940). Possibility of experimentally prolonging the duration of the corpus luteum after ablation of the pregnant uterus. (trans.) *Boll. Soc. ital. Biol. sper.* **15**, 381–382.

Mikulicz-Radecki, F. von. (1930). Untersuchungen über die Tubenkontraktionen mit Hilfe der Pertubation. *Zbl. Gynäk.* **54**, 2183–2191.

Mikulicz-Radecki, F. von and Nahmmacher, W. (1925). Zur Physiologie der Tube. II. Mitteilung. Beobachtung von Fortbewegung korpuskulärer Elemente in der Kaninchentube durch Muskelkontraktionen. *Zbl. Gynäk.* **49**, 2322–2327.

Miller, J. W., Kisley, A. and Murray, W. J. (1957). The effects of relaxin-containing ovarian extracts on various types of smooth muscle. *J. Pharmacol.* **120**, 426–437.

Miller, M. R. (1948). The seasonal histological changes occurring in the ovary, corpus luteum and testis of the viviparous lizard, *Xantusia vigilis. Univ. Calif. Publ. Zool.* **47**, 197–224.

Mingazzini, P. (1893). Corpi lutei veri et falsi dei rettili. *Ric. Lab. Anat. Norm. Univ. Roma*, **3**, 105.

Mishell, D. R. and Motyloff, L. (1941). The effect of hysterectomy on the ovary with reference to a possible hormonal action of the endometrium upon the ovary. *Endocrinology*, **28**, 436–440.

Mixner, J. P. and Turner, C. W. (1940). Rôle of oestrogen in the stimulation of mammary lobule-alveolar growth by progesterone and by the mammogenic lobule-alveolar growth factor of the anterior pituitary. *Endocrinology*, **30**, 591–596.

Mixner, J. P. and Turner, C. W. (1943). The mammogenic hormones of the anterior pituitary. II. The lobule-alveolar growth factor. *Res. Bull. Mo. agric. Exp. Sta.* No. 378.

Moore, W. W. and Nalbandov, A. V. (1953). Neurogenic effects of uterine distension on the estrous cycle of the ewe. *Endocrinology*, **53**, 1–11.

Mossman, H. W. (1937). The thecal gland and its relation to the reproductive cycle. A study of the cyclic changes in the ovary of the pocket gopher, *Geomys bursarius* (Shaw). *Amer. J. Anat.* **61**, 289–311.

Mossman, H. W. and Judas, I. (1949). Accessory corpora lutea, lutein cell origin, and the ovarian cycle in the Canadian porcupine. *Amer. J. Anat.* **85**, 1–39.

Murphy, D. P. (1934). The weight of rat ovaries after hysterectomy. *Anat. Rec.* **60**, 77–81.

Nalbandov, A. V., Moore, W. W. and Norton, H. W. (1955). Further studies on the neurogenic control of the estrous cycle by uterine distension. *Endocrinology*, **56**, 225–231.

Neher, G. M. and Zarrow, M. X. (1954). Concentration of progestin in the serum of the non-pregnant, pregnant and post partum ewe. *J. Endocrin.* **11**, 323–330.

Nelson, W. O. (1934). Studies on the physiology of lactation. III. The reciprocal hypophysial-ovarian relationship as a factor in the control of lactation. *Endocrinology*, **18**, 33–46.

Nelson, W. O. (1935). The effect of hypophysectomy upon mammary gland development and function in the guinea pig. *Proc. Soc. exp. Biol., N.Y.* **33**, 222–224.

Nelson, W. O. (1936). Endocrine control of the mammary gland. *Physiol. Rev.* **16**, 488–526.

Nelson, W. O. (1937). Studies on the physiology of lactation. VI. The endocrine influences concerned in the development and function of the mammary gland in the guinea pig. *Amer. J. Anat.* **60**, 341–360.

Newman, H. H. and Paterson, J. J. T. (1910). Development of the nine-banded armadillo from the primitive streak stage to birth: with special reference to the question of specific polyembryony. *J. Morph.* **21**, 359–423.

Newton, W. H. (1935). "Pseudo-parturition" in mouse and relation of placenta to post-partum oestrus. *J. Physiol.* **84**, 196–207.

Newton, W. H. (1938). Hormones and the placenta. *Physiol. Rev.* **18**, 419–446.

Newton, W. H. (1949). "Recent Advances in Physiology." Churchill, London.

Newton, W. H. and Beck, N. (1939). Placental activity in the mouse in the absence of the pituitary gland. *J. Endocrin.* **1**, 65–75.

Newton, W. H. and Lits, F. J. (1938). Criteria of placental endocrine activity in the mouse. *Anat. Rec.* **72**, 333–348.

Newton, W. H. and Richardson, K. C. (1940). The secretion of milk in hypophysectomized pregnant mice. *J. Endocrin.* **2**, 322–328.

Nicolas, J. S. (1947). Experimental approaches to problems of early development in the rat. *Quart. Rev. Biol.* **22**, 179–195.

Novak, E. and Everett, H. S. (1928). Cyclical and other variations in the tubal epithelium. *Amer. J. Obstet. Gynec.* **16**, 499–530.

2Q

530 E. C. AMOROSO AND C. A. FINN

O'Donoghue, C. H. (1911). The growth-changes in the mammary apparatus of *Dasyurus* and the relation of the corpora lutea thereto. *Quart. J. micr. Sci.* **57**, 187–235.

Olsen, A. G., Velardo, J. T., Hisaw, F. L., Dawson, A. B. and Braverman, L. E. (1951). Prolongation of pseudopregnancy associated with the presence of deciduomata in the rat. *Anat. Rec.* **111**, 460. (Abstr.).

Orsini, M. W. and Meyer, R. K. (1959). Implantation of the castrate hamster in the absence of exogenous oestrogen. *Anat. Rec.* **134**, 619–620 (Abstr.).

Panigel, M. (1956). Contribution à l'étude de l'ovoviviparité chez les reptiles: gestation et parturition chez le lizard vivipare, *Zootoca vivipara. Ann. Sci. nat. Zool.* **18**, 569–668.

Parkes, A. S. (1928). The rôle of the corpus luteum in the maintenance of pregnancy. *J. Physiol.* **65**, 341–349.

Parkes, A. S. (1931). Reproductive processes of certain mammals. Part I. Oestrous cycle of the Chinese hamster (*Cricetulus griseus* Milne-Edwards). *Proc. roy. Soc.* B. **108**, 138–147.

Parkes, A. S. and Bellerby, C. W. (1927). Studies on the internal secretion of the ovary. III. The effects of injection of oestrin during lactation. *J. Physiol.* **62**, 301–314.

Pearson, O. P. (1944). Reproduction in the shrew (*Blarina brevicauda* Say). *Amer. J. Anat.* **75**, 39–88.

Pearson, O. P. (1949). Reproduction of a South American rodent, the mountain viscacha. *Amer. J. Anat.* **84**, 143–173.

Pearson, O. P. and Enders, R. K. (1944). Duration of pregnancy in certain mustelids. *J. exp. Zool.* **95**, 21–35.

Pearson, O. P., Koford, M. R. and Pearson, A. K. (1952). Reproduction of the lump nosed bat (*Corynorhinus rafinesquei*) in California. *J. Mammal.* **33**, 273–320.

Peckham, B. M. and Greene, R. R. (1948). Prolongation of pseudopregnancy by deciduomata in the rat. *Proc. Soc. exp. Biol., N.Y.* **69**, 417–418.

Pencharz, R. I. (1940). Effect of estrogens and androgens alone and in combination with chorionic gonadotropin on the ovary of the hypophysectomised rat. *Science*, **91**, 554–555.

Pencharz, R. I. and Long, J. A. (1931). The effect of hypophysectomy on gestation in the rat. *Science*, **74**, 206.

Pencharz, R. I. and Long, J. A. (1933). Hypophysectomy in the pregnant rat. *Amer. J. Anat.* **53**, 117–139.

Pencharz, R. I. and Lyons, W. R. (1934). Hypophysectomy in the pregnant guinea pig. *Proc. Soc. exp. Biol., N.Y.* **31**, 1131–1132.

Perry, J. S. (1953). The reproduction of the African elephant, *Loxondonta africana. Phil. Trans.* B. **237**, 93–149.

Pfeiffer, C. A. and Hooker, C. W. (1940). Hormonal factors affecting the survival of adrenalectomized mice. *Amer. J. Physiol.* **131**, 441–448.

Pickford, G. E. and Atz, J. W. (1957). "The Physiology of the Pituitary Gland of Fishes." New York, Zoological Society.

Pincus, G. (1937). The metabolism of ovarian hormones, especially in relation to the growth of the fertilized ovum. *Cold Spr. Harb. Symp. quant. Biol.* **5**, 44.

Pincus, G. and Kirsch, R. E. (1936). The sterility in rabbits produced by injections of oestrone, and related compounds. *Amer. J. Physiol.* **115**, 219–228.

Pincus, G. and Werthessen, N. T. (1938). The maintenance of embryo life in ovariectomized rabbits. *Amer. J. Physiol.* **124**, 484–490.

Plotz, E. J. and Davis, M. E. (1956). The excretion of neutral steroids in the urine of pregnant women, following the administration of large doses of progesterone. *Acta endocr., Copenhagen,* **21**, 259–267.

Porto, A. (1942). Sobre a presenca de progesterone no corpo amarelo de serpentes ovovivipares. *Mem. Inst. Butantan,* **15**, 27–30.

Potter, E. L. (1953). "Pathology of the Foetus and New Born." Year Book Publishers, Chicago.

Prenant, L. A. (1898). De la valeur morphologique du corps jaune, son action physiologique et thérapeutique possible. *Rev. gén. Sci.* **9**, 646–650.

Raeside, J. L. and Turner, C. W. (1950). Progesterone in the maintenance of pregnancy in dairy heifers. *J. Anim. Sci.* **9**, 681.

Rahn, H. (1938). The corpus luteum of reptiles. *Anat. Rec.* **72** (Suppl.), 55.

Rahn, H. (1939). Structure and function of placenta and corpus luteum in viviparous snakes. *Proc. Soc. exp. Biol., N.Y.* **40**, 381–382.

Rasmussen, A. T. (1918). Cyclic changes in the interstitial cells of the ovary and testis in *Marmota monax. Endocrinology,* **2**, 353–404.

Ray, E. W., Averill, S. C., Lyons, W. R. and Johnson, R. E. (1955). Rat placental hormonal activities corresponding to those of pituitary mammotropin. *Endocrinology,* **56**, 359–373.

Reece, R. P., Turner, C. W. and Hill, R. T. (1936). Mammary gland development in the hypophysectomized albino rat. *Proc. Soc. exp. Biol., N.Y.* **34**, 204–207.

Renoult, M. (1931). L'hyperpituitarisme expérimental chez la poule. *Rec. Med. vét.* **107**, 604–613.

Robertson, D. C., Maddux, W. P. and Allen, E. (1930). Ovarian hormone effects in ovariectomized monkeys. *Endocrinology,* **14**, 77–88.

Robinson, T. J. (1951). Reproduction in the ewe. *Biol. Rev.* **26**, 121–157.

Robson, J. M. (1936). Maintenance of pregnancy in the hypophysectomized rabbit with progestin. *J. Physiol.* **86**, 415–424.

Robson, J. M. (1937a). Maintenance by oestrin of the luteal function in hypophysectomized rabbits. *J. Physiol.* **90**, 435–439.

Robson, J. M. (1937b). Maintenance of pregnancy and of the luteal function in the hypophysectomized rabbit. *J. Physiol.* **90**, 145–166.

Robson, J. M. (1938). Mechanism of oestrus inhibition in the mouse during pregnancy. *Quart. J. exp. Physiol.* **28**, 195–205.

Robson, J. M. (1939). Maintenance of pregnancy in the hypophysectomized rabbit by the administration of oestrin. *J. Physiol.* **95**, 83–91.

Robson, J. M. (1940). Prolongation of pregnancy in the hypophysectomized rabbit by progesterone and oestrogens. *J. Physiol.* **97**, 517–524.

Robson, J. M. (1947). "Recent Advances in Sex and Reproductive Physiology." Churchill, London.

Rogoff, J. M. and Stewart, G. N. (1927). Studies on adrenal insufficiency. III. The influence of pregnancy upon the survival period in adrenalectomized dogs. *Amer. J. Physiol.* **79**, 508–535.

Rogoff, J. M. and Stewart, G. N. (1929). Studies on adrenal insufficiency. VIII. The survival period of untreated adrenalectomized cats. *Amer. J. Physiol.* **88**, 162–172.

Romanoff, E. B. (1959). Steroidogenesis in perfused human placentas. *In* "Recent Progress in the Endocrinology of Reproduction" (C. W. Lloyd, ed.), pp. 283–295. Academic Press, New York.

2Q*

Rothchild, I. and Fraps, R. M. (1944). On the function of the ruptured ovarian follicle of the domestic fowl. *Proc. Soc. exp. Biol., N.Y.* **56**, 79–82.

Rowlands, I. W. (1947). Anterior pituitary-like hormones. *J. Endocrin.* **5**, xx.

Rowlands, I. W. (1956). The corpus luteum of the guinea pig. *Ciba Foundation Colloquia on Ageing*, **2**, 69–85.

Rowlands, I. W. and Short, R. V. (1959). The progesterone content of the guinea-pig corpus luteum during the reproductive cycle and after hysterectomy. *J. Endocrin.* **19**, 81–86.

Rugh, R. (1935). Ovulation in the frog. 2. Follicular rupture to fertilization. *J. exp. Zool.* **71**, 163–189.

Runner, M. N. (1947). Development of mouse eggs in the anterior chamber of the eye. *Anat. Rec.* **98**, 1–13.

Ruth, E. B. (1937). Metamorphosis of the pubic symphysis. III. Histological changes in the symphysis of the pregnant guinea pig. *Anat. Rec.* **67**, 409–419.

Sammelwitz, P. H. and Nalbandov, A. V. (1958). Progesterone induced regression of corpora lutea in pregnant and cycling gilts. *J. Anim. Sci.* **17**, 1233–1234.

Sammelwitz, P. H., Dziuk, P. J. and Nalbandov, A. V. (1956). Effects of progesterone in embryonal survival of rats and swine. *J. Anim. Sci.* **15**, 1211–1212.

Samuel, M. (1943). Studies on the corpus luteum in *Rhinobatus granulatus* Cuv. *Proc. Ind. Acad. Sci.* (B) **18**, 133–157.

Samuel, M. (1944). Studies on the corpus luteum in *Enhidryna schistosa* Daudin and *Hydrophis cyanocinctus* Daudin of the Madras Coast. *Proc. Ind. Acad. Sci.* **20**, 143–174.

Sandes, E. P. (1903). The corpus luteum of *Dasyurus viverrinus*, with observations on the growth and atrophy of the Graafian follicle. *Proc. Linn. Soc. N.S.W.* **28**, 364–405.

Sawyer, C. H. (1952). Progesterone initially facilitates and later inhibits release of pituitary ovulating hormone in the rabbit. *Fed. Proc.* **11**, 138.

Schofield, B. M. (1954). The influence of estrogen and progesterone on the isometric tension of the uterus in the intact rabbit. *Endocrinology*, **55**, 142–147.

Schofield, B. M. (1957). The hormonal control of myometrial function during pregnancy. *J. Physiol.* **138**, 1–10.

Schwabe, E. L. and Emery, F. E. (1939). Progesterone in adrenalectomized rats. *Proc. Soc. exp. Biol., N.Y.* **40**, 383–385.

Selye, H. (1934). Influence of the uterus on the ovary and mammary gland. *Proc. Soc. exp. Biol., N.Y.* **31**, 488–490.

Selye, H. (1939). Morphological changes in female mice receiving large doses of testosterone. *J. Endocrin.* **1**, 208–215.

Selye, H., Collip, J. B. and Thomson, D. L. (1933a). Effect of hypophysectomy upon pregnancy and lactation. *Proc. Soc. exp. Biol., N.Y.* **30**, 589–590.

Selye, H., Collip, J. B. and Thomson, D. L. (1933b). Effect of hypophysectomy upon pregnancy and lactation in mice. *Proc. Soc. exp. Biol., N.Y.* **31**, 82–83.

Selye, H., Collip, J. B. and Thomson, D. L. (1933c). On the effect of anterior pituitary-like hormone on the ovary of hypophysectomized rats. *Endocrinology*, **17**, 494–500.

Selye, H., Collip, J. B. and Thomson, D. L. (1935a). Endocrine interrelationships during pregnancy. *Endocrinology*, **19**, 151–159.

Selye, H., Collip, J. B. and Thomson, D. L. (1935b). Effects of oestrin on ovaries and adrenals. *Proc. Soc. exp. Biol., N.Y.* **32**, 1377–1381.

Selye, H., Browne, J. S. L. and Collip, J. B. (1936). Effect of combined administration of oestrone and progesterone in adult ovariectomized rats. *Proc. Soc. exp. Biol., N.Y.* **34**, 198–200.

Sharman, G. B. (1955a). Studies on marsupial reproduction. II. The oestrous cycle of *Setonix brachyurus*. *Aust. J. Zool.* **3**, 44–55.

Sharman, G. B. (1955b). Studies on marsupial reproduction. III. Normal and delayed pregnancy in *Setonix brachyurus*. *Aust. J. Zool.* **3**, 56–70.

Sharman, G. B. (1955c). Studies on marsupial reproduction. IV. Delayed birth in *Protemnodon eugenii* Desmarest. *Aust. J. Zool.* **3**, 156–161.

Siegmund, H. (1934). Ovarialfunktion nach Uterusextirpation (Tierexperimentelle Untersuchungen). *Arch. Gynaek.* **157**, 223–228.

Slotta, K. H., Ruschig, H. and Fells, E. (1934a). Reindarstellung der Hormone aus dem Corpus-luteum. *Ber. chem. Gest.* **67**, 1270–1273.

Slotta, K. H., Ruschig, H. and Fells, E. (1934b). Über die Hormone des Corpus-luteum. *Helv. chim. acta*, **17**, 1361–1362.

Smith, C. A. (1951). "The Physiology of the New-born Infant." Oxford.

Smith, C. L. (1955). Reproduction in female Amphibia. *Mem. Soc. Endocrin.* No. 4, 39–56.

Smith, G. W. and Smith, O. W. (1931). Studies on the urinary excretion of oestrin with special reference to the luteinizing hormone and progestin. *Amer. J. Physiol.* **98**, 578–584.

Smith, P. E. (1930). Hypophysectomy and a replacement therapy in the rat. *Amer. J. Anat.* **45**, 205–273.

Smith, P. E. (1946). Non-essentiality of hypophysis for maintenance of pregnancy in rhesus monkeys. *Anat. Rec.* **94**, 497.

Smith, P. E. (1954). Continuation of pregnancy in the rhesus monkey (*Macaca mulatta*) following hypophysectomy. *Endocrinology*, **55**, 655–664.

Smith, P. E. (1955). The endocrine glands in hypophysectomized rhesus monkeys (*Macaca mulatta*) with special reference to the adrenal glands. *Endocrinology*, **56**, 271–284.

Smith, P. E. and White, W. E. (1931). The effect of hypophysectomy on ovulation and corpus luteum formation in the rabbit. *J. Amer. med. Ass.* **97**, 1861–1863.

Smith, T. C. (1954). The action of relaxin on mammary gland growth in the rat. *Endocrinology*, **54**, 59–70.

Smithberg, M. and Runner, M. N. (1956). The induction and maintenance of pregnancy in prepubertal mice. *J. exp. Zool.* **133**, 441–458.

Smithberg, M. and Runner, M. N. (1957). Pregnancy induced in genetically sterile mice. *J. Hered.* **48**, 97–100.

Snyder, F. F. (1934). The prolongation of pregnancy and complications of progesterone in the rabbit following induction of ovulation near term. *Bull. Johns Hopk. Hosp.* **54**, 1–23.

Snyder, F. F. (1938). Factors concerned in the duration of pregnancy. *Physiol. Rev.* **18**, 578–596.

Sobotta, J. (1895). Zur Frage der Wanderung des Säugetiereies durch den Eileiter. *Arch. mikr. Anat.* **45**, 15–93.

Spies, H. G., Zimmerman, D. R., Self, H. L. and Casida, L. E. (1958). Influence of hysterectomy and exogenous progesterone on the size and progesterone content of the corpora lutea in gilts. *J. Anim. Sci.* **17**, 1234.

Spies, H. G., Zimmerman, D. R., Self, H. L. and Casida, L. E. (1960). Maintenance of early pregnancy in ovariectomized gilts treated with gonadal hormones. *J. Anim. Sci.* **19**, 114–118.

Steinetz, B. G., Beach, V. L. and Kroc, R. L. (1959). The physiology of relaxin in laboratory animals. *In* "Recent Progress in the Endocrinology of Reproduction" (C. W. Lloyd, ed.), pp. 389–423. Academic Press, New York.

Stewart, H. L. Jr. (1951). Hormone secretion by human placenta grown in the eyes of rabbits. *Amer. J. Obstet. Gynec.* **61**, 990–1000.

Strauss, F. (1939). Die Bildung des Corpus luteum bei Centetiden. *Biomorphosis*, **1**, 489–544.

Sussman, H. M. (1947). Quoted by Evans and Simpson (1950).

Susuki, Y. (1947). Studies on the physiology of the corpus luteum hormone. 2. The fate of the corpus luteum hormone during pregnancy in mares. *Jap. J. vet. Sci.* **9**, 149.

Svihla, A. (1932). A comparative life history study of the mice of the genus *Peromyscus*. *Univ. Mich. Misc. Publ. Mus. Zool.* No. 24, 1–39.

Sykes, J. F. and Wrenn, T. R. (1951). Hormonal development of mammary tissue in dairy heifers. *J. Dairy Sci.* **34**, 1174–1179.

Talmage, R. V. N. (1947). Changes produced in the symphysis pubis of the guinea pig by sex steroids and relaxin. *Anat. Rec.* **99**, 91–113.

Talmage, R. V., Buchanan, G. D., Kraintz, F. W., Lazo-Wasem, E. A. and Zarrow, M. X. (1954). The presence of a functional corpus luteum during delayed implantation in the armadillo. *J. Endocrin.* **11**, 44–49.

Teel, H. M. (1926). Effects of injecting anterior hypophyseal fluid on the course of gestation in the rat. *Amer. J. Physiol.* **79**, 170–183.

Teel, H. M. (1926). The effects of injecting anterior hypophysial fluid on the production of placentomata in rats. *Amer. J. Physiol.* **79**, 184–187.

Tenney, B., Parker, F. and Robbins, S. L. (1955). The effect of hysterectomy on ovarian function in the rabbit. *Amer. J. Obstet. Gynec.* **70**, 889–893.

Ten Cate Hoedemaker, N. J. (1933). Beitrag zur Kenntnis der Plazentation bei Haien und Reptilien. Der Bau der reifen Plazenta von *Mustelus laevis* Risso und *Seps chalcides* Merr. (*Chalcides tridactylus*). *Z. Zellforsch.* **18**, 299–345.

Te Winkel, L. E. (1950). Notes on ovulation, ova and early development in the smooth dogfish, *Mustelus canis. Biol. Bull., Wood's Hole*, **99**, 474–486.

Thorn, G. W. (1951). "Diagnosis and Treatment of Adrenal Insufficiency." Thomas, Springfield.

Tobian, L. Jr. (1949). Cortical steroid excretion in edema of pregnancy, preeclampsia and essential hypertension. *J. clin. Endocrin.* **9**, 319–329.

Trentin, J. J. (1951). Relaxin and mammary growth in the mouse. *Proc. Soc. exp. Biol., N.Y.* **78**, 9–11.

Tuchmann-Duplessis, H. (1945). Correlations hypophysoendocrines chez le triton. *Actualités sci. industr.* No. 987. Paris.

Turner, C. L. (1938). Adaptations for viviparity in embryos and ovary in *Anableps anableps. J. Morph.* **62**, 323–342.

Turner, C. W. (1939). The mammary glands. *In* "Sex and Internal Secretions" (E. Allen, ed.), pp. 740–803. Baillière, Tindall and Cox, London.

Turner, C. W. and Gomez, E. T. (1934). The experimental development of the mammary gland. II. The male and female dog. *Res. Bull. Mo. agric. Exp. Sta.* No. 207.

Ulberg, L. C. (1952). Modification of certain female reproductive functions in cattle, swine, and rabbits by means of progesterone. Thesis. University of Wisconsin.

Valle, J. R. and Valle, L. A. R. (1943). Gonadal hormones in snakes. *Science*, **97**, 400.

van der Horst, C. J. and Gillman, J. (1940). Ovulation and corpus luteum formation in *Elephantulus*. *S. Afr. J. med. Sci.* **5**, 73–91.

van der Horst, C. J. and Gillman, J. (1942). The life history of the corpus luteum of menstruation in *Elephantulus*. *S. Afr. J. med. Sci.* **7**, 21–41.

van der Horst, C. J. and Gillman, J. (1945). The behaviour of the Graafian follicle of *Elephantulus* during pregnancy, with special reference to the hormonal regulation of ovarian activity. *S. Afr. J. med. Sci.* **10** (Biol. Suppl.), 1–14.

Velardo, J. T., Olsen, A. G., Hisaw, F. L. and Dawson, A. B. (1953). The influence of decidual tissue upon pseudopregnancy. *Endocrinology*, **53**, 216–220.

Venable, J. H. and McDonald, L. E. (1958). Postparturient bovine uterine motility—normal and after experimentally produced retention of the fetal membranes. *Amer. J. vet. Res.* **19**, 308–313.

Venning, E. H. (1946). Adrenal function in pregnancy. *Endocrinology*, **39**, 203–230.

Venning, E. (1957). The secretion of various hormones and the activity of the adrenal cortex in pregnancy. *In* "Gestation" (C. A. Villee, ed.). Josiah Macy Jr. Foundation, New York.

Voss, H. E. (1927). Über die Funktion endokriner Heterotransplantate als Kennzeichen ihrer Einheilung. *In* "Biologia Generalis", Bd. III, p. 571.

Votquenne, M. (1936). Relations physiologiques hormonales au cours de la gestation chez la chienne. Hypophysectomie. *C.R. Soc. Biol., Paris*, **122**, 91–93.

Wagenen, G. van and Newton, W. H. (1940). Maintenance of the habitus of pregnancy and timely onset of labor after removal of the fetus. *Amer. J. Physiol.* **129**, 485.

Wagenen, G. van and Newton, W. H. (1943). Pregnancy in the monkey after removal of the fetus. *Surg. Gynec. Obstet.* **77**, 539–543.

Walaas, E. and Walaas, O. (1944). Studies on the compensatory hypertrophy of the fetal adrenal glands in the albino rat produced by adrenalectomy during pregnancy. *Acta path. microbiol. scand.* **21**, 640–672.

Wallace, W. (1903). Observations on ovarian ova and follicles in certain teleostean and elasmobranch fishes. *Quart. J. micr. Sci.* **47**, 161–213.

Watrin, M. (1924). Étude histochimique et biologique du corps jaune de la femme. *Arch. int. Méd. exp.* **1**, 97–276.

Watrin, M. (1926). Le corps jaune de la femme. *Arch. int. Méd. exp.* **2**, 203–212.

Watrin, M. and Brabant, H. (1932). Les repercussions de l'hysterectomie sur l'histo-physiologie ovarienne. *Arch. Biol., Paris*, **43**, 153–215.

Weekes, H. C. (1934). The corpus luteum in certain oviparous and viviparous reptiles. *Proc. Linn. Soc. N.S.W.* **59**, 380–391.

Weichert, C. K. (1942). Experimental control of prolonged pregnancy in the lactating rat by means of oestrogen. *Anat. Rec.* **83**, 1–17.

Westman, A. and Jacobsohn, D. (1936). Über Ovarialveränderungen beim Kaninchen nach Hypophysektomie. *Acta obstet. gynec. scand.* **16**, 483–508.

Westman, A. and Jacobsohn, D. (1937). Über Oestrin Wirkungen auf die Corpus luteum Funktion. *Acta obstet. gynec. scand.* **17**, 1–23.

Weymeersch, A. (1911). Étude sur le mécanisme de l'avortement après ovariotomie double et sur la restauration utérine consécutive. *J. Anat. Physiol., Paris*, **47**, 233–300.

White, W. E. (1933). The effect of hypophysectomy of the rabbit. *Proc. roy. Soc.* B. **114**, 64–79.

Whitney, R. and Burdick, H. O. (1936). Tube-locking of ova by oestrogenic substances. *Endocrinology*, **20**, 643–647.

Whitney, R. and Burdick, H. O. (1938). Acceleration of the rate of passage of fertilized ova through the Fallopian tubes of rabbits by massive injections of progynon B. *Endocrinology*, **22**, 639–642.

Whitney, R. and Burdick, H. O. (1939). Effect of massive doses of an estrogen in ova transport in ovariectomized mice. *Endocrinology*, **24**, 45–49.

Whitten, W. K. (1958). Endocrine studies on delayed implantation in lactating mice. Rôle of the pituitary in implantation. *J. Endocrin.* **16**, 435–440.

Wilkinson, J. F. and de Fremery, P. (1940). Gonadotropic hormones in the urine of the giraffe. *Nature, Lond.* **146**, 491.

Williams, P. C. (1940). Effect of stilboestrol on the ovaries of hypophysectomised rats. *Nature, Lond.* **145**, 388–389.

Williams, P. C. (1944). Ovarian stimulation by oestrogen in immature hypophysectomized rats. *Proc. roy. Soc.* B. **132**, 189–199.

Williams, P. C. (1945). Ovarian stimulation by oestrogens. 2. Stimulation in the absence of the hypophysis, uterus and adrenals. *J. Endocrin.* **4**, 125–126.

Williamson, H. C. (1910). Report on the reproductive organs of *Sparus centrodontus* (Delaroche); *Sparus cantharus* (L.); *Sebastes dactylopterus* (Delaroche); and on the ripe eggs and larvae of *Sparus centrodontus* and *Sebastes marinus*. *Fish, Glasgow Rep. Sci. Invest.* (1910), No. 1 (Sept. 1911), pp. 1–35.

Wiltbank, J. N. and Casida, L. E. (1956). Alteration of ovarian activity by hysterectomy. *J. Anim. Sci.* **15**, 134–140.

Wislocki, G. B. (1931). Notes on the female reproductive tract (ovaries, uterus and placenta) of the collared peccary (*Pecari angulatus bangsi*, Goldman). *J. Mammal.* **12**, 143–149.

Wislocki, G. B. and Snyder, F. F. (1933). The experimental acceleration of the rate of transport of ova through the Fallopian tube. *Johns Hopk. Hosp. Bull.* **52**, 379–386.

Wolfe, J. M. (1935). Reaction of mature female rats to injections of oestrin. *Proc. Soc. exp. Biol., N.Y.* **32**, 757–759.

Wood, J. (1859). In "The Encyclopaedia of Anatomy and Physiology" (R. B. Todd, ed.), vol. V, p. 164. Longman, London.

Yeates, N. T. M. (1949). The breeding season of the sheep with particular reference to its modification by artificial means using light. *J. agric. Sci.* **39**, 1–43.

Yeates, N. T. M. (1954). The effect of high air temperature on reproduction in the ewe. *J. agric. Sci.* **43**, 199–203.

Young, C. W. (1938). Quoted by Snyder (1938).

Zarrow, M. X. (1948). The rôle of the steroid hormones in the relaxation of the symphysis pubis of the guinea pig. *Endocrinology*, **42**, 129–140.

Zarrow, M. X. and Rosenberg, B. (1953). Sources of relaxin in the rabbit. *Endocrinology* **53**, 593–598.

Zeiner, F. N. (1943). Studies on the maintenance of pregnancy in the white rat. *Endocrinology*, **33**, 239–249.

Zimbelman, R. G., Pope, A. L. and Casida, L. E. (1959). The effect of exogenous progesterone on the corpus luteum in the bred ewe. *J. Anim. Sci.* **18**, 1327–1332.

Zondek, B. (1928). Die Schwangerschaftsdiagnose aus dem Harn durch Nachweis des Hypophysenvorderlappenhormons: Grundlagen und Technik der Methode. *Klin. Wschr.* **7**, 1404–1411.

Zuckerman, S. and Parkes, A. S. (1932). The menstrual cycle of the primates. V. The cycle of the baboon. *Proc. zool. Soc. Lond.* pp. 138–191.

CHAPTER 10

THE MENOPAUSE

A. SHARMAN

I. Introduction

The menopause is the cessation of menstruation. It is to be distinguished from the climacteric, although in its loose use, by both doctors and laymen, it is often made to apply to all the symptoms of the climacteric. The climacteric is the counterpart of puberty and the menopause is the counterpart of the menarche. In other words, the menopause is merely one manifestation of the climacteric, and may precede complete cessation of ovarian function by months or even years. This latter conception is of fairly recent origin, the traditional view being that the menopause is occasioned by the complete cessation of ovarian activity.

Exceptional prolongation of ovarian activity has been demonstrated by the occasional occurrence of ovulation after the menopause (this will be discussed more fully later), by the presence of oestrogens in the urine, by the persistence of glycogen in the vaginal epithelium and by the latter's failure to atrophy. Similarly, the tubal epithelium in postmenopausal women may remain quite high for a number of years; sooner or later, however, the tubal folds become rounded and of fibrous appearance, the epithelium becomes low or even flat and cilia disappear. Folsome et al. (1956), in a study of elderly institutionalized women, noted an oestrogenic effect in the stained vaginal smears in four women over the age of 81 years. It may be noted at this point that

539

there is considerable variability in the vaginal smears found at the menopause. Several types have been described by Papanicolaou and Shorr (1936). After the menopause, the female genital organs undergo atrophic changes in which the vaginal epithelium is also involved, and the atrophic menopausal type of smear gives the characteristic picture of many small round or oval cells, with relatively large nuclei, derived from the deep basal layers of the epithelium. Osmond-Clarke and Murray (1958) state that the main clinical value of the vaginal smear at the time of the menopause is to serve as a base-line for evaluating therapeutic progress. They claim that, although the smear is known to show individual variations, it is a valuable index regarding (a) the relative response of individual patients to various types of oestrogenic preparations; (b) any correlation between particular symptoms and the oestrogen deficiency at that period; (c) inadequate dosage; and (d) the question whether symptoms have another origin when they persist in the presence of a fully cornified smear. The traditional concept of the normal postmenopausal endometrium is of a mucosa which has become thin and atrophic, with a few small inactive glands, set in a sparse fibrous tissue. McBride (1955), however, has recently stated that this view is no longer tenable and inferences based upon it regarding the appearance of the endometrium in postmenopausal gynaecological disorders must therefore be reconsidered. This applies particularly to the association between cystic glandular hyperplasia and endometrial polypi and the development of cancer of the body of the uterus. Moreover, in certain cases of benign postmenopausal bleeding, considerable emphasis has been placed on the endometrial pattern present. The presence of cystic dilated glands in a senile endometrium has been considered abnormal. Variations in the endometrial pattern, however, do occur in the normal postmenopausal woman in whom bleeding is not a symptom. A variety of patterns other than atrophy in the normal postmenopausal endometrium occurs (see Figs. 1, 2 and 3). The speed of onset of atrophy and its completeness vary greatly in different individuals. This applies not only to the endometrium but even to different parts of the genital tract of the same woman (McBride, 1957). Novak and Richardson (1941) reported a 20 per cent incidence of active hyperplasia after the menopause, and a further 5 per cent with a proliferative endometrium.

Both the menopause and the climacteric are popularly known as the 'change of life'. The menopause is peculiar to the human race. In lower animals oestrous cycles and frequently ovulation continue into old age; this appears to be true of domestic animals like the mare, and laboratory ones such as the rat (cf. also Chapter 6, sect. IV B). Engle (1947) states that monkeys, obviously aged and grizzled, have

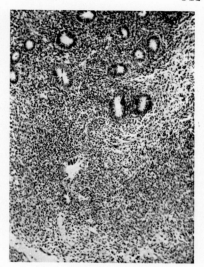

FIG. 1. Endometrium obtained by curettage from a woman aged 44 years, 7 weeks after presumptive menopause. This is a common type of menopausal pattern, showing an inactive proliferative pattern and a dense fibrous stroma.

FIG. 2. Endometrium obtained by curettage from a woman aged 45 years, 5 weeks after presumptive menopause. A type of atrophic endometrium is seen, with a dense fibrous stroma and a few inactive glands of proliferative pattern.

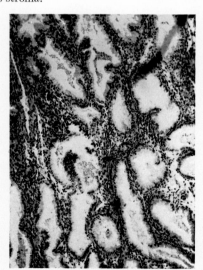

FIG. 3. Endometrium obtained by curettage from a woman aged 51 years, whose menopause had occurred 18 months previously. The histological pattern represents a mid-secretory phase of the menstrual cycle, indicative of presumptive ovulation. This is a very uncommon finding in a woman of this age.

been found to have normal follicles and oocytes and that lower animals
do not demonstrate any signs indicating a slowing of oestrous cycles or
the cessation of reproductive capacity. As Krohn (1955) expresses it,
nobody has seen a postmenopausal monkey. Comfort (1956) states that
senescence of the gonad regularly precedes or accompanies senescence of
the owner in a number of phyla—so much so that declining reproductive
capacity is a token of senescence almost as valuable as the direct
measurement of increasing mortality. He also states that the relation of
gonadal senescence to somatic senescence has clearly much evolutionary
interest, since once the first is complete in an organism to the point at
which that organism's contribution to posterity is no longer statistically
significant, any further adverse change in viability is, generally speaking,
inaccessible to the influence of natural selection, except in a very round-
about way. He suggests that the long post-reproductive period found
in women, being exceptional in mammals, probably represents a genuine
biological difference, quite apart from the far greater perfection of the
techniques for keeping human beings alive.

The fact that the end of the reproductive period, as well as the
beginning, is marked by changes in gonadal reactivity has led Swyer
(1954) to describe the menopause as the result of waning ovarian
activity, itself brought about by progressive loss of primordial follicles
and hence the main oestrogen-secreting apparatus of the ovary.
Hertig (1944) describes the exhaustion of a "capital" of ova, which is
not increased during postnatal life. Indeed, Bacsich (1951) refers to
the "postnatal slaughter of ova", which principally affects the most
immature and malformed elements of the ovary and includes multiovular follicles and multinuclear oocytes (cf. Chapter 4). In man, the
occurrence of oogenesis during postpubertal life has been doubted—
the case against it has been strongly put by Zuckerman (1951; see
also Chapter 1).

A. Age at the menopause

The average age of the menopause varies among different peoples
and in different climates, but it usually occurs between the age of 45
and 50 years, with an average of 47 years for Britain and close on 50
years in the United States. There are wide variations from this average
among normal healthy individuals and the age of the menopause does
not depend on the age of puberty, on the type of menstrual cycle,
or on marriage and the number of pregnancies. It is stated that known
factors governing it are familial and racial. Statistics collected by
workers in various countries differ. While one author states that
37·5 per cent of women cease to menstruate before 45 years, and
12·5 per cent after 50 years of age, another one gives the corresponding

figures as 25 per cent and 25 per cent, respectively. It is to be noted that there is no method of forecasting exactly when the last monthly period will occur and it is not known what the precise timing-mechanism is. One thing is certain, namely, that there is no definite sign in a woman that the menopause is at hand; greying of the hair, the appearance of wrinkles, etc. have nothing to do with it, because such changes may appear several years before or after the menopause. An increase in weight, however, is a frequent concomitant and is, in most cases, related to endocrine dysfunction. It has been stated that the menstrual cycle ceases because the ovaries no longer react to the stimulus of the anterior pituitary gland (Klebanow and Hegnauer, 1951). The pituitary continues to pour out follicle-stimulating hormone and indeed produces it in large amounts, this being probably due to lack of reactivity on the part of the ovary (cf. also Chapter 7).

B. Variations in onset and duration of the menopause

The onset and duration of the menopause vary greatly. It may occur quickly, with the sudden disappearance of menstruation which never again reappears. It may be gradual in its onset, with increasing intervals between periods and decreasing amounts of flow until it finally ceases completely. It may be preceded by the appearance of hot flushes, palpitation or attacks of excessive perspiration, or these may make their appearance only at some subsequent stage. The experiences of different patients in relation to the menopause vary greatly. Many of them have little trouble as they pass through it and a few of them none. In contrast, others are upset for long periods, physically and emotionally, and find the readjustment a long and trying process. In many women, these reactions are probably largely determined by the temperamental make-up of the individual rather than by hormonal dysfunction. One common factor that aggravates this situation for many women is the mistaken belief that after the menopause their sexual activities are at an end. Many fear the change because they believe that they will no longer be interested in sex, and may be unsatisfactory in their married life. This is, of course, untrue and indeed in many instances sexual relations are improved, if only for the reason that many women are relieved for the first time in years of the fear of pregnancy. A fundamental reason for emotional upset is that the menopause represents to many women the end of their reproductive phase and it is not uncommon for them to approach the menopause with a dread which may have been with them for several years. Some fear insanity, loss of femininity, loss of their husband's affection and, within comparatively recent years, partly due to increasing popular education, fear of the development of a gynaecological cancer.

2R*

It has already been stated that, after the menopause, the female genital organs undergo atrophic changes; but other physical changes occur as well. The breasts gradually diminish in size and become flat, but this may not occur in obese women because the atrophy affects the glandular tissue only. Changes occur in the activity of the thyroid and adrenal glands, as well as of the anterior pituitary. Probably as a result of these changes a woman tends to become coarser in build and appearance. There is a tendency for deposition of surplus fat, both on the shoulders and in the waistline. There may be a slight growth of hair on the face.

II. Systems affected

The systems which may be affected are: vasomotor; metabolic; nervous; alimentary; integumentary; articular; genito-urinary and sexual, including the breasts. The vasomotor symptom most commonly experienced is that of 'hot flushes'. Theories that have been advanced to explain such flushings are (1) lack of ovarian follicular hormone, evidenced by diminished total-oestrogen excretion in the urine; (2) excess of anterior pituitary hormone, manifested, according to the findings of some research workers, by a higher excretion of anterior pituitary hormone in the urine of women who have the most serious flushing, and (3) an unknown factor. The tendency to flush or blush affects mostly the face and neck, and the flushes are brought on particularly by excitement, nervousness and a warm atmosphere. They may occur by night as well as by day and sleep may be disturbed. Many other symptoms and signs are ascribed to the menopause, but their relationship to the latter is doubtful. They include painful and tender breasts, osteoporosis, fibrositis and 'menopausal hypertension'. It is probable that the relationship is coincidental and based on the age-factor.

It has been stated that 75 per cent of women experience some disturbance around the time of the menopause, but only about 25 per cent seek medical advice and only 10 per cent require more than reassurance. An enquiry conducted among 4,000 women doctors revealed that 90 per cent found that the menopause did not materially interfere with their work or private life.

III. Occurrence of ovulation around the time of the menopause*
A. Reports in the literature

Pregnancy at or near the menopause is uncommon. There are several possible explanations: contraception, relative infrequency of coitus,

---

* Being the substance of a chapter contributed to "Modern Trends in Obstetrics and Gynaecology" (1955) published by Butterworth and Co. Ltd., London, to whom the author is indebted for permission to quote liberally.

acquired pelvic pathological conditions, diminishing ovarian activity or infrequency of, or actual failure of, ovulation.

Pregnancy after the menopause is very rare. The Bible states that Sarah bore Isaac at the age of 90, but, as Snaith and Williamson (1947) have pointed out, Biblical estimates of age are perhaps more symbolic than factual; even so it seems to be indisputable that she was beyond the menopause " . . . for it had ceased to be with Sarah after the manner of women". These authors describe a case of a woman aged 45 years who was delivered of a normal full-term child after 3 years of amenorrhoea. The history was typical of the menopause, and the woman had every right to assume that her days of child-bearing were over. Neither menstruation nor a subsequent pregnancy occurred during a 3-year follow-up. These authors review the literature and state that they were able to trace only fifteen cases of pregnancy after the menopause; in several of these the duration of amenorrhoea prior to delivery was less than 2 years. They distinguish between cessation of menses and the incidence of the climacteric, and point out that oligomenorrhoea with a flow only once or twice a year and even amenorrhoea of 2 or more years' duration are often noted in younger women. Deliveries of living infants by postmenopausal women are described by Depasse (1891), 9 years, by Buckle (1910), 11 years, by Underhill (1879) and Levasseur (1873) 2 years, and by Hann (1902) 3 years after the menopause; the latter also quotes a case from Pearson (1865) in whom the period of amenorrhoea was 18 months. Ballon (1941) reports a twin pregnancy. Most of the infants appear to have been normal. In some of the other case reports details are not available. Snaith and Williamson state that it must be assumed that in each of the cases of pregnancy after the menopause, conception followed an ovulation which had not been associated with any menstrual cycle.

Newell and Rock (1952) have discussed the upper age limit of parturition, without special reference to the menopause. They state that the largest compilation of births by age of the mother is published in "U.S. Vital Statistics", the most recent issue of which, at the time of publication of their paper, being the one for 1948. There were approximately $3\frac{1}{2}$ million births during this year, of which 162 were recorded as being in women aged 50 years or over. This incidence of about 1 in 20,000 births is borne out roughly by preceding yearly statistics published in this compilation. These authors believe it to be highly significant that the maternal age, noted on the individual birth certificates, is dependent upon the accuracy and veracity of the mother and that even a birth certificate is not of itself indisputable evidence of an individual's age. Moreover, they point out that, in the numerous cases, recorded in the German literature, of pregnancies at an advanced age, unquestionable proof is lacking. They conclude, from their study of vital statistics and the medical literature, that parturition in a woman over 52 years of age has not been proved. Since their paper was written, "U.S. Vital Statistics" for the year 1949 has been published and shows a total number of live births at a little over 3½ million, with 150 mothers of 50 years old or older, an incidence of about 1 in 24,000 births. It may be of interest to compare these United States figures with the combined figures of England and Wales. The Registrar General's figures for England and Wales for the years 1952–1956 inclusive showed a total of approximately 3,400,000 live births, of which 95, or about 1 in 35,000, were noted as being in women 50 years old or older.

Davis and Seski (1948) reported that two women of 46 years and two of 48 years gave birth to children in over 50,000 deliveries at the Chicago Lying-in Hospital. Eastman (1950) stated that in 65,000 deliveries at the Johns Hopkins Hospital the oldest woman delivered stated that she was aged 49, but she was feeble-minded and may not have known her correct age.

Both the American and the British literature reveal several instances of more advanced ages at the time of delivery than those noted by the above-mentioned workers. These maternal ages were verified by reference to the mother's birth certificate. Gilbertson (1917) records a woman 50 years and 7 months of age at birth of her last infant. DeLee and Greenhill (1947) have delivered a woman of 52 years. Berkeley, Bonney and MacLeod (1938) state that they have knowledge of two cases of pregnancy followed by normal labour in women in their 51st year, as verified by their birth certificates.

Examination of the records of the Glasgow Royal Maternity Hospital for the period 1942–1956 inclusive reveals that no mother aged 50 or over has been delivered in this hospital, the total births for these years being 49,961.

B. Results of a special investigation

In order to explore the subject more fully by means of the detection of ovulation, the author (Sharman, 1955) made a study of ovulation, as indicated by the histological method, in women 40 years or older. They fell into three main groups:

(1) hospital in-patients, during the years 1951, 1952 and 1953, aged 50 years or older, who were curetted, the single curetting being examined microscopically;

(2) women aged 40–45 years, inclusive, who had repeated endometrial biopsies as out-patients; and

(3) women aged 46 years and over who had repeated endometrial biopsies as out-patients.

1. *In-patients aged 50 years and over*

In the Royal Samaritan Hospital for Women, Glasgow, Scotland, during the 3 years 1951, 1952 and 1953, an endometrial specimen has been microscopically examined in 333 women in the age group 50–59 years inclusive. Twenty-two showed a secretory pattern indicative of ovulation, eight of the women being 50 years old, nine being 51 and five 52. All but two of these women were still menstruating and most were suffering from menorrhagia or metrorrhagia. One of the exceptions, aged 51 years and 7 months, had 18 months' amenorrhoea when curettage was performed on account of bleeding of 2 weeks' duration. A follow-up 15 months later revealed that there had been no further bleeding or menstruation since curettage. An endometrial biopsy was thereupon attempted but no endometrium was obtained. The other exception, aged 52 years and 3 months, had 12 months' amenorrhoea when curettage was performed. From women 60 years or over, endometrium was obtained and examined in eighty-five cases: none showed a secretory pattern. There was thus no evidence of ovulation after the age of 52.

2. *Multiple biopsies in women aged 40 to 45 years*

In the next group studied, aged between 40 and 45 years inclusive, 184 endometrial biopsies were obtained from twenty-five women. Eighty-three of the biopsies were found to have been performed within 10 days of a supervening menstruation. Sixty-two were of the ovular (75 per cent) and 21 of the anovular type (25 per cent). In no case was a secretory pattern of the endometrium found earlier than 10 days before a menstrual period. Ten of the twenty-five women had multiple biopsies performed over a period of several months, the number of biopsies ranging from nine to forty. It is thought that these merit a little more detailed description. Of five cases who had each nine biopsies, one had ovular menstruations only, another had anovular ones only and the remaining three had both. Of two women who had each eleven biopsies, one had an anovular menstruation after 4 months of amenorrhoea and in the other case the biopsies followed after a curettage for incomplete abortion; although no biopsies were taken until after her first menstruation, all six succeeding menstruations were ovular. A woman in whom twelve biopsies were carried out had two anovular menstruations intermingled with seven ovular ones. Another subjected to fifteen biopsies had ten consecutive ovular cycles: she was aged 40 years. The woman who had forty biopsies performed over a period of 18 months was aged 45 years and 5 months at the start of her investigation and had 6 months' amenorrhoea after her eleventh biopsy. Two subsequent biopsies performed within 4 weeks of her last period yielded scanty proliferative endometrium, but ten further weekly attempts at biopsy yielded no endometrium whatsoever. During the next 8 months she had three irregular menstruations, two anovular and one ovular.

3. *Multiple biopsies in women aged* 46 *years and over*

In the next group studied, aged over 45 years, 149 endometrial biopsies were obtained from seventeen women. In one case thirty-seven biopsies were performed over a period of 17 months, in another thirty-one biopsies over a period of 12 months, and in another twenty-eight biopsies over a similar period. Twenty-seven of the 149 biopsies were found to have been performed within 10 days of a supervening menstruation. Sixteen were ovular (60 per cent) and eleven anovular (40 per cent). In this series, also, a secretory pattern was not seen earlier than 10 days before a menstrual period. In the case of one woman, aged 49 years and 9 months, a secretory biopsy specimen was obtained after amenorrhoea of 4 months' duration. Since menstruation did not supervene, this can be described as an instance of dissociated ovulation. Another such instance occurred in a woman aged 47 years and 7 months who had fifteen biopsies over a period of 7 months: in this case menstruation supervened 8 weeks later. These two cases recall the instances of pregnancy after the menopause already referred to. Two women in this series, in whom ovulation occurred, were aged 52 years at the time and another 51 years.

4. *Conclusions*

All these investigations, therefore, revealed no evidence of ovulation after the age of 52, although several women aged 50–52 did provide such evidence. Of the premenstrual specimens (taken within 10 days of a supervening menstruation), 75 per cent were ovular in the age group 40–45, while only 60 per cent were ovular in the age group 46 years and over. Thus there appears to be a high incidence of anovular menstruation, increasing with age, in women over 40. Two instances of ovulation dissociated from menstruation were found, so demonstrating the physiological basis of conception occurring during amenorrhoea. A change in the incidence of ovular menstruations— but in the reverse direction—also occurs in women after childbirth (Sharman, 1955).

IV. Treatment

A. Psychological approach

White (1944) states that a woman passing through the menopause should be advised how to conduct herself in order to experience the minimal amount of discomfort. It should be explained to her that it is a natural process in a woman's life, that many women experience no unpleasant symptoms of any sort, that there is no need to anticipate distressing complications, and that the menopause does not herald the onset of old age or a reduction in mental ability. Reassurance that the changes which occur are natural and not a sign of mental disturbance, that she will not lose her femininity, and may still lead a normal sex-life, often does much to allay her fears. A woman at the menopause should be advised to take plenty of exercise, fresh air, and a restricted carbohydrate diet to avoid putting on weight. The increased tendency to emotional instability and irritability may call for increased self-discipline. Psychologically, it is usually easier to deal with a married woman who has borne children, since to many of them the cessation of menstruation is in some respects a relief, but it is often much more difficult to deal with the spinster or childless married woman, where a measure of biological frustration enters the case.

B. Medical treatment

The use of ovarian hormones, either orally or intramuscularly, can be of considerable assistance, the best results being usually obtained by administration of small amounts over a long period. Bishop (1958) suggests that treatment should be discontinued every 6 weeks for a week or 10 days and that a synthetic oral oestrogen, Chlorotrianisene, is especially effective, since it is absorbed into the fat depots and gradually released from them into the blood stream. In no circumstances should a woman with menopausal symptoms be allowed to take as many oestrogen tablets as she thinks fit. Oestrogen can be given in its synthetic form, diethylstilboestrol, 0·5 mg daily with reduction after a few weeks to 0·1 mg daily. Similar preparations such as hexoestrol and dienoestrol are preferable since they are less toxic. It is well established that symptoms may be alleviated by dosages of oestrogens which are too low to affect hormonal excretion. But oestrogens should be given with caution, as not only high doses but prolonged administration of small doses sometimes produces uterine bleeding and may necessitate diagnostic curettage. Tablets containing both male and female hormones may be prescribed, e.g. methyl-testosterone with ethinyl oestradiol. Menopausal vulvar and vaginal ailments, e.g. 'senile' vulvitis and vaginitis, may be treated with the local application of oestrone pessaries. Recently an oral oestrogen, containing 0·25 mg oestriol, has been marketed and is claimed to have a powerful selective action on the uterine cervix and vagina, but no endometrial effects. It is also claimed that it restores atrophic vaginal and cervical epithelium, promoting rapid healing of lesions with low doses. If this claim is substantiated this new preparation, having the advantage of not stimulating the endometrium, should not produce withdrawal bleeding. Apart from hormone therapy, it may be necessary to prescribe sedatives to those who show emotional crises.

REFERENCES

Bacsich, P. (1951). Some observations on near-term human foetal ovaries. *J. Endocrin.* **7**, 14–15.

Ballon, L. (1941). Twin pregnancy after menopause. *Brit. med. J.* **1**, 121.

Berkeley, C., Bonney, V. and MacLeod, D. (1938). "The Abnormal in Obstetrics", p. 10. William Wood & Co., Baltimore.

Bishop, P. M. F. (1958). The oestrogens. *Practitioner*, **180**, 5–12.

Buckle, L. (1910). Childbirth after apparent menopause. *J. Amer. med. Ass.* **55**, 568.

Comfort, A. (1956). "The Biology of Senescence", p. 180. Routledge and Kegan Paul Ltd., London.

Davis, M. E. and Seski, A. (1948). Childbearing in the twilight of the reproductive period. *Surg. Gynec. Obstet.* **87**, 145–152.

DeLee, J. B. and Greenhill, J. P. (1947). "Principles and Practice of Obstetrics", p. 87. W. B. Saunders Company, Philadelphia.

Depasse, E. (1891). Grossesse à cinquante-neuf ans. *Gaz. de Gynécol.* **6**, 241–243. (Quoted by Hann).

Eastman, N. J. (1950). "Williams Obstetrics", p. 200. Appleton-Century-Crofts Inc., New York.

Engle, E. T. (1947). *In* "Progress in Gynecology" (J. V. Meigs and S. H. Sturgis, eds.), pp. 58–60. Grune and Stratton, New York.

Folsome, C. E., Napp, E. E. and Tanz, A. (1956). Pelvic functions in the elderly institutionalized female patient: a gynecic survey of six hundred and eighty patients. *J. Amer. med. Ass.* **161**, 1447.

Gilbertson, J. H. (1917). The oldest age of parturition. *Brit. med. J.* **1**, 378.

Hann, R. G. (1902). A case in which pregnancy occurred after the menopause. *J. Obstet. Gynaec., Brit. Emp.* **2**, 290.

Hertig, A. T. (1944). Ageing ovary—preliminary note. *J. clin. Endocrin.* **4**, 581–582.

Klebanow, D. and Hegnauer, H. (1951). Die germinative Insuffizienz der alternden Frau. *Z. Altersforch.* **5**, 157–171.

Krohn, P. L. (1955). Tissue transplantation techniques applied to the problem of the ageing of the organs of reproduction. *Ciba Foundation Colloquia on Ageing*, **1**, 141–161.

Levasseur. (1873). *Gaz. Hebdomadaire.* (Quoted by Hann).

McBride, J. M. (1957). Estrogen excretion levels in the normal postmenopausal woman. *J. clin. Endocrin.* **17**, 1440–1447.

Newell, J. W. and Rock, J. (1952). Upper age limit of parturition: a review of the literature. *Amer. J. Obstet. Gynec.* **63**, 875–876.

Novak, E. and Richardson, E. H. (1941). Proliferative changes in the senile endometrium. *Amer. J. Obstet. Gynec.* **42**, 564–579.

Osmond-Clarke, F. and Murray, M. (1958). Some clinical applications of vaginal smears in gynaecological endocrinology. *Brit. med. J.* **1**, 307–310.

Papanicolaou, G. N. and Shorr, E. (1936). Action of ovarian follicular hormone in menopause, as indicated by vaginal smears. *Amer. J. Obstet. Gynec.* **31**, 806–831.

Pearson. (1865). *Bulletin de la Soc. de Méd. d'Angers.* (Quoted by Hann).

Registrar General's Statistical Review of England and Wales (1956). Part II, Tables, Civil, Table B, pp. 8–9 and Table AA, pp. 144–145.

Sharman, A. (1955). *In* "Modern Trends in Obstetrics and Gynaecology" (K. Bowes, ed.), pp. 97–100; 216–227. Butterworth & Co. Ltd., London.

Snaith, L. and Williamson, M. (1947). Pregnancy after the menopause. (A case report and a review of the literature). *J. Obstet. Gynaec., Brit. Emp.* **54**, 496–498.

Swyer, G. I. M. (1954). "Reproduction and Sex", pp. 58–63. Routledge and Kegan Paul Ltd., London.

Underhill, J. W. (1879). The female generative organs in their medico-legal relations. *Amer. J. Obstet. Gynec.* **12**, 91–111. (Quoted by Hann.)

U.S. Vital Statistics (1948). **35**, 10.

U.S. Vital Statistics (1949). Part II, 100.

White, M. M. (1944). "The Symptomatic Diagnosis and Treatment of Gynaecological Disorders", pp. 158–163. H. K. Lewis & Co. Ltd., London.

Zuckerman, S. (1951). The number of oocytes in the mature ovary. *Recent Progr. Hormone Res.* **6**, 63–109.

CHAPTER 11

DERANGEMENTS OF OVARIAN FUNCTION

P. M. F. BISHOP

I. Introduction

Normal ovarian function depends on complete differentiation of the gonad during embryonic life, the awakening of gonadotrophic activity at puberty, the integrative action of the endocrine system and the absence of endogenous abnormalities affecting the production of its hormones.

Derangements of ovarian function must therefore be considered under the headings of those that arise during embryonic life, those that result from abnormal activity of other parts of the endocrine system and abnormal behaviour of the ovary itself. This may be due to the development of an ovarian tumour which is producing excessive quantities of one or other of the three principal ovarian hormones, oestrogen, progestogen or androgen, or else producing them in an abnormal ratio, one to another.

This chapter deals exclusively with derangements of the human ovary and is mainly concerned with the clinical manifestations of disorders affecting the normal production of the ovarian hormones.

In describing these clinical pictures it is necessary to discuss their differential diagnosis. This could lead to a detailed enumeration of the features of disorders not directly concerned with abnormalities of ovarian function. To avoid this, the various hypothalamic syndromes and some pituitary tumours have been mentioned only briefly.

II. Ovarian deficiency of embryonic origin

A. 'Gonadal dysgenesis'

In 1938 Turner described a syndrome of which the essential features were infantilism (retardation of growth and sexual development), webbing of the skin of the neck and cubitus valgus. Varney *et al.* (1942) found high urinary gonadotrophin titres in four young women of short stature and referred to the condition of ovarian 'aplasia' found at autopsy in seven short women. Albright *et al.* (1942) reported eleven cases of primary ovarian insufficiency and decreased stature, and Wilkins and Fleischmann (1944) described the findings at laparotomy in five such cases and applied the term 'ovarian agenesis' to the condition, pointing out that the stunted growth is a congenital anomaly. It was clear that the cases described by Turner fell into this category, and it is now customary to refer to those cases that show webbing of the neck as Turner's syndrome. Barr and his co-workers (Barr and Bertram, 1949; Graham and Barr, 1952; Moore *et al.*, 1953) showed that it is possible to determine the genetic sex of an individual according to whether there is a chromatin mass present on the inner surface of the nuclear membrane of cells with resting or intermitotic nuclei. If this sex chromatin is present in the majority of such nuclei of cells studied by means of skin biopsy, buccal smears or blood films, the individual is a genetic female or 'chromatin positive'. If the sex chromatin is absent the individual is a genetic male, or 'chromatin negative'. Wilkins and his co-workers (1954) and Polani and his colleagues (1954) simultaneously discovered that some patients suffering from 'ovarian agenesis' or Turner's syndrome are in fact genetic males. It therefore became no longer appropriate to refer to this syndrome as 'ovarian agenesis'. As some of these patients are genetic males and others are genetic females the logical term would seem to be 'gonadal agenesis'. Cases of this syndrome have been reported, however, in which certain androgenic features such as enlargement of the clitoris or hirsutism are found to be associated with nests of Leydig cells or tubules of the rete testis in the depths of the typical primitive fibrous streaks which lie in the position of the gonads. In these cases one cannot speak of gonadal 'agenesis' because in fact there are structural elements of gonadal origin present and, indeed, unless one were to section the primitive streaks serially in all cases it would be impossible to ensure that no gonadal structural elements were present. It would therefore seem prudent to use the expression 'gonadal dysgenesis' suggested by Grumbach *et al.* (1955) as a general term to include all cases of 'ovarian' deficiency of embryonic origin. Nevertheless, when it is reasonably certain that no gonadal development has occurred at all, one can logically speak, as Wilkins (1957) does, of gonadal 'aplasia', so that one may refer to cases with vestigial gonadal elements found in the depths of the primitive streak as instances of gonadal 'dysplasia' and to cases in which further development, say of primordial or Graafian follicles, occurs as examples of gonadal 'hypoplasia'.

1. *Turner's syndrome*

The classical triad of Turner's syndrome consists of sexual infantilism, short stature and congenital anomalies. The sexual infantilism is associated with gonadal aplasia and, though the genetic sex is male in about 80% of cases, the bodily configuration is feminine. (There are, however, cases of Turner's syndrome occurring in phenotypical—and genetic—males: they also have webbing of the neck and other congenital anomalies, as well as short stature and small testes.) Furthermore, the genital tract is female, though the uterus, vagina and labia minora remain infantile. The vaginal smear shows no evidence of oestrogenization and the vulval mucosa is pink and glistening. Some sexual hair develops, though it is usually extremely scanty. The breasts, areolae and nipples remain completely underdeveloped. A possible explanation of this feminine physique, albeit with lack of secondary sex characters, is supplied by the experiments of Jost (1947), who showed that castration of the rabbit foetus at an early stage of embryonic life led to normal differentiation of the Müllerian duct system and female external genitalia no matter what sex the foetus was originally destined to be.

Bishop and his collaborators (1960) collected seventy-five cases of gonadal dysgenesis and related syndromes, of which twenty-four were examples of Turner's syndrome and thirty were classified as gonadal dysgenesis without neck webbing. The height had been recorded in sixteen of the cases of Turner's syndrome and only in one was it greater than 5 feet. In three of the other group it was 5 feet or greater. Urinary gonadotrophins were raised in the majority of cases, as one would expect in a lesion that is primarily gonadal and not pituitary in origin. In about half the cases the urinary 17-ketosteroids were below 5 mg per 24 hours. Two of the patients with Turner's syndrome had experienced a few spontaneous menstrual periods at the age of puberty and should probably therefore be regarded as examples of gonadal hypoplasia.

All the other cases in both groups had primary amenorrhoea. Estimation of the bone age according to the standards of Greulich and Pyle (1950) showed that it usually lagged about 2 years behind the chronological age.

Various congenital anomalies may be associated with gonadal dysgenesis and are most commonly seen in the group of cases of Turner's syndrome. They include congenital heart disease, of which the commonest form is coarctation of the aorta, and renal anomalies, such as horseshoe kidney, double ureter and pelvic kidney; these are invariably associated with some deformity of the ears. Pigmented moles are a striking feature of the clinical picture and may be evidence of a disorder of the embryonic neural crest. Bony abnormalities of the digits, metacarpals and thorax, and soft tissue anomalies of the hands as indicated by palm prints are not unusual.

Of the forty-three patients with gonadal dysgenesis and webbing of the neck collected in the series of Grumbach et al. (1955), Hoffenberg and Jackson (1957a) and ourselves, seven were mentally retarded.

The incidence of red-green colour blindness is of considerable interest as being a sex-linked congenital anomaly which might be used to check the chromatin pattern as a marker of the genetic sex of the individual. Red-green colour vision defects are due to the behaviour of genes located in the non-homologous segment of the X-chromosome and are recessive. In order to manifest the trait in females it would be necessary for both X-chromosomes to be affected, whereas in males the unopposed action of the genes of the one X-chromosome is sufficient. Thus the incidence of the anomaly is not more than 0·6 per cent in women, whereas it occurs in 7 to 8 per cent of normal males. Polani and his colleagues (1956) studied the incidence in patients with gonadal dysgenesis and continued the study in the larger series of cases reported (Bishop et al., 1960). Of twenty-nine chromatin-negative cases of gonadal dysgenesis four were red-green colour blind. This observation confirms that the presence or absence of the chromatin mass is an indicator of the nuclear sex. Recent advances in cytological technique have enabled the chromosomes to be counted and identified. In consequence the sex chromosomal pattern in cases of Turner's syndrome has been shown to be XO (Ford et al., 1959) and not that of a normal male, namely XY, as had been assumed from the fact that these cases are chromatin-negative so far as their nuclear sex is concerned. By contrast, in the condition of Klinefelter's syndrome—'seminiferous tubule dysgenesis', which is to some extent the mirror image of Turner's syndrome—the majority of cases are chromatin positive though they are phenotypical males. Polani et al. (1958) found four cases with red-green colour blindness out of thirty-eight in which the nuclear sex was female.

Hoffenberg and Jackson (1957a) have propounded the theory that the complete picture of Turner's syndrome is of genetic origin and involves three closely connected genes situated on the same chromosome, one responsible for sexual infantilism ('I'), one for shortness of stature ('S') and one for other various anomalies of the skeletal, cutaneous, cardio-vascular, renal and other systems ('A'). I + S + A would give rise to the full Turner's syndrome. The 'webbing' syndrome (status Bonnavie-Ullrich) might involve A and possibly S but not I, whereas I + S might lead to gonadal dysgenesis in patients of short stature but without other congenital anomalies, and indeed such cases do exist. Perhaps the greatest interest, however, centres round the syndrome produced by I alone. This defect would be consistent with the clinical picture of a phenotypical woman of normal height but eunuchoid appearance with no congenital anomalies but with primary amenorrhoea and lack of secondary sex characters such as breast development, scanty pubic and axillary hair, infantile uterus and external genitalia. The nuclear sex may, of course, be male or female. Swyer (1955) described two such cases, in which he thought it unjustifiable to inspect the gonads by laparotomy. He assumed that they were unusual cases of a syndrome described by Goldberg and Maxwell (1948) in which the bodily habitus is female and the breasts are fully developed. No uterus or cervix, however, is present and the vagina ends blindly (in Swyer's cases the vagina was normal in size and the cervix and uterus were present though small). In the Goldberg-Maxwell syndrome the gonads are immature testes and it is an example of the feminine type of male pseudohermaphroditism (sometimes known as the 'testicular feminization syndrome of Morris' (1953)). The testes are often palpable in the inguinal region, though they may be intra-abdominal. The blind vagina, however, is characteristic. The normal differentiation of the genital tract in Swyer's cases suggests that they belong to the group of gonadal dysgenesis. Furthermore, one of his patients had marked enlargement of the clitoris and probably therefore falls into the category of gonadal dysplasia with vestigial testicular elements developing in the deeper layers of the primitive streak. Hoffenberg and Jackson's suggestion that this case was an example of gonadal dysgenesis rather than male pseudohermaphroditism makes it clear that an inspection of the gonads is essential before such cases can be properly assessed.

2. *Gonadal dysplasia*

Numerous examples have been cited of cases of gonadal dysgenesis with some evidence of abnormal androgenic influence (Meyer, 1925;

Baer, 1927; Pich, 1937; Gordan *et al.*, 1955; Grumbach *et al.*, 1955; Greenblatt *et al.*, 1956; Hoffenberg and Jackson, 1957b). In these cases the clitoris is found to be considerably enlarged, even at birth; hirsutism subsequently develops and the pelvis is android in shape. Nests of mature epithelioid cells resembling Leydig cells are seen in the primitive streak, and rete tubules and other tubules derived from the mesonephros may also be present. It is thought that in these cases, although no cortical element of the gonad succeeds in differentiating, the mesonephric medullary elements reached an early stage of embryonic development and may have released a male evocator sufficiently potent to cause abnormal enlargement of the phallus.

3. *Gonadal hypoplasia*

Occasionally, cases of gonadal dysgenesis have been reported in which spontaneous menstrual bleeding has occurred (Albright *et al.*, 1942; Varney *et al.*, 1942; Lisser *et al.*, 1947; Briggs and Kupperman, 1956; Hoffenberg *et al.*, 1957). Indeed, two of the author's cases experienced occasional spontaneous menstrual bleeding. Direct inspection of the gonads has seldom been made in these cases; when it has the results have sometimes proved extremely puzzling, since no gonadal elements have been found in the primitive streaks, as in one of the two patients described by Hoffenberg *et al.* (1957). In this case, however, a withdrawal bleeding occurred following removal of the primitive gonads which strongly suggests that they were producing oestrogen. In other cases, however, some ovarian elements have been found, as in one of the two reported by Kerkhof and Stolte (1956) in which serial sections of biopsy specimens of the very small ovaries showed primordial follicles, a follicle cyst, granulosa cells and luteinized theca interna cells. The authors suggest that this condition is due to partial primary agenesis of the gonia rather than of the gonad. These patients actually had primary amenorrhoea, and it would seem possible that other cases of primary amenorrhoea associated with development of normal secondary sex characters may be due to failure of primordial germ cells to reach the genital ridge in adequate quantities, with subsequent degeneration of the ones that succeed in doing so.

B. Sex reversal

Ashley and Jones (1958) have reported the case of a child who at the age of 10 days was referred because of doubts as to its true sex. The phallus was suggestive of an enlarged clitoris and there were two urethral openings on to the surface, one resembling a complete hypospadias and the other being situated on the anterior wall of the vagina.

The urinary levels for 17-ketosteroids were within the normal neonatal range. A laparotomy was performed at the age of 17 months and revealed a uterus and Fallopian tubes of normal size. The ovaries were in their normal position and were slightly enlarged and cystic. A small section was removed from one ovary and contained a follicular cyst and many oocytes, though few formed Graafian follicles. The nuclear sex as determined by buccal smears and skin biopsy was male. This would appear to be the only case so far reported in which a male nuclear sex has been associated with ovarian tissue (all the cases classified under 'Gonadal Hypoplasia' that had their nuclear sex investigated so far have been chromatin positive).

C. True hermaphroditism

Although this condition might have been discussed under a separate main heading, it has been classified here as a type of gonadal dysgenesis in so far as both male and female tissues go to make up the gonads. According to Witschi and his colleagues (1957), the condition may be due to uneven distribution of germ cells in the gonadal folds when the number of primordial germ cells migrating to the genital ridges approaches the threshold for normal development. Relatively well supplied regions of the gonadal folds can achieve ovarian differentiation whereas poorly supplied regions will only manage to produce testicular differentiation. Whether or not this explanation is valid (and it would depend on an XX chromosomal pattern being present so that ovarian differentiation is attempted; according to Barr (1955), out of nine cases studied six possessed female type nuclei and three male type nuclei), the gonads consist of an ovary on one side and a testis on the other, or of an ovotestis on one side and an ovary or testis on the other, or of bilateral ovotestes. A recent case has been described by Clayton et al. (1957) in which both an ovary and a testis were found lying in the scrotal folds.

About eighty cases of true hermaphroditism have so far been reported. The bodily configuration varies from almost normal male to almost normal female and in cases where there is a testis on one side and an ovary on the other differentiation of the genital ducts tends to conform to the sex of the adjacent gonad. There are also many possible variations in the development of the external genitalia. Wilkins (1957) points out that it is impossible to predict whether at puberty the secondary sexual development will be predominantly male or female. Hormone studies are of little diagnostic value and the condition can be established only by submitting both gonads to biopsy (Bishop and Sommerville, 1957). There is no recorded case of a true hermaphrodite achieving parenthood either as a father or as a mother.

III. Ovarian deficiency of endocrine origin

In this classification it is proposed to include ovarian deficiency of hypothalamic origin, for not only is the hypothalamus an endocrine gland (cf. Zuckerman, 1954), but there is no doubt that it exerts a fundamental control over the anterior pituitary gonadotrophins, possibly releasing small amounts of luteinizing hormone which may be essential for the secretion of oestrogen by the Graafian follicle. Sudden withdrawal of hypothalamic influence may, through the pituitary, have a profound effect on ovarian activity.

A. Hypothalamus

1. *Impulses from the higher centres*

The pituitary-ovarian axis is very sensitive to variations in its hypothalamic control resulting from impulses from the higher centres, and probably the majority of menstrual disorders which may manifest themselves as amenorrhoea, oligomenorrhoea or menorrhagia are due to ovarian deficiency of hypothalamic origin. Examples are *environmental amenorrhoea* which may occur when a woman changes her mode of life. Girls often develop amenorrhoea during term-time at a boarding school, whereas their menstrual cycles are regular during the holidays. The incidence of amenorrhoea in nurses when they commence their training is significant. A journey overseas sometimes leads to sudden amenorrhoea. *Emotional disturbances* may interrupt the menstrual cycle. Obesity of hypothalamic origin often accompanies these menstrual disturbances. Indeed sudden change of weight is frequently associated with amenorrhoea or oligomenorrhoea. This applies also to sudden loss of weight, the extreme example of which is *anorexia nervosa*, a condition that usually affects adolescent girls who lose weight at an alarming rate because they develop an obsession that they are overweight and acquire a psychopathic aversion to food. The amenorrhoea appears very early in this sequence of events and is not primarily due to the malnutrition.

2. *Hypothalamic syndromes*

The clinical features of these vary according to which hypothalamic nuclei are involved, but include diabetes insipidus, somnolence, disturbances of temperature regulation, obesity and evidence of gonadal deficiency leading in women to amenorrhoea. Lesions may be caused by inflammation, infiltration (for instance, with cholesterol deposits, as in the Hand-Schüller-Christian syndrome), or by tumours such as craniopharyngioma. This may give rise to Fröhlich's syndrome, the classical features of which are sexual infantilism, retardation of growth and obesity.

B. Pituitary

Ovarian failure secondary to pituitary deficiency may occur as the result of a tumour, chromophobe or eosinophil, compressing the functional cells or, in the case of eosinophil tumours, the basophils; alternatively, it may result from complete necrosis of the pituitary cells which is usually due to thrombosis of the hypophysial vessels following post-partum haemorrhage; or again, there may be 'selective' pituitary failure involving the gonadotrophic hormone complex only. Idiopathic pituitary infantilism leads to permanently retarded puberty.

1. *Pituitary tumours*

(*a*) *Chromophobe adenoma.* This is the commonest pituitary tumour. Endocrine symptoms are not a prominent feature, but amenorrhoea is not infrequent.

(*b*) *Eosinophil adenoma.* This produces the clinical picture of acromegaly in which scanty periods or amenorrhoea commonly appear as early symptoms. It is generally believed that both luteinizing hormone (LH) and follicle-stimulating hormone (FSH) are produced by the basophil cells. Using the mouse uterine-weight method of assaying urinary gonadotrophin (? FSH) none was detected in some female cases of acromegaly (Paschkis *et al.*, 1954). Absence of FSH would explain the deficient ovarian function, though excessive production of LH by the basophil cells might equally well account for the amenorrhoea.

2. *'Panhypopituitarism' (Simmonds' disease)*

The commonest cause of this condition is post-partum haemorrhage which renders the anterior pituitary temporarily ischaemic and results in either total or partial necrosis of the gland. Lack of gonadotrophic stimulation leads to secondary ovarian failure resulting in amenorrhoea, atrophy of the breasts, loss of pubic and axillary hair (also to some extent due to adrenocortical failure), hypoplasia of the external genitalia, involution of the uterus and absence of cornified cells in the vaginal smear. The urinary 17-ketosteroids drop to less than 2 mg per 24 hours. There is also evidence of thyroid and adrenocortical deficiency and the clinical picture is that of myxoedema. Pituitary cachexia with gross loss of weight is uncommon. Simmonds' disease may also result from craniopharyngiomas, chromophobe adenomas or inflammatory disease such as basal meningitis or encephalitis.

3. *'Selective' pituitary failure*

Pituitary failure may be partial rather than complete and may involve only one of the triad of trophic hormones. When it affects the gonadotrophic hormones only, the classical example is that of a rather tall woman of eunuchoid proportions resulting from late closure of the epiphyses of the long bones, in the absence of oestrogen production by the ovaries ('Pituitary Eunuchoidism'). Other evidence of oestrogen deficiency is provided by the failure of development of nipples, breasts, labia minora, vagina and uterus. These cases can be distinguished from those of ovarian eunuchoidism by the absence of urinary gonadotrophin which in the latter group of cases would be considerably raised. There may, however, be patients suffering from relative gonadotrophic deficiency that show no evidence of failure of secondary sex characters and complain only of amenorrhoea or oligomenorrhoea. In such cases urinary gonadotrophins may not be demonstrable. Unfortunately, however, the present methods of gonadotrophin assay are not sufficiently sensitive to distinguish clearly between their complete absence, which would denote pituitary deficiency, and the low titres which might be compatible with normal pituitary function.

4. *Pituitary infantilism or dwarfism*

In about a third of these cases the condition is due to a tumour developing in infancy or childhood. Puberty is indefinitely retarded and there is complete absence of pubic and axillary hair and, in the female, of mammary development.

C. Adrenal cortex

Adrenocortical deficiency, such as occurs in Addison's disease or following bilateral adrenalectomy (with inadequate substitution therapy), may sometimes be accompanied by signs of gonadal deficiency, but this is not always the case and amenorrhoea is not invariable.

The most profound effect on ovarian activity, however, is produced by excessive adrenocortical function due to congenital adrenal hyperplasia or to a tumour or bilateral hyperplasia of the cortex leading to the clinical picture of the adrenogenital syndrome or Cushing's syndrome.

1. *Congenital adrenal hyperplasia*

This condition arises during foetal life and if the patient is deprived of treatment until after the normal age of puberty, menstruation does not take place. The appropriate treatment is to give cortisone. This acts not simply as substitution therapy but also by suppressing excessive production and output of corticotrophin. This in its turn leads to the release of pituitary gonadotrophin which can now stimulate the ovary, with the result that the patient becomes completely feminized so that normal, regular ovulatory cycles and breast development take place. Provided enough cortisone is given to keep the urinary 17-ketosteroids well within the normal range, the patient continues to live as a normal female, and there have been reports of patients thus treated becoming pregnant (Blizzard and Wilkins, 1957).

The condition frequently occurs in sibs, though so far it appears to have been confined to a single generation (Wilkins, 1957).

Congenital hyperplasia is by far the commonest type of *female pseudohermaphroditism*, but cases have been described in which abnormalities of the urogenital sinus and external genitalia were found in the absence of adrenal hyperplasia, but due to masculinizing influences derived from the mother during pregnancy.

2. *Adrenogenital syndrome*

The development of excessive adrenocortical activity after birth will give rise to virilism, though of course there will be no congenital deformity of the external genital tract or urogenital sinus as in congenital adrenal hyperplasia, and this is an important diagnostic distinction. Enlargement of the clitoris and other signs of virilism such as those described in the case of congenital adrenal hyperplasia are likely to occur. One of the characteristic features is suppression of ovarian activity resulting in amenorrhoea.

3. *Cushing's syndrome*

Amenorrhoea is regarded as a classical manifestation of this condition. Since the 'androgenic' signs of Cushing's syndrome are usually slight and the disease is principally due to overactivity of gluco- and mineralocorticoids, it is perhaps surprising that amenorrhoea develops so early in many cases. Possibly the excessive production of corticotrophin is accompanied by a shift in pituitary hormone production away from gonadotrophic, somatotrophic and lactogenic hormones. Reduction in gonadal activity, however, does not occur invariably, and pregnancy has been reported even in the active stage of the disease. Restoration of normal ovulatory cycles is one of the earliest signs of remission in some cases.

IV. Abnormal ovarian activity in the absence of ovarian tumours

Primary ovarian failure may occur and the menopause is the most obvious physiological example. Normal ovarian activity may become established at an abnormal age and give rise to precocious puberty, or abnormal ovarian activity may return after the menopause. Excessive or abnormal production of hormones by the ovary may occur in association with pathological conditions of the ovary, so that follicular cysts may give rise to excessive oestrogen production, and hyperthecosis may lead to androgenic manifestations.

A. Primary ovarian failure

The gradual failure of ovarian activity that leads to the menopause is associated with a complicated clinical picture, which is dealt with fully in Chapter 10. This type of primary ovarian deficiency is characteristically accompanied by hot flushes, and estimation of urinary gonadotrophins shows abnormally high values, whereas in cases of primary pituitary failure urinary gonadotrophins cannot be detected. It is important to realize that this picture is not confined to women in their fifth and sixth decades, but that primary ovarian failure may occur comparatively early and that climacteric symptoms may be experienced in the thirties or even in the twenties. Maintenance of ovarian endocrine activity depends, among other things, on the number of potentially functional oocytes in the ovaries. There are circumstances in which these may have been grossly depleted leading to secondary amenorrhoea of ovarian origin supervening at an early date, for instance between the age of 20 to 30, or even to primary amenorrhoea.

B. Precocious puberty

In 80 to 90 per cent of girls in whom the menarche occurs before the age of 10 years the condition is 'constitutional', and the menstrual cycles will be ovulatory as demonstrated by a biphasic basal temperature pattern or the finding of pregnanediol in the urine in the second half of the cycle. Very occasionally neurogenic causes leading to a destructive lesion of the hypothalamus, particularly in the region of the mamillary bodies or posterior hypothalamus, may bring about precocious puberty. Weinberger and Grant (1941) postulated that during childhood impulses from the anterior hypothalamus which would release gonadotrophins from the pituitary are prevented from doing so by the inhibitory influence of the posterior hypothalamus.

Polyostotic fibrous dysplasia is a condition described by Albright and his colleagues (1937) in which scattered bone lesions, consisting of osteitis fibrosa, are associated with areas of pigmentation of the skin, often overlying the sites of the bone lesion. The condition almost always occurs in girls and is accompanied by precocious puberty. Thannhauser (1944) has suggested that there may be overgrowth of the bone at the base of the skull leading to pressure on the hypothalamus.

C. Abnormal postmenopausal ovarian activity

About 5 to 10 per cent of all cases of postmenopausal bleeding occur without any cause being found to account for it, such as exogenous administration of oestrogen, carcinoma of the uterine body or the presence of oestrogen-producing ovarian tumours (McBride, 1955). No adequate explanation has been given for the bleeding, which may occur as long as 20 years after the last menstrual period, or the fact that the endometrium is sometimes atrophic, sometimes metropathic and sometimes even secretory (cf. Chapter 10). In the last case its bleeding is thought to be the result of the belated ripening of a stray oocyte (Jeffcoate, 1957).

D. Follicle cysts

'Single' follicle cysts, so called to distinguish them from polycystic ovaries, are lined by granulosa cells and may persist for variable periods of time continuously producing oestrogen and thereby causing endometrial hyperplasia and metropathic bleeding. They may rarely occur in childhood and give rise to sexual precocity (Fischer, 1940; Kimmel, 1947). They apparently never produce postmenopausal bleeding.

E. Polycystic ovaries, hyperthecosis ovarii and the Stein-Leventhal syndrome

Stein and Leventhal (1935) called attention to a 'polycystic ovarian syndrome' which was accompanied by amenorrhoea and infertility, and six years previously Stein had performed his first wedge resection of bilateral polycystic ovaries and restored normal cycles following a prolonged period of amenorrhoea. The classical features of the Stein-Leventhal syndrome are bilateral enlargement of the ovaries, amenorrhoea, hirsutism, obesity and vague and intermittent abdominal pain.

The ovaries are usually considerably enlarged and therefore may be palpable at bimanual examination, although in some cases the obesity makes this examination difficult. They are firm, smooth, flattened, sclerotic and bluish-white in colour and resemble giant oysters ('oyster' ovaries). On cutting into them they are seen to have a thick and fibrotic cortex and to be polycystic, though all the cysts are small. On microscopic examination many microcystic follicles are found and they are surrounded by hyperplastic theca interna cells, mostly luteinized. Furthermore, the hyperthecosis spreads into the ovarian stroma where islands of thecal cells may be found. There is some doubt as to whether these hyperplastic thecal cells produce androgen or excessive quantities of progesterone which may give rise to androgenic manifestations clinically. Hirsutism is present in about half the cases and may be accompanied by signs of virilism such as acne, enlargement of the clitoris, voice changes, atrophy of the breasts and a muscular physique. Dorfman and Shipley (1956) record that in twenty-nine reported cases in which virilism was present the urinary 17-ketosteroid excretion was elevated in only five cases. The evidence for excessive progesterone production is rather tenuous. Fischer and Riley (1952) found a persistently high urinary pregnanediol level in one case, but even so Klinefelter and Jones (1954) question the specificity of the colorimetric method of assay used in this case. Culiner and Shippel (1949), impressed by the fact that both ovaries are affected in every case, concluded that the cause of the condition must be outside the ovary and presumably in the pituitary and attributed it to excessive and continuous production of LH. Urinary gonadotrophins are, however, within the normal range.

In some cases it is difficult to arrive at a diagnosis. Obesity is marked in the majority of patients and may make it difficult to palpate the enlarged ovaries. Secondary amenorrhoea is the characteristic menstrual disorder, though metropathia, menorrhagia or even oligomenorrhoea may occur. If one favours the mechanical explanation of the amenorrhoea, infertility and presence of microcystic follicles, one believes that the Graafian follicles cannot rupture because of the tough capsule. It is therefore difficult to reconcile evidence of ovulation with the Stein-Leventhal syndrome. Hirsutism is found in only about half the cases. It is thus possible that this pathological syndrome of polycystic ovaries may be the cause of infertility in a woman with secondary amenorrhoea who may or may not be hirsute, and who, if rather obese, may not have palpably enlarged ovaries. Nevertheless the results of surgical treatment of the genuine syndrome are spectacular. Stein and his colleagues (1949) restored normal menstrual cycles in sixty-seven of a series of seventy-five cases, and twenty-six of forty infertile patients conceived within a few months. It is therefore of great importance to distinguish between the Stein-Leventhal syndrome and simple hirsutism or even cases of menstrual irregularity attending a Fertility Clinic. This can often be accomplished only by inspection of the ovaries either by 'gynaecography' (injection of air into the pelvis and subsequent X-ray examination), culdoscopy or laparotomy. There has been a tendency recently to extend the criteria for the diagnosis to include impalpable ovaries, and even ovaries which on inspection are atypical, on the theory that the condition must start some time and one may have encountered an early case in which the ovaries have not assumed the classic appearance. Stein (1959) has recently reaffirmed his conservative views regarding the essential requirements for making a diagnosis, namely sterility accompanied by non-ovulatory amenorrhoea and consistently enlarged, symmetrical ovaries. He feels that laparotomy is not justifiable as a diagnostic procedure, and regards the aetiology as being still obscure. Surgical treatment consists of removing a wedge of tissue from both ovaries. If failure to ovulate is due to the mechanical difficulties of the Graafian follicles to rupture this would seem to be a logical procedure. It should be emphasized that this operative technique has little, if any, effect on the hirsutism. The only indication for surgery, therefore, is infertility.

V. Endocrine tumours of the ovary

The majority of ovarian tumours produce no endocrine effects. When they do, the effects are either feminizing or masculinizing. Very rarely they produce a decidual reaction in the endometrium, suggesting that they are secreting progesterone. There is still considerable difference of opinion concerning the origin of some of the so-called lipoid-cell tumours and whether some of them arise in adrenal rests. Teilum (1951), for instance, does not accept the view that any ovarian tumour is derived from adrenal cells. Novak (1947), on the other hand, supports the existence of adrenal adenomas of the ovary, though he considers them to be very rare. Very occasionally lipoid-cell tumours have been found in which symptoms and signs of Cushing's syndrome are present, such as obesity, polycythaemia, hypertension and a tendency to diabetes. Morris and Scully (1958) have collected eleven reports from the literature. This suggests the possibility that they may be of adrenal origin (see also Chapter 23).

So far as is known at present (Morris and Scully, 1958), only one tumour has been recorded as having given rise to heterosexual precocity. On the other hand, feminizing sexual precocity has occasionally been produced by ovarian tumours.

A. Feminizing tumours of the ovary

These are either *granulosa-cell tumours, thecomas* or *granulosa thecomas*. A luteoma is a tumour in which the granulosa cells have been completely transformed into lutein cells (Novak, 1948). It is usually classified as a lipoid-cell tumour, the endocrine manifestations of which are masculinizing. Novak refers to one case which was associated with a typical decidual appearance in the endometrium and to another occurring after the menopause in which progestational changes in the endometrium were associated with a partially luteinized thecoma.

The tumour which most commonly produces sexual precocity is a granulosa-cell tumour. Seckel (1946), however, has collected thirty-one reports from the literature between 1926 and 1944 of cases of precocity produced by ovarian tumours, and six of these were *teratomas* and four *chorion-epitheliomas*. Hain (1949) reported a dysgerminoma which gave rise to sexual precocity in a girl of 5 years of age, and Lloyd (1955) recorded a luteoma associated with precocity in a 4-year-old child. Though granulosa-cell tumours are the commonest cause of sexual precocity in girls, in contrast to precocious puberty, they occur in fact very rarely in childhood. Novak (1944) encountered only one record of an ovarian tumour giving rise to sexual precocity in 60 years in the gynaecological department of the Johns Hopkins Hospital during which 60,000 patients were dealt with. Uterine bleeding is usually the first clinical sign, whereas in cases of precocious puberty breast development and pubic hair growth appear before the onset of the first menstrual period. Usually the bleeding is of the metropathic type and non-ovulatory, although sometimes menstruation is fairly regular. Under the influence of the oestrogen produced by the tumour the uterus grows rapidly and may reach pregnancy dimensions. Oestrogen stimulates osteoblastic activity and consequently the long bones increase in size, but there is little advance in bone age as there would be under the influence of androgen. So far few hormone studies have been recorded in these cases, but the introduction of improved methods of estimating urinary oestrogens (Brown, 1955; Bauld, 1955) should make such studies extremely valuable in the differential diagnosis between this condition and constitutional precocious puberty. Treatment should consist of removal of the affected ovary and tube, and the prognosis is usually good.

Such tumours occur more commonly in adult life than in childhood, but even then they must be considered unusual. The majority develop after the age of 40, and postmenopausal bleeding is therefore the commonest sign, though their rarity is shown by the fact that Fahmy (1933) collected only three instances in the records of 937 patients complaining of postmenopausal bleeding. In women before the menopause, menstrual disturbance is often the only clinical symptom and this is usually of the metropathic pattern. Sometimes, however, there is no interference with the normal menstrual rhythm. The uterus is almost always enlarged, sometimes greatly.

Some of these tumours are undoubtedly malignant, and the incidence of recurrence and metastases is stated to be 20 to 25 per cent. Novak (1948) felt that more extensive follow-up studies would lead to a much higher figure.

Of considerable interest is the question as to whether the continuous endogenous oestrogen production may give rise to cancer. In fact, endometriosis, fibroids, and carcinoma of the breast and endometrium have been described as occurring in association with these tumours. Carcinoma of the breast and endometrium are probably the only significant lesions. Novak (1953) was of the opinion that thecomas are more carcinogenic than granulosa-cell tumours. Ingram and Novak (1951) reviewed the literature on feminizing ovarian tumours from 1920 to 1949 and found fifty cases in which carcinoma of the endometrium was associated with such tumours. Carcinoma of the breast was found co-existing with a thecoma in two out of twenty-three cases by Macafee (1954) and in three cases of a series of eighty-seven feminizing tumours reported by Dockerty and Mussey (1951).

B. Virilizing tumours of the ovary

These tumours arise from embryonic remnants of the developing gonad.

1. *Dysgerminoma*

In its indifferent state the gonad contains primitive cells which will later differentiate into both cortical and medullary elements. Some of the primitive cells of medullary origin may remain dormant throughout embryonic life and, very rarely, may differentiate in adult life, giving rise in the male to a testicular seminoma, and in the female to a dysgerminoma (which French workers usually refer to as a seminoma of the ovary). This tumour is fairly common and appears usually during adolescence ('carcinoma puellarum') and is generally supposed to produce no hormones. Very rarely cases have been reported with endocrine manifestations. Hain (1949) recorded such a tumour that gave rise to precocious puberty and was associated with a positive Aschheim-Zondek reaction, and refers to four other cases in which excessive urinary gonadotrophin was found. Possibly abnormal pituitary gonadotrophic activity reawakens the dormant gonadal cells and leads to their differentation. Plate (1953) reported a case in a girl of 17 years of age in which virilism was associated with a 17-ketosteroid output of between 23 and 28 mg per 24 hours. Fractionation showed uniform increase of all the components. The level dropped to normal figures 3 months after removal of the tumour. Ber (1949) described a dysgerminoma the size of a man's head that was removed from a 25-year-old virilized woman. The Aschheim-Zondek reaction was positive, but the urinary androgen level was within normal limits.

2. *Arrhenoblastoma*

In the early stages of gonadal differentiation primary sex cords develop from the mesenchyme and would become canalized to form seminiferous tubules if the gonad were to become a testis. If, however, the gonad develops into an ovary, a secondary wave of differentiation is superimposed on the original testicular scaffolding, but some of these mesenchymal sex cords may persist to differentiate in later life into an arrhenoblastoma.

There are three types of arrhenoblastoma, of which the two extremes are exceedingly rare. One is highly differentiated and contains tubules, a rete testis and islets of Leydig cells. This is the 'testicular adenoma of Pick' which seldom produces endocrine manifestations. At the other extreme is a completely undifferentiated growth resembling a sarcoma and giving rise to virilism. In the commonest, intermediate group the tumour consists of a mass of dense fibrous tissue which looks like a fibro-sarcoma and contains embedded tubules, sex cords and Leydig cells. It gives rise to masculinization only if it achieves reasonable dimensions. The urinary 17-ketosteroid output was within the normal range in ten of twelve such cases (Dorfman and Shipley, 1956). In the other two cases it was elevated. Nevertheless, the postoperative levels in all cases studied were significantly lower than before operation.

3. *Leydig cell tumours*

These and the next group, luteomas, are usually classified as lipoid-cell tumours. They arise from cells lying in the ovarian hilus and are sometimes referred to as hilus-cell tumours. Similar cells are also found in the rete ovarii and mesovarium. They contain crystalloids of Reinke which are characteristic of testicular Leydig cells and differentiate them from cells derived from adrenal rests. Up to 1954 the author was able to find records of only nine undoubted cases (Bishop, 1954), but Segaloff and his colleagues (1955) regard this as being one of the commonest virilizing tumours of the ovary. In the few cases in which the urinary 17-ketosteroids have been estimated they were usually within normal limits (Dorfman and Shipley, 1956). Chromatographic fractionation showed that dehydro*epi*androsterone (derived from the adrenal cortex) accounted for only 1% of the total 17-ketosteroids (Pedersen and Hamburger, 1953). These authors suggest that there is a distinct syndrome which consists of a Leydig cell tumour of small size with marked masculinization, increased total 17-ketosteroid output with low or normal output of the β-fraction (dehydro*epi*androsterone), uterine fibroids, hyperostosis cranialis, polycythaemia and diminished glucose tolerance. The two last signs have been singled out by Morris and Scully (1958) as manifestations of Cushing's syndrome and, according to them, would suggest an adrenal origin for the tumour, though the presence of crystalloids of Reinke and the fractionation studies of Pedersen and Hamburger would be in favour of a gonadal derivation.

In one case described by Scully (1953) a Leydig cell tumour gave rise to postmenopausal bleeding (a feminizing rather than masculinizing trait) which supports the view that Leydig cells may produce oestrogen as well as androgen.

4. *Luteomas, adrenal-rest tumours and masculinovoblastomas*

It is in connection with this type of tumour that there is real confusion of classification. The tumours are usually characterized by high levels of urinary 17-ketosteroids, which is in favour of their being adrenal rather than gonadal in origin; gonadal androgens, though biologically very active, give rise to a relatively small amount of urinary metabolites in the form of 17-ketosteroids, whereas the opposite is the case with adrenal androgens. Some of them, however, show evidence of producing progesterone. For instance there was a high output of urinary pregnanediol in the case of masculinovoblastoma reported by Merivale and Forman (1951). Friedman *et al.* (1955) collected records of nine cases in which virilism occurred during pregnancy. In their own case virilization had been marked in the first pregnancy but had disappeared after parturition, only to return in a subsequent pregnancy, the urinary 17-ketosteroid value being 273 mg per 24 hours at the 8th month. Both ovaries, removed some time later, contained nodular collections of lipoid cells. One of the nine cases was reported on by Searle and his colleagues (1948) in which the immediate ante-partum 17-ketosteroid level was 158 mg per 24 hours, whereas 3 weeks after delivery it had dropped to 23 mg. An 'ovarian cyst' was removed with a further diminution in the 17-ketosteroid level. The authors found patches of marginal thecal cells pointing to a luteal origin, but the Ovarian Tumor Committee of the American Gynecological Society placed the 'tumor' in the 'adrenal-like' group. This emphasizes the degree of confusion concerning this type of tumour.

REFERENCES

Albright, F., Butler, A. M., Hampton, A. O. and Smith, P. (1937). Syndrome characterized by osteitis fibrosa disseminata, areas of pigmentation and endocrine dysfunction, with precocious puberty in females. *New Engl. J. Med.* **216**, 727–746.

Albright, F., Smith, P. H. and Fraser, R. (1942). A syndrome characterized by primary ovarian insufficiency and decreased stature; report of eleven cases with digression on hormonal control. *Amer. J. med. Sci.* **204**, 625–648.

Ashley, D. J. B. and Jones, C. H. (1958). Sex reversal: ovarian tissue associated with male nuclear sex. *Lancet*, **1**, 74–76.

Baer, W. (1927). Vollkommene angeborene Aplasie beider Ovarien, infantiles Genitale, viriler Habitus. *Zbl. Gynäk.* **51**, 3241–3245.

Barr, M. L. (1955). The skin biopsy test of chromosomal sex in clinical practice. *Anat. Rec.* **121**, 387.

Barr, M. L. and Bertram, E. G. (1949). A morphological distinction between neurones of the male and female, and the behaviour of the nucleolar satellite during accelerated nucleoprotein synthesis. *Nature, Lond.* **163**, 676–677.

Bauld, W. S. (1955). Sources of error in the chemical determination of urinary oestrogens. *Mem. Soc. Endocrin.* No. 3, 11–22.

Ber, A. (1949). A case of dysgerminoma ovarii tested hormonally. *Acta med. scand.* **133**, 411–426.

Bishop, P. M. F. (1954). "Recent Advances in Endocrinology", 7th ed., p. 130. Churchill, London.

Bishop, P. M. F. and Sommerville, I. F. (1957). *In* "Biochemical Disorders in Human Disease" (R. H. S. Thompson and E. J. King, ed.), p. 740. Churchill, London.

Bishop, P. M. F., Lessof, M. H. and Polani, P. E. (1960). Turner's syndrome and allied conditions. *Mem. Soc. Endrocrin.* No. 7, 162–172.

Blizzard, R. M. and Wilkins, L. (1957). Present concepts of steroid therapy in virilizing adrenal hyperplasia. *Arch. int. Med.* **100**, 729–738.

Briggs, D. K. and Kupperman, H. S. (1956). Sex differentiation by leucocyte morphology. *J. clin. Endocrin.* **16**, 1163–1179.

Brown, J. B. (1955). A chemical method for the determination of oestriol, oestrone and oestradiol in human urine. *Biochem. J.* **60**, 185–193.

Clayton, G. W., O'Heeron, M. K., Smith, J. D. and Grabstald, H. (1957). A case of true hermaphroditism: possible relationship to Klinefelter's syndrome. *J. clin. Endocrin.* **17**, 1002–1005.

Culiner, A. and Shippel, S. (1949). Virilism and theca-cell hyperplasia of the ovary: a syndrome. *J. Obstet. Gynaec., Brit. Emp.* **56**, 439–445.

Dockerty, M. B. and Mussey, E. (1951). Malignant lesions of the uterus associated with estrogen-producing ovarian tumours. *Amer. J. Obstet. Gynec.* **61**, 147–153.

Dorfman, R. I. and Shipley, R. A. (1956). "Androgens", p. 416. Wiley, New York.

Fahmy, E. C. (1933). An analysis of 937 cases of post-menopausal haemorrhage. *J. Obstet. Gynaec., Brit. Emp.* **40**, 506–512.

Fischer, H. S. (1940). Sexual precocity and accelerated growth in a child with a follicular cyst of the ovary. *Amer. J. Obstet. Gynec.* **39**, 525–527.

Fischer, R. H. and Riley, C. L. (1952). Pregnanediol excretion in a masculinizing syndrome. *J. clin. Endocrin.* **12**, 890–900.

Ford, C. E., Jones, K. W., Polani, P. E., de Almeida, J. C. and Briggs, J. H. (1959). A sex-chromosome anomaly in a case of gonadal dysgenesis (Turner's syndrome). *Lancet*, **1**, 711–713.

Friedman, I. S., Mackles, A. and Daichman, I. (1955). Development of virilization during pregnancy. *J. clin. Endocrin.* **15**, 1281–1290.

Goldberg, M. B. and Maxwell, A. F. (1948). Male pseudohermaphroditism proved by surgical exploration and microscopic examination: case report with speculations concerning pathogenesis. *J. clin. Endocrin.* **8**, 367–379.

Gordan, G. S., Overstreet, E. W., Traut, H. F. and Winch, G. A. (1955). A syndrome of gonadal dysgenesis: a variety of ovarian agenesis with androgenic manifestations. *J. clin. Endocrin.* **15**, 1–12.

Graham, M. A. and Barr, M. L. (1952). A sex difference in the morphology of metabolic nuclei in somatic cells of the cat. *Anat. Rec.* **112**, 709–723.

Greenblatt, R. B., Carmona, N. and Higdon, L. (1956). Gonadal dysgenesis with androgenic manifestations in the tall eunuchoid female. *J. clin. Endocrin.* 16, 235–240.

Greulich, W. W. and Pyle, S. I. (1950). "Radiographic Atlas of Skeletal Development of Hand and Wrist." Stanford University Press, California.

Grumbach, M. M., van Wyk, J. J. and Wilkins, L. (1955). Chromosomal sex in gonadal dysgenesis (ovarian agenesis): relationship to male pseudohermaphroditism and theories of sex differentiation. *J. clin. Endocrin.* 15, 1161–1193.

Hain, A. M. (1949). An unusual case of precocious puberty associated with ovarian dysgerminoma. *J. clin. Endocrin.* 9, 1349–1358.

Hoffenberg, R. and Jackson, W. P. U. (1957a). Gonadal dysgenesis in normal-looking females. *Brit. med. J.* 1, 1281–1284.

Hoffenberg, R. and Jackson, W. P. U. (1957b). Gonadal dysgenesis: modern concepts. *Brit. med. J.* 2, 1457–1462.

Hoffenberg, R., Jackson, W. P. U. and Muller, W. H. (1957). Gonadal dysgenesis with menstruation: a report of two cases. *J. clin. Endocrin.* 17, 902–907.

Ingram, J. M. and Novak, E. (1951). Endometrial carcinoma associated with feminizing ovarian tumours. *Amer. J. Obstet. Gynec.* 61, 774–789.

Jeffcoate, T. N. A. (1957). "Principles of Gynaecology", p. 499. Butterworths, London.

Jost, A. (1947). Recherches sur la différenciation sexuelle de l'embryon de lapin. III. Rôle des gonades foetales dans la différenciation sexuelle somatique. *Arch. Anat. micr. Morph. exp.* 36, 271–315.

Kerkhof, A. M. and Stolte, L. A. M. (1956). Two cases of 'hypoplasia' of the ovaries. *Acta endocr., Copenhagen,* 21, 106–114.

Kimmel, G. C. (1947). Precocious menstruation. *J. Pediat.* 30, 686–690.

Klinefelter, H. F. and Jones, G. E. S. (1954). Amenorrhoea due to polycystic ovaries (Stein-Leventhal syndrome). *J. clin. Endocrin.* 14, 1247–1259.

Lisser, H., Curtis, L. E., Escamilla, R. F. and Goldberg, M. B. (1947). The syndrome of congenitally aplastic ovaries with sexual infantilism, high urinary gonadotrophins, short stature and other congenital abnormalities. Tabular presentation of twenty-five previously unpublished cases. *J. clin. Endocrin.* 7, 665–687.

Lloyd, C. W. (1955). Precocious puberty of the female type. *J. clin. Endocrin.* 15, 1518–1523.

Macafee, C. H. G. (1954). Address to the Edinburgh Obstetrical Society. Cited by Matthew, G. D. (1955). Oestrogenic tumours of the ovary: clinical features. *Proc. R. Soc. Med.* 48, 724–730.

McBride, J. M. (1955). In "Modern Trends in Obstetrics and Gynaecology" (K. Bowes, ed.), p. 335. Butterworths, London.

Merivale, W. H. H. and Forman, L. (1951). A case of masculinovoblastoma. *Brit. med. J.* 1, 560–563.

Meyer, R. (1925). Zum Mangel der Geschlechtsdrüsen mit und ohne zwittrige Erscheinungen. *Virchows Arch.* 225, 33–46.

Moore, K. L., Graham, M. A. and Barr, M. L. (1953). The detection of chromosomal sex in hermaphrodites from a skin biopsy. *Surg. Gynec. Obstet.* 96, 641–648.

Morris, J. M. (1953). Syndrome of testicular feminization in male pseudohermaphrodites. *Amer. J. Obstet. Gynec.* 65, 1192–1211.

Morris, J. M. and Scully, R. E. (1958). "Endocrine Pathology of the Ovary." Kimpton, London.

Novak, E. (1944). The constitutional type of female precocious puberty with a report of nine cases. *Amer. J. Obstet. Gynec.* **47**, 20–42.

Novak, E. (1947). "Gynaecological and Obstetrical Pathology." Saunders, London.

Novak, E. (1948). Functioning tumours of the ovary, with special reference to pathology and histogenesis. *J. Obstet. Gynaec., Brit. Emp.* **55**, 725–738.

Novak, E. (1953). Hormone-producing ovarian tumours. *Obstet. and Gynec.* **1**, 3–14.

Paschkis, K. E., Rakoff, A. E. and Cantarow, A. (1954). "Clinical Endocrinology", p. 36. Cassell, London.

Pedersen, J. and Hamburger, C. (1953). Virilizing Leydig cell tumour of the ovary. Report of a case with special reference to the hormone secretion. *Acta endocr., Copenhagen*, **13**, 109–122.

Pich, G. (1937). Über den angeborenen Eierstockmangel. *Beitr. path. Anat.* **98**, 218–263.

Plate, W. P. (1953). Dysgerminoma of the ovary in a patient with virilism. *Acta endocr., Copenhagen*, **14**, 227–234.

Polani, P. E., Hunter, W. F. and Lennox, B. (1954). Chromosomal sex in Turner's syndrome with coarctation of the aorta. *Lancet*, **1**, 120–121.

Polani, P. E., Lessof, M. H. and Bishop, P. M. F. (1956). Colour-blindness in 'ovarian agenesis' (gonadal dysplasia). *Lancet*, **2**, 118–120.

Polani, P. E., Bishop, P. M. F., Lennox, B., Ferguson-Smith, M. A., Stewart, J. S. S. and Prader, A. (1958). Colour vision studies and the X-chromosome constitution of patients with Klinefelter's syndrome. *Nature, Lond.* **182**, 1092–1093.

Scully, R. E. (1953). An unusual ovarian tumour containing Leydig cells but associated with endometrial hyperplasia in a post-menopausal woman. *J. clin. Endocrin.* **13**, 1254–1263.

Searle, W. N., Haines, M. and Baker, J. K. (1948). Virilizing tumours of the ovary with report of a case associated with pregnancy. *J. Obstet. Gynaec., Brit. Emp.* **55**, 135–141.

Seckel, H. P. G. (1946). Precocious sexual development in children. *Med. Clin. N. Amer.* **30**, 183–209.

Segaloff, A., Gordon, D., Horwitt, B. N. and Weed, J. C. (1955). Differential diagnosis of virilism. *J. clin. Endocrin.* **15**, 142–147.

Stein, I. F. (1959). Hirsutism. *Brit. med. J.* **1**, 301.

Stein, I. F. and Leventhal, M. L. (1935). Amenorrhoea associated with bilateral polycystic ovaries. *Amer. J. Obstet. Gynec.* **29**, 181–191.

Stein, I. F., Cohen, M. R. and Elson, R. (1949). Results of bilateral ovarian wedge resection in 47 cases of sterility. *Amer. J. Obstet. Gynec.* **58**, 267–274.

Swyer, G. I. M. (1955). Male pseudohermaphroditism: a hitherto undescribed form. *Brit. med. J.* **2**, 709–712.

Teilum, G. (1951). Classification of ovarian tumours. *Acta obstet. gynec. scand.* **31**, 292–312.

Thannhauser, S. J. (1944). Neurofibromatosis (von Recklinghausen) and osteitis fibrosa cystica localisata et disseminata (von Recklinghausen). *Medicine*, **23**, 105–148.

Turner, H. H. (1938). A syndrome of infantilism, congenital webbed neck, and cubitus valgus. *Endocrinology*, **23**, 566–574.

Varney, R. F., Kenyon, A. T. and Koch, F. C. (1942). An association of short stature, retarded sexual development and high urinary gonadotrophin titres in women. *J. clin. Endocrin.* **2**, 137–145.

Weinberger, L. M. and Grant, F. C. (1941). Precocious puberty and tumours of the hypothalamus: report of a case and review of the literature, with a pathophysiologic explanation of the precocious sexual syndrome. *Arch. intern. Med.* **67**, 762–792.

Wilkins, L. (1957). "The Diagnosis and Treatment of Endocrine Disorders in Childhood and Adolescence." Thomas, Springfield.

Wilkins, L. and Fleischmann, W. (1944). Ovarian agenesis; pathology, associated clinical symptons and bearing on theories of sex differentiation. *J. clin. Endocrin.* **4**, 357–375.

Wilkins, L., Grumbach, M. M. and van Wyk, J. J. (1954). Chromosomal sex in ovarian agenesis. *J. clin. Endocrin.* **14**, 1270–1271.

Witschi, E., Nelson, W. O. and Segal, S. J. (1957). Genetic developmental and hormonal aspects of gonadal dysgenesis and sex inversion in man. *J. clin. Endocrin.* **17**, 737–753.

Zuckerman, S. (1954). The secretions of the brain. *Lancet*, **1**, 739–743; 789–796.

AUTHOR INDEX

Numbers in italics refer to pages on which references appear at the end of the chapter.

Abramowicz, H., 4, *71*

Abramowitz, A. A., 277, *305*, 367, 390, *408*, 498, 502, *522*

Ackerman, A., 113, *117*

Adam, A. B., 165, *177*

Adams, A. E., 47, *71*, 397, 399, *408*

Adams, C. E., 88

Adams, E. C., 4, *82*, 151, 173, *186*, 192, 200, 208, 211, 216, 217, 219, 221, 223, *240, 241, 244*, 316, *358*

Addison, W. H. F., 249, *266*

Aeby, C., 437, *447*

Agate, F. J., Jr., 465, 469, 494, *508*

Agduhr, E., 30, *71*

Ahrens, W., 101 *117*

Aikawa, J. K., 150, *181*

Aitken, W. A., 170, *174*

Alba, J. de, 169, *175*

Albert, A., 277, *305*, 362, 377, 379, 381, 384, *408, 409, 410*, 502, *522*

Albert, S., 196, *234*

Albright, F., 554, 558, 564, *571*

Alden, R. H., 30, *71*, 144, *174*, 477, 478, 479, *508*

Aldman, B., 202, *234*

Aldred, J. P., 475, *508*

Alexander, D. P., 487, *518*

Alexander, S. S., 131, *138*, 397, *408*

Alfert, M., 44, *71*, 192, *234*

Allan, H., 466, 492, 494, *508*

Allanson, M., 446, *447*

Allen, B. M., 4, 6, 9, 11, 13, 15, 20, 21, 22, 23, 49, *71*, 250, *266*

Allen, E., 55, 70, *71*, 145, 150, 166, 167, *174, 180, 185*, 249, 250, 257, *266*, 292, *301*, 320, 332, 333, 335, *344*, 439, *447*, *448*, 454, 465, 469, 477, 494, *508, 518*, *531*

Allen, P., 146, *174*, 456, *508*

Allen, W. M., 324, 339, *345, 347*, 452, 453, 454, 465, 474, 486, *508, 521*

Allende, I. C. L. de, 130, *138*, 398, *408*

Alpatov, V. V., 393, *430*

Altland, P. D., 283, 284, *301*, 402, *408*, 505, *508*

Amoroso, E. C., 156, 170, *175*, 280, 281,

288, 299, *301, 306*, 318, 324, 340, 341, *345, 352*, 391, 395, *408*, 452, 454, 455, 457, 459, 460, 461, 462, 463, 464, 465, 467, 468, 477, 480, 483, 484, 491, 496, 501, 502, *508, 509, 516, 519, 523*

Ancel, P., 296, 299, *302*, 452, 478, 488, 489, 491, *509, 511*

Andersen, D. H., 158, 159, 169, *175*, 331, *345*, 477, 494, *509*

Anderson, E. M., 374, *412*

Anderson, L. L., 486, *515*

Andreu, B., 39, *7*

Andrews, J. S., 196, *237*, 253, *267*

Arai, H., 57, 58, *71*, 137, *138*, 255, 260, *266*

Aron, C., 56, 70, *71*, 374, *408, 423*, 474, *509*

Aron, M., 374, *408, 423*, 474, *509*

Aronson, L. R., 129, *139*, 396, *412*

Artemov, N., 397, *408*

Artunkal, T., 483, 485, *509*

Arvy, L., 215, *234*

Asami, G., 248, 249, 250, 256, 258, *266*

Asana, J. J., 15, *85*

Aschheim, S., 362, *408*

Aschner, B., 156, *175*, 361, *408*

Aschner, I., 466, *509*

Asdell, S. A., 169, 172, *175*, 287, *301*, 315, 316, 328, 339, 343, *345*, 454, 472, 485, 486, *509, 510, 516*

Ashbel, R., 196, *234*

Ashby, K. R., 14, 19, 40, *71*

Ashley, D. J. B., 558, *571*

Ashley-Montague, M. F., 288, *301*

Ask-Upmark, M. E., 485, *510*

Astrada, J. J., 398, *408*

Astwood, E. B., 297, *301*, 335, 337, *345, 357*, 362, 374, 375, 376, 385, *408*, 467, 468, 482, 496, 499, *510*

Athias, M., 156, *175*, 249, *266*

Atkinson, W. B., 468, *523*

Atwell, W. J., 397, *409*

Atz, E. H., 393, *409*

Atz, J. W., 315, *356*, 389, 391, 393, 395, 407, *426*, 502, *530*

SUBJECT INDEX

SUBJECT INDEX

613

Ovarian-pituitary relationships
—*continued*
in mammals, 369
in reptiles, 400
Ovariectomy, during pregnancy, effect on mammary growth, 492
effects of, 332
on course of gestation, 483, 484–488
on gonadotrophin storage, 376
in snakes, effect on gestation, 506
partial, effect on number of oocytes, 58
unilateral, effect on follicular atresia 260
Ovarioles, in insects, 101
Ovary, abnormal activity in absence of tumours, 563–567
activity during pregnancy, **451-508**
adrenocortical relationships with, 331
agenesis, 554
and behaviour; *see* Vol. II
arterial supply, 157
asymmetry, 25, 121, 132, 143; *see also* Ovary, structure
at puberty, structural and physiological changes, 342
atresia, **247-266**
bursa, 29, 143, 144
cellular components, modification, 26
cortex, 125, 126
development, 22
proliferation, 13
cyclical changes in vertebrates, 126
deficiency of embryonic origin, 554–559
of endocrine origin, 560–563
development, **1-32**
experimental modification; *see* Vol. II
phases, 2
effects of external factors on; *see* Vol. II
of hypophysectomy, in amphibians, 396
in birds, 403
in mammals, 369
in reptiles, 400
in teleosts, 391
of injection of follicle-stimulating hormone preparations, 372, 373

Ovary, effects of injection
—*continued*
of luteinizing hormone preparations, 373
endocrine activities, **319-340**
physiological manifestations, 328
failure, primary, 564
foetal, interstitium of, 463
luteal structures in, 462
follicle cells, 26
follicle cysts, 565
functions, in non-pregnant female, **311-344**
alternation, 315
at cessation of reproductive life, 344
at puberty, 342
at reproductive maturity, 343
before onset of puberty, 340
derangements, **553-571**
during pregnancy, 451–508
in relation to age, 340–344
steroid control, 474
grafts, effect on oocyte population, 58; *see also* Vol. II
histochemistry, **189-234**
histology, 124; *see also* Ovary, structure
hormonal activities before puberty, 341
hormones, biological effects, 333
production, 319
production, disorders in, 553–571
secretion during ovarian cycle, 325
influence of nutrition on; *see* Vol. II
influence on secondary sexual characters; *see* Vol. II
interrelationships with other endocrine organs, 330, 369–408
irradiation, effects; *see* Vol. II
mammalian, vascular supply, 157
medulla, 125, 126
development, 21
in birds, 134
in reptiles, 130
origin, **13-16**, 20
secondary, 125
morphology, comparative, in vertebrates, 121, 124
paired, in vertebrates, 122

614   SUBJECT INDEX

Ovary—*continued*
  physiology, in non-pregnant female,
    311–344
  in pregnant female, **451–508**
  polycystic, 565
  post-menopausal activity, abnormal,
    565
  pre-pubertal, hormonal activities,
    341
    sensitivity to hormonal stimuli,
      340
  pubertal changes, 342
  right, suppression of development, in
    birds, 25, 122, 132
  rupture at ovulation, 437
  secretions, in amphibians, 399
    in birds, 405
    in elasmobranchs, 390
    in fish, 395
    in reptiles, 402
    paradoxical effects; see Vol. II
  secretory cells, 27
  steroid control of function, 474
  stroma, 26, 28
  structure, in invertebrates, **89-117**
    in mammals, 136, **143-174**
    in vertebrates, **121-138**
  thyroid relationships, 330
  transplantation, effect on oocytes,
    263
    experiments, 381; see also Vol. II
  tumours; see also Vol. II
    endocrine, 567–569
    experimental; see also Vol. II
    feminizing, 567
    virilizing, 569–571
Oviduct, secretory activity, 476
  transport of ovum through, 477
Oviductin, 278
Ovigerous folds, 20, 128
Ovulation, alternation in ovaries, 315
  at menopause, 544–548
  causes, 440–443
    chemical factors, 443
    hormonal theory, 443
    mechanical factors, 441
    pressure theory, 441, 443
  dependency on mating, 291
  during pregnancy, 314
  effect of progesterone on, 385
  effect of unilateral ovariectomy on,
    260

Ovulation—*continued*
  fossa, 145
  in amphibians, 436
  in birds, 437
  in fishes, 128, 436
  in insects, 436
  in mammals, 288, 439
  in marsupials, 288
  in rat, 63, 65
  in reptiles, 131
  in teleosts, 128
  induction by pituitary preparations,
    in amphibians, 397
    by pituitary preparations, in rep-
      tiles, 401
  inhibition, in lactation and preg-
    nancy, 297, 299, 454
  interval in relation to gestation
    period, 277
  mechanism of, **435-447**
  post-menopausal, 539
  provoked, 444
    in birds, 445
    in insects, 444
    in mammals, 447
  spontaneous, 444
    with functional corpora lutea, 293
    with inactive corpora lutea, 292
  suppression, 317
Ovum, implantation, delayed, 480
  role of corpus luteum, 479
  number produced in different verte-
    brates, 314
  size at ovulation, 314
  transport through oviduct, 477
'Oyster' ovaries, 565

Pachytene stage of meiotic prophase,
    33
Palpigrada, ovary in, 104
Pancreatin, effect on follicle-stimula-
    ting hormone, 366
Panhypopituitarism, 561
Parabiosis, ovarian–pituitary relation-
    ships in, 382; see also Vol. II
Paradidymis, 30
Para-luteal cells, 173
Paroöphoron, 30
Parturition, induction, role of gonadal
    hormones and relaxin, 499
  upper age limit, 545